Geography and a Crowding World

PARTICIPANTS AND OBSERVERS

From left to right, FRONT ROW: P. Sen Gupta, Shinzo Kiuchi, Jacqueline Beaujeu-Garnier, Harold C. Brookfield, V. Nath, Gurdev Singh Gosal, Gerhard Sandner, Glenn T. Trewartha, Xavier de Planhol; SECOND ROW: Irene B. Taeuber, Pierre George, John M. Hunter, R. Mansell Prothero, Wilbur Zelinsky, Leszek Kosinski, John E. Brush, John I. Clarke, Gordon DeJong; THIRD ROW: Kempton E. Webb, Jean Tricart, Peter F. M. McLoughlin, Colin G. Clarke, John Fraser Hart, George Kay, Harley L. Browning; FOURTH ROW: M. J. Mortimore, Peter N. D. Pirie, Philip W. Porter, Edward Hawkins, Ester Boserup, Paul I. Mandell, Warren C. Robinson, Akin L. Mabogunje, Paul D. Simkins.

GEOGRAPHY AND A CROWDING WORLD

A Symposium on Population Pressures
upon Physical and Social Resources
in the Developing Lands

Edited by
WILBUR ZELINSKY
LESZEK A. KOSIŃSKI
R. MANSELL PROTHERO

OXFORD UNIVERSITY PRESS
New York London Toronto
1970

Copyright © 1970 by Oxford University Press, Inc.
Library of Congress Catalogue Card Number: 77-82999
Printed in the United States of America

FOREWORD

Although one of the organizers and editors of this work, I take the opportunity to write this Foreword as Chairman of the Commission on the Geography and Cartography of World Population of the International Geographical Union. The Commission was set up in 1964 with its members coming from India (the late Miss P. Sen Gupta), Japan (S. Kiuchi), Poland (L. A. Kosiński), United Kingdom (R. M. Prothero), U.S.A. (W. Zelinsky), and the U.S.S.R. (V. V. Pokshishevskii). During the period 1964-68, the Commission organized a number of projects, of which the one represented by this volume was the most important. This work has been an example of truly international co-operation, and in it Leszek Kosiński, Wilbur Zelinsky, and I have been particularly associated. Leszek Kosiński and I want here to express our special thanks to our colleague and friend, Wilbur Zelinsky, who has been the key person at all stages in this project. He has given so much of his time, boundless energy, and infectious enthusiasm to bring it to completion. Our work together has been a happy and satisfying experience. We hope that others will judge it to have been worthwhile.

R. MANSELL PROTHERO
University of Liverpool

March 1969

PREFACE

A growing concern over the imbalance between rapidly increasing population and limited resources in the developing world is shared by members of many scientific disciplines. Population pressure poses major theoretical and practical questions that will be occupying the attention of geographers and others in the immediate future. Realizing the importance of these questions, we, the organizers and editors of this Symposium, working as members of the International Geographical Union's Commission on the Geography and Cartography of World Population, met during the 1965 World Population Conference in Belgrade, and decided to promote a cooperative study of the geography of population pressure upon resources in developing countries.

It was proposed that the Symposium be not only international, but also interdisciplinary in character so as to bring about a productive exchange of methods, facts, and ideas between geographers and scholars in other fields concerned with population matters. It was further agreed that the discussion should be restricted to the developing countries and that the regional examples should be drawn predominantly, though not entirely, from South Asia, West Africa, and Middle America. Regional contributions were to be supplemented by treatment of various general aspects of population pressure, so that the systematic and regional approaches would be mutually reinforcing.

A brief prospectus was thereupon prepared, a list of potential participants was drawn up and their cooperation solicited. The enthusiastic and almost unanimously affirmative response—even before we had been assured of the funds to bring our colleagues together at a conference—further reinforced our belief that the time was right for this sort of endeavor. An application to the National Science Foundation of the U.S.A. resulted in a generous grant which made it possible to proceed to put our ideas into practice. Further details of the content and organization of the symposium were worked out at discussions held in Warsaw in May 1966, and in University Park, Pennsylvania, in November 1966. During the early months of 1967, working papers were prepared by the invited participants; and copies were then circulated among the entire group. These papers were issued in two successive "generations," the second reviewing and commenting on those submitted in the first.

The Symposium was held on the campus of the Pennsylvania State University September 17-23, 1967. Some 33 scholars from 11 countries were present as official participants, along with three observers from interested institutions. Their names and affiliations, as of September 1967, are as follows:

Edward A. Ackerman	Carnegie Institution of Washington
Mme Jacqueline Beaujeu-Garnier	Institut de Géographie, Université de Paris
Mme Ester Boserup	Institute of Economics, University of Copenhagen
H. C. Brookfield	Research School of Pacific Studies, Australian National University
Harley L. Browning	Department of Sociology, University of Texas
John E. Brush	Department of Geography, Rutgers University
Colin G. Clarke	Department of Geography, University of Liverpool
John I. Clarke	Department of Geography, University of Durham
Gordon DeJong (observer)	Department of Sociology, Pennsylvania State University
Pierre George	Institut de Géographie, Université de Paris
Gurdev Singh Gosal	Department of Geography, Panjab University
John Fraser Hart	Department of Geography, University of Minnesota
Edward A. Hawkins (observer)	Economics Department, International Bank for Reconstruction and Development
Chiao-min Hsieh	Department of Geography, University of Pittsburgh
John M. Hunter	Department of Geography, Michigan State University
George Kay	Department of Geography, University College of Rhodesia
Shinzo Kiuchi	Institute of Human Geography, University of Tokyo
Leszek A. Kosiński	Institute of Geography, Polish Academy of Sciences
Akin L. Mabogunje	Department of Geography, University of Ibadan
Paul I. Mandell (observer)	Food Research Institute, Stanford University
Peter F. M. McLoughlin	Department of Economics, University of Santa Clara
M. J. Mortimore	Department of Geography, Ahmadu Bello University (Zaria, Nigeria)

V. Nath — Kuwait Institute of Economic and Social Planning in the Middle East, Kuwait (on leave from Indian Planning Commission)

Peter N. D. Pirie — Department of Geography, University of Hawaii

Xavier de Planhol — Faculté des Lettres et des Sciences Humaines, Université de Nancy

Philip W. Porter — Department of Geography, University of Minnesota

R. Mansell Prothero — Department of Geography, University of Liverpool

Warren C. Robinson — Department of Economics, Pennsylvania State University

Gerhard Sandner — Institut für Geographie und Wirtschaftsgeographie, Universität Hamburg

Miss P. Sen Gupta — Office of the Registrar General, New Delhi

Paul D. Simkins — Department of Geography, Pennsylvania State University

Mrs. Irene B. Taeuber — Office of Population Research, Princeton University

Glenn T. Trewartha — Department of Geography, University of Wisconsin

Jean Tricart — Centre de Géographie Appliquée, Université de Strasbourg

Kempton E. Webb — Institute of Latin American Studies, Columbia University

Wilbur Zelinsky — Department of Geography, Pennsylvania State University

Much to our regret, the following participants were unable to attend the Symposium.

Vadim V. Pokshishevskii — Institute of Ethnography, Academy of Sciences of the U.S.S.R.

William Vogt — The Conservation Foundation, New York

Andrzej Bonasewicz — Institute of Geography, University of Warsaw

Bohdan E. Kikolski — Institute of Geography, University of Warsaw

Marcin Rościszewski — Institute of Geography, Polish Academy of Sciences

We have been shocked and saddened in recent months by the news that two of our participants have passed away—Dr. William Vogt on July 11, 1968, and Dr. P. Sen Gupta on November 13, 1968.

During the months following the Symposium, the working papers were substantially revised by authors and editors, additional editorial matter was composed, and transcripts of the discussions abridged and prepared for publication. In the present volume, the papers have been arranged into six sections, divided into General Problems and Regional Problems, which are related to the various sessions of the Symposium. Each section begins with a brief introduction that reviews the major questions and findings of the subsequent papers. It is hoped that this publication will be useful to all who are concerned with problems of population pressures upon resources, and that it will prove to be a point of departure for further, more extensive research by geographers and others in this vital field of study. If these objectives are achieved, then the four arduous years spent on the project will be fully justified.

The serious student will find the references appended to most of the essays in this volume useful points of departure for further reading and research on particular regions and topics. In lieu of a general bibliography on population pressures and related matters—one that would be very difficult to select out of a vast, diversified literature and would also go quickly out of date—it is suggested that the interested reader consult the better current bibliographies. In the case of demography, virtually all material of interest is listed in:

> *Population Index,* Office of Population Research, Princeton University and Population Association of America (Princeton, 1935-). Quarterly.

The most comprehensive geographic indexes are:

> *Bibliographie Géographique Internationale,* Association de Géographes Françaises (Paris 1891-). Annual.
>
> *Current Geographical Publications,* American Geographical Society (New York, 1938-). Monthly except July and August.
>
> *Referativnyi Zhurnal. Geografiia,* Akademiia Nauk, S.S.S.R., Institut Nauchnoi Informatsii (Moskva, 1954-). Monthly.
>
> *Geographical Abstracts. Part D—Social Geography and Cartography,* University of East Anglia (Norwich, 1966-). Bimonthly.
>
> *Documentatio Geographica; Papers of Geographical Periodicals and Serials* (Bad Godesberg, 1967-). Bimonthly.

The participants in the Symposium agreed that any royalties accruing from the sales of this volume should be used to promote further scholarly activities. Accordingly, a Population Geography Trust is being established, with the editors serving as trustees. The principal objective of the Trust is to sponsor further development of population geography.

We should like to express our gratitude to various institutions and individuals, without whose assistance the Symposium and this publication would never have come to fruition:

The National Science Foundation, whose generous financial aid made possible the Symposium and subsequent editorial work;

The International Geographical Union and its past General Secretary-Treasurer, Prof. Hans Boesch, for moral and material aid in the planning phases of this project;

The Institute of Geography of the Polish Academy of Sciences and its Director, Prof. Stanislaw Leszczycki, for warm hospitality during our meeting in Warsaw, May 1966;

Dr. E. F. Osborn, Vice President for Research, Pennsylvania State University, for many kindnesses, financial and otherwise;

Prof. Peirce F. Lewis, Department of Geography, Pennsylvania State University, organizer and guide for a thoroughly enjoyable and memorable tour of central Pennsylvania, September 20, 1967;

Messrs. Gary Fuller and Robert Ziegenfus for technical assistance in the tape-recording of the discussions;

Mrs. Hannah Lattman, who provided English translations for four papers initially submitted in French;

Miss Joan Treasure and Messrs. A. G. Hodgkiss and J. Sebunya, University of Liverpool, for their expert redrafting of the maps and diagrams in this volume;

Mr. James J. Anderson, Oxford University Press, for agreeing to publish this volume, and for aid and sympathetic understanding well beyond the call of duty;

And, last but far from least, Mrs. Mary S. Neilly, State College, Pennsylvania, secretary and factotum extraordinary, without whose calm and cheerful expertise we should have been utterly lost.

WILBUR ZELINSKY
LESZEK A. KOSIŃSKI
R. MANSELL PROTHERO

April 1969

CONTENTS

Dawna

xiii

PART TWO   REGIONAL PROBLEMS

Africa: Introduction   329

Asia and the Pacific: Introduction   389

Latin America: Introduction   509

PART THREE CONCLUSIONS

Geography and a Crowding World

GENERAL INTRODUCTION

Growth of World Population

One of the most striking phenomena in the contemporary world is the rapid, accelerating growth of its population. The annual increase, which had averaged 0.5 per cent during the late eighteenth and nineteenth centuries, increased to almost 1 per cent in the first half of the present century, and is now slightly over 2 per cent. The world population, estimated to have been between 200 and 400 million in A.D. 1, reached almost a billion in 1800, 2.5 billion in 1950, 3.4 billion in 1967. It is likely to exceed 6 billion by the year 2000 (22; 5: 137).

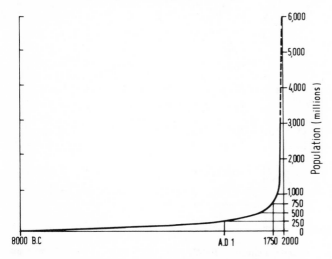

Fig. 0-1. LONG-RANGE TREND OF WORLD POPULATION GROWTH
(after J. D. Durand, "Population Problems," *Proceedings of the American Philosophical Society*, Vol. III, No. 3, 1967).

In a recent publication, J. D. Durand, former head of the U.N. Demographic Division, suggests that the acceleration "probably began somewhat before 1750 in parts of Europe, Russia and America and possibly before 1700 in China" (5: 139). To explain this almost simultaneous upturn of population in such different and distant parts of the world, Durand puts forward the hypothesis "that the potential stimulus to population growth resulting from the strengthening of agriculture was counteracted during the sixteenth and seventeenth centuries, in varying degrees in different areas, by the transmission of diseases around the globe; and that in the eighteenth century growing natural resistance to the new diseases opened the way for an upturn of the population trend in several areas" (5: 142).

Acceleration since World War II has far exceeded the projections pub-

3

TABLE 0-1   "MEDIUM" ESTIMATES OF POPULATION OF THE WORLD AND
MAJOR AREAS 1750-1950, AND PROJECTIONS TO 2000

Areas	Population (millions)						Annual rate of increase (per cent)				
	1750	1800	1850	1900	1950	2000	1750-1800	1800-1850	1850-1900	1900-1950	1960-2000
World total	791	978	1,262	1,650	2,515	6,130	0.4	0.5	0.5	0.8	1.8
ASIA*	498	630	801	925	1,381	3,458	0.5	0.5	0.3	0.8	1.9
China (Mainland)	200	323	430	436	560	1,034	1.0	0.6	0.0	0.5	1.2
India and Pakistan	190	195	233	285	434	1,269	0.1	0.3	0.4	0.8	2.2
Japan	30	30	31	44	83	122	0.0	0.1	0.7	1.3	0.8
Indonesia	12	13	23	42	77	250	0.2	1.2	1.2	1.2	2.4
Remainder of Asia*	67	69	87	118	227	783	0.1	0.5	0.7	1.3	2.5
AFRICA	106	107	111	133	222	768	0.0	0.1	0.4	1.0	2.5
North Africa	10	11	15	27	53	192	0.2	0.5	1.2	1.4	2.8
Remainder of Africa	96	96	96	106	169	576	0.0	0.0	0.2	0.9	2.5
EUROPE*	125	152	208	296	392	527	0.4	0.6	0.7	0.6	0.6
U.S.S.R.	42	56	76	134	180	353	0.6	0.6	1.1	0.6	1.4
AMERICA	18	31	64	156	328	992	1.1	1.5	1.8	1.5	2.2
Northern America	2	7	26	82	166	354	–	2.7	2.3	1.4	1.5
Middle and South America	16	24	38	74	162	638	0.8	0.9	1.3	1.6	2.8
OCEANIA	2	2	2	6	13	32	–	–	–	1.6	1.8

* (exc. U.S.S.R.)

ᵃ Calculated by assuming that Indonesia's share in the projected total for South-East Asia would be the same in 2000 as in 1980.

— This table presents the most recent estimate, differing slightly from the estimates by the same author and by G. Ohlin, presented at the U. N. World Population Conference in 1965.

— Estimates which lack a firm foundation are shown in italics.

Source: J. D. Durand: The Modern Expansion of World Population, in *Proc. Amer. Philos. Soc.,* Vol. 111, No. 3, p. 137.

lished by various demographic authorities. G. Ohlin quotes several forecasts by leading demographers which indicate that the world population would reach 3.5 billion in 1990 (C. Clark in 1949) or 3.3 billion in 2000 (F. W. Notestein in 1950) (16: 18). In fact, this number has already been reached, and subsequent forecasts, including those by the U.N. Population Division, suggest at least 6 billion for the year 2000. This "demographic boom" has also experienced an important territorial shift. In the nineteenth century the rates of growth for Europe, the U.S.S.R. (Russia), and the Americas exceeded the world average (Table 0-1). The most dynamic stage of the "demographic revolution" first took place in Europe. From there it was exported overseas as millions migrated to the New World. Whereas the population in areas of European settlement (in Europe, the present area of the Soviet Union, Oceania, and North America) represented only 22.2 per cent of the world total in 1800, by 1900 it had risen to 31.4 per cent. Similarly, the annual growth rate of 0.7 per cent from 1800 to 1850 accounted for 33.5 per cent of the world increase. In the second half of the nineteenth century, this figure rose to 1 per cent, representing 53.1 per cent of the world increase. However, from 1900 to 1950 the rate of growth was once again 0.7 per cent and the percentage of world increase fell to 26.9—less than average (5: 141), as the "boom" shifted to the "non-European" countries. It is in these parts of the world that rates of growth are the highest, reaching 3 per cent *per annum* in some countries, and where most of the 60-70 million of the present annual increment is located.

The experience of Europe and countries settled by people of European stock was generalized in the theory of the "demographic transition" or the "demographic revolution," which explains the expansion of population as a result of improved economic and social conditions accompanying the industrialization or modernization process. Such improvements produced a decline of mortality rates that preceded and exceeded the decline of fertility rates, thus causing the transitional upsurge of population growth. The decline in fertility rates was a product of relatively slow, but far-reaching changes in social and economic structure, patterns of behavior, in particular the acceptance of the small-family model so typical of modern urban society. Reduced fertility and mortality characterize what is sometimes called "demographic maturity."

The developing countries, on the other hand, now in the most dynamic stage of their demographic evolution, are experiencing a precipitous decline in mortality following the effective application of public health measures (such as the campaigns to eradicate malaria), undertaken at relatively small cost and organizational effort, and very often subsidized or carried on directly by foreign or international bodies. Mortality has also been reduced by clinical measures and introduction of new pharmaceuticals, such as antibiotics and sulfa drugs. However, because these measures have usually been imposed from outside, they have had little if any bearing on the structure of society and patterns of behavior. In most instances these predominantly rural and nonindustrial countries do not have the knowledge, desire, or means to reduce a fertility level that is not only high but increasing. Thus it may be asked whether the earlier experience of more developed countries has any relevance for the developing countries and the concept of the "demographic transition" can be safely applied to them. The question is one of resources.

The Question of Resources

Resources are defined by demographers as the "means available to maintain the population" (23: 49). Economists and geographers, however, hasten to point out that existing raw materials cannot be called resources until their usefulness is determined by man. As Zimmerman states, "the word 'resources' does not refer to a thing nor a substance but to a function which a thing or a substance may perform . . . (in order to) attain a certain end" (12:8). There are also two basic types of resources: those that are destroyed by being used and those that can be regenerated. These are defined as exhaustible (or nonrenewable) and replaceable (or renewable), respectively. The distinction is crucial to any discussion of development process.

Although the use of the concept of resources, as defined above, has been generally adhered to in the papers and discussions in this volume, there are some alternative suggestions. J. Tricart would use instead the term "limitations" and "bases," limitations being those physical and social features which hinder or constrain development and the bases those which facilitate it. M. Rościszewski's "barriers" or obstacles to economic growth, such as the "environment barrier," the "institutional barrier," or "demographic barrier," are similar to Tricart's "limitations." Mme J. Beaujeu-Garnier suggests that we can usefully apply the concept of an "assimilation capacity"—especially to urban situations. This term is basically economic in character—the ability of a metropolis to absorb new migrants by providing worthwhile employment and adequate housing, as well as other physical facilities. The absence of such a capacity is all too frequently demonstrated through statistics or field observations in the major cities of the developing countries. P. W. Porter's "environmental potential" is essentially the same; but instead of being applied to the capacity of cities to support newcomers, it refers to the size or density of population that could be maintained by the biological yield from a particular tract of land. Although the idea is an intriguing one, Porter makes it clear that its precise definition and the ways in which it might be effectively measured are hedged about by many technical difficulties.

Relationship between Population and Resources

The problem of relations between resources and population has been studied and discussed by numerous scholars. It has obvious practical importance and is implicit in ideological arguments or political decisions. The controversial pronouncements of T. Malthus toward the end of the eighteenth century gave rise to endless arguments that continue even now. Malthus argued that if the growth of population exceeds that of food (he suggested that populations tend to grow in geometric progression, doubling in size every 25 years, while food supplies can at best grow in arithmetic progression), preventive checks such as continence and delayed marriage, must be introduced, or positive checks, such as starvation, disease, and war, will plague the society. He grouped these checks under the heading of "misery and vices."

Malthus proved to be wrong in his computations. On the one hand, he underestimated the pace of economic and social growth in Europe in the last century; and on the other he did not foresee the impact of emigration and birth control on European populations. Thus, as we discussed above, the more developed nations avoided a population crisis in the nineteenth and early twentieth centuries because their rate of economic growth exceeded that of population growth, the latter being reduced by lower fertility, following reduced mortality. In less developed societies, of course, there was no build-up of excessive pressure at this time because of a very high rate of mortality.

All this recently has changed with the "demographic explosion." Consequently, the argument put forward by Malthus in 1798 is becoming relevant once again. The wide spectrum of current opinion, reflected to some degree in the present volume, ranges from the extreme attitude of those who feel that population increase should be limited (on the regional, national, or global scale) to avoid imminent catastrophe, to those who believe in the unlimited capacity of Earth to house ever-increasing numbers of people, whose talents and productivity will multiply the means of subsistence. The views declared and adhered to are not only of academic interest; they can and sometimes do reflect ideological attitudes and/or influence directions of explicit or indirect population policy.

The Malthusian argument today centers on the question of food. The United Nations Food and Agricultural Organization (FAO) offers a skeptical view of the present situation anl prospects for the near future. The Third World Food Survey based on data for 1957-59 estimated that 10-15 per cent of the world population are undernourished and up to one-half suffered from hunger, malnutrition, or both (9: 9). The latest report of FAO on food and agriculture (1967) indicates that while food production increased both in absolute terms and per capita output during the postwar years, more recently per capita output has become relatively stable. Although the four developed regions of the world experienced growth far exceeding the rates for the rest of the globe, the less developed regions showed little progress. In fact, from 1964 to 1966 Latin America and Africa, having suffered an absolute decline of food production, retreated to per capita production levels of the late 1940's.

The inequality of the present terms of trade is working against the developing countries. Even the commercial import of food becomes difficult, and philanthropic gifts are not always obtainable, and if gifts do arrive, they may aggravate the position of local food producers, as argued in the case of India (Nath, p. 406). Thus hunger and starvation not only threaten but actually occur in different regions of the world. The recent striking example of Biafra is an instance of human tragedy caused by political instability so often encountered in developing nations.

FAO experts warn that, in view of the expected growth of population (according to the "medium" U.N. projection), "the world's total food supply would have to be trebled by the year 2000 in order to provide a

TABLE 0-2   INDICES OF WORLD* AND REGIONAL FOOD PRODUCTION IN 1948-1966

Regions	Average Annual 1948-52	1952-56	1962	1963	1964	1965	1966 Preliminary Data
			Total Food Production				
Western Europe	84	100	126	128	129	130	134
Eastern Europe & U.S.S.R.	83	100	141	134	147	150	166
North America	92	100	113	121	119	121	124
Oceania	93	100	135	138	144	136	153
Four above regions	87	100	125	127	131	132	140
Latin America	88	100	125	132	138	138	136
Far East*	87	100	128	132	137	133	138
Near East	83	100	134	138	139	141	144
Africa	88	100	125	130	132	132	130
Four above regions	87	100	128	132	137	135	137
World total	87	100	126	129	133	133	139
			Production per Caput				
Western Europe	87	100	118	118	118	118	120
Eastern Europe & U.S.S.R.	88	100	125	118	128	129	141
North America	99	100	98	104	100	101	102
Oceania	102	100	112	113	116	106	118
Four above regions	92	100	113	113	115	115	120
Latin America	98	100	100	102	104	101	97
Far East*	93	100	108	109	110	105	106
Near East	92	100	110	111	108	107	106
Africa	96	100	103	104	104	101	97
Four above regions	94	100	106	108	108	105	104
World total	93	100	108	109	109	108	110

* Excluding China
Source: *The State of Food and Agriculture*, F.A.O. Rome 1967 (C 67/4), p. 12

reasonably adequate level of nutrition. For the less developed areas, total food supplies would have to be quadrupled and the supplies of animal products should be raised to six times the present volume" (9: 9-10). Although many are very skeptical about the feasibility of such an expansion, there are some relatively optimistic views. G. Ohlin claims that "Contrary to the widespread beliefs, the statistical evidence of past agricultural performance in the underdeveloped countries does not point to an inescapable food crisis" (16: 43), and concludes: "Of all the possible consequences of the current population explosion that of catastrophic food shortage seems the most remote" (16: 51).

Indeed, it should be emphasized that food is not the only item on the long list of needed resources. An increasing demand for water, which at the same time is bcoming more and more polluted, leads some people to believe that pure water rather than food may be the decisive factor in further development. There are other needs as well in a modern society, the satisfaction of which requires resources other than food or water. Both quantity and quality of supplies of energy, minerals, industrial raw materials of all sorts, transport facilities, residential space, and the amenities may be critical to the success of a community. Consequently, the problem of resources become rather complex, as shown by Zelinsky (26).

An estimate by J. L. Fisher is worth mentioning. He suggests that "a whole effective demand for resources by the year 2000 might require increases in supply of the following magnitudes: (1) a tripling of aggregate food output just to provide adequate calories, and considerably more to provide adequate proteins and vitamins; (2) a fivefold increase in energy output; (3) perhaps a fivefold increase in output of iron ore and ferro-alloys, and somewhat less in copper, but a much larger increase in bauxite-aluminum; (4) a possible tripling or more of lumber output" (7: 105).

Views as to the feasibility of achieving those goals vary, and they seem to reflect to a great extent the beliefs and convictions of those expressing them, since scientific forecasting is extremely difficult. Some authors have tried to evaluate the ultimate carrying capacity of the earth. The highest estimate "ever calculated by a responsible scholar," as P. Hauser put it (15: 59), is an estimate by Harrison Brown—50 billion. K. M. Malin suggests fantastic figures of several hundreds of billions (16: 32), but it is difficult to take him seriously. The present size and the projections for the rest of this century deal with much smaller numbers; nonetheless growing concern is reflected in several recent publications (2; 11; 15; 16).

It has also been pointed out that "probably the race against time is more urgent than that against space. . . . In time, the capital may be formed; in time, the necessary social reforms will be undertaken. But as things stand, the developing world faces a transitional period of uncertain length in which time will be exceedingly short" (16: 131). One obvious way to buy time is to slow down population growth. Consensus is slowly evolving that if death rates are "artificially" reduced, indiscriminate procreation must be stemmed as well. There have been efforts and experiments to develop more efficient, less expensive contraceptive techniques. Possibly the real issue is not contraceptive technology but a desire to limit the family size. Surveys aimed at finding more effective ways of persuading people to change their fertility behavior are being conducted. More important, birth control and family limitation have become a public issue for a growing number of governments or public bodies who are trying to repeat the postwar success of Japan, a nation confronted by the loss of her imperial dependencies and the sudden influx of 6 million repatriates.

General agreement also appears to be materializing around an even more basic point—that a program of general economic development cannot be pursued successfully in any of the currently undeveloped countries without also encouraging a retardation in population growth, and, conversely, that any program that seeks to reduce fertility is a questionable proposition without a simultaneous modernization of economy and society. Thus neither is a substitute for the other, although the two sets of problems are inextricably bound together. Most analysts now also accept the notion that rapid expansion of human numbers in a community existing at a low socioeconomic level siphons an undue proportion of scarce physical, social, and financial resources away from the investments which are so badly needed to generate significant development into expenditures for mere day-to-day subsistence. Consequently, any slowdown in population increase would almost automatically mean a more rational exploitation—and building up—of resources. Once such a forward developmental momentum is achieved, new social resources can be created, the older physical resources can be utilized more rationally, while new ones, requiring greater skills and organization for their use, can be tapped. And the greater the supply of known, reliable physical and social resources, the less the need for parents to invest heavily in large families as a form of social insurance.

Definition of Concepts

In planning this Symposium the organizers raised the question of whether the participants should be given suggestions and guidelines for the terminology to be used. The existing terminology is confused, but it was decided to leave the matter open rather than to initiate arguments which could take up valuable time during the discussions. Thus the use of terms throughout this volume is not consistent. Further, while some authors assumed that the terms they used were known, others, notably A. L. Browning, attempted to define them. Two concepts, however, that of *population optimum* and *population pressure*, should be discussed briefly here.

POPULATION OPTIMUM

The concept or theory of the population optimum evolved slowly in the eighteenth and nineteenth centuries; to many people it is John Stuart Mill who first promulgated the theory of optimum welfare in *Principles of Political Economy* (1848). Around 1900, three economists independently undertook studies that led to the theory of an economic optimum of population: E. Cannan in England (1888), who did so without using the term "optimum," J. Wolf in Germany (1901 and 1908), who set forth a theory of "optimum output," and K. Wicksell in Sweden (1911), who is credited with first using the term "optimum populations" (3: 25-40). In the interwar period, the concept of the population optimum was further developed, and several schools of thought could be distinguished. Although the "birth control" movement promptly adopted it, the concept was not universally accepted (3: 40). The World Population Congress in Geneva in 1927 offered an opportunity for discussion, the repercussions of which were later reflected in numerous publications edited and summarized by I. Ferenczi in 1938 (6).

The theory of the population optimum is basically economic in character, but it is also relevant to geographers who are interested in the relationships between population and resources. At present the idea seems to be especially popular among French scholars (3; 10; 19; 20; 24). A. Sauvy considers it a useful tool, even if in practice there are some difficulties in its measurement. Irene Taeuber thinks that "the idea is enticing, but the attempt to use the concept is disillusioning" (p. 56). At the other end of the spectrum is the view of W. Robinson: "In retrospect, much of the discussion of population optimum which consumed so much time strikes one as an interesting, often ingenious, but altogether sterile exercise." Robinson quotes F. Osborn who likened optimum population to the ideal of feminine beauty—a thing which continues to fascinate men but which is incapable of precise definition (18: 384).

For A. Sauvy, optimum population assures, in the best possible way, the achievement of a given end (20: 50). The end can be defined in various ways: the maximization of the average standard of living (economic optimum), the maximization of means that can be employed to obtain a collective end (power), or full employment, longevity and good health, knowledge and culture, social harmony and family stability. In his discussion of the economic optimum, A. Sauvy uses a model graph that relates production to population. Population optimum is achieved at point $P = n_o$, where the per capita output is the highest (R), marginal productivity still exceeds the average productivity, and the rates of growth of total production are the highest. Sauvy suggests in his model that the subsistence level is defined by the line V-S, and all production above this level can be used differently, depending on the desired ends.

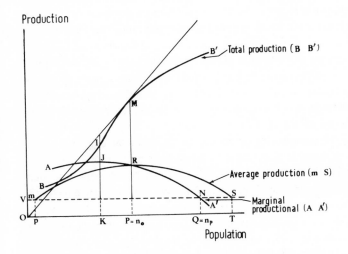

Fig. 0-2. OPTIMUM PRODUCTION, STANDARD OF LIVING, AND POWER (according to A. Sauvy)

G. Veyret-Verner is more specific, and suggests that in economic terms, the optimum situation occurs when there is full employment, a satisfactory level of life, a daily intake of food exceeding 2500 calories and absorbing no more than 50 per cent of income, and resources are exploited in a rational way—to a full extent but not excessively. In demographic terms, the optimum is achieved when the structure of population is such that the adults are not overburdened and the division of labor allows for purely intellectual functions (24: 163). The population optimum is regarded by demographers as a certain state of equilibrium, one that can vary in time and space, but in each case satisfying the needs of members of a community. This, in turn, requires that the needs be defined. Most authors define needs vaguely, whereas Mme Veyret-Verner suggests specific means by which to measure them, as does E. Ackerman, who suggests the following lengthy formula: $PS = RQ\,(TAS_t) + E_s + T_r \pm F - W$, where P = number of people; S = standard of living; R = amount of resources; Q = factor for natural quality of resources; T = physical technology factor; A = administrative techniques factor; W = frugality element (wastage or intensity of use); F = institutional advantage and "friction" loss element consequent upon institutional characteristics of the society; E_s = scale economies element (size of territory, etc.); T_r = resources added in trade.

It can be argued that PS, according to this formula, represents the carrying capacity of the land. The existing equilibrium can be upset if the carrying capacity is diminished or does not grow fast enough, if the number of population increases, or if the desired standard of living is rising. A. Mabogunje emphasizes in particular the multiplier effect of growing expectations which only adds to the burden of a growing population.

If the equilibrium is upset, we can speak of maladjustment or overpopulation. The latter term was introduced into the literature long ago. An economic definition of overpopulation given by W. T. Thornton some 130 years ago was brought to the attention of the editors by G. Kay. "Over-population may be shortly defined to be a deficiency of employment for those who live by labour, or a redundancy of the labouring class above the number of persons that the fund applied to the remuneration of labour can maintain in comfort" (21).

Reviewing the concept of overpopulation, W. Winkler emphasizes that in each society there is the possibility of redirecting surpluses from one region or social group to another that happens to be deficient, and only the net result can indicate whether the size of a population enjoying a certain level of living (defined as *Existenz-minimum*) exceeds the carrying capacity of an area (*Nahrungssplielraum* or *Tragfähigkeit des Lebensraumes*) (25: 89).

P. George suggests that there is a difference between *surpeuplement* and *surnombre organique*. The first term refers to the relations between two variables, population and resources. If the resources are being used to a full extent, and the maladjustment is apparent, then it is *surpeuplement absolu;* if there are still some unused reserves, then the apparent disequilibrium can be defined as *surpeuplement relatif.* On the other hand, *surnombre organique* is a function of an economic and social system that prevents people from fully enjoying the fruits of the environment (10).

A. Sauvy reminds us that overpopulation has always been a form or manifestation of underdevelopment (19: 480) and emphasizes the dynamic concept of the *rythme optimal d'accroissement* or, more generally, *rythme optimal de variation de la population* (19: 475) (the notion that there is some optimal rate of population increase as related to economic growth). This last view attracted much attention during the discussions of the Symposium. Some participants suggested that, instead of talking about the land-man ratio, one should compare two processes—population change and economic growth. But as V. Nath pointed out, the literature of development theory does not treat this relationship extensively; in fact, there is no theory that would relate these two processes. Many people tend to believe that eventually economic growth will serve to slow down or arrest demographic growth. This view is based on the experience of European societies and is generalized in the theory of the Demographic Transition. However, there is no proof that it will hold true in presently undeveloped countries. Others emphasize that population growth has always accompanied economic growth. But, in fact, there is no convincing empirical evidence of a significant statistical correlation between the two processes, and it would be even more difficult to prove the existence of causal association. Yet at the same time, population pressures are mounting and certain policies have to be adopted and priorities assigned.

It seems that a compromise consensus is gradually emerging that the solution to the problems facing underdeveloped countries can be found only when both aspects are considered at the same time, and a policy of economic growth must be accompanied by measures aimed at limiting excessive population increase.

POPULATION PRESSURE

This term has never been defined *a priori* and is used in different senses in a number of the papers presented here. Irene Taeuber suggests a dynamic interpretation: "Population pressure implies that equilibrium between population and resources is being shaken as a result of a mounting pressure but does not specify whether the pressure exceeded the ideal optimum level, thus leading to overpopulation" (p. 56). This approach is shared by C. Clarke: "Pressure is caused by the imbalance between human numbers and needs and the physical and human resources of the area in question" (p. 305). Similarly, H. L. Browning defines population pressure "as a maladjustment between the resources of a community or society and the population living within it . . ." (p. 72). Some authors, however, use the term "population pressure" as a synonym for overpopulation. Thus G. Kay states that "use of these terms (overpopulation or population pressure) is prompted by maladjustment between population numbers and either resources or production, and problems of population pressure consist of adverse consequences of such maladjustment upon resources or human beings or both" (p.   ). In addition, some authors explicitly used the term "overpopulation" (i.e., M. Ročsciszewkski, Miss P. Sen Gupta, G. Kay) or "overcrowding" (C. Clarke).

Even if a definition of the concept of population pressure could be worked out satisfactorily and accepted unanimously, there would still remain the question of how to measure it operationally. Should one consider short-term or long-term trends? What territorial scale would be the proper one? Should the study deal with average situations, or should one take into account the existing social disparities? The last question was extensively discussed, and the conclusion was that social structure does indeed play a very important role. No general answers were found to the other questions.

Conclusion

The relationship between population and resources is a basic question of geography. Yet geographic studies on population pressure have not been as numerous as might be expected. It is hoped that this volume will help to promote interest among geographers in the problems under discussion.

Although much has been said and written about the problems of population pressure on the global and continental scale, the amount of detailed reliable information on the regional and local scale is decidedly smaller and certainly insufficient. The papers here reflect the special attention given to relatively small selected regions: The Indian subcontinent, Central America, and West Africa in particular.

There is also a great need for a theory of population pressure which might serve as a unifying base of empirical studies. If the theoretical base of a case study is not firm enough, its relevance may be questioned. A base must be sufficiently broad, well-enough known, and generally accepted to allow comparisons. Theory-building is an involved proposition and cannot be done in haste. Because the organizers of the Symposium felt that summaries of existing knowledge can be a useful step toward this end, several persons were asked to prepare systematic papers as a background for discussion.

One might wonder whether a general theory of population pressure can be developed by geographers alone. It seemed that the participation of the representatives of other disciplines in both a theoretical discussion and a review of empirical studies would be highly desirable; and, consequently, the Symposium was planned as an interdisciplinary meeting.

In sum, the present volume reflects three basic assumptions accepted by the organizers of the Symposium: (i) the approach to the problem of population pressure should be interdisciplinary; (ii) although the most immediate contributions of geographers may be on a local or regional level, the underlying theoretical base should be developed at the same time; and (iii) the best results would be obtained if one alternates between the synthetic and analytical approaches as represented by regional and systematic contributions.

This is only a single step toward the better understanding of the problems facing not only the developing countries but indeed the whole world. Better understanding is a necessary precondition for more successful measures to solve these problems.

REFERENCES

(1) E. A. Ackerman: Population and Natural resources, in: P. M. Hauser & O. D. Duncan, eds.: The Study of Population (Chicago, 1959. Reprinted in: I. Burton & R. W. Kates, eds.: Readings in Resource Management and Conservation (Chicago, 1965), pp. 127-52.

(2) G. Borgstrom: The Hungry Planet. The Modern World at the Edge of Famine (New York, 1967).

(3) L. Bouqet: L'Optimum de Population (Paris, 1956).

(4) R. C. Cook: Soviet Population Theory from Marx to Kosygin, *Population Bulletin* Vol. 23, No. 4, 1967.

(5) J. Durand: The Modern Expansion of World Population, *Population Problems. Proceedings of the American Philosophical Society* Vol. III, No. 3, 1967, pp. 136-59.

(6) I. Ferenczi: The Synthetic Optimum of Population, International Institute of Intellectual Co-operation, League of Nations (Paris, 1938).

(7) J. L. Fisher: Perspectives on Population and Resources, in: I. Burton & R. W. Kates, eds.: Readings in Resource Management and Conservation (Chicago, 1965), pp. 104-9.

(8) Food and Agriculture Organization: The State of Food and Agriculture 1967 (Rome, 1967).

(9) Food and Agriculture Organization: Third World Food Survey, Freedom from Hunger Campaign, Basic Study No. 11 (Rome, 1963).

(10) P. George: Introduction à l'Etude Géographique de la Population du Monde. Institut National d'Etude Démographiques, Cahier No. 9 (Paris, 1951).

(11) P. M. Hauser, ed.: The Population Dilemma (Englewood Cliffs, 1963).

(12) H. L. Hunker, ed.: Erich W. Zimmermann's Introduction to World Resources (New York, 1964).

(13) S. Kuznets: Population and Economic Growth, *Population Problems. Proceedings of the American Philosophical Society,* Vol. III, No. 3, 1967, pp. 170-193.

(14) T. R. Malthus: A Summary View of the Principle of Population, in: Three Essays on Population (New York, 1960).

(15) S. Mudd, ed.: The Population Crisis and the Use of World Resources (Bloomington, 1964). Abridged and revised version published as a paperback by L. K. Y. Ng and S. Mudd, eds.: The Population Crisis (Bloomington, 1965).

(16) G. Ohlin: Population Control and Economic Development, Organisation for Economic Co-operation and Development, Development Centre Studies (Paris, 1967).

(17) R. Revelle: Population and Food Supplies: the Edge of the Knife, *Proceedings of the National Academy of Science,* Vol. 56, No. 2, 1966, pp. 328-51, reprinted by *Harvard University Center for Population Studies,* Contribution no. 21.

(18) W. C. Robinson: The Development of Modern Population Theory, *American Journal of Economics & Sociology,* Vol. 23, No. 4, 1964, pp. 375-92.

(19) A. Sauvy: Evolution Récente des Idées sur le Surpeuplement, *Population,* Vol. 15, No. 3, 1960, pp. 467-84.

(20) A. Sauvy: Théorie Générale de la Population, 3rd edition (Paris, 1963).

(21) W. T. Thornton: Over-Population and its Remedy or an Inquiry into the Extent and Causes of the Distress Prevailing among the Labouring Classes of the British Isles and into the Means of Remedying It (London, 1846).

(22) United Nations: Demographic Yearbook 1967 (New York, 1968).

(23) United Nations: Multilingual Demographic Dictionary, Population Studies No. 29 (New York, 1958).

(24) G. Veyret-Verner: Population. Movements, Structures, Répartition. (Paris, 1959).

(25) W. Winkler: Uebervoelkerung, Untervoelkerung. Begriffe, Verfahren, Tatsachen, *Metrika,* Vol. 9, No. 2, 1965, pp. 85-102.

(26) W. Zelinsky: The Geographer and His Crowding World, *Revista Geografica,* Vol. 65, 1966, pp. 7-28. Reprinted in the present volume.

PART ONE

GENERAL PROBLEMS

THEORY AND METHODS

Within the field of population studies there exists a body of theory relating to population growth and change and to the factors which influence them. The Demographic Transition, the passage from a near-balance between fertility and mortality, both fluctuating at high levels through a period of disequilibrium to the situation of the advanced countries in which fertility tends to stabilize above an even lower mortality, is a well-established concept, but one susceptible to oversimplification. The papers contributed to this Symposium clearly indicate that while the Demographic Transition has a number of common elements, it does not everywhere and at all times maintain uniform characteristics. An examination of recent population data causes one to hesitate in using the Demographic Transition, as generalized from the experience in the developed world, as a model for examining and understanding the population problems and future prospects of the developing world. Although contemporary situations frequently require considerable modification of the concept, it provides a theoretical base for the study of population.

Little comparable theory or established methodology exists for the study of population-resource relationships and the pressures which may arise from them. What does exist is lacking in co-ordination, systematization, and detailed development. We have progressed relatively little from the propositions advanced by Thomas Malthus more than a century and a half ago. Population-resource relationships have created major contemporary problems, yet their study often has been neglected or less than rigorously pursued. The terms "overpopulation," "underpopulation" and "optimum population" continue to be used in such an absolute sense as to be almost meaningless, though *Hart** maintains that optimum population can be useful if considered in strictly relative terms.

As an example of the neglect, *Browning* notes that sociologists have studied population pressure to a limited extent only, attributing this to "Western experience," a tendency to underemphasize human ecological factors, and the nonbehavioral nature of PPR. They are, however, by no means alone in their largely negative approach, and *Mrs. Taeuber,* a distinguished demographer, stresses the need for developed theory and hypothesis to encompass the complexities of man, land, and resources within the changing contexts of culture, history, and technology. To accomplish this would involve "the procuring of data, the relating of people to space at specific points of time and over time." Even given these data, she notes the small likelihood of our generating a deterministic model for future population-resource developments that would have much predictive value.

* Names in italics, in this introduction and in those following, are those of participants in the Symposium.

The papers in this section were neither intended or expected to produce a body of acceptable theory; nevertheless they discuss many important concepts and methods relevant to such theory building. They identify and illustrate, drawing attention to many of the gaps, flaws, and fallacies in studies of population-resource relationships. *Zelinsky* says that there is a need to define our goals more clearly, and his introductory essay explores critically some of the basic assumptions commonly made about population and resource problems. Many of these are based on false, or at best inadequate, premises.

Pokshishevskii, as he reaches back to the past and forward to a reasonably attractive future in a broad global view of population and resources, is consistently critical of the pessimism of Malthusians and neo-Malthusians alike, whose views he associates with the ideas and methods of the capitalist system. The neo-Malthusians, he says, have substituted "poor countries" for their predecessors' "poor people," and he advocates the need for developing countries to develop resources actively and to adapt levels of population growth to the existing limited levels of development. He also acknowledges the need for *family planning,* though not *family limitation.* With such developments he foresees reasonable prospects for the future, even though the next few decades may present difficulties.

Having referred to the sociological view of the nonbehavioral nature of the concept of population pressure, *Browning* points to the ways in which pressures may manifest themselves in social terms. As a result of scarcity —an inevitable characteristic of pressure—communities retreat inward upon themselves, seeking refuge in the relative security of the nuclear family, with a breakdown in communal attitudes and cooperation. Such a breakdown—or "break-up," to use the term adopted in our symposium discussions—may ultimately be beneficial if it serves to stimulate the individual incentives and initiatives crucial for socioeconomic development.

Unlike many economists, *McLoughlin* regards human beings as the prime variable in economic development, and accords population growth and distribution their own special theoretical and practical importance rather than treating them as abstract data in an equation or a model. This attitude is further developed in his discussion of the need to see problems from the points of view of those who experience them. He recognizes that what may be technically possible may not be humanly acceptable. *Mrs. Boserup,* another economist, is also concerned with developments that are technically feasible but which present problems in application. She views population as an independent variable which can stimulate resource development and whose growing needs can be met through an intensified use of land by increasing the frequency of its use. This desired situation can be achieved, provided that the rates of population growth are not so rapid as to overwhelm the rate of economic development. Those factors which bring resource development into phase with population growth are largely economic and usually viewed from the point of view of their economic implication. The most important factors are capital and its organization, and the major problems are political and social obstacles to capital investment.

Social factors in population pressure on resources are examined particularly by *Brookfield* and *Mabogunje*. The former regards pressure as a single force operating on a society, or as the result of a group of forces. He reviews the socio-political institutions of various groups and their management of resources under the influence of increasing population, differentiating between "flexibility" and "restriction" in access to and use of resources. *Mabogunje* also emphasizes the importance of socio-political systems in achieving a relatively favorable balance between population growth and the development of resources. He argues the importance of the various standards of living which different people expect from their resources, and identifies these "expectations" as perhaps the most crucial factor in understanding population pressure (cf. *McLoughlin* who also queries the importance of "aspirations"). On the basis of combinations of high or low levels of resources, population, and expectations, *Mabogunje* elaborates a framework for population-resource relationships in which population pressure may be identified as occurring in three of the possible combinations. Each combination is illustrated with West African examples, two of which show that population pressure can have positive as well as negative effects.

In sum, the papers in this section suggest a variety of ways in which theory and methods may be developed for the study of population-resource relationships. They illustrate marked similarities in approach and attitudes between individuals and between disciplines concerned with the study of these relationships. These similarities are encouraging in suggesting base-lines for further study. There are also important differences among contributors which are not to be regarded negatively, but rather as positive contributions to interdisciplinary co-operation. Several authors stress this interdisciplinary need either directly or otherwise. *Mrs. Taeuber* writes of attempting to involve "all human experiences" in this most urgent of human problems. *Browning* suggests that, as well as being interdisciplinary, the strategy for study must be essentially comparative.

Whatever the approach may be, it is clear that further studies of population pressures on resources, the factors which give rise to them and the problems that result are urgently needed. The understanding and evaluation so gained should contribute measurably toward solutions of these problems. *Zelinsky* rightly disclaims any charge of "congenital pessimism" against the views he expresses, but also stresses the need for positive thinking leading to positive action in respect to population-resource relationships as "the era of spontaneous change and piecemeal decisions draws to a close." If solutions are to be achieved, there may be the need, as *Mrs. Boserup* suggests (and as *Pokshishevskii* regards as axiomatic) for increasing authority at all levels. But authority can only be exercised successfully in the long-term if there is a full appraisal and an understanding of existing problems.

1. THE GEOGRAPHER AND HIS CROWDING WORLD: CAUTIONARY NOTES TOWARD THE STUDY OF POPULATION PRESSURE IN THE DEVELOPING LANDS

Wilbur Zelinsky

If anything is safely predictable for the final third of this most complex, dynamic, and crucial of mankind's many centuries, it is that the management and consequences of rapid, massive population increase will engross the attention of more and more of our best minds. Parallel with that ominously steepening arc graphing the total accumulation of human beings, there has been a recent upsurge of interest in such matters not only among social scientists but also among statesmen and the public at large. For anyone who recalls with chagrin the apathy concerning matters demographic in places both high and low a mere twenty years ago, the current general consternation over the "Population Explosion" is scarcely credible, and even a bit disconcerting. What is implied thereby is an expectation that somehow, however late in the game it may be, the "experts" will save the day with some brilliant panacea or technical legerdemain. The main burden of this essay is that there is as yet little grounds for such faith. The enormity and uniqueness of the huge twentieth century proliferation of human numbers has caught population scientists unawares, or at least technically and methodologically unequipped. I can say this with some assurance for the still rather underdeveloped field of population geography; but I suspect that the situation is not much better among demographers in general.

The basic argument can be stated quite simply: We are about to confront practical decisions of the utmost gravity in our social, economic, ethical, political, and ecological affairs brought about, in large part, by very great population increments in recent years in most inhabited areas and by the even greater growth forecast for the immediate future. Furthermore, theoretical problems of major interest and importance are being posed by the radically novel situations now coming into being. Unfortunately, our existing body of population doctrine was distilled from the experience of past or vanishing epochs of decreasing relevance to this strange new "crowded" world. Indeed, the inertia of ideas being what it is, we may find ourselves positively hindered in the scientific study of developing population pressures by some of our scholarly legacy or the related folk wisdom of the literate. As a contribution toward the more realistic, meaningful, and utilitarian theoretical framework still to be erected—a ground-clearing operation so to speak—I propose to examine eleven important ideas that are either explicit or implicit in recent statements and thought on population matters, and are also of some interest to geographers. It will be argued that all can be classed as either fallacies or unproved assumptions, the latter to be used with caution awaiting the time they can be either certified or discredited. The casual reader may infer congenital pessimism or malicious mischief in this approach. In actuality, the mood is one of painful self-scrutiny and the intent that of breaking through to deeper levels of understanding and ultimately to truly constructive approaches to the long-term welfare of our species and its habitat. In this process, it is necessary to concede that a lively appreciation of one's ignorance is the beginning of true wisdom.

From *Revista Geografica* (Rio de Janiero), 65, December 1966, pp. 7-28. Reprinted by permission of the publisher.

Attention is confined to the so-called "underdeveloped" world, or "developing lands," more for the sake of convenience than through conviction. It is quite possible that the arithmetically less alarming rates of population growth in the advanced nations, combined as they are with virtually unlimited expansion of economic production and consumption and by more mischievous manipulation of the environment, may ultimately engender crises more pernicious and insoluble than those so visibly looming over less affluent countries. It is also arguable that both the ultimate causes and cures for the population-resource afflictions of the underdeveloped world are to be found in the advanced nations. Currently, neither proposition is so nearly generally accepted as the imminence of trouble in the former class of areas. And since a separate essay would be needed to validate these theses, the question of the advanced nations is bypassed reluctantly for the time being.

Before this review of dubious propositions can be begun, two premises must be stated: that a critical situation is indeed being produced in the developing lands by the amount and rate of population growth; and that,

quite aside from the sheer magnitude of this expansion, the new sets of man-earth and man-man relationships that are linked to this growth are qualitatively distinct from anything that has preceded them historically.

Scientists are obliged to be skeptical creatures, by virtue of temperament and their professional charge. The sheer raucousness of some of the Neo-Malthusian canon and the fear-mongering of various journalistic approaches to the population problems of developing lands will automatically induce some students to assume that so much sound and fury may well signify nothing. Unfortunately, though the shriller criers of havoc may be doing their cause more harm than good, the simple facts are incontrovertible.

There are many ways to indicate the severity of the approaching crisis, even though, admittedly, we are still quite uncertain as to exactly what forms it will take or what the outcome will be. One device, as effective as any, is to consider the probable change in total population of the developing lands during the expected lifetime of children already born. For the following six, randomly chosen nations, I have projected the aggregate population that will reside in each at the time the

	Population[1] 1964 (millions)	Annual Rate[2] of Increase 1964	Expectation of[2] Life at Birth, Female	Projected Population, Year of Death of Average Female Born 1964 (millions)
Brazil	78.8	+2.81%	45.5 (1940-50)	289.2
Costa Rica	1.4	3.82	57.0 (1949-51)	12.3
Egypt	28.9	2.73	53.8 (1960)	132.4
Jordan	1.9	4.08	50.0 (est.)	13.7
Indonesia	102.2	2.2	50.0 (est.)	302.5
South Korea	27.6	2.76	53.7 (1955-60)	125.9

1. Population Index, 32:1 (1966).
2. Population Index, 31:4 (1965).

average female inhabitant born in 1964 can be expected to die. These projections, based on 1964 population figures, the most reliable estimates of annual rate of increase for the same date, and the most recent data on female expectation of life at birth, are somewhat conservative. The indicated rate of change for 1964 may understate the true rate in some instances; in addition, mortality rates are susceptible to lowering, or are actually declining in some of these countries; and almost certainly the 1964 life expectation value in every case well exceeds that given here.

Thus we must quite soberly contemplate the prospect that an Egyptian girl born in 1964 will breathe her last in a nation containing over 132 million inhabitants. Given Egypt's present social and physical resources, I find it impossible to imagine how so many individuals could live in reasonable material comfort without some truly revolutionary remodeling of the social and economic structure of the country. Such a development is, of course, not necessarily undesirable or impossible, but would be quite a feat during the next 54 years. The same argument applies to the other nations, although the immediate environmental constraints upon demographic growth are not nearly as great in Brazil, Costa Rica, or (outer) Indonesia. The dilemmas of large populations pressing upon limited, immediately exploitable resources could be circumvented by a rapid reduction in fertility; but this too (unless implemented by brute force) would imply a rather implausible degree of skill in social engineering or incredibly good luck. The more probable alternative is a serious depression of level of living and a return to the former pattern of high mortality rates and low expectation of life. In any event, the status quo cannot be maintained; difficult, painful, and even disastrous alternatives must be pondered.

The argument that the present or impend-

ing population-resource situation of the developing lands is historically unique could be sustained quite firmly on quantitative grounds. Never before in human history has there been so rapid and persistent an increase in population involving so large a percentage of mankind; and, although there is little comfort in this fact, it seems highly unlikely that the experience can ever be repeated during a later epoch. The sheer mass and rapidity of this change would in itself induce major qualitative social and geographic innovations. But there are more fundamental reasons for the uniqueness of the developing situation. There is growing evidence that the current extraordinary demographic situation is but a single phase of a larger unique episode in human history—the phenomenon that has received the unfortunate, but probably indelible, designation "underdevelopment." Poverty, in many forms and degrees, has always been with us; and there have been earlier large, rapid, localized spurts of population. But the existence of large, impoverished masses of people undergoing rapid numerical increase for several decades is indeed quite unprecedented; and the profound disequilibrium between demographic growth and a relatively slow expansion or exploitation of physical and social resources appears to be symptomatic of some quite deep structural changes—possibly of a pathological character—in the nature and organization of human society. Thus the so-called "Population Explosion" is both a symptom of and a contributing factor to a much larger process, of which "Underdevelopment" is another relatively visible manifestation. This observation leads logically to the first of the ideas to be scrutinized:

1. *The fallacy that the population-resource disequilibrium of the developing lands is an isolated phenomenon, and the unproved assumption that it constitutes their single most important problem.*

The first portion of this statement is one that few thoughtful scholars would endorse, since it collapses the moment the real world is examined. Nonetheless, it merits our attention since this is a notion that much recent non-academic literature would tend to convey. There is also the ever-present danger that the population student may unconsciously slip into this fallacy when, as he often must, he disaggregates the fearsome complexities of social reality into manageable fragments. In any event, the image of a simple, stable underdeveloped community, idyllically undisturbed and unchanging for centuries, suddenly erupting demographically with the arrival of a few physicians, nurses, wonder drugs, and DDT is patently misleading. In almost every instance, the community had, for some time, been experiencing radical changes, either under the direct impact of the advanced nations or through endogenous processes initiated by such contacts. Thus a great many new things had been going on; and the rather abrupt onset of a decidedly lower death rate (and possibly also a significantly higher birth rate) came as the culmination of a whole series of changes, not as a whimsical trick of fate. Furthermore, the new demographic regime is associated with major revisions in socioeconomic and psychological patterns and with innovations in transportation, communications, education, and many aspects of technology. The interactions among all these are real and important; and this functional interrelatedness, which may frequently find spatial expression, is a quality that should endear the study of population change to the geographer.

A major reason for belief in this fallacy—or allegiance to the unproved assumption that population-resource disequilibrium, i.e. the "Population Problem," is the most urgent of problems in the underdeveloped world—is its exceptional statistical visibility. The number of inhabitants is probably the most widely available statistic for underdeveloped countries taken as a whole. Rapid change in this index can be detected quickly and easily even by the most amateurish of observers. On the other hand, it is reasonable to suggest, at least for the sake of argument, that even more momentous upheavals have been going on in the basic socioeconomic structure, in ideas, values, and attitudes, in the nature of the relations among communities, among individuals, and between man and the land, or even in the essential psychological makeup of the people—and that, in fact, one or more of these sets of changes comprise the truly central and decisive problem. If such is the case, then we are faced with problems of observation, measurement, and analysis that will tax our most resourceful social scientists. The more radical transformations that may underlie an abrupt demographic change could involve entities not easily quantifiable and, in any case, ones not immediately rising to any statistical surface. Least of all are they likely to reveal themselves in the visible landscape; and in much of the underdeveloped world revolutionary new generations of social and economic geographies may have reached an advanced embryonic stage and be ready for hatching within the shell of old, traditional vistas.

In brief, then, recent population growth in underdeveloped countries at a pace well beyond the demonstrated capacity of social and economic systems to provide adequately for human needs is a phenomenon inextricably bound to other less well observed, or poorly understood, ongoing processes. Until we learn the true nature and interrelations of this complex of processes, the chain of causes and effects, and the hierarchy of forces among them, there is no sound basis for claiming that excessive population growth is the most crucial problem confronting these areas.

2. The fallacy that any consensus exists concerning the kind of resolution to be sought for the population-resources problems of the developing lands (disregarding the means to be employed to attain this desideratum).

The discovery that the foregoing notion is indeed a fallacious one is probably more unsettling philosophically and more suggestive of future practical difficulties than any of the other negative or cautionary statements offered in this essay. Virtually every writer and social scientist who has been responsive to the demographic distress of the underdeveloped world has instinctively adopted the idea that he, or the people concerned, clearly visualizes the sort of normalcy, the demographic or economic good health to which the community must be restored. In actual fact, almost no methodical thinking has been done on this crucial issue.

A rough medical analogy may be in order. Imagine that some students of natural history acquire in a young, immature form the only known specimen of a rare animal species, one never before observed in its adult stage, and attempt to rear and study it in captivity. During the process, this unique creature contracts a serious chronic disease, one which finally becomes acute, produces serious malformations, and threatens its life. All the attending veterinarians agree that everything possible must be done to save it. They have succeeded in describing the symptoms and are able to diagnose intelligently the probable causes. Several possible courses of treatment suggest themselves. They have, of course, never previously been applied to this particular animal; and although it is not certain whether any of the possible therapies will be efficacious, it is agreed to try the most promising one. At this juncture, one of the more reflective veterinarians points out that during the course of his illness their patient has apparently entered the adolescent stage and

may, in fact, be on the verge of full adulthood. How are they to tell just when the treatment has succeeded, i.e. when the creature begins to look and act like a healthy, normal *adult* of its species? How can they be sure that, although the therapy may save its life, it may not also produce a permanently crippled, abnormal organism and, incidentally, spoil forever their earlier plans for studying its behavior and biological characterics?

As we leave our imaginary friends with their unresolved quandary, it must be admitted that this is a defective analogy. Strictly speaking, no discussion of either immediate action or ultimate results is absolutely necessary in the case of "runaway" population growth in the underdeveloped lands. It is simple to demonstrate mathematically that the problem is self-limiting, that within a very few generations the current rate of growth must come to an end because of the finiteness of terrestrial mass and space and the existence of certain basic physical laws. And the patient will not necessarily die if left unattended. Even though the final results may be most unpleasant, the prognoses are, in order of declining plausibility, an arresting or reversal of growth through (a) a death rate rising well above present levels, (b) a spontaneous decline in fertility, or (c) any of the many possible combinations of the two foregoing changes. The countries passing through this experience of letting their population crisis run its course may find themselves subsisting under wretched conditions; but the population will have survived somehow.

Many of the affected countries still remain at the stage where the problem is unrecognized or where, through disinterest, indecision, or positive choice, a laissez-faire policy is being followed. But more and more—and eventually possibly all—will agree that it is desirable and urgently necessary to avoid major catastrophe. And that, finally, returns us to the main point of this discussion: Is it possible to adhere to a policy that limits itself to the purely negative objective of substantially reducing rates of population growth? It seems much more intelligent, more common-sensical tactically, to recognize that, willy-nilly, such a policy will result in a country basically different from what it has been, or that the negative program is more likely to be consummated if it is combined with a positive push toward useful and desirable goals. The status quo ante cannot possibly be patched together again. And so what sort of world are we getting in its stead? Or what sort of world *can* or *should* we strive for?

We are, in fact, being coerced by the huge, inexorable mechanism of the "modernization" process into thinking seriously about which utopias, or sub-utopias, or reasonable facsimiles thereof, we can put on the drawing boards. It is even conceivable that this compulsory review of means and ends may be a blessing in disguise. Gone are the leisurely days when history took care of itself. Until recently, one could hopefully contemplate the autonomous forces of social and economic change propelling mankind forever forward and upward along the erratic, but ascending, paths of Progress toward some glorious, if rather indistinct, destiny. Now it is abundantly clear that active, skillful human intervention is mandatory for survival or for the qualitative enhancement of human existence.

No agreement has been reached, and none is possible without great difficulty, over the goals—the signs of returning health—that might be striven for in any campaign to deal with extremely rapid population growth. Or perhaps the issue has already been settled tacitly. Many writers claim that the underdeveloped countries have been undergoing a "Revolution of Rising Expectations" (though without much specificity as to what is being

expected). It is not really clear, and certainly has not been verified by any rigorous research, that any truly fundamental revision of material appetites or life-goals has taken place; but if it has, these new values must be reckoned with in any demographic programs. In any case, what aspirations can be proclaimed concerning the size, composition, dynamics, economic status, environmental ecology, or any of a variety of relationships between man and physical and social resources in the populations that will have survived their period of trauma? Even more basically, which (or whose) values—cultural, philosophical, or whatever—are to be preserved and strengthened? What of our obligations to other species of life or to the quality of the inanimate environment? For whose benefit are plans to be made and implemented—for that of the locality, the nation, or all of mankind? Or for which segment of the population—the business community, the military, the administrative bureaucracy, the intelligentsia, or the "common people"? And for which generation—those who are now alive, or their children or grandchildren? Or do we think in terms of perpetuity? These are profound questions of intent to be debated, questions of scale, duration, conflict of interest, and philosophic bias. I would suggest that the time has arrived when we should begin asking them.

3. The preoccupation with population numbers as items of essential importance per se.

Population scientists are so accustomed to dealing with statistics as a useful surrogate for the reality with which they are, in fact, truly concerned that they may impute to them an importance not actually inherent in them. More specifically, scholars, and many laymen as well, may tend to view population-resource problems in the light of numerical indices rather than the grosser, and partly unmeasurable, world that underlies them. It is self-evident that for any given area or community a particular population size is not absolutely good or bad in itself as long as it stands somewhere above the minimum needed for biological and cultural survival and below that maximum where sheer physical congestion inhibits the movement or physical and mental health of individuals. This statistic is important, of course, but only takes on meaning in the context of specific conditions and specific value systems (even though, incidentally, it is extremely difficult to assign hard numerical values to the concepts of "underpopulation," "overpopulation," or "optimum" population even when all the facts and assumptions are open to inspection). In the same vein, no specific rate of population change is necessarily good or evil—unless it is prolonged to the point where the population either disappears or expands to calamitous dimensions. Thus, during a limited time span, population growth or decline, or stasis, or a complex cycle of change may be good, bad, or indifferent, depending on the character of the place and the period. An annual net reproductive increase of + 4.0 per cent or thereabouts in Kentucky in 1790 was an occasion for rejoicing; in El Salvador in 1990 it could be disastrous.

Excessive preoccupation with population counts may lead to treatment of symptoms rather than causes. We may find ourselves worrying over how to slow down the annual population increment in some area from 3 per cent to 1 per cent or less, while omitting any real concern about gains or losses in human and social values. Conversely, the absence of any perturbations on the demographic fever chart may lead to a false sense of well-being. A stable population is not necessarily a happy or a fundamentally healthy one. Just as we can delude ourselves into believing that all is well with the body politic if the citizens are not actively rioting in the streets, so too it is possible to postpone dangerously any serious investigation of the population/resource situation in a region that seems stationary in its behavior.

4. The fallacy of demographic predestination—the belief that mankind is moving teleologically toward a happy resolution of its population problems or, conversely, directly toward demographic doom.

This is a fallacy that is much more likely to be implicit, or sometimes even subconscious, rather than explicitly avowed by the student. It may be the result of belief in supernatural forces or simply a matter of temperamental outlook. The scholar is, of course, entitled to harbor his own private credo, whether it be melioristic or fatalistic, but should guard against letting it warp his judgment when attempting to deal in systematic, scientific fashion with the facts at hand. In particular, there is genuine danger that this kind of innate bias may predispose the population scientist to write as though man were either utterly impotent or else all-powerful in grappling with his demographic destiny. As it happens, no very convincing evidence is yet visible in the pattern of history or the innate logic of current facts to support belief in either brand of teleology—the inevitable ascent of mankind to higher levels of social and geographic grace or the imminence of Doomsday. Is it not the better part of wisdom for the population scholar to take nothing for granted, but rather proceed to test the limits of the necessary and the possible through careful observation and analysis and through the design of action programs that are not circumscribed by unproved, a priori assumptions?

5. The fallacy that the population-resource problem in developing lands is simply one of adequate food production.

This is a fallacy that is widely and explicitly current in both the scholarly and popular literature on demographic problems. And since food production is a favorite subject for geographic investigation, geographers may be particularly vulnerable to it. It is, of course, axiomatic that the day-to-day problem of feeding most of the low-income citizens of low-income lands is a matter of large, lasting concern. During the millennia when most communities were small, self-contained, nonmonetary economic units operating outside any large regional or world market, local food production could indeed be the paramount problem in survival; and insofar as population-resource crises appeared, food shortages might be cause or effect. But it does not follow, now that all the world's peoples are more or less integrated into the world market economy, that either the population-resource problem or the phenomenon of underdevelopment can be defined solely, or even primarily, in terms of the calories people consume or how much food they can grow. To see them as such, even at the rudimentary level of immediate human needs, is a gross distortion of reality, a sort of alimentary determinism.

For his animal survival, man everywhere requires food, potable liquids, and breathable air and, in those areas with winters or cold nights, clothing, shelter, and domestic fuel. But even the most primitive communities have other needs; and in those lands that can be realistically called "developing," there is an imposing inventory of necessities. Industrial fuel and energy requirements must be met; a wide range of industrial raw materials is called for; various services—among them, transportation, education, and administration—must be supplied; and the amenities are in ever increasing demand. Indeed, as the country climbs up the developmental scale, the problem of producing and supplying food recedes as other problems come to the fore; yet population-resource crises may still occur. Indeed, I believe it is possible for even the most advanced of nations to anticipate severe population-resource situations in which the issue of food supply may be totally irrelevant. And the irrelevance of food production as the critical element in population-resource imbalances may also be demonstrated in those various countries, past or present, that have produced food surpluses but, nonetheless, have displayed acute symptoms of "underdevelopment" or of an incapacity to provide for the wants of rapidly increasing populations.

A country may be said to have mastered its population-resource problems when it is living within its own technical, institutional, and ecological means and at the same time offering its inhabitants the wherewithal for acquiring all the goods and services they regard as basic for a decent existence. This "wherewithal" simply means purchasing power. And money, in turn, implies the existence of reasonably well-paying jobs for all, or nearly all, the labor force, and a labor force with a reasonably high level of productivity, or, more precisely, the capacity for producing in abundance goods and services other people wish to buy. Where a market demand exists, in the form of would-be purchasers willing and able to spend money, food or any other commodity can be furnished to the inhabitants of either underdeveloped or advanced countries from either external or internal sources.

It is quite inaccurate to characterize an area as suffering from "population problems" if it does not produce all the foodstuffs it consumes. (Most advanced nations would fall into this class.) It is equally erroneous to believe that an underdeveloped land experiencing food shortages will shed its status as an area undergoing population-resource problems simply by importing or producing more food—unless the augmented production yields a marketable, transportable surplus that will generate capital for the developmental process. This is not the solving of a problem, but simply the temporary staving off of starvation or malnutrition. In any case, it is unfair to expect the underdeveloped lands to be what nearly all the advanced nations are not—self-sufficient in the basic raw materials for human existence.

Even on a planetary scale, the availability of food cannot be said to be an essential issue in present or impending population-resource crises, at least for the next few generations. If consumers in the underdeveloped areas were, through some magic, to acquire instantaneously large amounts of cash for food purchases or, better still, the negotiable goods and services which such cash represents, the nations possessing advanced agricultural techniques could probably double, or perhaps triple, their output of foodstuffs within the next few years, using currently known techniques and capital equipment already on hand or readily obtainable. And it is quite thinkable that this brisk demand might also induce farmers in the less developed countries to extend and upgrade their activities and vastly increase their output. It has been estimated that if all the world's present and potential food-producing surfaces were exploited to maximum capacity, using current technologies or those that can be reasonably anticipated for the future, it should be possible to feed as many as 50 billion persons. We are ignoring, of course, the supply of other physical and social needs or the quality of human existence that would result from such single-minded agricultural zeal.

Thus, until a genuine impasse in agricultural expansion is reached, the real problem is employment and productivity, how an underdeveloped society can rearrange and revolutionize its socioeconomic structure so that its citizens can produce enough goods (in-cluding edibles, but certainly much else besides) and services that can be exchanged with other peoples for other goods and services and thus also, one hopes, makes life comfortable, purposeful, and interesting. Unfortunately, the steps whereby these revolutionary changes are initiated are still rather mysterious; and there is no guarantee that any country can enjoy such a transformation just by wanting and struggling for it. However, anything else, including the simple expansion of food production for subsistence within the traditional economy, will not provide a way out of the economic dilemma faced by such areas; at best, it would merely postpone the crucial period. In summary, then, population-resource problems in developing lands can be neither defined nor solved solely in terms of food production.

6. The unproved assumption that processes already in operation will rid the developing countries of their population-resource problems.

Under this dubious proposition, we can group several rather different notions, but ones that all imply strong faith in some deus ex machina or in the long-term rightness and equilibrium induced by the autonomous workings of basic geographic, social, economic, and political processes. They are thus not unrelated to the teleological dogma discussed above as Item 4. Perhaps the most interesting and attractive of these various sub-assumptions is:

(a) The unproved assumption that rapid, massive population growth under contemporary conditions will of itself trigger major economic advance or, at least, contribute materially to its success.

The chief inspiration for this notion is, of course, the fact that among the advanced nations both phenomena—rapid growth and qualitative change in the economy; and a great expansion in the population—have been roughly concurrent. Furthermore, under certain conditions, within these same countries, it is clear that population growth is a positive stimulant to the economy. But it would appear that this is a dangerous analogy as applied to the underdeveloped countries. Although the two events do much overlap in time, the evidence indicates that it was significant economic innovation that tended to precede the demographic revolution, not the other way around. An even greater difficulty is the fact that the preconditions for both demographic and economic growth in the advanced nations were so strikingly different from those prevailing in the currently "developing" lands. In brief, then, there is as yet no well-authenticated instance in modern demographic history of rapid demographic growth in any sort of country preceding, or becoming one of the significant reasons for, basic improvements in the economy. It is true enough that such might seem superficially to have happened in Hong Kong, Taiwan, Puerto Rico, Jamaica, Mexico, and Venezuela; but I believe that the facts indicate quite the contrary in each case—that large population increments have been economic hindrances or, at best, of neutral value.

It is not impossible that rapid population growth may become the main instrument for significant economic advance in some underdeveloped land in the future; but for the moment we have no proof that this has ever happened or that it is likely to happen. It is, of course, also possible that an awareness of rapid population growth may precipitate a course of action leading to economic progress; but this is quite another matter.

There are persuasive arguments, as put forward by Ester Boserup (*The Conditions of Agricultural Growth: The Economics of Agrarian Change under Population Pressure,* Chicago, 1965) for a related hypothesis—that sustained, relatively slow population growth may have been the prime genetic factor in bringing about the intensification of agricultural output per unit of land and, ultimately, radical changes in land-use systems and a complex train of consequences in the spheres of social and political behavior. There may be much truth in this argument (although I suspect that the actual situation has been rather more complicated and ambiguous than such a simple one-way cause-and-effect formula would indicate); but the author is careful to refrain from any claim that her idea is valid for places currently undergoing rapid rural population increases.

(b) A mystic belief in national salvation through the more or less spontaneous development of "great, untapped natural riches."

This amounts to a visceral feeling rather than any coherent doctrine, and is simply faith in the prospect that somehow through the exploitation in some unspecified ways of natural resources, whose nature and extent are at best quite approximately surveyed, the nation will arrive at some unspecified answer to its demographic, social, and economic worries. A careful inventory of possibilities and a detailed set of working plans for their realization may or may not be necessary eventually; but they are incidental to the central article of this faith: the transcendent goodness and wonder-working nature of these as yet untouched gifts of Nature. Although this sort of feeling will not withstand logical analysis, it is influential among large sections of the general population, as well as the governing elite, at least in Indonesia, Mexico, Guatemala, Brazil, and other nations sharing the Amazon Basin, and in several African nations.

(c) Present and future pioneer settlement as the way out of the demographic dilemma.

This notion is, of course, closely related

to the preceding one. And it is also a most appealing option in the diminishingly few underdeveloped countries that do still have any considerable amount of land suitable for pioneer settlement—particularly in the light of the historical experience of Anglo-America, Siberia, Australia, Argentina, and a few other areas where rapid frontier advance seems to have had a salutary effect upon the national welfare. Unfortunately, only a few realistic observations will quickly deflate one's confidence in the frontier as the great hope of underdeveloped nations suffering from population pressure upon available resources. Recent experience indicates that the supply of empty land meriting any sort of capital input under present conditions is quite finite and likely to be exhausted rapidly, that (with the one, quite temporary, exception of Costa Rica) the frontierward migration removes only a minor fraction of the redundant population from overcrowded areas, that these frontier zones contribute little, if anything at all, to the net worth of the national economy of underdeveloped lands, and that where, as so often happens, unplanned or unsupervised settlement occurs, the effects may be most deleterious to the habitat and to its agricultural and general biotic productivity. However, this is not to deny the possibility that pioneer settlement may be a most useful and profitable device as part of a larger, well-organized national development plan.

(d) The continuing export of permanent or temporary emigrants to foreign lands as a demographic "safety valve."

There is little doubt that this device has worked well to alleviate population pressures in a number of smaller nations or dependencies. Among those that come readily to mind are Jamaica, Puerto Rico, several of the Lesser Antilles, the Azores, the Canary Islands, Algeria, Malta, Syria, Lebanon, Greece, and Western Samoa. In these cases and others, there are two obvious advantages: the immediate reduction in the ranks of the unemployed or the underemployed; and the return flow of remittances from abroad. But there is one major drawback. Those most likely to leave are usually those who are also the least expendable—the skilled, well-educated, and ambitious—precisely the persons most needed to man the growth points in the national economy and infrastructure. Mass emigration is, in any case, not a valid general solution, and least of all in those countries with more than a very few million inhabitants. It is ludicrous even to think of it in connection with the Chinese, Indians, or Pakistani, or even the much smaller Egyptian population. And it is the most irresponsible, pseudoscientific sort of folly to suggest extraterrestrial outlets for potential emigrants.

Even the maintenance of the *status quo* may be difficult for the various smaller areas that are postponing a basic solution to their population-resource difficulties through vigorous emigration. The historic trends of the present century point clearly to further restrictions on international movements of migrants not to their relaxation. Even where the channels are left open for small, but crowded, lands enjoying a privileged political or economic relationship with a larger, more affluent patron, the relative demand for unskilled labor is likely to shrink, while the flow of the skilled and semi-skilled may quicken, to the benefit of the latter and detriment of the former.

(e) The transfer of redundant population from rural tracts to urban centers as a major contribution toward the solution of population-resource problems.

The urbanization process is well begun and rapidly accelerating in nearly all underdeveloped lands. Thus, if this cityward movement does indeed offer much hope as a way of eliminating population pressures, it has the added advantage of calling for little artificial encouragement. Largely for lack of sufficient research, we know much too little about the economic and demographic consequences of rapid urbanization in the underdeveloped world. The few broad generalizations that can be offered, however, do little to support the stated assumption. In virtually every instance, the removal of migrants from countryside to town or city is much less rapid than the natural increase of rural populations. Although the availability of social services and amenities may be greater in the cities, it has yet to be demonstrated that, as a general rule, the chances for full employment are greater or that real incomes are significantly higher in an urban milieu. There may be certain cost-saving advantages for the national economy in the centralization of skills and markets; but there are also severe strains upon poorly developed supply systems. Thus we may be rapidly approaching the danger point in the logistics of water, food, fuel, and raw materials in several large metropolises, not to mention grave difficulties in waste disposal and the provision of vital social services.

Another disappointment is the finding that the depression of fertility rates has been much less in the metropolises of developing lands than in their counterparts in advanced nations. The urban birth rates, though appreciably lower than in the countryside, are still high enough so as to ensure a vigorous growth of city population even without further recruitment of rural migrants. Thus, as with pioneer settlement, the urbanization process is far from a complete answer, even though it may well play a significant role in a larger, more effective program.

(f) The belief that many demographically distressed underdeveloped lands can survive indefinitely through charitable contributions from the richer nations.

This is a doctrine seldom proclaimed publicly, but one implicit in the actions of the client countries. In a sense this notion underlies all the various aid programs in the developing lands financed by a few rich nations, but with the critical distinction that most of such programs are intended to be catalytic in effect, to furnish "seed money" for what will hopefully become self-sustaining socioeconomic processes rather than a long-term dole. The simple facts of world economic life are adequate prima facie evidence that, even with a maximum effort on the part of the donors, international alms would suffice for only a few fleeting years to support all countries who are acquiring more inhabitants than they are able to provide for. There is little doubt, however, that for a few small, poorly equipped areas—among them, Malta, Okinawa and other Pacific islands, the Gaza Strip, the Netherlands Windward Islands, and French Guiana—present and future survival is contingent upon the uninterrupted flow of outright subsidies. It is also clear that foreign subsidy, though often in disguised form, is a large component in the economic life of many other dependent territories and nominally independent nations; and it is possible that their ranks may swell rather than dwindle during the next few decades.

(g) The fallacy that through the age-old more or less "normal" institution of warfare, a reasonable balance between people and resources can be restored.

This doctrine, one that only rarely erupts into print, but unquestionably lurks in the minds of many individuals, is shaky on some fundamental points. First, there is little evidence that, in the past, warfare has been a *major* long-range determinant of population size among human communities, except among those small, relatively primitive tribal societies for whom a rather ritualized form of battle has been the major outdoor recreation. Secondly, the extension of European economic and political control over nearly the whole of the non-European world during the past few centuries has resulted (despite some notable lapses) in the gradual imposition of a *Pax Europaea* on those areas. Furthermore, the structure of the modern world has become such, specially during the past 20 years, that general agreement seems to have been reached, however tacitly, that military conflicts within and among the underdeveloped nations will be suppressed or contained, the alternative being devastation and bloodletting on an unimaginable planetary scale. In short, as a demographic constraint, mid-twentieth century warfare appears to be a cure much worse than the disease.

The fallacy posed above is quite patently a variant of another subterranean notion, seldom uttered aloud in politer academic circles, that perhaps, after all, it is best to be "hard-boiled" and realistic about the situation and let the imbalance between people and resources take care of itself by doing nothing to avoid a rebounding of mortality to pre-modern levels in the underdeveloped areas, or by even actually encouraging the restoration of the old demographic regime. When it is objectively reviewed, however, this policy fails to make any sense on social, economic, or political grounds, quite aside from moral considerations.

(h) The fallacious hope that the traditional, approximate balance between births and deaths can be maintained in the last few areas beyond the reach of the modernization process, or that somehow the developing countries can reverse course and return to the simple, equilibrial demographic ways of the past.

This nostalgic aspiration has no basis in fact. Again what we have is hardly a coherent, articulate doctrine but rather a set of emotions that do not altogether reach the surface of conscious deliberation. But this is an attitude that may well have affected the treatment of relatively primitive folk within certain advanced nations as well as the handling of relatively retarded communities within the developing lands. Unless another small, remote tribe or two still remains to be found in New Guinea, northern Australia, or some obscure recess of the Amazon and Orinoco basins, all of contemporary humanity has been launched upon the modernization process, with all that that implies in a demographic sense, as well as in other ways. Furthermore, there is a great mass of evidence proving beyond any reasonable doubt that this is an irreversible process. Thus there is no way of erasing the impact of the advanced nations upon the underdeveloped, to make people forget what they have learned and shun the Great World, or to declare a moratorium on change. The question is not whether the peoples of the developing lands must move forward, but rather how, at what rate, and toward what specific destinations.

7. *The unproved assumption that rapid population growth per se will damage man's habitat.*

This widespread idea, which is, of course, of peculiar interest to geographers, rests precariously on two technical questions: the definition of the quality of our physical environment; and the measurement of changes therein. There appears to have been confusion of three distinct items among those who have expressed concern over the human impact upon the face of the earth—the present or potential economic productivity of the affected areas; their aesthetic attractiveness; and the preservation of the ecological integrity of "wild" areas. It must be admitted immediately that no one has yet devised ways of measuring these conditions, much less any techniques for describing their dynamics. But, even assuming that we could, it is most doubtful whether there is, in general, any direct correlation between population density or rate of increase in a specific place on the one hand and its economic worth or visual beauty on the other. Per-unit area output of agricultural and other economic goods may, in fact, increase as fast or faster than population numbers (at least to that point of total, hopeless congestion that has never yet been achieved over any appreciable land surface). Indeed the argument is credible that augmented population density is a major genetic factor in bringing about major increments in soil productivity or in the discovery, creation, or more efficient exploitation of various "natural" resources. Furthermore, archaeological evidence indicates that, among other areas, portions of Mexico, Ceylon, and Iraq maintained for long periods of the past populations greater than those now resident there and without any apparent adverse effects upon the food-producing qualities of the land.

The aesthetic quality of an area is, of course, a highly subjective matter. Nevertheless, a consensus might be reached for the view that some of the loveliest landscapes in the world are to be seen in some of the most crowded, e.g. Japan, the Low Countries, or Highland Guatemala, and that further humanization of many areas, as growth proceeds, may enhance rather than detract from their aesthetic appeal. It is equally apparent that any number of very distressing, contrary examples could be cited to show that population growth has meant both environmental and aesthetic degradation. The point to be made here is that the kinds of changes induced in the appearance and economic utility of an area undergoing brisk demographic growth is most decidedly a function of the nature, structure, and operations of the specific culture or community, not of such growth per se, and that universal postulations are probably not feasible. Thus there exists a wide spectrum of situations, from the thin, nearly static or transient population that commits the most horrendous vandalism upon its surroundings to the very dense, rapidly multiplying groups that husband their physical resources with jealous devotion and constantly add to the value and beauty of their land.

There is no logical riposte to the adherents of the wilderness mystique who are so profoundly distressed by the damage being wrought by man's activities to the delicate ecological fabric of relatively empty areas. There is little doubt that the further spatial extension or intensification of the human pesence will further violate much that is priceless ethically or in any ultimate economic reckoning. As it happens, however, the virginity of even the wildest tracts has already been compromised; and there, as in the more obviously humanized areas, it is urgent that some modus vivendi be contrived that metes out the maximum benefits possible to all species of living things. But this is a concern peripheral to the agenda of the population geographer and the demographer.

8. The unproved assumption that demographic salvation is possible through modern contraceptive technology and exhortation.

If one accepts the thesis that a sharp reduction in fertility is a necessary condition for solving the population-resource pressures of underdeveloped lands, then the means for effecting such a reduction become an issue of transcendent importance. Historically, the only proved method for inducing a lasting and significant lowering of the birth rate has been to raise quite substantially a population's levels of living—and aspiration for further gains. Unfortunately, this process is difficult to initiate, requires the generation and input of considerable capital, and consumes much valuable time. This time lag is a significant one, for not only does it take a number of years to push a population upwards to a higher socioeconomic stage but there is also a further, roughly equivalent period before the new fertility pattern reflects this achievement.

It is understandable, then, that ways are being sought whereby fertility reduction can be realized without waiting out the difficult passage through the "Demographic Transition." Two obvious techniques are not normally feasible either politically or financially—the physical separation of the sexes for prolonged periods (including the enforced postponement of marriage), or massive programs of subsidies designed to limit the number of children or to encourage voluntary sterilization. Nor are any other coercive measures likely to be considered seriously in the near future.

Currently much stress is being laid on the mass distribution of new contraceptive devices and information in the underdeveloped countries. The theory behind such programs is that a number of developing countries have now reached the point where parents realize it is to their economic and social advantage to limit family size even before the inception of significant socioeconomic advances and that they need only some cheap, simple, safe, effective, and psychologically acceptable techniques and perhaps a little official encouragement and propaganda to become successful contraceptors. The two items which seem best to meet the stringent requirements for widespread acceptability among underdeveloped populations are the oral contraceptive pill and the intra-uterine device, or coil (IUD's); and field trials for both have been initiated on a rather ambitious scale.

It is still somewhat too early to have collected and analyzed enough data from Korea, Taiwan, India, Pakistan, and elsewhere to determine whether these programs have had any significant results within the test groups, whether the new fertility pattern, if any, is likely to be a lasting one, or whether the method in question can be extended to the total population of reproductive age. A further complication is the fact that some of these experimental efforts are being carried on in areas, such as Taiwan, where significant socioeconomic development may have already initiated some spontaneous declines in fertility. Organized family limitation programs may, in such cases, simply accelerate an ongoing process, as appears to have happened in Japan during the 1940's and 1950's. Demographic history tells us that possession of advanced contraceptive technology is an incidental matter, while the truly crucial question is whether the potential contraceptors genuinely wish to achieve the small-family pattern. Quite probably the ease with which each community accepts a new, lower fertility pattern will depend upon the fundamental character of its culture and other spatially variable factors. When the need for fewer children is felt, even old, rather primitive contraceptive methods will suffice. But, insofar as the present and impending population-resource impasse is a unique episode in human history, past precedents are not necessarily binding. It is not unthinkable that major, rapid declines in the birth rate can be engineered on a national scale in advance of any important socioeconomic breakthrough, however implausible this may seem in the light of earlier experience. We do not know; we must await the evidence. But, in the interim, it would be imprudent not to examine other alternatives.

9. The unproved assumption that major socioeconomic advance can somehow be achieved in every underdeveloped country that wishes to do so.

If a nation elects to strive for a more comfortable balance between population and resources—and also to achieve other social and economic ends generally deemed desirable—by initiating major socioeconomic development, there is no assurance that it will succeed. Some nations undoubtedly can and will reach their declared goal; but historical precedents are too few in number and too distinct in character from the territories in question to offer any grounds for unqualified optimism. The various European and Neo-European nations and Japan were (with a few exceptions in Southern Europe) launched upon their developmental careers in the nineteenth century or earlier. In any event, their start was made under conditions radically different from those confronting our contemporary underdeveloped countries. Economic development preceded or ran parallel with demographic expansion. Population growth was not racing ahead of economic and social capabilities so as to absorb most of the short supply of capital and physical resources.

A critical survey of the assets and liabilities for economic development of the various underdeveloped countries would indicate that the former are greatly outweighed by the latter. In addition to the severe braking effect of disproportionately rapid population growth, it is obvious that most of these territories are seriously deficient in some of the more elementary physical resources. That this is not an insuperable obstacle is shown by the attainments of such areas as Iceland, New England, Israel, Switzerland, Japan, or Finland, all of whom are at best marginal with respect to natural endowments—or perhaps best of all by the near-miracle of Hong Kong.

What is discouraging is the fact that the combination of advantages necessary to surmount physical handicaps may be lacking. Thus there may be an acute shortage of venture capital, domestic or foreign, available for developing critical components in the economy of the national infrastructure; and, in fact, much in the way of locally generated investment funds may have been exported to safer or more lucrative havens. The exploitation and export of abundant local mineral and agricultural resources can produce funds that may or may not be channeled into local growth-producing enterprises; but future problems in procuring materials needed for an advanced society may also be created thereby.

Many, perhaps most, underdeveloped countries are plagued by chronic political instability, or even military disorder, that makes it difficult to execute even the best-laid development schemes. Paradoxically, the small size of the population and market of many rapidly growing underdeveloped countries makes the formulation of valid economic plans a trying task. One's imagination strains at the prospect of any development plans that are both efficacious and primarily reliant on local resources in such "ministates" as the Maldives, Tonga, Basutoland, Bhutan, Singapore, Mauritius, Jordan, or some, such as Panama, Jordan, Malawi, or Ruanda, that are a bit ampler.

Along with the annoyances of deficiencies of physical resources, investment capital, effective government, and markets of noneconomic size, there are at least two other handicaps that may prove even more frustrating: the dearth of skilled or experienced personnel, native or alien, capable of designing and managing the developmental process; and our quite limited knowledge of how best to draw up intelligent, realistic, and effective developmental blueprints to fit the peculiar needs of each individual country.

It is not even certain whether, under the best of conditions, a more or less sovereign nation can escalate itself upward to genuinely advanced socioeconomic status, and to the demographic concomitants thereof. In this connection, it will be interesting to learn whether such states as Kuwait and Bahrein, with their windfall economies—or Libya, Iraq, and Venezuela—can force-feed themselves and buy their way quickly into advanced status. The answer should be available in a few years. One final uncertainty looming over every country (except China) that aspires to better its socioeconomic standing is the attitude of the two superpowers who monopolize so much of the world's economic and military power. Without their moral, technical, and financial support—or at least acquiescence—it would be foolish to count upon much progress.

10. The unproved assumption that the demographic consequences of major socioeconomic progress in the developing countries will replicate those experienced in the advanced nations.

Once again, we should be restrained by lack of solid historical precedent from declaring that economic development is not only a possible but is a necessary and sufficient means for achieving an efficient demographic budget, i.e. a pattern of low fertility closely approximating a low mortality rate. The assumption that the attainment of advanced socioeconomic status is *always* followed, after an interval of some years or decades, by a major reduction in fertility has not yet been fully tested in enough different countries with different historic and cultural settings. To date, the Demographic Transition and the modernization process have indeed always accompanied each other; but in every instance, development was well under way by the end of the nineteenth century (as was the case in Japan, incidentally), or the country in question is European or Sino-Japanese in culture, and, without exception, the country did not start out after it had begun to suffer the symptoms of underdevelopment. Is there not some possibility that the causal connection between socioeconomic development and fertility may be culture-specific? And may it not be possible that a nation beginning its development program in an underdeveloped condition may follow a rather separate demographic course from that previously observed? In any case, is it safe to extrapolate a universal principle to cover all countries from the experience of a limited number of rather special countries?

The answers to these questions may be forthcoming in the next few years. In addition to the oil-rich states of the Middle East, there are several situations in Latin America where sustained or increasing prosperity should test the hypothesis that family limitation is a necessary sequel to socioeconomic development. These would include portions of Mexico and Venezuela, Puerto Rico, Curaçao, and possibly Jamaica, but would exclude Cuba, Argentina, Uruguay, and Southern Brazil, areas that enjoyed major influxes of European migrants during the past several decades. It may be noteworthy that substantial rises in standardized birth rates have occurred in most Latin American countries, starting in 1920 or later, even where there has been no appreciable socioeconomic progress. It must be admitted, however, that some of our difficulty in knowing just what to expect can be attributed to the fact that the earlier stages of the Demographic Transition were rarely well documented in the currently advanced nations. Thus we cannot be certain whether or not the dynamics of vital rates in the developing lands are paralleling those of earlier travelers through the Demographic Transition.

11. The unproved assumption that developing lands that succeed in attaining advanced socioeconomic status quo and then duplicate the demographic pattern of currently advanced nations will thereby have permanently solved their population-resource problems.

Entry into the charmed circle of advanced nations by no means guarantees any final, absolute resolution of imbalances between people and resources. It may simply change the terms of the problem. The advanced nations comprise a highly unstable system. Population growth does continue at a fairly brisk rate (as compared to the pre-modern period) in nearly all such countries; and economic product and per-capita wants and consumption are climbing an upward slope that has no visible crest. The problems being engendered by large, growing, affluent masses of people caught in the grip of an accelerating technology that seems to have no essential rationale except its own perpetuation and expansion are likely to be much more intense, perverse, and resistant to simple answers than those of the underdeveloped lands. But proper exploration of this point takes us into territory well beyond the range of this essay.

I hope it is evident from the foregoing discussion that we do not yet have enough facts, historical models, or general theory concerning the demography and population geography of the underdeveloped lands to describe, evaluate, and interpret their population-resource problems at all adequately, to predict the future course of these problems, or to prescribe infallible solutions. It should also be plain that it is urgent that much work and thinking be done and the proper research questions asked before much more time has elapsed. For the first time in human history, we are forced to take a hard look at the conditions of humanity in general and the forces that control our lives. And as the era of spontaneous change and piecemeal decisions draws to a close, we are being compelled not only to grasp what has been happening but also somehow to take our futures into our own hands. It is difficult; it is painful; it is necessary; and it is a tremendous challenge to the scholar.

For the geographer, the questions are particularly intriguing. Barring some catastrophe, the underdeveloped world will have at least twice its present population by the end of the century. And it is difficult to conceive how near-stability of numbers can be managed before these countries have three or four times the population now inhabiting them. What will be the geography of these crowding lands, with their burgeoning cities, their ever more mobile citizens, their intensifying ecological stresses, and tremendous, if still unforeseen, new social tensions? Some of the answers may be reportable soon in places such as Haiti, Egypt, El Salvador, Java, Mauritius, and South Korea, possibly even in the 1970's. In any case, we must begin to learn how to study this new geography of mounting population pressures, clearly, analytically, and without the incubus of myth or obsolete dogma. Then perhaps we can help in the effort to realize the full potential of our species and our planet, sanely, richly, and for many millennia to come.

2. WORLD POPULATION AND RESOURCES: THE LARGER HISTORICAL CONTEXT OF THE PROBLEM

V. V. Pokshishevskii

The relationship between human population and the material riches at its disposal is one of the age-old problems that have troubled mankind. It has now become a world-wide problem, and no one can regard it with indifference.

The population of the world is growing, and the rate of its growth has accelerated notably during the last decades. Yet the real (or potential) resources of mankind appear to be finite, even renewable resources such as water power, timber, grain, or fish. As for nonrenewable resources, notably minerals, there are gloomy forecasts that many, if not all, of these resources will be depleted in the near future. Many estimates have indicated that oil reserves may be sufficient for a few decades only. But, in fact, such forecasts have usually been discredited—the discovery of new resources has increased much more quickly than the rate of consumption. Often in the course of history, new resources have been suddenly made available, ones previously without value such as coal, oil, and most recently, uranium. This constant increase of known mineral reserves is especially noteworthy under the conditions of systematically planned geological survey.

HOW HAS WORLD POPULATION BEEN GROWING?

In the past, population growth was so slow that some scholars of the seventeenth and eighteenth centuries considered that it was actually declining relative to a past "Golden Age." Montesquieu, for example, wrote along these lines in *Persian Letters*. In reality, nothing of the kind was taking place, although in some periods a decrease of population, occasionally a catastrophic one, did occur.

It is estimated that some 8000 to 9000 years ago (that is, when man occupied only part of his present *ecumene,* or populated area, and agriculture was only in its beginings) our planet contained only five to ten million people, scarcely more than now live in the Moscow region or the Paris conurbation. By A.D. 1 the population of the earth, as estimated by United Nations experts, approximated 300 ($\pm$ 50) million. At that time, there were 54 million people in the Roman Empire, 23 million of whom lived in Europe (2). By the beginning of the Christian era, there were possibly some 33 million persons in the whole of Europe (20: 21), 71 million in China (6), and between 140 and 150 million in India and Pakistan (4).

By the mid-seventeenth century, the world's population had reached about 553 million (9). Beginning with the eighteenth century, when statistics became more reliable, the following figures can be offered (9):

> 1725— 726,000,000
> 1850—1,325,000,000
> 1900—1,663,000,000
> 1950—2,509,000,000
> 1960—3,010,000,000
> 1964—3,256,000,000

Before our era and as late as the end of the Middle Ages, the period required to double the earth's population fluctuated between 1000 and 2000 years. But since then, the "doubling period" has decreased rapidly. In the eighteenth century, it was already under 200 years; in the nineteenth roughly 100 years; now it is about 40 years, corresponding to an annual natural increase of 1.7

per cent. In many areas the increase rate is still higher, especially in the larger part of Asia outside the U.S.S.R., Canada, and many countries of Africa and Latin America. In still other countries the rate of natural increase comes very near the 1.7 level. We should note, however, that in the most highly developed countries natural increase is far from the forty-year doubling level. In almost all of Western Europe, it is under 1 per cent; in the U.S.A. about 1.3 per cent.

During the seventeenth and eighteenth centuries, settlers appeared in increasing numbers in areas of North America, Australia, and Siberia that were previously almost unpopulated. Here it is convenient for the author to refer to migration processes in northern Asia, of which he had made a special study. Although Russians began to settle in Siberia in the seventeenth century, there were only about 400,000 inhabitants in the area at the beginning of the eighteenth century. Migration to Siberia, accelerated after the abolition of serfdom in 1861, brought about an agrarian crisis in the central provinces of Russia; as a result, approximately 4.2 million migrants had firmly settled in Siberia by the 1917 Revolution or, if East Asia is included, 5 million (11:12). In Soviet times, with the inflow of settlers to the Asian part of the R.S.F.S.R. and the high natural increase there, its population had reached almost 26 million by 1965. In North America during the second half of the nineteenth and the beginning of the twentieth century, from one-quarter to one-third of the total increase of population was due to the influx of people mainly from Europe.[1] Nevertheless, the overwhelming mass of world population is still concen-

trated in the densely settled regions of eastern, southern, southeastern, and southwestern Asia, and in Europe. About three-quarters of the total lived in this belt at the beginning of our era; in the eighteenth century up to 80 per cent; by 1900, 75 per cent; and at present about 70 per cent. Indeed only one new focus of very high population density has been added to the world map—the northeastern United States.

The over-all increase in the earth's population results from an excess of births over deaths. Death rates, of course, fluctuate considerably. This is particularly true for the past, when widespread epidemics and famines were not uncommon; within our own memory the death rate has experienced upward leaps during time of war. However, over the earth as a whole, during the last two hundred years, the death rate has steadily decreased, largely because of improvements in health services: the suppression of epidemics, the eradication of foci for such diseases as malaria and yellow fever, and, in particular, special measures to decrease infant mortality. With regard to death rates, it is characteristic that *people always value life.* Although the death rate depends primarily on socioeconomic conditions, the subjective aspirations of human beings strongly and consistently impel them to seek its reduction. These aspirations are naturally limited by the apparently inevitable process of biological aging and the finiteness of an individual life. Only in exceptional cases, usually among isolated primitive peoples living in especially difficult natural conditions, do social institutions arise that encourage mortality (infanticide or the killing or suicide of the aged).

Only in the remote past was birth a purely instinctive biological process, regulated by physiology and ecology (abundance or shortage of food, etc.). Even at a comparatively early stage, birth rates were influenced by various social institutions and even by social

1. In calculating the long-period immigration balance of the United States, influx of Negro slaves is often omitted. Because the death rate among them was very high, the inflow was in fact considerably higher than is usually estimated from the number of Negroes at the time of the suppression of the slave trade.

"doctrines" of population (the propensity of tribes to strive for greater cohorts of warriors, etc.). It is true that although contraception was known and widely practiced in primitive cultures, it had but little influence on the birth rate. The belief that the wealth and power of a country (and of *latifundi* or feudal fiefs) depended on size of population prevailed among philosophers and historians in antiquity, the Middle Ages, and the Age of Absolutism. This belief gave birth to "populationist" doctrines, which proclaimed population increase to be a blessing. The political economists of ascendant capitalism declared labor to be the father of riches (Adam Smith) and accordingly favored population increase. The rise of the opposing theory of Malthusianism with the first economic crises and other symptoms of the acute contradictions of capitalism will be mentioned below.

Birth rates are now largely determined by many varied *social, economic, and psychological* factors. At the 1965 Belgrade Congress on population problems, the English anthropologist, E. Southall, very aptly emphasized that modern fertility is first and foremost "social fertility." Following are some instances relating largely to certain social classes: the system of land inheritance, adopted among peasant landowners in European countries to avoid subdivision of farms, has strongly influenced the birth rate. Communal land property periodically redistributed according to the number of males in a family (as in the Russian pre-revolutionary village) encourages a high birth rate, as does abundant, easily accessible land for new settlement. The high birth rate among the French colonists in Canada in the eighteenth and nineteenth centuries is a classic example; the physiological limit seems to have been reached there. The widespread use of child labor in early capitalist factories also strongly promoted the rise of the birth rate.

The Demographic Present

The present birth rate situation is well known. In the old, highly developed countries of Europe birth rates remain moderate, although in some countries, as in France, they are higher than at the beginning of the century. This, together with the prolongation of life, results in the aging of the population. Thus, although the general birth rate seems to be continually falling, it is in fact the proportion of nonfertile age groups that is increasing, while the fertility index (births related to the female population in all the fertile age groups or by individual age groups), may not be falling at all. A contrasting situation prevails in developing countries (particularly those recently liberated from colonial oppression) that have not yet succeeded in tangibly raising their economy, and in most Latin American countries where birth rates are as a rule two or three times as high as in the old European countries. It may be supposed that hopes of a better future have noticeably influenced the increase. Some of these hopes are already being realized in the shape of agrarian reforms and revision of disadvantageous agreements with foreign companies or nationalization of their properties. Since death rates, which are still high in these countries, are decreasing very rapidly (even the most primitive medico-hygienic measures are effective), more and more of mankind is characterized by a high fertility–low mortality reproductive pattern. The principal socioeconomic processes (the rise of education and urbanization, development of manufacturing, and increase of women in industry) which led to the slowing down of population growth in the older centers of capitalism have not yet materially restricted the rise of the birth rate.

The character of reproduction in the relatively poor countries, seems to confirm the "law" of inverse relationship between welfare and the number of births supported by the majority of sociologists (although they express interrelationships not in terms of countries, but rather in class divisions). On the other hand, crude birth rates in the countries of Western Europe with the highest living standards (Belgium, Great Britain, Sweden, Switzerland, the German Federal Republic, the Netherlands) are sometimes below, but often above the average for the region—about 19. Birth rate trends in these countries have varied greatly since World War II in spite of the almost universal rise in the standard of living, and frequently the level of fertility has moved upward in positive correlation with the expansion of income and social welfare.

A *third group* is formed by those countries with moderately high birth rates and fairly low death rates. This results in a high natural growth, although not so high as in the developing regions. To this group belong the countries of widely varying socioeconomic structures, for example, the U.S.S.R. and the United States, Poland, Canada, Rumania, and Australia.

The interdependence between economic and demographic phenomena is very complex. It would be presumptuous to assume that the character of this interdependence has been completely explored by science. Thus the controversy among demographers about the *inverse relationship between birth rates and material well-being* is still going on. The presence or absence of this relationship is very important, especially for developing countries, which must choose between alternative demographic policies.

In the U.S.S.R. research indicates that this inverse relationship might also exist in socialist societies. According to the Soviet Academician S. G. Strumilin, "the fall of the birth rate in the U.S.S.R. during the period

of rapid industrialization is a perfectly legitimate and consistent result of the constant growth in wages and in the well-being of the workers in our country" (17: 20). Other Soviet researchers are generally in accord (22; 5; and 18), but some demographers and sociologists have reached less definitive, or even contrary conclusions (8; 16).

In this context, the reasonable remark of B. C. Urlanis should be recalled: "The classification of families according to per capita income may easily lead to erroneous conclusions. . . . The birth of each child causes a reduction of per capita income." He similarly connects the influence of housing conditions on the birth rate: "Families with many children are included in the group with smaller dwelling space, since it is only the birth of the children that has resulted in the lowering of housing conditions. Cause and effect easily change places here" (21). Cause and effect evidently do not act directly and simply, but through a complex set of intermediate factors. Analysis leads us to stochastic factors which must be examined as a whole system of interacting influences; here we must seek not simple but multiple correlations. As each country develops, all these factors operate increasingly through the conscious participation of the people in internal family planning (planned motherhood). The Czechoslovak demographer Z. Pavlik may have been right when he said that the basic cause of the modern reduction in fertility lies in the aspiration of our families to raise their living standards by limiting the number of their children.

THE SECOND ASPECT OF THE PROBLEM—
RESOURCES

The concept of resources is only beginning to be clearly delineated in geographical science. A new "Resources" school is at present being formed in the field of Soviet economic geography. It draws upon adjacent branches of knowledge (geology, mining, agro-climatology, hydroenergetics, forestry, etc.) for objective ideas. Thus we hope to arrive at a realistic concept of resources based upon actual experience.

In other countries the term "resources" is sometimes interpreted by geographers rather too broadly. "Physical and social resources" are construed as including minerals in the bowels of the earth, technical equipment, and even potential capital. The well-known work *Resources in America's Future* (13) suffers basically from this type of diffuseness. Often people are considered as "resources," but this makes a comparison of population with resources meaningless.[2]

Resources can exist only for the use of human society and the degree to which they are developed is all important. The possibilities range from mere potential to virtual exhaustion.[3] In this sense, it is essential to distinguish *renewable* from *nonrenewable* resources. (Among the former, food resources are of particular concern.) However, this distinction is far from absolute. Timber, for instance, may be felled at such a rate and by such methods that it can never be renewed. Yet correct felling methods will ensure replacement of the timber in its former state.

It is important always to think of re-

2. In the United States, "labor resources" is a technical term in which the word "resources" sounds like a metaphor. In the practice of economic planning in the U.S.S.R., the term designates all able-bodied persons of working age. It excludes invalids and pensioners of working age-groups, and sometimes mothers with many children, but includes persons in the pension age-groups working in industry.

3. Exhaustion may occur even in the case of *renewable* resources, for example, if a stream is completely utilized in a cascade of hydroelectric stations. For *nonreproducible* resources, exhaustion indicates their disappearance. For example, in a completely worked-out mine or quarry (one depleted of deposits relevant to the existing level of the development) minerals simply no longer exist as resources.

sources *historically*. Since the existence of resources is only relative, they can only be evaluated historically in accordance with the development of productive forces and varying social needs. The problem of correlating population and resources was very different before and after the agrarian-technical revolution (the introduction of agriculture 8000 or 9000 years ago), and again before and after the Industrial Revolution, when many kinds of raw materials and sources of energy suddenly acquired new significance. Very probably we are again at such a turning point. The development of technical equipment permits an ever wider utilization of a steadily increasing range of resources. However, success should not go to our heads: for example we still cannot count on utilizing many of the useful chemical elements dissolved in the waters of the oceans, unlike marine food resources, or desalinized sea water.

It should also be noted that, although *the dominion of society over nature* (the possibilities of drawing natural materials into production) *is on the whole increasing,* certain reserves once at the disposal of mankind will no longer be suitable. For instance, the quantities of iron ore needed in the industries of the sevententh and eighteenth centuries could be obtained from small ore lenses or marsh ores. Iron smelting using wet-blast furnaces, manually operated forges, etc. was possible almost everywhere, or, at any rate, within very broad geographical limits. Today, when a modern iron foundry demands ore reserves in the hundreds of millions of tons, the number of deposits that can serve as industrial bases are very limited. On the other hand, the carrying capacity of transport has increased immeasurably, and geological surveys bring to light more and more new deposits.

The entire development of the productive forces of society may be presented as a con-

	U.S.S.R.			UNITED STATES		
Year	Total Products	Products of Agriculture	Per cent of Total	Total Products	Products of Agriculture	Per cent of Total
1913	781.0	635.8	81.4	2108.7	1080.0	51.4
1940	1431.6	786.7	54.9	2665.6	1197.0	45.1
1960	3137.6	1049.5	33.4	4089.7	1441.0	35.2

tinual broadening of man's utilization of the planet's resources. The speed of this process is increasing. In material terms, it comprises mainly the extraction and processing of ever greater quantities of various materials from lithosphere, hydrosphere, and biosphere. Human labor and the controlled forces of nature have become the motive force of the newly arising circulation of matter. Besides material substances, it is important to command the "immaterial" forces of nature, such as water power and solar radiation.

The volume of various materials extracted from the natural environment has been partially estimated for different historical periods. The Soviet geographer I. V. Komar recently attempted to determine the volume by weight of primary natural materials extracted in the U.S.S.R. and the United States and then, allowing for the amount added or subtracted through the export-import balance, the total volume consumed during the years 1913, 1940, and 1960 (7).[4] Allowing 10 to 15 per cent for incompleteness of calculation, Komar's output figures are (in million tons) in the table above.

The gross volume of consumption does not differ markedly from the volume of national output, especially for the U.S.S.R., where the former is slightly lower. In the United States the volume of consumption is higher by several millions of tons, due to excess of imports over exports by weight. The extraction of natural materials in these two countries amounts to probably not less than 30 to 40 per cent by weight of the world materials budget.

Though the period studied is less than half a century, a marked increase can be plainly seen in the extraction of natural materials and their utilization; the proportion of food products is perceptibly falling.

We have no similar estimates for the rest of the world,[5] but it is reasonable to assume that a comparable growth and acceleration, one that outstrips the growth of population, is taking place. Komar estimates per capita consumption of primary materials in the U.S.S.R. as follows: 4.9 tons per year in 1913; 7.4 in 1940; and 14.3 in 1960. He envisages a prospective growth up to 35-40 tons per person (7). However, simple extrapolation is scarcely possible here because the growing use of synthetic materials and atomic energy may introduce marked changes. In a number of areas, fresh water may soon beome a special kind of "raw material"; in some places it is near depletion.

4. For livestock raising, Komar included in the total not the weight of its products, but the weight of fodder as extracted from the phytosphere; he believes internal processes in livestock raising (the "distillation of milk, meat, etc. from fodder) should not be attributed to the sphere of extraction of primary natural materials.

5. In 1958, Y. G. Saushkin estimated the volume of natural materials extracted by man as 4 to 5 billion tons per year (15: 227). Komar considers this estimate to be very low since it equals the consumption of only two countries in that year—the U.S.S.R. and the United States (7).

Desalinization of sea water and reclamation of waste waters are urgent problems for the immediate future.

The growth in volume of resources used by man is a concomitant of the progressive evolution of human society. Only under conditions of historical stagnation will growth cease or usage decline. Of course, we realize that to express level of use through the weight of various materials is a simplification. The increase in the amount of materials extracted from nature is mainly due to greater use of nonorganic resources. The growth of agricultural production is bound to correspond in the main to population growth, since these are overwhelmingly food substances for people or livestock, and stomach capacity is fairly constant. Fluctuations may be attributed to patterns of consumption —especially concerning animal substances— or to export-import ratios.

RESOURCES MUST GROW MORE QUICKLY THAN POPULATION

The basic relationship of population to resources is composed of a series of partial equations linked with one another. The per capita demand for resources is growing simultaneously with the growth of population, which results in a strong over-all increase of the total demand. On the other hand, the growth of the known volume of potential resources goes on constantly, and with it a corresponding growth of their actual utilization. Thus, per capita utilization should be compared with per capita demand. If this per capita utilization keeps ahead of demand, the problem may be satisfactorily resolved.

But in fact it is only at the simplest levels of human existence that this primitive relationship is valid: that for every 1 per cent of population increase there should be a corresponding increase in the means of consumption. The continually rising demand for housing, clothing, tools, and equipment has destroyed this equation. The higher a society develops the more its members are drawn away from the direct production of food to other activities. Moreover, society does not simply reproduce itself year by year, generation by generation; it progresses. This progress, and the quantitative increase of material culture, demands technical equipment for building new cities, railways, and factories, and educating new and larger generations of technicians seeking improved training. A recent estimate by Burke shows that a continuous annual world population growth for the next few decades of 2 per cent calls for an annual increase in food production of at least 3 per cent. According to his calculations for the period 1935-61, the mean per capita annual increase of food production was only 0.3 per cent; for some countries, mainly in Asia, it was even negative (3). Many demographers consider that an annual population growth of 1 per cent, if the Western standard of living is to be retained, demands a 4 per cent growth of national income, and that only a higher rate will create preconditions for raising a country's well being.

We cannot here determine the increase rates of national income and food production necessary to balance the growth of population. But it is certain that, firstly, these rates must exceed population growth, and, secondly, be differentiated according to the level of a country's industrialization and urbanization. The more a country is developed and industrialized the heavier is the burden of "demographic investment," although the means for such investment are easier to find. But we should not find consolation in the idea that countries lagging considerably in development may, for a time, be satisfied with correspondingly lower "demographic investments." First, in absolute terms, these investments are not actually low, because the incease of population is much faster than in

$$\text{RATIO} - \frac{\text{POPULATION}}{\text{RESOURCES}}$$

Technical Equipment	*High* *"European Type"*	*Low* *"U.S.A. Type"*
High	All Europe, Soviet Middle Asia, Japan, the Nile Delta, the eastern shore of the Mediterranean.	U.S.A., Canada, Southern and Middle Siberia and the south of Australia, New Zealand, some regions of Brazil and the Argentine
Low	*"China and India Type"* Southern and Eastern Asia, excluding Indochina; Java, the Philippines, Northern Africa and the internal part of the U.A.R.	*"Brazilian Type"* Almost all Southern and Central America, Africa (excluding the South African Republic, northern U.A.R. and deserts), South Eastern Asia, the north of Australia together with New Guinea

the highly developed countries. Secondly, and this is the main point, if investment continues at a low level, then the economic lag of these countries will not be overcome.

At the United Nations World Population Conference in Belgrade (1965), the summing up of the discussion on the problem of "Population and Natural Resources" was entrusted to the American geographer and resources expert E. Ackerman. In his report (1), Ackerman divided all areas of the world, excluding sub-polar areas, high mountains and deserts, into four types as shown in the table above.

It is his opinion that the Population-Resource Ratio shows how heavily population presses upon resources, and reveals the degree of their insufficiency. The essential utility of this idea, in my view, is the way it stimulates a geographically differentiated approach to the problem, and brings out the actual correlations between "masses of people" and "masses of resources" (in simple cases primarily food resources). However,

Ackerman sometimes includes entire countries under particular types (which has a point since each national economy possesses internal regulators for the redistribution of resources); sometimes only regions or parts. The latter is an especially questionable method for countries with planned economies. Also included in the report is an index of technical equipment which is very significant at any given date. But this index is subject to rapid variation, as is illustrated by the examples of the U.S.S.R. or Japan over the past few decades.

GEOGRAPHY OF RESOURCES AND POPULATION AGGLOMERATIONS

Theoretically speaking, the geography of human resources in future centuries will depend on two principal, mutually dependent series of factors.

1. *On the distribution in the earth's crust of chemical elements necessary for humanity.* The deposits must be in accessible horizons and in sufficient concentrations for in-

dustrial use. The availability of mineral deposits for human use—their industrial significance—depends on the level of development of productive forces and technical progress. Thus the range of human possibilities is very great. At present, scientific theories of the composition of the earth's crust do not yet give us full and exact knowledge of the laws of distribution of specific elements and their combinations. But certain geochemical concepts, such as those concerning the connection of oil and gas deposits with marginal depressions and salt domes, or the belt of nonferrous ores ringing the Pacific, have been developed. Now, after the notable research of Vernadsky, Fersman, and other founders of geochemistry, it is no longer possible to consider the distribution of mineral wealth in the bowels of the earth to be purely fortuitous.

2. *On the distribution of solar radiation reaching the earth's surface.* The energy of solar radiation is utilized by the biosphere, which man is learning to control. Another vital component utilized by the biosphere is water, which is often in short supply, especially where solar radiation is the greatest and, consequently, the transpiration rate of plants is very high. But as humanity acquires increased skill and technical facilities for the redistribution of water and control of runoff, the zones with the most abundant solar radiation may ultimately become the richest in bioenergy which is especially important for food production. A time may be foreseen when deserts and zones of tropical forests (with the exception of equatorial forests which receive less radiation because of more extensive cloud cover) will become the major granaries of the earth. In addition, the world distribution patterns of other resources, such as hydroenergy might be noted.

The over-all picture of the distribution of the major natural resources of the earth is roughly as follows:

First among *mineral energy resources* comes coal, which still provides almost half of all energy poduced. Mankind is comparatively well supplied with coal, especially if *brown coal* is included; and with the modern development of transport, the location of supply bases may be regarded as adequate. The reserves of coal are largest in the U.S.S.R., China, the U.S.A., Canada, England, the Federal Republic of Germany, Poland, Czechosolvakia, India, and the Republic of South Africa; those of brown coal are most extensive in the U.S.S.R., the German Democratic Republic, the Federal Republic of Germany, the U.S.A., Canada, and Australia. The known reserves of coal are poorest in South America, the western part of Australia, and in equatorial Africa.

Oil and gas resources are represented by a narrower circle of world bases, but their number is growing fast. The main belt extends in a meridional direction from the Near East across the Caucasus to the Volga-Ural geological province. This belt has now become wider with the inclusion of areas in the Ob Basin to the east of the Urals. The second major oil region occurs in the Western Hemisphere, extending from western Canada and the U.S.A. across Texas, Mexico, and under the bed of the Gulf of Mexico to Venezuela and Colombia. In addition to these main bases and subsidiary smaller ones (in Indonesia, Rumania etc.), new deposits are constantly appearing, such as those in the Sahara, under the North Sea, in South America, Alaska, and Eastern Siberia.

If the role of oil and gas resources is growing, the role of *iron ore* may begin to decline with increasing turnover of metal already mined, and the consumption of synthetic substitutes. The main bases of iron ore are located in the U.S.S.R., India, Brazil, China, the United States, Venezuela, Cuba, Sweden, and France. One can foresee the concentration of iron ore mining only at the most convenient deposits, those high in metallic content and with few harmful impurities, or those permitting open-cut mining methods. The role of nonferrous metals (both heavy and light) is also growing, although changes may occur as chemical engineering advances. Geographically, the bases form a very irregular pattern and are widely scattered. These ores are characterized by a low concentration of useful constituents and by high value, which determine the profitability of smelting, or the export of concentrates from the most remote areas. Copper from Katanga and Chile, bauxites from Jamaica and Guinea, tin from Malaysia and Bolivia, uranium ores from remote regions of Africa, Australia and Canada, become sufficiently profitable for exploitation.

Bioenergetic resources are quite "zonal." The land areas which receive annually 200 and more kilocalories per square centimeter include the northern Sahara, the U.A.R., the Arabian peninsula, southern Iran, West Pakistan, and the extreme northwest of India. In the Western Hemisphere, the same intensity of radiation is received over a considerably smaller area—northern Mexico and the southwestern United States. The zone which annually receives 160-200 kilocalories per square centimeter is much wider. It covers all but the southernmost part of southern China, the Indochinese peninsula, Burma, India, Ceylon, Afghanistan, the south of the Middle-Asian Soviet Republics; and the southern, eastern (including Madagascar), and northwestern parts of Africa. In the Western Hemisphere the same zone covers the southern United States, Central America and the Caribbean, Venezuela and the Guianas, the eastern extension of Brazil, and some regions in the far interior of the South Ameican continent. Finally, the zone with an annual radiation of over 120 kilocalories per square centimeter forms a wide band around the planet: the whole of the Old World, except that part of Eurasia north of the 45th or 50th parallel (in eastern Asia, north of 35°-40°), Oceania (except Tasmania and the South Island of New Zealand), all of the Americas (except Southern Patagonia, Tierra del Fuego, Alaska, Canada, the northeastern United States, and Greenland) (10).

In principle, the most favorable regions for habitation are those where a sufficiently high bioenergetic potential coincides with bases of mineral resources useful for industrial development. Comparison of the areas described above with a population map shows that many closely settled regions, for example those in Asia, or northeastern Africa, have a very high economic development potential, especially for food production: they lie in the belt of rich solar radiation, permitting, for example, the harvesting of two or three rich crops per year.

At the same time, a detailed realistic geographical survey shows much greater variations of combinations of factors than is roughly outlined in Ackerman's scheme. For example, it is doubtful if the average "United States Type" fits the eastern part of the country, where the thousand-kilometer strip from Boston to Washington forms an almost completely urbanized megalopolis with a population of about 40 million. It is far from rich in resources: Pennsylvania oil in the rear of this strip is practically depleted; Appalachian anthracites are no longer profitable; and miners' settlements in this region are officially classified as distressed areas. Megalopolis suffers intensely from shortages of fresh water. In a word, the proportion of population to resources in this region is unfavorable—the numerator is big and the denominator small. There are also many thinly populated other localities that do not fit into Ackerman's scheme, such as petroleum-rich desert regions of the Near East.

It has been shown that in a number of

regions a high resource potential coincides with a dense population. In other cases, it is the proximity of resources and population concentration that is favorable. But the size of population in many developing countries should be compared not with "theoretical" (potential) resources but with those economic possibilities that are already available.

In this light it appears that a tremendous "belt" of unfavorable conditions surrounds the planet. It includes those former colonies of Asia and Africa which have not yet succeeded in creating a sufficiently powerful economy, and the South American continent, which is still undergoing concealed exploitation by highly developed capitalist countries. There are, of course, many variations in the specific combinations of population and resources. Again, the diversity of forms of social organization under which development of resources has occurred, or is occurring, is no less significant. Thus, in Mexico, oil mining and refining are nationalized under the state corporation PEMEX, and this has become an important progressive factor in the utilization of fuel and energetic resources. In a number of other countries, such as the newly formed African states, the capital of former colonizers retains its supremacy, which greatly restricts economic development.

Some examples may be given showing the immediate prospects for certain regions in this belt. In the Near East, the most densely populated region is lower Egypt; since it lies in the zone of very rich solar radiation, it has major possibilities for strengthening its control over water resources. According to the evaluation of foreign experts, the completion of the Aswan High Dam, which is being built with the aid of the U.S.S.R., will enable the U.A.R. to produce food for twice its present population (14). Agrarian reforms have also created social and economic preconditions for a more favorable ratio of population to resources. The same evaluation shows that the extremely tense situation in densely populated Northern India might be ameliorated to a great extent by storage of part of the runoff in the Ganges-Brahmaputra Basin. Solar radiation would permit the switch-over of about half of the cultivated area from one to three crops a year, thus doubling the food resources (14). The tremendous efforts of the government and peoples of India to fulfill the Five-Year Plans may ensure the achievement of this, along with other objectives designed to overcome the lag. In the Sahara, the discovery of large underground fresh-water reserves may serve to revive the life of the desert regions of the Maghreb countries, Sahara petroleum providing the necessary power.

The fate of those countries in which the balance between population and resources seems to have been upset must be decided primarily by improvement of their national economies,[6] and by profound socioeconomic transformation which may promote quicker development and fuller utilization of their resources.

The high road to progress for countries of non-Soviet Asia, Africa, and Latin America is in the active development of resources, not in passive adaptation of population growth to their present limited level of development.

FROM MALTHUS TO THE MODERN MALTHUSIANS

The policy stated above is the most progressive approach to what are becoming extremely acute problems. However, some so-

6. As for loans, the developed countries of old capitalism are, in general, paid a sufficiently high interest. Only when these loans are utilized in especially profitable branches of the economy can they upbuild the national economy. But it is often these branches that have already been seized by foreign capital.

ciologists, economists, and demographers steadfastly declare to the contrary that the full range of measures for birth rate reduction is the only panacea against the calamities threatening the less developed countries. This point of view is not new. Even at the beginning of the nineteenth century, the reproduction of the "poorer classes" and population growth were declared to generate social misery automatically. When the first internal contradictions of capitalism appeared in acute form, when its progress was shaken by the first crises, the doctrines of Malthus arose and became fashionable in certain circles. This conception was directly contrary to the populationist doctrine then dominant, and arose in response to the appearance of relative overpopulation, the reserve army of labor caused by the development of capitalism. The social meaning of Malthusianism is clear: it declares poverty to be a natural phenomenon and sees the "path to salvation" in the limitation of population growth.

During the nineteenth and early twentieth centuries, this doctrine lost its prestige, owing to the rapid growth of productive forces, which provided a growth of wealth obviously faster than the growth of population. The scientific literature of the time maintained a reasonably optimistic approach to the growth of world population. Triumphant agrotechnics declared 40 to 50 per cent of the world's total land area to be arable (Prasolov and Zimmermann), though reserves of land seem easiest to consider finite (with the "end" visible to the naked eye). Clark's estimate of arable land based on Thornthwaite's climatic classification of territories is 61.7 millions of "standard" square kilometers (equivalent in productivity to modern fertile fields in Northwestern Europe). This provides for an increase of the cultivated areas of the earth by 7 to 8 times. The interpretation of the problem dominant in the 1950's is recorded in a number of surveys, notably the works of

D. Stamp, and has been sufficiently optimistic in its general tone.

Quite recently, however, the emergence on the world scene of a number of developing and populous, but poor and technically lagging, countries in Asia, Africa, and Latin America galvanized, as it were, the Malthusian attitude. The place of the poor classes is now taken by "poor" countries. As in former times, paupers, for whom there was no place at the great feast of life (Malthus), were exhorted to abstemiousness, so that modern neo-Malthusians now persistently call upon backward countries to intensify the struggle to limit their birth rates.

THE GROWTH OF POPULATION WILL BE
REDUCED IN ANY CASE

Meanwhile it must be recognized that, irrespective of the correlation of birth rates with material well-being, the natural increase of population in those countries where it is now especially high will begin to decrease, possibly quite soon.

Social progress will create the conditions for a change in psychology, in the traditional view of large families as a blessing sent by the gods. The rise of the cultural and hygienic level of the population, urbanization and industrialization, a wider participation of women in the industrial labor force and in services will lead to a slower population growth. The historical experience of the U.S.S.R. is a most instructive example. There the transformation of the backward agrarian economy of tsarist times to a highly developed socialist economy altered fundamentally the entire regime of natural reproduction of the population.

The neo-Malthusians cite the example of Japan where the propaganda for birth control has been supposedly quite effective. The birth rate for the postwar period fell from 3.0 to 1.7 per cent, the lowest in Asia. Despite a considerable decease in the death rate, the total rate of population increase has fallen substantially, and is now below 1 per cent. But, in fact, this was determined not only by the official birth control policy (and abortions are far from being the best method of control), but by the socioeconomic pre-conditions for a change in the over-all character of population reproduction—rapid industrialization, the growth of cities, etc. As a result, demographic processes in Japan became similar to those typifying the "old" countries of developed capitalism.

With the rise in cultural and economic levels, the development of industry, changes in agrarian relationships and in social psychology, demographic processes are bound to change in other countries as well. An important factor, but not an independent or primary one, will be birth control employing modern medical contraceptive means. On the other hand, the widening range of resource utilization, the transfer from a "raw materials" to a "processing" economy, will lead to a more favorable population-resources ratio both through the direct growth of the denominator and through social and cultural transformations, which are bound to retard the growth of the numerator.

It is possible that in countries where the correlation between population and resources is most disturbed, such as India and a number of African and Latin American countries, the period of greatest difficulties will last only for the next few decades. The duration and intensity of the crisis will depend on the mix of specific resources, on population characteristics, on the existence of certain cultural traditions which may need to be modified, and on the effectiveness of the economic transformation policy.

Thus there is hope that the balance will gradually be restored fom both sides at once, as it were: from the decisive rise and profound reconstruction of the economy, and from the ensuing changes in social psy-chology, with a resultant decrease in population growth.

Apart from social and economic causes, the decrease of the birth rate will proceed also from technical demogaphic causes.

1. There is a clear connection between the levels of birth and death rates, especially the infant mortality rate. The desire to have many children is always nourished by the fear of losing some of them; but demographic progress leads to a steady decrease of the death rate, and especially during childhood.

2. With the over-all aging of the population due to improvement in hygienic conditions and greater longevity, the larger proportion of nonfertile age groups will certainly lead to a decline in the crude birth rate.

It is to be expected that these tendencies, which are not socioeconomic, but purely demographic in character, will shortly begin to operate within the developing countries.

In the U.S.S.R., the paths of demographic policy are quite clear. Our planned economy will allow us to keep a favorable relationship between a very rapidly growing population and the volume of resources that are being ever more actively drawn into circulation. The only problem is in accomplishing the most effective distribution of the labor force between branches of industry and between regions. Here, of course, maladjustments may occur, but they are fortuitous and temporary, and will be overcome by virtue of the main trend of planned economy: an urge to provide correct proportions between the population and the economy. In principle, the problem is solved in the same way for every socialist country.

As for the developing countries, they must strive for a considerable rise in living standards through social transformation and the strengthening of the planning principles in their economies. Population increase will probably begin to taper off gradually through an upsurge in the economy and for purely demographic reasons as well. To help realize these tendencies it is very important to spread ideas of family planning.

It is clear that the acute problem of correlating population and resources will be solved by different methods and at different rates. For many countries the forthcoming decades will be very difficult. It must be remembered that the modern world is becoming more and more a system of interacting units, and that the whole problem of correlation has not only local significance for the "belt" of countries suffering from calamity, but also for all mankind. The difficulties of the "belt of hunger and poverty" may be considerably softened by action of the developed countries, although the problem cannot be fully solved without considerable investments made on sufficiently favorable terms. We should note that investments in these countries would be facilitated under conditions of disarmament or reduction of defense expenditures. The task of humanity is to wipe from the face of the planet the shameful "hunger belt" and to call persistently for the cessation of the arms race. To fulfill this task, the ideals of peace, friendship, and coexistence of all peoples should become universal. For that we need good will. The author hopes that such good will is growing in the hearts of the peoples of the whole world.

REFERENCES

(1) E. Ackerman: Population and Natural Resources, in: United Nations, Department of Economics and Social Affairs: Proceedings of the World Population Conference . . . 1965. Volume I: Summary Report (New York, 1966), pp. 259-68.

(2) J. Beloch: Die Bevölkerung des griechisch-römisch Welt (Leipzig, 1886).

(3) T. Burke: Food and Population, Time and Space: Formulating the Problem, *Journal of Geography,* Vol. 55, 1966, pp. 58-66.

(4) K. Davis: The Population of India and Pakistan (Princeton, 1951).

(5) L. M. Davtian: On the Relation between Living Conditions and Birth Rate, *Problemy Demograficheskoi Statistiki* (Moscow, 1966). [In Russian]

(6) J. D. Durand: The Population Statistics of China, A.D. 2-1953, *Population Studies,* Vol. 12, 1959-1960, pp. 209-56.

(7) I. V. Komar: Dynamics and Structure of Using Resources in the USSR, *Izvestia Akademia Nauk SSSR, Seria Geografitscheskaia,* 1966, No. 3. [In Russian]

(8) A. D. Kuznetsov: The Labor Resources of the USSR and their Utilization (Moscow, 1960). [In Russian]

(9) G. Ohlin: Historical Outline of World Population Growth, United Nations World Population Conference, 1965, WPC/WP 486.

(10) Physical-Geographic Atlas of the World (Moscow, 1964). [In Russian]

(11) V. V. Pokshishevskii: Settlement of Siberia (Irkutsk, 1951). [In Russian]

(12) V. V. Pokshishevskii: On the Geography of Pre-Revolutionary Colonization and Migration Processes in the Southern Part of the Soviet Far East, *Sibirskii Geograficheskii Sbornik,* Vol. 1 (Moscow, 1962). [In Russian]

(13) H. H. Landsberg, L. L. Fishman, and J. L. Fisher, eds.: Resources for the Future: Resources in America's Future; Patterns of Requirements and Availabilities, 1960-2000 (Baltimore, 1963).

(14) R. Revell: Water, *Scientific American,* September, 1963.

(15) Yu. G. Saushkin: Introduction to Economic Geography (Moscow, 1958). [In Russian]

(16) G. A. Slesarev: Methodology of Sociological Population Research (Moscow, 1965). [In Russian]

(17) S. G. Strumilin: Problems of Labor Economics (Moscow, 1957). [In Russian]

(18) N. A. Tauber: Influence of Some Conditions of Life on the Level of Fertility of Married Women, *Problemy Demograficheskoi Statistiki,* Moscow, 1966. [In Russian]

(19) United Nations: The Determinants and Consequences of Population Trends, Population Studies, No. 17 (New York, 1953).

(20) B. C. Urlanis: The Growth of Population in Europe (Moscow, 1941). [In Russian]

(21) B. C. Urlanis: Birth Rate and the Duration of Life in the USSR (Moscow, 1963). [In Russian]

(22) A. M. Vostrikova: Some Data on Natality in the USSR, *Vestnik Statistiki,* No. 12, 1962. [In Russian]

3. POPULATION DYNAMICS AND POPULATION PRESSURES: GEOGRAPHIC-DEMOGRAPHIC APPROACHES

Irene B. Taeuber

The dimensions of space, the relations of man to earth, are neglected aspects of contemporary demography. The natural dynamics of populations and the mobilities of peoples are neglected aspects of contemporary geography. Developments in population, in population distribution, and in research are reducing the historic separatisms (7, 15, 25, 26). This Conference attests the geographers' recognition of the population crisis that now exists throughout much of the less developed world and the search for a role in the research that underlies resolution. Ecology and regional science are areas of contact. Increasingly demographers and geographers are concerned with the increases, differentiations, expansions, and linkages of metropolitan areas. As we attend each other's conferences, we move forward in understanding and in ability to communicate across disciplinary lines. The joint conference on strategic problems in critical areas would seem a logical advance.

If this were a relatively stable era and populations were changing gradually within traditional societies, the hiatus of the disciplines concerned with man and earth could be left to close slowly and naturally. This is not a stable era. Populations in the less developed areas are increasing at 2, 3, or even 4 per cent a year. Traditional societies are permeated with the disquiets and instabilities of aspirations that are beyond achievement. Economic development lags; problems of civil and political order disturb many peoples. In great areas life itself is dependent on the vagaries of harvests and international largesse. In the advanced industrial regions of the earth, science and technology contribute toward increasing productivity and widening affluence. The gulfs between the populations who achieved modernization in past periods and those who struggle for it today are widening.

The diverse population dynamics and the divergent man-land relations that characterize the areas of the world in the late twentieth century are not subject to simple theoretical or philosophical interpretations. Science is in swift forward movement. Technologies now known are adaptable to expanded and effective contraceptive practice and rapidly declining birth rates in agrarian societies. Technologies are available that permit the multiplication of agricultural yields. The questions are incisive, but the answers are difficult. Neither demographic nor geographic analysis yields close estimates of the future for the troubled areas. The essential needs go beyond the extension of geography and demography to most of the sciences of man and earth, of behavior and culture. Moreover, in a period of demographic crisis, economic hazard, and political instability, the needs concern the present rather than some future period.

It is not contradictory to this emphasis on crisis in some two-thirds of the world's population to stress the immensity of the needs for intensive and coordinated research in the developed countries. There are not likely to be close replications of the past of countries now developed in the future of countries now euphemistically called developing. But neither are there total dissimilarities. That advanced science which alone contributes substantially to the knowledge of structure, relations, and processes is not specific to

55

space, time, culture, economy, or society.

The associations of population, space, resources, economies, and social structures are almost infinitely complex in static cross section and in change. There are fundamental interrelations, though, and there are regularities in change. In the long record of man on earth, no population survived unless the birth rate was high enough to maintain numbers against continuing and episodic hazards. High death rates and high birth rates were alike attributes of the continuing cultures. Declining death rates and concurrent or delayed declines in birth rates were aspects of the economic and social development in all countries that are now modernized or modernizing. Is it essential, then, that comprehensive modernization accompany or precede decline in birth rates? Are the historic evolutions in countries now modernized explainable in deterministic economic contexts? Are there associations that are essential in the sense that they have occurred in all countries? What are the roles of culture, indigenous adjustments, location, and time in demographic transitions in diverse regional, climatic, and resources contexts?

The research approach to the relations of man, land, and resources must recognize the divergent states and processes among peoples differing in historic origins, cultures, and economies and living in one or the other of the earth's many and distinctive regions and subregions. The basic queries concern movement rather than stability, change rather than continuity, the ranges of the possible or the plausible in the future rather than simple projection of past and present into the future. The concepts and the usages in past and even present descriptions of man's relations to space and resources have been basically static. Moreover, they are evaluative with reference to problems and social pathologies.

Such terms as "overpopulation" and "underpopulation" have been discarded rigorously in scientific approaches, perhaps unduly so. The validities that may inhere in the concepts are difficult to define in measurable form,[1] while the concepts themselves are exploited in generalizing propagandistic ways. A generation ago there were major attempts to define man's relations to space, resources, and economy in terms of an optimum (4). The idea was enticing, but the use was disillusioning. It may be sufficient to note two difficulties. First, those attributes or characteristics whose incidences are to be evaluated must be defined in specific and measurable terms. Second, the optimum which is to be assessed must itself be defined. Is an optimum simply a maximization for the nation? Are distributional elements involved? What is the criteria of selection or of aggregation if the maxima for several variables do not coincide?

It was fairly simple to throw aside the specific language of over and underpopulation and optimum population. The need for a term to refer to maladjustments remained. Population pressure is a simple word to use in descriptive fashion when density of settlement occurs alongside economic and social deprivation, but the definition of pressure as a demographic variable is difficult. Resource deficiencies may or may not be factors in economic, social, and political deprivation. The absence of advanced economic development cannot be equated with the absence of the resources for that development (1). Countries with very limited re-

1. Neither geographic nor demographic bibliographies classify literature in analytical categories of population-land-resources relations. But see (5), (7), (25), and (26). The works of Pierre George are notable in the integration of demographic and geographic analysis; see, particularly, (6). For an early, but incisive, statement of the concepts of over-population and under-population, the problems and the difficulties, see (10).

sources in the conventional sense have yet achieved advanced development through science, technology, high levels of competence, and international trade. There is a further complication. Population pressure, as it is usually viewed in terms of increasing, ill-educated, and ill-nourished peasants, may be due primarily not to the limitations of resources, the productivity of the land, or the redundancy of the people, but to the nature of the social structure and the characteristics of the distribution system.

The essay on population pressure is not the assignment here. The demolition of the concept as research tool would be premature. Multi-disciplinary explorations of that which is now labeled population pressure are basic to advance. There are problems, but there are also realities. Population growth and man-land-resource relations as they now exist are among the deepest and the most intractable of the hazards to economic, social, and political advance for one-half to two-thirds of the world's total population.

The definitions and the logical structuring of those phenomena of man-land-resources relationships commonly designated as population pressure are the primary tasks in this Symposium. If these activities are to contribute to research rather than further debates on concepts, there are coordinate tasks. These are the development of methodological approaches, particularly the definitions of those measurable states, relationships, and changes that indicate the existing and the changing relations of population to resources, not as exclusive or deterministic processes but as aspects of the process of movement that may be labelled simply as modernization (18).

A focus on the new concepts and methodologies is spectacular and exciting. This is not sufficient, however. The work that underlies all others is the procuring and ordering of the data, the relating of people to space at specific points of time and over time, and the measurements of the relations in distributions.[2]

The urgency of the work is related to the present priority of research on the status and the dynamics of populations, and the types and speeds of the processes of resolution or intensification. In the revolutionary world and among the aroused peoples of the present, those variations in existing states of livelihood and anticipated future states that were once accepted quietly would not now be accepted with equanimity even if the dynamics of population had remained unchanged. Those dynamics have not remained unchanged. The most revolutionary of the many changes in the world of the last quarter-century was the swift reduction in mortality without correlated or delayed declines in fertility. There was, and there now is, rapid population growth without the correlated economic developments and educational advances that lead toward declining birth rates and slowing increase.

Population, Space, and Change

It may be unduly repetitive to state again that the critical questions for analysis are not limited to the size and the characteristics of the populations that are currently disadvantaged. They are, rather, the directions of and the potentialities for economic growth, educational advance, and demographic modernization. The research approach that contributes both to science and to planning involves the relations of people, space, and resources in historic and current perspective among all populations in all areas.

Some general statements on population, space, and intervening variables may be

2. The statistical data compiled by the United Nations are increasingly valuable, particularly, (20), (21), and (22).

phrased as hypotheses amenable to quantitative testing.

1. Demographic processes are biological and therefore universal, but demographic processes are socially conditioned and therefore distinctive, if not unique.

2. Space is generally conditioning rather than determinative of demographic process. This is valid whether the term is used in simple definition or in successive refinements as space usable to the people inhabiting it.

3. Culture, technology, economy, and organization condition the dynamics of population through the modifications of biologic processes and the redefinitions or transformations of space.

4. Population dynamics may so alter the relations of men to used and usable space that culture, society, economy, technology, and political stability become dependent variables at risk of retrogression. The process of change may involve the birth rate, the death rate, or both; it may involve increase or decline. Migrations within or outside the local, regional, or national area are components in change, whether of adjustment or of retrogression.

5. Cultural relativity and social conditioning are alike operative only within the range of responses and relations that yield continuing viability of the population in the space available to it.

6. Inharmonious relations are necessarily transitory. There are usually alternate resolutions rather than inevitabilities in the directions of movement and the types of resolution.

In some areas, the abundance of resources has been critical in evolution and status. The westward expansions of Americans and Canadians to the Pacific and the eastward movements of Russians to the far shores of the same vast ocean document the growth of population, technology, and capital in lands where peoples were trained and the resources for the industrial society abundant. There are converse situations. The associations of density, pressure, physical vulnerability, and recurrent political instability are not easily denied in the deltas of the Hwang-Ho and the Yangtse, the Ganges and the Indus. Whatever the technical possibilities, crises in the availability of food for densely settled and increasing people are existent or emerging in such countries as Indonesia, India, and perhaps China.

In those regions where spaces and resources are now plentiful, utilization evolved as industrialization and urbanization rather than as traditional agrarian expansion. Science and technology were bases of development; people were increasingly educated. Birth rates declined with industrialization, urbanization, and education. In the United States, birth rates that were 50 to 55 per 1000 total population in 1790 declined throughout the nineteenth century and into the early decades of the twentieth century. The postwar upsurge carried birth rates to half the levels of the early nineteenth century. And now again, for almost a decade, birth rates have been declining.

The areas that are centers of the world's problems of population, poverty, illiteracy, ill health, and instability retain major aspects of the ancient ways of living and thinking. (For illustrative materials, see 11 and 13.) Birth rates remain high; population increase is rapid.

Demographic factors may seem paramount in the determination of population-space relationships if the argument is based on selective case studies. However, there are countries such as the Netherlands where density is high but economy is highly developed, people educated and skilled. There are countries in Africa, Asia, and Latin America where densities are low but economies little developed, the people insufficiently educated and generally pre-modern. The poverty of the Amazon is scarcely less than that of the Indus.

Space, Pressure, and Development: Japan[3]

Analyses of the relations of population, space, and resources are increasingly prevalent and increasingly sophisticated. If the focus is pressure on resources, if the orientation is the less developed countries, the generalization of conclusions and arguments over space and time presents intricate problems. Research proceeds within contexts of location, culture, time, and contact. Interrelations of population and resources in the place and time of study may be described objectively. The determination of the scientific and technical possibilities for change within the place at the time may also proceed in empirical frame. Judgments become critical if assessments involve human feasibilities, alternate paths, and probable futures. Broad social, political, and philosophical climates seem to create directional drifts in the selection of problems and areas of study, in modes of approach, and in evaluations of that which is, that which may be, and that which should be.

The complexities in the interrelations of people and space over time, the diversities among peoples and cultures, and the limited concurrence of philosophies and realities need not be argued in hypothetical form. There is Japan.

3. The background of this discussion is the writer's volume (12). The major sources for information after 1955 were the publications of the Censuses of 1960 and 1965. Population and vital statistics information is included in summary form in (20). Analyses of the historic and contemporary demography of Japan are concentrated in the Institute of Population Research, Ministry of Health and Welfare, Government of Japan. They are presented in the journal of the Institute, *Jinko Mondai Kenkyu Sho,* and in research bulletins. The alternative illustration would have been the USSR. In the present context, see (9) and (17).

The one non-Western population that has achieved modernization has done so with increasingly dense settlement of an ever-increasing population on limited land. This most advanced development outside the European cultural area was achieved in the country that was the classic example of the pressure of population on resources. The paradox merits analysis. Perhaps wider definitions of pressures, concepts of the multiple relations of pressure to development, and new orientations to population as resources are indicated. Perhaps social and cultural dimensions in stability and in change are as significant as the physical and demographic variables that are presently considered basic.

The Japanese space consists of islands off the coast of Asia. One-sixth of the land is cultivable. Iron, coal, and the other resources essential to industrialization are missing or limited. The climate was hospitable to early agricultural man, however, for no section of the islands had either annual or seasonal deficiencies of moisture. Access to the islands was difficult but feasible; movement beyond them was hardly possible. Internal migration, transport, and communication were difficult except by sea. The migrants to these marginal islands of late settlement in the northern Pacific included northward-moving islanders and eastward-moving peoples from the mainland. Migration was almost completed by the beginning of the Christian era. The evolution of a culture that was distinctly Japanese involved early periods of intense contact with the more advanced culture of China, later periods of contact, and then long insulation from the culture of the West. Social structure became firmly manorial, then feudal, then modern. Political continuity and social discipline were unparalleled in world history. The increasingly intensive irrigated rice agriculture yielded increasing and increasingly regular subsistence. In these islands there were no major diversities of people, language, or culture. Religion became eclectic rather than divisive. Internal policies and island location alike protected against invasion, conflict, or ideological fragmentation.

The area of occupation, the intensity of land use, and the numbers of the people increased slowly, almost cyclically, over the centuries. The fact or belief in population pressure persisted from the legendary period to the years after the Pacific War. It remains in the folklore and the popular literature today, whether within or outside Japan.

The population of Japan reached about ten million in the twelfth century. It was 18 million in the late sixteenth century. In 1726, the commoners in secluded Tokugawa Japan numbered 26.5 million. A century and a quarter later, in 1852, the last of the Tokugawa counts of commoners showed 27.2 million. Death rates and birth rates need not have been in balance in all local areas within any one year, or in all Japan from year to year. Over-all, though, the forces of death equaled those of reproduction. Famine, epidemic, and catastrophe reinforced the normally high mortality of a pre-modern population densely settled on the land. Exactions from farmers maintained great cities and a nonproductive sector of *daimyō, samurai,* and retainers distributed across the countryside. Family ideals and reproductive habits did not remain apart from the milieu in which life was difficult, survival conjectural. There was abortion among the elite, infanticide among the people. The term for rationality in suvival, pragmatism in family size, was *mabiki,* the thinning of the rice.

This relative stability of population in a cloistered Japan occurred as colonial order, dual economies, and death-preventive measures were initiating and maintaining long cycles of population growth elsewhere in Asia; as Chinese order, society, and economy deteriorated in the late Ching; as Euopean countries moved in industrialization and urbanization; as the North Americans advanced westward from the Atlantic to the Pacific, and the Russians advanced eastward from the Urals to the Pacific.

Japan's extraordinary century of modernization cannot be summarized here. In 1868, at the time of the Meiji Restoration, the state of science, technology, and economy is symbolized by the samurai swords with which the Japanese faced the guns of Western warships. In 1968, Japan ranks below only the U.S. and the U.S.S.R. as an industrial power. In 1868, rates of births and deaths were pre-modern, with population change the narrow range between them. Total population was perhaps 35 million. In 1968, rates of births, deaths, and natural increase are all very low. The population is 100 million. Demographic transition was completed in less than a century; increase in numbers was threefold. There is still growth, a product of the age structure that is heritage of past years of higher fertility. Continuation of the childbearing patterns and frequencies of the present with the low mortality now prevailing would yield decline in total numbers within a few decades.

The development of a statistical rather than a counting and record system was an aspect of Japan's modernization. The first of the quinquennial enumerative censuses was taken in 1920. Registration of births and deaths reached high levels of completeness and accuracy. Thus there is a prolific and intricate record of the almost miraculous transformations of the last half-century. There can be analyses of the initial, changing, and terminal relations of population, resources, and technology at the macrolevels of the imperial structure, the nation, and the rural and urban areas within it. Data are sufficient for the micro-levels of detailed geographic study.

The population in the 47 prefectures of

Japan, including Okinawa, increased from 55.4 million in 1920 to 72.5 million in 1940. In the years from 1940 to 1950 there was the Pacific War, the loss of empire, and the repatriation of all Japanese to a homeland now constricted to Tokugawa boundaries. There had been losses of military and home population through direct action and bombing. There was a period with heightened death rates and reduced birth rates. There was a major baby boom. Then, swiftly, the precipitately declining death rates were outpaced by the even more precipitately declining birth rates. The population that had been 72.5 million in the Japan of 1940 was 83.2 million in the Japan of 1950. It was 98.3 million in the Japan of 1965.

The population of Japan increased 6 to 8 per cent in each five-year period from 1920 to 1940. There was a net loss of about 1 per cent between 1940 and 1945, an increase of 16 per cent between 1945 and 1950. In the three intercensal periods from 1950 to 1965, per cent increases were 7.3, 4.6, and 5.2 respectively. The number of people per square kilometer was 146 in 1920. It increased to 195 in 1945 and 226 in 1950. It was 266 in 1965.

The still prevailing discussions and forebodings of the fact and role of population pressure in a modernizing and a modern Japan are belied by the course of urbanization. In 1920, the cities (*shi*) included 18 per cent of Japan's population; the rural areas (*machi* and *mura*) included 82 per cent. The per cent urban increased from 18 in 1920 to 38 per cent in 1940; in 1950 it was more than 50; in 1965 it was 68.

The population of Japan almost doubled in the 45 years from 1920 to 1965. The proportion of the population that was rural declined from 82 to 32 per cent.

The urbanization of Japan's population involved both concentration and dispersion. In 1920, 0.4 per cent of the land area was in cities, 99.6 in rural areas. In 1965, 24 per cent of the land was in *shi*—officially delineated cities—while 76 per cent was in *machi* and *mura*—usually defined as rural. The urban population per square kilometer of urban land was 7326 in 1920, 760 in 1965. The rural population per square kilometer of rural land was 120 in 1920, 112 in 1965. If these figures are meaningful, density was declining in cities and in rural areas; the increasing national density reflected the increasing proportion urban, the declining proportion rural.

The distinction of urban (*shi*) from rural (*gun,* or *machi* and *mura*) is a blurred, even erroneous, reflection of the realities of the Japanese distribution. In 1960 and in 1965, Densely Inhabited Districts (DID) were delineated on the basis of enumeration districts. More than 47 million of Japan's 98 million people lived in DID that occupied 1.3 per cent of the land area. Population density was $10,263/km^2$ in the DID, 140 outside them. In the five years from 1960 to 1965, the population of the DID's increased 38.8 per cent. The population outside DID's declined 5.2 per cent.

There is widespread and progressive depopulation in contemporary Japan. Twenty-eight of the 46 prefectures lost in total population between 1955 and 1960; 27 lost between 1960 and 1965. Twenty-two prefectures declined from 1955 to 1960, again from 1960 to 1965. The areas of increase were highly concentrated. The center was Tokyo, but Tokyo was no longer simply a great city or even a Densely Inhabited District. It was a megalopolis involving four prefectures. Almost two-thirds of Japan's total increase between 1960 and 1965 went into Tokyo and the surrounding prefectures of Saitama, Chiba, and Kanagawa.

The economic, social, and demographic processes that underlay this transition from a rural and agricultual to a metropolitan and industrial population were similar to those that had occurred earlier in Western countries, but they were also distinctively Japanese. The single fact perhaps most relevant to the reassessment of theories of population pressure and modernization is the absence of any pile-up of people on the land. The numbers of households changed little from the early days of the Restoration to the years after the Second World War. There was primogeniture in status and in inheritance. All sons except the first had either to secure another farm or to seek nonagricultural employment. Land was limited, but the combination of industrialization, conscription, and imperial migration provided employment or living for all maturing youth except the replacement sons in agriculture.

Compulsory education was introduced early for boys and girls alike. Girls worked in factory industry, particularly textiles, prior to marriage. The arranged marriages transferred the girls to the cities where the men had gone. Thus marriages were advanced to later ages. Urban social and demographic structures were more normal, and children born to more mature parents were educated in urban settings.

The Japanese process of modernization could proceed as it did because death rates did not decline swiftly under ancient ways, levels, and hazards of living. Industrialization under conditions prevalent in the late nineteenth and early twentieth centuries introduced new threats to health and longevity. Tuberculosis and other respiratory diseases became national scourges. Birth rates in traditional Japan were not high in comparison with those now prevalent in South Asia or Latin America. Slowly declining fertility and mortality were alike aspects of the urban and industrial transformation. There was no massive widening of the gap between birth and death rates. The rate of natural increase neither reached nor exceeded 2 per cent a year prior to the upsurge in the years from 1947 to 1949.

The demographic transition proceeded with seeming inevitability in Japan in the years from 1920 to 1935. Fertility declined in each of Japan's 47 prefectures in each intercensal period. The national birth rate was 36.1 in 1920, 30.8 in 1935. It declined to 27 in 1938 and 1939, rose to 29 in 1940. Japanese predictions of the future indicated deficiencies in the manpower needed for the Co-Prosperity Sphere. A comprehensive population policy was adopted to ensure the 200 million Japanese needed for imperial destiny. In the defeated Japan of 1945 and later years, concern over the population problem was deep. Pessimism was pervasive as new marriages and reunited families produced the births that carried the rate in the stricken nation to 34 in 1947 and 1948, 33 in 1949. Birth control policy was debated but not adopted. In 1948, though, a Eugenics Protection Law designed to purify the race and protect the lives and health of mothers legalized contraception, sterilization, and induced abortion. Contraception was to be available through health services; sterilization and abortion in the private sector. The legalization of contraception and its placement in the health services was quite ineffective; the numbers of sterilizations were limited, particularly of men. The resort to abortion was massive. Successive modifications of the law made abortion available virtually on request.

The incidence of induced abortion in Japan was believed to be somehow peculiarly Japanese. The later experiences of the U.S.S.R., the countries of Eastern Europe, perhaps even Mainland China, suggest that here, as in so many other areas, Japan was precursor of a future rather than deviant in a present. Whatever the relative roles of delayed marriage, induced abortion, and contraception, the consequences in declining fertility were spectacular. The crude birth rate, 33.0 in

1949, dropped to 23.4 in 1952, 19.3 in 1955, 17.2 in 1960. Quinquennial birth rates were 23.7 in 1950-54, 18.2 in 1955-59, 17.2 in 1960-64. In 1966, the Year of the Horse and Fire, when girl babies are destined to be obnoxious and dangerous mates for men, the rate was 13.7.

The variations in crude birth rates contain elements of artifact through changing age structures. Gross and net reproduction rates obviate the difficulties. The gross rate for Japanese nationals in Japan was 2.3 in 1930, 2.0 in 1937. These are relatively low rates, far below those of 3.0 to 3.5 that characterized such countries as Ceylon and Taiwan in the years around 1950. The postwar surge of births carried the gross rate in Japan to 2.3 in 1937, 2.1 in 1948 and 1949. These, it should be noted, are the levels of 1930 to 1937 in Japan itself. Thereafter decline was swift, to 1.8 in 1950, 1.4 in 1952, 1.2 in 1954. In 1957 the gross reproduction rate was below unity. In 1963 it was .96. The net reproduction rate went below unity in 1956; it was .93 in 1963.

The decline of the birth rate in Japan involved delayed marriage and severely limited fertility within marriage. Government was permissive, but induced abortions were performed in the private sector, not in government clinics or health centers. The driving force was neither government pressure nor means of limitation. It was, rather, the determination of the people of Japan to limit children to two, generally as a maximum. Determination, practice, and achievement were not limited to Tokyo and the great cities. The deceleration diffused from Hokkaido in the far north to the once-Japanese Islands of the Ryukyus in the far south. Regional differences narrowed so rapidly that crude birth rates were often lower in remote rural prefectures than in the Tokyo conurbation itself.

Population problems remain in Japan, but the greatest and the most nearly insoluble are those of the large cities. They involve smog and water pollution, transportation and housing, discipline and civil order. The problems of agriculture are those of manpower as a labor force composed mainly of women, the very young, and the aged. There are deficiencies of young manpower; soon, as the survivors of the years of precipitant decline reach labor force ages, there will be declining entrants to the labor force from one year to the next. Families will decline in numbers; two births per family will produce declining total numbers. The aged are increasing in numbers as the children and the youth decline. The structure of the population is becoming ever more weighted with the aging and the aged. If there is population policy in Japan in future years, it will be concerned with how to raise the birth rate, not how to lower it. Perhaps in Japan, as in the United States, the people of the affluent society will develop the norms and the aspirations of the larger family, perhaps two or three children rather than one or two. Perhaps the population of Japan is stabilizing with the two-child ideal.

The questions of population pressure in Japan are no longer those of the national population, of land, of resources. They are, rather, those of concentration, density, and dispersion within the cities and the urban areas. They are particularly the relations between reproduction, longevity, productivity aspirations, and the physical milieu of living and working in Tokyo, the most populous city that has yet existed in the world.

Man and Space within the Nations

Some unifying theory or interpretation is required if the population-space relationship is not to be relegated to the sphere of the historically unique or the coincidental. Such relegation is not rationally plausible, nor is it an intellectually satisfying solution. Any sufficient tentative hypotheses must involve the replacement of cross-sectional analyses at points of time by developmental analyses over time. The space that is relatively favorable to simple agricultural techniques contributes to the establishment of an economy and an increase of the people. Given this space context, familistic values and high fertility are conducive to economic growth; economic growth is favorable to relatively controlled death rates, the persistence of the high fertility, and the continuing growth of the population. Continuity in rapid growth is necessarily time-limited; the question is not the fact but the process of the slowing growth. Fertility and mortality are alike variable, whatever the time or continent of reference.

Ancient Asian empires and European or other colonial and imperial powers that fostered irrigation, improved agricultural practices, and regularized distributions raised the ceilings of maintenance and so introduced interludes of growth, but provided no solutions to the problems of growth. Transformations in ways of living, values, and rates of reproduction were essential if there was to be continuing advance. Among Europeans themselves and among the Japanese, these transformations came with industrialization and urbanization. The traditional continuities in social orders and stabilities in areas of residence yielded to substantial and continuing mobilities. These related transformations are now in process in those countries where the demographic transition to low birth rates is occurring.[4]

If population increased within the traditional society until high densities were achieved, the adoption of new technologies and institutions was retarded. As this happened, the probabilities of successful modernization were reduced. There was space and time for natural development in nineteenth-century America. There is neither space nor time for slow change in Java. In Northern America, culture, technology, economy, and organization redefined and transformed space. The biologic processes of human reproduction were largely dependent variables. In Java, as elsewhere in the densely settled traditional societies, population growth so altered the relations of man to used and usable space that culture, society, economy, technology, and political stability became dependent variables at risk of retrogression.

The relations of people to living space within national boundaries are critical in a world of increasingly fragmented sovereignties and ever more formidable barriers to movement among the economically lowly nations and between them and the more prosperous sectors of the world. There is another dimension to the problem of space. This is the association and redistribution within nations where people have hypothetical if not always feasible choices in the locations of their residences. Here relations between people and space may be measured in more precise terms, and variables in culture, economy, social organization, and political structure may be controlled.

In the United States, the internal dynamics of man-space relations developed from a limited agrarian base to a continental metropolitan form without the generation of physical pressures on space in other than local and exceptional situations.[5] The population-resources structure and its dynamics in

4. Birth rates are now low or declining in all the Chinese or Chinese-related populations of the China perimeter. Elsewhere in the under-developed areas, birth rates remain high and apparently unyielding. For an overview of levels and projections, see (19).

5. The analyses of the population of the United States are based on a study in process on the changing population in the twentieth century. Three volumes of basic data have been published: (14), (23), (24).

China provide almost maximum contrast.[6] The comparative analysis of population dynamics in these two areas refute arguments of inherent bio-demographic relationships to space, but they sustain arguments of the interrelations of geographic, demographic, and cultural factors. Japan provides an almost experimental testing of hypotheses derived from the analysis of Chinese dynamics, for the creators and participants in the modern economy and the metropolitan society of Japan were Asian in ethnic origin and in culture (2, 3, 12, 16).

UNITED STATES

The role of space in the population dynamics of the United States is little explored, despite the duration and extent of the statistical records and the empiricism of the social scientists. We shall not attempt to remedy this deficiency. Rather, we shall note the seeming contradictions in the space and privacy-oriented values of the culture and the continuing concentration of the population in a limited portion of the national domain.

Many of the physical and psychological processes in the mobile population of the United States are related to the plethora of space. The problems have been the capabilities of people and the caliber of management rather than the deprivations of nature. From the earliest years, when settlers struggled for subsistence along the Atlantic Coast to the last decade where California and the Southwest were the mecca of a nation, there was always a region beyond in which aspiring youth could seek larger and freer futures than those anticipated in the area of origin.

In the years from the Revolution to the Civil War the frontier was the Northwest

6. The analyses for China and Manchuria are portions from an ongoing study of the population of the Chinese cultural area.

Territory. The latter half of the nineteenth century spanned the westward movement of the men in the covered wagons who made the trans-Mississippi region the granary of the world. This region, incidentally, is the area that Thomas Jefferson suggested would postpone the day of crisis for rapidly multiplying Americans. By 1890 the frontier of the homestead was gone; by 1900 or 1910 the most productive agricultural population the world had yet achieved was beginning a long period of voluntary liquidation through the movements of youth to greater opportunities in the growing cities and the advancing industrial regions. The destinations of increasing proportions of the migrants of the twentieth century were areas once Spanish or Mexican: Florida, Texas, the Southwest, and California.

This is the broad geographic frame of migration in the expanding area of the United States. Fundamental redistribution was more than regional, however. The urban population increased more rapidly than the rural in all regions at all times from 1790 to the present. Most of the forty million immigrants of the years from 1820 to 1960 entered the great cities. Most of the maturing youth who left the farms and towns went to urban areas. As technologies developed, the manpower needs of the country declined in agriculture, increased outside it. (Table 3-1) Advancing technologies contributed both to the expansion of the physical cities and to the diffusion of their products, their ways of living, their ideals, and their codes of behavior. Concentration became metropolitan rather than simply urban. In the interpenetrations of urban and rural, rural areas were urbanized and the cities absorbed the impact of rural in-migrants and their descendants.

In 1960, 63 per cent of the total population of the United States lived in Standard Metropolitan Statistical Areas. The concentration was a continuing process. Almost

TABLE 3-1   LEVELS AND CHANGES IN AGRICULTURAL EMPLOYMENT,
STATES GROUPED BY DENSITY IN 1960, CONTERMINOUS UNITED STATES

Population per sq. mile (and km²), 1960	1900	1910	1920	1930	1940	1950	1960
			Per cent of employed in agriculture				
Conterminous U. S.	38.8	32.5	25.6	21.4	17.5	11.6	5.9
Less than 10 (3.9)	50.1	47.0	45.9	44.4	37.5	27.8	16.8
10 to 50 (3.9—19.3)	56.0	48.0	40.7	36.4	30.6	19.9	10.4
50 to 100 (19.3—38.6)	57.3	50.7	42.0	35.3	28.5	18.6	8.5
100 to 250 (38.6—96.5)	32.3	23.3	17.3	13.0	10.8	7.0	3.8
250 to 500 (96.5—193.0)	15.4	10.9	7.9	6.1	4.8	3.3	1.9
500 and over (193.0 and over)	7.9	5.8	3.7	4.4	2.4	1.8	1.0
			Per cent change in numbers in agriculture				
Conterminous U. S.	...	9.8	−13.9	−1.8	−16.9	−20.0	−41.5
Less than 10 (3.9)	...	64.6	2.2	7.3	−17.4	−9.8	−30.3
10 to 50 (3.9—19.3)	...	19.7	−11.7	3.1	−17.2	−21.5	−40.5
50 to 100 (19.3—38.6)	...	10.4	−17.0	−4.9	−16.4	−22.0	−48.3
100 to 250 (38.6—96.5)	...	−7.0	−10.5	−4.4	−15.0	−14.7	−33.4
250 to 500 (96.5—193.0)	...	−8.5	−19.3	−10.6	−19.7	−21.5	−36.3
500 and over (193.0 and over)	...	−4.3	−23.3	7.2	−31.4	−11.2	−39.3

Source: Irene B. Taeuber, *Population Trends in the United States: 1900 to 1960.* U.S. Bureau of the Census, Technical Paper No. 10, and unpublished tabulations. Washington, D.C., Government Printing Office, 1964. Table 7.

two-thirds of the population increase of the first decade of the twentieth century was absorbed in the metropolitan areas as defined in 1960; the proportion was three-fourths from 1910 to 1920 and more than four-fifths in all later decades except that of the 1930's. There was also a regional concentration of metropolitan areas and the emergence of metropolitan subregions. Again in 1960, some 32 million people, one-sixth of the total population of the United States and almost three-fifths of the metropolitan population, lived in 33 metropolitan areas that lay in almost unbroken succession from Boston to Washington, D.C.

The national process was concentration within metropolitan areas; the metropolitan process was dispersion to the peripheries. In the decade of the 'fifties the concentration of Negroes in central cities continued, but that of whites declined or even reversed itself as movements to the rings quickened. For all metropolitan areas, central city populations increased less than 5 per cent in the decade, ring populations almost 50. In 1960 more than half the entire white population of the metropolitan areas lived outside the central cities. In 1966 the population outside central cities exceeded that within them.

The correlate of metropolitan concentration was slow growth or decline outside the SMSA. In the 20 years from 1940 to 1960, there was negligible increase or decline in the nonmetropolitan populations of the area that had been the Louisiana Purchase and the Oregon Cession, Appalachia, and the Deep South. Half the counties of the entire United States lost population each decade; a substantial portion lost population both decades. Metropolitan concentration and nonmetropolitan depopulation were related processes.

Today, as throughout the period of record, fertility is related inversely to density. Since the populations of the less densely settled areas are more agricultural, less educated, and disproportionately native of native parentage, psychological relations of space and fertility can be affirmed only cautiously. The evidence of the urban and metropolitan experience is more conclusive. Age at marriage is higher, the fertility of the married lower, in those areas that were metropolitan in 1900. Indigenous urbanites are less oriented to reproduction than rural migrants and the immediate descendants of such migrants. The fertility of the white population is higher in the areas outside central cities than in the central cities themselves. Presumably the migration from central city to outer area was related to a decision for greater space by those having or desiring children.

The historical developments and present status in the United States illustrate both the continuing relevance of space as a dimension of demographic processes and the diverse ways in which that dimension manifests itself. Space has priority value provided it is within the orbit of the ways of living that are the contemporary metropolis. Perhaps the repudiation of isolation is a heritage of the vast spaces of the past; perhaps the movement to the urban fringe or to exurbia is a persistence of the values of privacy. The specific point is speculative, but the inference that depopulation merits research attention along with concentration is affirmed.

CHINA

If the comparison of the United States and China were simply the widely known divergences, there would be little contribution to the restatement. The striking aspect of these two great continental populations is the similarity in the process of expansion

and adjustment to space in periods of demographic and technological change. The Chinese process was expansion on the perimeters of the developed areas; the direction of the migration and the new space utilization reflected the vitality or decrepitude of administration, the persistence or diffusion of crops and techniques, and the state of the pressures from the central area. In Ch'ing, major expansions occurred in Szechwan and the southwest; in the Republic, there were major movements to the northeastern provinces. The populations of the deltas and plains of the Hwang-Ho and the Yangtze and the lesser areas of intense utilization increased in developmental periods, when people and production were in such precarious balance that the rates of dying approached the rates of generation, and declined through death or flight in such cataclysms as the Tai'ping Rebellion.

In the United States, the movement from the settled areas to the frontiers was so great that manpower deficits were met by immigration from abroad. In China, the movements from the settled areas were insufficient to reduce the pressures or the vulnerabilities; death rather than migration was the prime regulator of numbers. In the United States, the base population was small, the resources major. In China, the base population was large, the resources limited. In the United States there was a scientific, technological, and managerial revolution. In China there were persistent ways of production, distribution, and consumption. In the United States birth rates declined to low levels along with death rates. In China neither birth nor death rates declined prior to the establishment of the Peoples Republic. Normalization in age and sex structures occurred rapidly through the assimilation of other peoples and the identification of the children of Chinese men and indigenous women as Chinese.

This aspect of Chinese expansion was

distinctive. There were similarities in the paths of migration and in migrant-space adjustment. The destinations of most of the migrants were urban areas and industrial regions, not the land and agriculture. In the rural areas of Manchuria where frontier settlement had occurred a generation earlier, fertility was associated negatively with density. The major differentiation was that between rural areas or industrial and commercial cities. The fertility of women was far lower in the cities and the areas of divergent contacts than in remote rural areas; the fertility of women in areas near cities was at intermediate levels. Youths were moving from rural areas to great cities, as were the migrants from the longer distances of China Proper. There were major ecological variations within cities, with associations comprehensible in American historic experience.

The migrations and the transformations of the Chinese in China and in developmental situations outside China sustain a hypothesis that is not limited to China and the Chinese. The relations of population dynamics, space and resources use, and social and economic levels cannot be projected into the future on the basis of cross-sectional analysis of developed, developing, and underdeveloped nations. Time, technology, and drives to modernization are major dimensions. If these are integrated in analysis, in retrospect, in projection, or in the eventual test of time itself, it is possible that the interrelations of population dynamics and the dimensions of space may involve regularities in bio-social response.

Relevances and Queries

If this paper had been written sometime in the twenty-first century, it could have had intellectual symmetry. Today the populations of most of the world are in revolutionary change. Technologies now known and diffusing, technologies likely to be achieved, and scientific advances yet to be made yield new definitions and changing realities in the relations of population to resources. Present rates of population growth, resources definitions, and resources use are inherently transitory. The concepts and the theories of the past condition the thinking of the present; they are bases for its literature. The concepts are insufficient, the literature superficial, if the focus is the relations of men to resources and the physical, biological, and social-psychological consequences of such relations in time perspective. The intellectual history of the diffusion of technology, the dynamics of cultures, and the processes of change sustain affirmations of mobility but skepticism with reference to the directions and dimensions of the movements in the analytically approachable future.

Populations, as resources, seem almost immutable factors or forces at specific times. The stabilities of the distributions, structures, and relations of the slowly changing populations of the great traditional societies permitted research approaches in analytical frames of pressures, stresses, and responses. There were movements but not transformations within the enduring economy, social organization, and value matrix of the culture. Starvation and malnutrition, epidemic and endemic hazard, and cataclysms were episodic or recurrent within the pressure system. The expansions and contractions of resources bases were processes to which populations responded with altered growth and migration but here, as in cataclysmic extinctions, culture and demographic process were continuing verities.

Today, populations in the less developed areas are increasing year by year with seeming inevitability. The ever larger cohorts of births mature almost as tidal waves moving upward through the age groups. In the 'fifties and the early 'sixties, the massively increased numbers of youth were preschool and school age populations. In this decade they are in the ages when the normal sequences move from employment to marriage, home, and children. The insufficiencies and frustrations are more than economic, whatever the geographic region, the culture, or the political and social organization.

There are regions and countries that have achieved economic development of advanced types, educated populations, politically stable social systems, and generally sufficient levels of living if not affluence. The human correlates of modernization include the increasing diversification of the occupational structure, the increasing urbanization of the population distribution, the advancing education of youth, and the slowing of population growth through declining fertility. No country has yet achieved demographic balance without modernization, and no country has achieved modernization without demographic balance. The level of the fertility is perhaps the most incisive single index of place in a modernization continuum. In countries now developing, fertility is moving downward. In countries where fertility is declining, economies are developing. Increasingly fertility itself is a planning variable, subject to program, facilities, and service as a component in health services at personal, family, and community levels and economic growth at regional or national levels.

The questions for population geographers and resources demographers are simple to state. They concern the relations of increasing numbers to resources availability and use, the requirements for and the processes of integration of the increasing youth into man-land-resources structures geared over generations or millennia to slowly changing numbers, and the economic and political correlates of the success or failure of such integrations at acceptable levels of living.

REFERENCES

(1) Edward Ackerman: Population and Natural Resources, in: Philip M. Hauser and Otis D. Duncan, eds.: The Study of Population (Chicago, 1959), pp. 621-48.

(2) J. Lossing Buck: Land Utilization in China (Nanking, 1937; New York, 1964).

(3) George B. Cressey: Land of the 500 Million; a Geography of China (New York, 1955).

(4) Imre Ferenczi: The Synthetic Optimum of Population; an Outline of an International Demographic Policy (Paris, League of Nations, 1938).

(5) F. R. Fosberg, ed.: Man's Place in the Island Ecosystem; a Symposium, Tenth Pacific Science Congress, Honolulu, Hawaii, 1961 (Honolulu, 1963).

(6) Pierre George: Introduction à l'Etude Géographique de la Population du Monde (Paris, 1951).

(7) Preston E. James: The Geographic Study of Population, in: Preston E. James and Clarence F. Jones, eds.: American Geography: Inventory and Prospect (Syracuse, 1954), pp. 106-22.

(8) Owen Lattimore: Inner Asian Frontiers of China (New York, 1940).

(9) Materialy i Mezhduvedomstvennogo Soveshchaniya po Geografii Naseleniya, Proceedings of the First Inter-Agency Conference on Population Geography, Moscow University (Moscow and Leningrad, 1961).

(10) E. F. Penrose: Population Theories and Their Application with Special Reference to Japan (Stanford, Cal., 1934).

(11) A. Grenfell Price: White Settlers and Native Peoples (Cambridge, 1950).

(12) Irene B. Taeuber: The Population of Japan (Princeton, 1958).

(13) Irene B. Taeuber: Demographic Instabilities in Island Ecosystems, in: F. R. Fosberg, ed.: Man's Place in the Island Ecosystem; a Symposium, Tenth Pacific Science Congress, Honolulu, Hawaii, 1961 (Honolulu, 1963), pp. 226-52.

(14) Irene B. Taeuber: Population Trends in the United States: 1900 to 1960, U.S. Bureau of the Census, Technical Paper No. 10 (Washington, 1964).

(15) Glenn T. Trewartha: The Case for Population Geography, *Annals of the Association of American Geographers,* Vol. 43, 1953, pp. 71-97.

(16) Glenn T. Trewartha: Japan, a Geography (Madison, Wisc., 1965).

(17) I. P. Gerasimov and Chauncy D. Harris, eds., Lawrence Ecker, trans.: U.S.S.R. Geograficheskoe Obshchestvo: Soviet Geography: Accomplishments and Tasks (New York American Geographical Society, 1962).

(18) United Nations, Population Division: The Determinants and Consequences of Population Trends, Population Studies, No. 17 (New York, 1953).

(19) United Nations: World Population Prospects as Assessed in 1963, Population Studies, No. 41 (New York, 1966).

(20) United Nations: Demographic Yearbook (New York, annually).

(21) United Nations: The Population Bulletin of the United Nations (New York, 1951-   ).

(22) United Nations: Population and Vital Statistics Report, quarterly (New York, 1948-   ).

(23) U.S. Bureau of the Census: U.S. Census of Population: 1960. Selected Area Reports. Standard Metropolitan Statistical Areas. Final Report PC(3) – 1D (Washington, 1963).

(24) U.S. Bureau of the Census: U.S. Census of Population: 1960. Selected Area Reports. Type of Place. Final Report PC(3) – 1E (Washington, 1964).

(25) Wilbur Zelinsky: A Bibliographic Guide to Population Geography, University of Chicago, Department of Geography, Research Paper No. 80 (Chicago, 1962).

(26) Wilbur Zelinsky: A Prologue to Population Geography (Englewood Cliffs, N.J., 1966).

4. SOME SOCIOLOGICAL CONSIDERATIONS OF POPULATION PRESSURE ON RESOURCES

Harley L. Browning

The history of the concept of Population Pressure on Resources (PPR) shares many of the features that long have been associated with optimum population theory. Over the years economists have been alternatively attracted and repelled by the latter (10). Efforts to generate a scientifically acceptable formulation of optimum population have met with little success. No one has been satisfied either with the conceptualization or measurement of this elusive and relative concept. Periodically it has been suggested that the task be abandoned because "optimum" by its very nature cannot be given a scientific basis. Yet in spite of the many severe and damaging criticisms repeatedly fired at it, the concept of optimum population refuses to die. It survives, I submit, because it represents a fundamental problem that must be confronted in one way or another, a problem certain to increase rather than diminish in the immediate future. In a world in which planning both by public and private sectors becomes more and more common and the optimal allocation of resources occupies a central position in the planning process, population as a variable cannot be left free to vary in ways unrelated to economic and social goals.

Population Pressure on Resources (PPR) and its allied concepts of Over- and Under-population and Population Equilibrium and Disequilibrium, are in the same theoretically muddled and unsatisfactory state as optimum population theory. A survey of its usage in the papers prepared for this conference reveals a considerable variation in the way the authors approach the definition and measurement of the term. If there is a general tendency, it is to treat PPR in a loose and in-

formal manner. Some contributors, in fact, give scarcely *any* consideration to the theme of this conference but instead go directly to the specialized topics that interest them.

Now I freely admit that I too have been unable to wrap up PPR in a neat package with no loose ends. As a matter of fact, it is loose ends that most interest me, and I would like to spend the first part of my paper in an unsystematic consideration of some of the reasons why we have difficulty in defining and working with PPR. Specifically, I want to take up problematic aspects of the scope of PPR, its definition and operationalization, the appropriate territorial units of analysis, and, finally, the dynamics of PPR. Following this review I will turn my attention to specifically sociological features of PPR.

THE SCOPE OF PPR

To begin on a positive note, the inherent complexity of PPR is now well recognized. The early naïve belief that PPR could be expressed adequately by crude density figures has been wholly abandoned. As a number of papers have demonstrated, PPR may be found in areas of very low population densities and, conversely, high population densities are not invariably indicative of PPR. (Sen Gupta, p. 427) But if the early simplistic man-land formulas have been abandoned, there now exists, in my opinion, the danger that we will go to the other extreme and so extend and broaden PPR that it will become a "sponge" concept, absorbing indiscriminately all sorts of disparate factors and meanings. In effect, PPR may be used to explain too much. I will argue throughout that it is advisable to restrict the scope and content of PPR rather than converting it into a "global" concept such as modernization or economic development.

A good example of the way the scope of PPR is being extended may be found in the growing divergence in the way PPR is conceived in developing and developed countries. In the former, "resources" are still defined in the traditional manner, with a heavy emphasis upon those providing for the necessities of life (food, clothing, and shelter). And there is great concern about the shortage of these vital sustenance requirements. In contrast, the trend in the developed countries (and it has very recently become quite pronounced in the United States) is to redefine PPR so as to minimize the basic necessities.[1] With the exception of proportionally small disadvantaged sectors of the populations, the fulfillment of basic sustenance requirements does not offer great problems. Instead, much more is heard about resources affecting the "quality" of life. Thus dwelling requirements are expanded to include recreational facilities away from home. And in discussing the environment, attention is now directed to problems related to clean air, pure water, etc. Now the above *are* resources, and physical ones at that, but it is also clear that a discussion of PPR may take quite different directions, depending upon the kind of country.

DEFINITION AND OPERATIONALIZATION OF PPR

If PPR is identified as a maladjustment between the resources of a community or society and its population, then an increase in PPR may be due to an increase in population, a deterioration of resources, or both. The major cause currently is to be found in the very high and sustained rates of natural increase in most developing countries. It is also possible for PPR to occur when the population size remains constant or even declines somewhat, provided there is a rapid and marked deterioration of the resource base, but this is not a common occurrence. Sharp alterations in the patterns of international trade can produce much the same result, at least temporarily.

There is sometimes a tendency to think of PPR in static terms, the relationship of population to resources without reference to time. It should be emphasized that it is not so much the absolute size of the population that brings about an increase in PPR, but rather the rate of population growth. Significant differences in rate of growth will greatly influence the ability of a community or society, and the individuals living within it, to adjust satisfactorily to the increase in numbers. Let us assume a doubling of population. If this takes place within a fifty-year span, accommodation may be quite successful, but a time period half as long will be insufficient to allow for a satisfactory adjustment. Since a sizable number of developing countries are reproducing themselves at the present time within a period of twenty years or so, a circumstance without precedent in human history, they are operating, so to speak, with pistols to their heads. Unfortunately, at the present time we cannot speak with any certainty about the probable consequences of an increase of .5 per cent or 1.0 or 1.5 in the per annum rate of growth of a country. Is there such a thing as a critical point, and, if so, is there much variation among societies in this respect?

Another problem in the definition of PPR is whether short-term fluctuations in the economy (i.e. depressions) that may temporarily affect PPR are to be included. During the 1930's many industrialized countries in Europe, for example, could be defined as experiencing PPR, but it was in these same countries only twenty years later that so severe a manpower shortage developed that large numbers of laborers had to be im-

1. This has permeated even official publications. See (11) for example.

ported from other countries. In line with my "restrictive" bias, I believe we should ignore such cyclical fluctuations and stick to long-term trends.

Perhaps the most important question I would like to raise concerning the definition and scope of PPR has to do with the proper place of "social" factors. This is, it will be recalled, a Symposium on the Geography of Population Pressure on Physical and Social Resources, but I must confess to a certain "uneasiness" about the inclusion of "social" in this title. Presumably as a sociologist I should be delighted with the expansion of scope to include social as well as physical resources, but it may be unwise to do so, for reasons that I am at the present time unable fully to articulate, hence my "uneasiness." To be truthful, I'm not at all sure what social resources *are* or, perhaps better stated, what things social would be excluded from this category. We could, as has been suggested in one of the papers, classify the labor force as a social resource. But doesn't this procedure invite confusion? The members of the labor force are also part of the growing population that is putting pressure on this social resource.

For rather related reasons I have reservations about the tendency in a number of the papers to make the factor of "expectations," the "frustration gap," or whatever else it is called, an integral part of the definition of PPR. Surely this position will brand me a traitor to my profession. I am not, however, in any way denying the importance of this factor. Indeed, I believe the various authors are correct in assigning it so much attention and I find, for example, Mr. Mabogunje's use of "expectations" in his typology of West African areas very helpful for his subsequent analysis. (Mabogunje, pp. 115-18) But I would still prefer to define PPR only in terms of population and physical resources *and then* to determine PPR's effects upon social

institutions and the expectations of the people. It is, after all, not easy to identify the relevant population variables, and it is even more difficult, as is lamented in many of the papers, to assemble adequate information on the physical resources. Do we really want to further burden ourselves with the problem of measuring "expectations"? If so, we are asking for trouble. Mostly, "expectations" and the "frustration gap" are imputed to people rather than being empirically demonstrated. I'm not suggesting that it is impossible to empirically ground these concepts, but I am saying that it's terribly difficult to do so and that it requires skills most geographers do not possess. At the very least it would mean extensive (and therefore expensive) field interviews. And besides, for reasons I will not consider here, I believe expectations and the like to be more directly related to the process of modernization than PPR as such, so it would be more prudent to let others concern themselves with the problems of its measurement.

There remain a few comments to be made about how best to operationalize PPR so as to obtain quantitative indices for it. For purposes of ensuring comparability, emphasis should be given to measures that can be applied in a variety of contexts. There is no need, however, to fix upon any single measure as being the only appropriate one. Underlying most of them will be a decline in productivity. In more strictly economic terms, we can express it as a declining productivity per unit of factor of production used ("labor," "land," and "capital"). Particularly important is the decline in productivity of the labor force. This will be reflected by increasing unemployment and underemployment and by declining per capita or family income.

We would expect that the various direct measures of lower productivity would move in the same direction, although they will vary somewhat. Whatever the measure or measures adopted, it is most desirable to have them for as long a time period as possible. Unfortunately, it is in the developing countries, where the problem of PPR is most acute, that we are least likely to have an adequate time series.

THE APPROPRIATE TERRITORIAL UNITS
OF ANALYSIS OF PPR

Most generally, the units of analysis are communities, regions, and countries. While one can make meaningful comparisons among countries, it is well to keep in mind, as has amply been documented by papers presented to this conference, that most countries have considerable internal variation with respect to PPR. For some countries the national average is scarcely to be encountered at the local level. Internal diversity has a favorable aspect, for it implies that the country's planners can formulate programs designed to redistribute the population more in accord with available resources.

While it complicates the analysis and is often cumbersome to execute, it is strongly recommended that PPR be considered on *both* the local and national level, particularly in the investigation of the responses generated by PPR. Ultimately, of course, successful adaptations to PPR must be made at the level of the community and by the people who inhabit it. But even in the most retarded countries and in their most remote villages, the influence of outside forces penetrates, particularly the actions of the central government. Local government generally is very weak and wholly unable to respond effectively, so the vacuum, if it is to be filled at all, must be filled from federal sources. The interplay among local, regional, and national governmental sources generally is more complex and subtle than is often portrayed and it warrants explicit attention. This topic is closely linked to the problem of fostering economic development on the local level and, as McLoughlin suggests, there is often a great distance, in more ways than one, between the planners and other top governmental elites concentrated in the capital city and the inhabitants of small villages. (McLoughlin, p. 90)

There remains one more point to consider in terms of the appropriate unit of analysis, and this is the question of whether PPR lends itself equally well to urban and rural areas. Most of the work that has been done, and this conference is no exception, has been carried out in agrarian situations. I find it difficult to apply many of their findings, and certainly their techniques, to urban areas. In C. G. Clarke's study of metropolitan Kingston, unemployment is used as a measure of PPR. (C. G. Clarke, pp. 308-11) I have already suggested that as an index it is equally applicable to urban as well as to rural areas, particularly if some combination of unemployment and underemployment can be made. Nonetheless, I once again find myself "uneasy" in trying to think of PPR in terms of urban areas, without knowing quite why. Perhaps it is because for agricultural areas we can determine, within broad error limits, the "carrying capacity" of the land under various combinations of labor, capital, and other inputs. There are no comparable ways of estimating the limits to the growth of urban areas for reasons that I need not consider here. In line with my inclination to restrict rather than to amplify the scope of PPR, I would prefer to concentrate upon agricultural communities and, even more, only upon those in developing countries.

THE DYNAMICS OF PPR

If it is true that there are many troublesome and unresolved problems in the definition, scope, and units of analysis of PPR, I believe the greatest barrier to our understanding is that we often think of PPR as a condition rather than as a process; and even when we consider it from the latter standpoint we have very few empirical studies to draw upon. It is, obviously, a very complex process and there is nothing at all mechanical or deterministic about its unfolding. Indeed, our very terminology is perhaps misleading. Just as the catch phrase "population explosion" is a misnomer when applied to the steady and rather imperceptible increment of human numbers—day by day, week by week—so too it is apt to be misleading to think of population "pressure" as something analogous to a pressure cooker in which, if there is no escape valve or if it does not function properly, the pressure is built up to the point where the lid is blown off. At least I know of no societies that have been torn apart as a consequence of PPR.

So dynamic is the relationship between population and resources that the notions of equilibrium and disequilibrium lose much of their meaning, for it is only during short periods that equilibrium states can be maintained. Population rates of increase have shown marked fluctuations in the past, much to the embarrassment of the demographers who have sought to predict the future. Eventually mankind may be able to develop stable or stationary populations, but this still is a rather distant prospect. On the side of resources, their discovery or reappraisal can be important, although it is doubtful that there are many undiscovered treasures that will miraculously transform poor countries into rich ones. Possibly more important are sudden shifts in world trade patterns that greatly increase *or* reduce demand for certain commodities. The consequences of this can be dramatic. To illustrate, let us suppose a cheap synthetic coffee were developed, by no means a remote possibility, that would eliminate the demand for natural coffee. The effect on certain Latin American countries is not pleasant to contemplate.

To repeat, we are very much deficient in our knowledge of exactly what happens to a community and to a country as PPR manifests itself over a period of time. In what ways is it cumulative and, if sustained, are qualitative changes the result? Since we have a fairly adequate understanding of the causes of PPR, it is consequences that represent the real problem. In one way or another the remaining sections of this paper will grapple with this problem of consequences.

SOCIOLOGICAL DIMENSIONS OF POPULATION PRESSURE UPON RESOURCES

In terms of any explicit and direct consideration of PPR on the part of American sociologists, the sad truth is that very little either has or is being done. You will not find PPR or overpopulation in the indexes of sociological periodicals, even though most demographers in the United States belong to sociology departments.

How can we account for the barren scene and the neglect? I would suggest several reasons. For one thing, sociology is a relatively young science whose development has been almost entirely within this century. As important, it originated and has developed to a large degree within Western Europe and the United States. As a consequence it has evolved in countries already industrialized and not generally subject to PPR, at least under the circumstances now confronting most developing countries. PPR simply has not been "visible" to most Western sociologists.

Second, population variables, and PPR in particular, are not an integral part of the theoretical orientation and conceptual framework of the great majority of sociologists. This is in spite of the fact that demographers and human ecologists (a discipline that, as we will soon see, is well suited to a consideration of PPR) are most often to be found in the same departments. The "communication gap" between them and other sociologists generally is distressingly great. Some sociologists would explicitly exclude demography and human ecology from the field, and a number (by no means all, fortunately) of general textbooks simply ignore demographic and human ecological factors. PPR, if it is considered at all, is treated as an exogenous variable, not as one central to the main sociological concerns. There is an irony here, for a number of prominent sociologists, among them Talcott Parsons, have made the problem of the social "order" (what serves to hold a society together or to tear it apart) central to the field (9). As I will attempt to indicate, one of the most important consequences of PPR precisely is that it introduces into the community and the society the strains that serve to weaken and undermine the social order unless vigorously counteracted. Yet these sociologists seem to be unaware of the importance of PPR in this respect.

As a third reason why sociologists have not paid much attention to PPR, we must acknowledge the nonbehavioral character of the concept. Norms and role expectations governing behavior are not seen as relevant to PPR because there are no "actors" to act. And for most sociologists causality cannot be imputed to such an "impersonal" force. Of course sociologists are not the only ones who do not think in these terms. Whatever else the great majority of people worry about, they don't spend much thought on PPR. For them its meaning and importance are mediated and transmitted in more concrete ways: lack of land, lack of work, etc. And, of course, they rarely attribute to PPR responsibility for their difficulties. They blame the government, landlords, minority groups, imperialists, etc.

In spite of the general lack of explicit attention to PPR on the part of sociologists and the genuine difficulties that arise in try-

ing to fit the concept within a sociological framework, I believe sociology to be useful, at least in exploring the consequences of PPR. But before considering this point, I would like to mention a subfield of sociology, human ecology, whose basic framework *is* well suited for consideration of PPR. In the United States, within the last decade or so, human ecology has undergone a reformulation of the earlier work of Park, Burgess, and others of the Chicago school. Led by such men as Duncan, Gibbs, Martin, and Schnore, the new formulation seeks to make "organization for sustenance" the core concern of human ecology and the "ecological complex" a central feature of the field (4; 5; 7). The latter is conceived of as four major mutually interactive concepts:

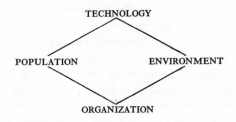

If we substitute resources for environment (and they are virtually synonymous), it can be seen that this schema is very well suited for the analysis of PPR. More and more it is recognized that technology and organization mediate between population and resources (environment), and they serve to make quite problematic what otherwise would be a rather direct relationship between population and resources. (Human ecologists look with a certain envy at the "animal" ecologists who do not have to deal, at least directly, with technology and organization. It is for this reason, however, that the two fields pursue separate ways.)

Unfortunately, to date human ecologists have been unable to specify with any exactness what is to be included under each of these four key concepts, to operationalize them, or to state the ways in which they interact.[2] Undoubtedly the most weakly developed of the four is organization, and it has not even been identified successfully. The distinction between technology and organization is a rather fine and subtle one, generally difficult to distinguish in reality, and a change in one generally is accompanied by a change in the other. Nevertheless they are conceptually distinct and it is likely that as we learn more about them the differences between them will become more apparent. While there is much study of "organizations" in sociology, very little of it seems relevant for ecological considerations as the emphasis is upon interpersonal relationships within organizations rather than features of organizations in their own right. So far human ecologists have done very little themselves with the concept except rather vaguely to link it to the structure of the labor force. Their data are not based upon productive organizations, but are aggregate figures of individuals in the labor force as enumerated by the census.

I would assign a high priority to the development of the concept of organization and its applicability to empirical situations. If I understand McLoughlin correctly, what he calls farm systems or farm management could be included under organization. I concur in the importance he assigns to it, and his judgment that there are "terribly few reliable farm management studies" can be applied equally to other organizations. If we are to arrive at a satisfactory knowledge of the importance and functioning of organizations, they must be studied from the perspective of many academic specialties. And, to emphasize the point once again, we need to construct indices and develop techniques that apply directly to the organizations themselves and not simply to rely upon indices

2. A provocative effort along these lines is (1).

based upon aggregates of individuals in the organizations.

To return now to the ways in which mainstream sociology could contribute to our understanding of PPR, we need to think about what *can* happen—what alternatives are open to the community—as a means of accommodation to the stresses introduced by PPR.

In analyzing the ways a community has of "coping" with PPR several distinctions can be made. Accommodation may be *ameliorative* or *transformative*. In the former the social structure of the community is essentially unchanged, whereas in the latter fundamental structural changes take place. The source of the accommodation, whether ameliorative or transformative, may be classified as *internal* or *external* to the community. (It should be pointed out that all four of these modes of accommodation may take place in the same community at the same time, although their relative importance will vary greatly.) Under the classification of external, I would put forms of assistance by central or state governments, foreign aid and relief agencies, and by ex-natives of the community. This assistance is often, though not necessarily, ameliorative and is, in effect, a subsidy that maintains the existing social structure without seriously altering it. This is not uncommon in many communities, and they are rendered increasingly vulnerable (often without being aware of it) because of their growing dependence upon outside aid. Should it be cut off for any reason, the shock to the community would be great. Political scientists could make significant contributions through the study of this phenomenon.

Another major means of adaptation I would classify as external is out-migration, whether it is of a temporary, seasonal, or permanent nature. This is, of course, a frequent and extremely important mode of adaptation to PPR and since it is covered in another paper (Kosiński and Prothero, pp. 251-58) I will make only a few comments. As a mechanism of adjustment requiring little or no structural transformation of the community, migration, especially permanent migration, might be considered an ideal solution to PPR. Yet there are a number of features of this form of adaptation that have negative implications. For one thing, out-migration does not function as a safety valve that works automatically to keep the population at a proper relation to resources. The volume of net out-migration (there is, even in the poorer communities, an appreciable amount of return migration and in-migration) is dependent upon many factors. There must be superior opportunities elsewhere that serve to attract the prospective migrant and he must be made aware of them in some fashion. If out-migration is to be heavy enough to be effective, a substantial part of the population must be willing to leave, and their willingness to do so is associated with a host of factors, such as family commitments, levels of aspirations, and education. Because of the inherent complexity of the situation, demographers and others who have attempted to predict migration have been really successful only in predicting whether the net will be positive or negative rather than accurately estimating the magnitude of the migratory flow or in anticipating important changes in its pattern.

The age-selective character of out-migration has negative implications for the community, especially if the outflow persists for a lengthy period. One of the few migratory patterns that approximates a "law" because of its occurrence in all parts of the world is the concentration of migrants in the young adult years. Once past age 30 both the objective circumstances favoring migration and the propensity to migrate decline markedly. In the developing countries most migrants from rural areas are deficient in education and lacking in occupational skills useful in urban areas. They have only their physical strength to offer in the labor market and this asset declines rapidly with advancing age. From the standpoint of the sending community, the fact that over a period of years perhaps 30 to 50 per cent of the age cohorts entering their late teens and early twenties leave the community means a heavy loss of the more vigorous members just at a time when the long period of caring for and rearing them is finished and the "returns" on this investment would begin to flow in.

But there is also a more subtle but equally important loss to the community that derives from sustained out-migration. The selectivity of migrants is more than an age phenomenon. Even though there are embarrassingly few studies that have empirically documented it, there is general agreement that migration from small communities is selective of the more enterprising and ambitious individuals.[3] Over the years, then, the community sends out its best sons to other places, generally urban areas. The loss of these potential leaders and innovators, with the implication that those who remain are psychologically disinclined to take risks, means that the community becomes less and less able to generate solutions internally to the various problems arising from PPR.[4] This feature of the migratory process enters into the "vicious circle" that makes it so difficult for rural communities to generate their development from within. In most cases, to reverse the flow of talented and enterprising individuals back to these small communities requires special incentives, either a tremendous moral commitment or high economic rewards.

In considering the consequences of PPR for the social structure of the community,

3. A major recent study of the United States supports this point (2).
4. For a perceptive account of southern Italy, long a region of sustained out-migration, see (8).

the contributors to this conference have many useful things to say. I believe we are especially indebted to H. C. Brookfield for his incisive analysis. Despite his disclaimer that "the only refuge open to an empiricist such as myself is to carve out a quite limited field," he has provided us with a wide-ranging survey that turns up a host of generalizations that can be applied not only to primitive or archaic groups as he suggests but also to most peasant communities. I am indebted to him throughout the following section, though he may not be happy with the result. To be consistent with his treatment, as well as for reasons I have earlier stated, my discussion will be restricted to agrarian communities such as are to be found in most developing countries.

Let us first assume that PPR has made itself manifest, and I will venture no generalizations as to how long it will take before the full force of PPR is felt for this will depend upon many factors, including the rate of population growth and the importance of out-migration and external aid. If I were to use one word to describe the situation, that word would be *scarcity*. There will be a growing scarcity of land, of full and remunerative employment, of access to public services such as schools. While the production of goods and services for the community need not decline in absolute terms, the community is not an "expanding" one in various meanings of this term; it tends to become "closed" rather than "open." This leads, as Brookfield suggests, to an increasing "rigidity" of the system as people and institutions become more "defensive" in their actions. Such a course is hardly calculated to encourage the community and the people living within it to seek innovative or "radical" solutions to community problems resulting from PPR. People adopt an increasingly pessimistic appraisal of the future in general and their own prospects in particular. Brook-

field mentions "a general *tristesse*" that has increased in Mauritius in the last few years. It is uncertain how "alienated" (a much used, and probably overused, concept by American sociologists) the populace becomes, but they can hardly be enthusiastic about a social system that provides them with less and less.

A key question of interest to sociologists is the effect of PPR upon the cohesiveness of the community. From what has just been said it would appear that conflict and divisiveness would increase and a decline in social cohesion invariably would result. While this route is in my opinion the most probable one, it is by no means inevitable. The "challenge" of PPR may result in a "response" that serves to increase the cohesiveness of the community, to make it more, rather than less, close-knit, and there occurs a kind of collective tightening of the belt. Brookfield suggests this type of reaction to be characteristic of "chronically disadvantaged groups in a Western cultural milieu, such as depressed coal mining communities, urban slum dwellers, Irish or Appalachian small farmers." I would agree, if fishing villages and logging communities can be substituted for "urban slum dwellers." A common feature of all of these communities is a certain isolation and a communal and occupational homogeneity that increases solidarity and the "we" feeling. These conditions are not typical of urban slum dwellers for they have neither the institutions nor the stable and homogeneous population that is required.[5]

Turning to agrarian communities in the non-Western world, Brookfield cites the very instructive study of Java by Geertz (6) to show how "agricultural involution" works

5. This is, of course, one of the prime problems of Negro leadership (Black Power or otherwise) in U.S. slums: to develop sufficient cohesiveness and solidarity so as to become a strong political force.

to absorb an increasing population with re-markably little alteration of the social system. The resulting "shared poverty" based upon "flexibility within fixity" can only take place where there are common values, well-developed networks of reciprocal obligations, and effective forms of social control. It is also dependent upon a special kind of agriculture. In Java it is "the wet-rice terrace, an ecosystem of great stability and with a remarkably elastic response to additional inputs of labor." The *milpa* system of cultivation still common in Middle America, for example, does not have such an elasticity.

While over the short run the kind of adaptation described above is effective in coping with PPR, the long-run consequences are likely to be disastrous. As Brookfield well put it in discussion, ". . . while flexibility within a society can distribute stresses, it cannot by itself create new opportunity; indeed, by its equalizing tendencies, it may inhibit the adoption of more constructive responses." Here is a situation where social cohesion (so highly esteemed by many sociologists) may be inimical to the long-run survival of the society. While the reckoning may be postponed, it cannot be put off indefinitely, and the longer the delay the more severe, even catastrophic, the consequences. No known society has reached this stage, but if the current rates of population growth are to be maintained for so much as another generation, the situation in some countries may reach the critical stage. So novel and so recent are the current high rates of population growth that we really cannot depend upon the historical record as a reliable guide to the future.

All things considered, my guess is that the majority of the agrarian communities will not go the route of "flexibility within fixity," but instead will follow a path by which PPR serves to increase conflict within the community. With a growing awareness on the part of the inhabitants that the "good" things in life are in short supply, there will be an increasing unwillingness to engage in cooperative enterprises and to work toward communal goals. Perhaps the pattern of southern Italy, as described by Bonfield some years ago is appropriate (3). What he called "amoral familism" represents an unwillingness of individuals to make any commitments to the community or to mass institutions within it and even less to those on the national level. Instead, there is a retreat to the security of the family (and not a very "extended" family at that), as it becomes the only secure haven in a hostile world. Any means to obtain the limited goods of the society are sanctioned, for if one doesn't use all the measures at his disposal, he surely will be bested by someone else who has no qualms about their use.

This pattern of minimal communal cohesion contrasts with the "shared poverty" of communities with high social cohesion. In the former the various forms of social inequality are heightened. Differences deriving from social stratification are likely to be further sharpened as a consequence of PPR. While class antagonisms may be deep and bitter, this will not necessarily lead to an increase in class consciousness in the Marxian sense, for most people will be reluctant to extend their allegiance and commitment to any group outside of the family. When the chips are down there may be a good deal less willingness to act, rather than talk, for one's class than would be anticipated.

It is evident that I have only been able to scratch the surface in indicating ways in which sociology can be brought to bear upon PPR. There has been, for example, no consideration of the key sociological concept of "anomie" as applied to PPR nor of the way generational differences are widened in the course of continued PPR. In particular, the position of ethnic and other minority groups within the community or society is likely to be much affected by PPR. An appreciable increase in the latter generally will exacerbate traditional animosities. But to do justice to these and other features would require a far more lengthy treatment than can be offered here.

In closing this paper I would like to make a few comments regarding the empirical study of PPR. One can speculate at length about the possible effects of PPR upon social institutions and go on to generate any number of hypotheses, but it is obvious that sooner or later these formulations must be tested in the field. Fortunately, a number of the papers of this conference do report the results of well-conceived and painstaking investigations. But they are, as I am sure the authors would agree, only the beginning, for only upon the basis of a great many more field studies carried out in many parts of the world can our understanding of PPR be much advanced.

The use of public information, such as population and agricultural censuses, economic data, etc. will be most helpful in the initial stages of the investigation and in supplementing it, but these kinds of data cannot be direct substitutes, for they are too limited and gross in character. Their value will be in matters such as the selection of the community or communities for study and in the formulation of crude but serviceable indices of PPR that can enable the investigator to classify communities into those with high, medium, and low PPR. And if data are available to form a time series, so much the better, for they can provide some idea of trends.

The kind of field study that I would like to see carried out would be "interdisciplinary" in character, and this is not intended as the conventional pious incantation, for I believe that much scientific investigation

should *not* be interdisciplinary. But in the case of PPR and its consequences the problem inherently cuts across the boundaries of a number of disciplines. I do not suggest that all conceivably relevant disciplines be represented, if for no other reason than the danger that the investigators might out-number the villagers. What is important is that the skills of the key disciplines be adequately represented.

At the very least one would want data on land use and land tenure provided in detail and for as long a period as possible. Demographic expertise would be needed to make estimates of trends not only of fertility, mortality, migration, household formation, age structure, etc., but also for census-derived data on education, ethnic background, labor force, etc. I say "estimates" because even in the unlikely circumstance of the availability of abundant data, many adjustments will be necessary before they can be used with confidence. The social structure of the community (i.e. the stratification system, power dimension, ethnic relationships, amount and kinds of extra-community contacts) must be known in sufficient detail to link it to the other aspects of the investigation. One would also want to find out the way in which people "perceive" PPR, their degree of satisfaction with their life and their expectations for the future.

The selection of the community or communities to be studied is particularly important. Since communities rather than individuals are the unit of analysis, one is severely limited in the number of cases. "Random" selection is not feasible, at least for the sort of investigation in depth that I am suggesting, so selection should be such as to emphasize rather than minimize differences. For example, if finances and personnel permitted, my strategy would be first to select a rural region known to be characterized by PPR. Within this culturally and demographically homogeneous region as many as four villages of similar size would be selected:

1. a village with mounting PPR but relatively little out-migration
2. a village with mounting PPR but with substantial recent out-migration
3. a village with mounting PPR that has, at least relative to the others, an unusual amount of contacts with external agencies
4. a village that has much less PPR than any of the others to serve as a sort of control.

There are, of course, other possible selections, but I believe that whenever possible the field investigations should have built into their design a comparative framework. Otherwise we shall be quite uncertain about the importance of certain key variables. Probably the single most difficult aspect of the investigation will be the time dimension. It is vital to consider PPR as a process, but admittedly it is often virtually impossible to obtain reliable retrospective information, particularly for a subject matter of this nature.

REFERENCES

(1) Kenneth D. Bailey: Human Ecology: a General Systems Approach (Ph.D. dissertation, University of Texas, 1968).
(2) Peter M. Blau and Otis Dudley Duncan: The American Occupational Structure (New York, 1967).
(3) Edward C. Bonfield: The Moral Basis of a Backward Society (Glencoe, Ill., 1958).
(4) Otis Dudley Duncan: Human Ecology and Population Studies, in: Philip M. Hauser and Otis Dudley Duncan, eds.: The Study of Population (Chicago, 1959), pp. 678-716.
(5) Otis Dudley Duncan and Leo F. Schnore: Cultural, Behavioral, and Ecological Perspectives in the Study of Social Organization, *American Journal of Sociology,* Vol. 65, September, 1959, pp. 132-46.
(6) Clifford Geertz: Agricultural Involution; the Processes of Ecological Change in Indonesia (Berkeley and Los Angeles, 1966).
(7) Jack P. Gibbs and Walter T. Martin: Towards a Theoretical System of Human Ecology, *Pacific Sociological Review,* Vol. 2, Spring, 1959, pp. 29-36.
(8) Joseph Lopreato: Peasants No More (San Francisco, 1967).
(9) Talcott Parsons: The Social System (Glencoe, Ill., 1951).
(10) Joseph J. Spengler: Population Optima, in: Daniel O. Price, ed.: The 99th Hour (Chapel Hill, N.C., 1967), pp. 29-50.
(11) U.S. Department of the Interior: Conservation Yearbook. No. 2. Population Challenge, What It Means to America (Washington, 1966).

5. INCREASING AGRICULTURAL OUTPUT TO HELP WITH THE POPULATION "PROBLEM"

Peter F. M. McLoughlin

Basic Problems of the Development Economist

The economist's core function is the raising of the standards of economic performance. The economist's tasks have fragmented themselves into numerous particular specialties, even among the minority who concern themselves actively with the problem of development of the world's poorer nations. Economists thus see the matter of population growth through many sets of academic and operational spectacles.[1]

With such a large subject, there are, similarly, numerous vantage points from within the international and national economies involved from which to regard the question of population and its growth. One may take the Olympian view, and try to conceptualize in broad mental strokes the complete demographic panorama of the many poor nations. Or, moving to the foothills, one may examine the population growth and distribution picture with a nation's senior politicians and economic decision-makers such as those in the national planning organizations. At the lowest level, the condition may be witnessed from behind the hoes and plows, or the shop counters, of those in the individual economic institutions of a particular society, the lowest level of economic decision-making —how do they see, and how are they affected by, population growth?

Regardless of level of examination, how-

1. My own bias in recent years has been more heavily on the operational—what is to be done, how it is to be done, and who is going to do it. As indicated later, the theoretical structure of Western economics, at least, has been of little use in solving these more practical development problems. My emphasis here is production.

ever, the core issue for the economist remains much the same. This is the changing relationship between production levels and distribution on the one hand, and the number and distribution of people on the other. This is a dynamic and mutually interacting relationship; the world, the economy, or the household is usually in trouble of one kind or another (economic, social, political) when the rate of population increase over any sustained period exceeds the rate of increase in production.

I say "usually" because it might be the case that at relatively high levels of average productivity, a failure of per capita production to rise may be tolerated for brief periods under certain conditions. This situation obtained, for example, during parts of the 1930's in Western Europe and North America. Or it might be tolerated temporarily in low output nations if commodities may be imported so that per capita consumption does not fall too drastically.

Obviously, however, broad generalizations on output or consumption per person, while used to dramatize and advertise the problem, are of only limited value to the economist, policy-maker, or anyone else whose function it is to do something about declining or constant levels of per capita production and consumption. It is normal for a nation to experience different and varied rates of change in both population and production levels within its borders. Some activities may be increasing the productivity of those employed in them: this group may include railroads, and dock and warehouse activities; mining and directly associated work; office techniques and the expediting of paper work in some commercial organizations; certain forms of communications such as radio and telephone; the production and transmission of power; the processing of vegetable oils; the manufacture of cotton fabrics, or even steel, etc.

Within the broad area of agricultural production itself, worker and family productivity will vary enormously from place to place, from agricultural system to agricultural system, and from farm to farm within any one system. Rates of change in average productivity levels, upwards or downwards, may be long or short.

Quite aside from the technological, psychological, and economic factors which influence productivity, it is a matter of record that rates of population growth differ significantly from one society and sub-economy to another within a nation. The sometimes enormous differences in birth and death rates, as well as immigration and emigration, mean striking contrasts in demographic structures and rates of population growth, and hence a wide range of milieux with which the economic developer has to work.

As a practical proposition, therefore, the development economist is faced with the enormous task of appraising dozens, if not hundreds, in some of the larger and less homogeneous nations, of separate economic-demographic systems. In other words, while one may generalize by stating that the rate of increase in production should be greater than the rate of increase in population, this has little operational significance in view of the complexity of the problem. This is true whether one wishes to increase production, or desires to reduce the rate of population growth—the diverse factors which influence productivity, as well as those affecting birth and death rates, combine in a unique package for each particular society and economic system. A set of policies and procedures which may get results in one region, or even village or family, may be quite ineffective only a few miles away.

The Inadequacy of Orthodox Economic Doctrine in Non-Western Areas

Economists from the Western-developed economies, generally speaking, have approached the problem of population growth in the low-output nations along theoretical paths which have not, in my opinion, been too fruitful. There are two broad reasons for this. One is the nature of received doctrine, the body of theoretical tools which has been developed in the stream of economic thought in the Western, heavily "capitalist," now industrialized nations. Our ability to adapt this analytical and policy-making equipment has been circumscribed and slow. I expect that present-day economists working from other streams of economic thought, such as the Socialist, experience similar problems.

The tasks of the high-productivity economies, whatever their politics, and those of the low-output nations, are essentially the same: decisions must be made on what to produce, when and how much; on who receives this production (income distribution); on how to motivate the population to perform all those tasks which need doing (the problem of incentives); and on the institutional framework in which all these things take place. In a broad but meaningful sense these are essentially political and cultural matters on which the values and motivations of a given population and their leaders have a significant bearing—economic development is a political-social process.

The assumptions underlying Western economic theory reflect Western society: the assumptions as to human motivation and values as they affect people's economic behavior, the role of government and the legal structure, the nature of the political system, and the nature of economic institutions and decision-making processes. Our Western theories, hence, and policies stemming from them to deal with the problems of growth of both population and production, need severe re-casting, if not revamping, when faced with bundles of facts of life so different from those of North America and Western Europe. I suspect the same strains among the Soviet and Eastern European economists. This theoretical metamorphosis is proceeding, albeit slowly.

The second reason is not completely unrelated. The relative barrenness of Western economic theory has been due also to the economists' sometimes incorrect and, more usually, incomplete, appraisal of the nature of the development problem itself. If the basic characteristics of the environments in which we examine population growth and its relationship to productivity are not described and analyzed clearly and completely, it follows that the theoretical models and structures which are built, as well as the policies and procedures of developers, will be equally incorrect or incomplete, and are bound to experience limited success. This is, of course, much less true for those sectors in which the technology, including management systems and skills, may be transferred from developed economies with relatively minor adaptations—transport, power, manufacturing of many varieties, and so on. But where the human being is the prime variable, where economic decision-making is assumed by tens of millions of individual household units, and where the technology by which to raise productivity is virtually absent—in the agricultural sector—the Western-trained economist is rather helpless, at least so far.[2]

2. Needless to say the writer is not too enamored of the more "conventional" theoretical structures as they apply to the problems of low-output nations at the micro level.

The economist trained in the economics of a developed economy, whether a native of such an economy or a native of a low-output nation, generally is taught to view development as a process of the most rapid accumulation of capital, and the expansion of manufacturing and industry. The logic of our theoretical structure leads to this conclusion: one solves the problems of population growth, therefore, by the rapid creation of high-productivity employment in manufacturing and associated industries. However cursory one's examination of the economic development literature, it will be clear that, historically, the theoretical and practical emphases have been on the transfer of resources, including the foreign exchange earned by agricultural exports, from traditional and rural activities to the "modern," "urban," "industrial," "nontraditional" activities. Domestic planners, members of international agencies, and expert advisers from the governments of developed countries have generally followed this line.

Population Growth as a Crucial Problem

Much more recently, however, a slowly increasing number of economists have been shifting their ground with respect to the means to cope with population growth. Population growth and distribution have begun to assume a theoretical and practical life of their own, worthy of direct attention instead of just more figures in an equation or in a two- or three-sector model. There are a number of reasons for this, all well known. Basically, they have to do with the economic effects and implications of the population growth itself. Partly because statistics are improving, and partly because there is a slowly growing body of research and analysis, it is now possible to identify much more effectively than in the past the more precise outlines and magnitude of the major development problems. In principle, we have always known that the single most important fact of life, anywhere, has been population growth. But the developed countries have been able to turn this to advantage, to spur economic growth, another reason why our orthodox economic theories have not recognized "population" as a crucial problem.

In recent years the accelerated rate of population growth in the low-output world has demanded the attention of economists somewhat indirectly, as it were, through two related problems: these are unemployment and agricultural development. It has become clear in the majority of low-output nations that even a relatively rapid rate of increase in investment and employment in manufacturing, mining, and other nonagricultural activities (as dictated by economic theory, as well as by such factors as national pride) is not, by itself, solving the problem—it is too little, too late.

Balancing Population Increase, Agricultural Improvement and Felt Needs

There is evidence, in fact, that such a concentration is rendering the situation worse, and for two basic reasons. Because of the relative lack of income-earning opportunities in the countryside, the flow of labor from the land is progressively greater than the number of jobs available to such labor, many of which jobs require skill levels beyond those possessed by such migrants. So urban unemployed and underemployed pile up, and development resources have to be allocated to such groups to keep the political peace. Secondly, the failure of rural incomes to rise significantly has curtailed the ability of industry itself to expand; the rate of growth of effective domestic markets is terribly slow.

The policy implications from this, on the surface, seem quite clear: improve the level of agricultural income by increasing the level of agricultural production. In this manner more employment will be created in the rural areas, directly and indirectly; migration from the land will slow down; and markets will be provided for the products of industry (inputs needed by a modernizing agricultural as well as consumer goods), thus increasing the demand for workers in industry as well. With rising living standards in rural areas, where the majority live, the birth rate will gradually fall more quickly than the death rate, and lower net rates of population growth will be experienced.

A great deal of our recent literature thus has been devoted to the discussion of the nature of the required "balance" between the agricultural sector and the rest of the economy. We have been involved in long deliberations on the meaning and effects of "dual" economies; on the pros and cons of increased investment in agriculture for export or for domestic markets; on the nature of the planning process by which to organize and effect increases in agricultural production; on the internal implications of fluctuations in world market supplies; on the demand and prices for basic commodities exported; and so on. Much of this thinking and writing has been helpful to policymakers. Far too much of it has been rather academic, in that it abstracts too highly for practical purposes. Other parts of it are based on assumptions about the nature of these economies which are not entirely realistic, either because of the lack of facts, or because of the need to use the theoretical structures of developed countries.

The basic question behind it all, however, still remains unanswered, by economists or by any other group. This critical gap is the answer to the question "What do you have to do, *in practice*, to raise the level of agricultural production?" Virtually everywhere throughout the low-output world a satisfactory answer to this question has not been provided in practical, operational terms, with accomplishment. The successful attempts to raise the productivity of the scores of millions of typical African, Asian, or Latin American farmers cover only a small fraction of such farmers. We do not seem to be able to raise output with any general competence, or certainly with any speed. Over the centuries an intensification of land use has occurred in land-short regions, and/or more new land has been cultivated, to feed net additions to the populations. But the accelerated rate of population growth in recent decades, and the fact that little new land is available any longer to put to the plow in most regions, call for a *rate* of intensification of land and labor use much more rapid than in even the recent past. The typical agricultural system cannot as yet move at this higher rate; evolution must be near revolution in many areas to preclude falling per capita levels of production and income, if not now, then in a few years' time.

Given population increase in the rural milieux, combined with the development and expansion of other forces such as education, travel, and a generally rising political and social awareness, there has been experienced a growing "frustration gap." That is, the gulf is increasing between the felt need for income (for subsistence for a growing population and for a better standard of living per capita), on the one hand, and the opportunities for providing that income, on the other. Both are increasing over time, but the former at the more rapid rate in most (not all) communities in the underdeveloped world. The economist has been trying to describe and analyze the economic effects of these pressures, attempting to use them to development advantage. What has been done so far is generally useful, but of course inadequate: I wish we had several thousand more economists in the field.

Raising Agricultural Productivity: The Main Bottlenecks

For these reasons, the balance of this paper, therefore, will be devoted to an economist's summarized appraisal of how some of the economic implications of population growth for agriculture must be dealt with.[3] The following comments are not original, but they are based on field experience over a range of cultures and ecologies, much of which has been "practical"; the writer has been involved directly or indirectly in the formulation, appraisal, or execution of projects which attempt to raise agricultural productivity (irrigation, settlement, tree crop, livestock, transportation, extension, mechanization, and other schemes).

In view of the abundance of literature on the economics of agriculture and rural development, there is no need here, nor space, to list once again all those things which the economist and agricultural economist deem important to rural development. In view of the orientation and spirit of this symposium, it is thought preferable, instead, to deal with the economics of the problem in terms of research and knowledge areas on which attention must be focused by social scientists if per capita production is to be maintained, let alone raised. In the course of discussion of these priority research areas (as seen by an economist), it should be possible to suggest or infer those tasks in which the geographer and the economist may assist one

3. It is appreciated that this is not "population pressure" *per se*. But "pressure" comes from a relationship—people and production. We have enough people, and perhaps their *rate* of increase may be retarded somewhat over the next 50 to 100 years. Until then, and certainly now, the problem is one of production.

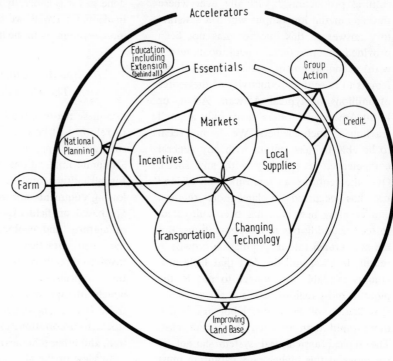

Fig. 5-1. A GENERAL MODEL FOR AGRICULTURAL DEVELOPMENT
(*Source:* Agricultural Development Council, New York)

another. This is done in the final section of this paper.

Priority areas of economic research are so because they are aimed at solving the priority problems. One may put one's finger on any segment of the diverse economic processes in underdeveloped countries and label that segment a "problem," in that difficulties of one kind or another are experienced with it. These several discussed here are felt to be priorities because the problems the research is trying to cope with are the prime bottlenecks to the accelerated expansion of production. Unless we break open, or widen, these bottlenecks, not very much is going to happen. Not that other bottlenecks will not arise, they will; but these several discussed below should be, in my opinion, the prime targets for current research in every low-output nation I know about.

Generalizing severely, and abstracting still further, agricultural development is dependent upon three broad and interrelated factors:
1. a sound knowledge of each of the existing farm systems in an area or country—why do farmers do as they do, and what are the economic, technical, and social constraints on the expansion of output;
2. a knowledge of the new inputs—methods, tools, systems, services, institutions—which will relax those constraints; and
3. the means to demonstrate to the farmer that all of this is both possible and rewarding—how do you motivate the farmer to adopt the new technology?

Virtually nowhere in the low-output world have these three conditions been met. Though there may be one or a few "successful" agricultural projects or activities in most countries, the mass of farmers have barely been touched. The three priority research items discussed below thus relate to these requirements.

1. *The economics of farm systems and, within that, the economics of the smaller farmer.* Before a farm, or a community of farmers may be induced (or forced, as far as that goes) in the direction of higher production, it is necessary to know the exact nature and rationale of the *existing* farm system. An incredibly high percentage of effort so far expended has been based on inaccurate or incomplete awareness of these actualities. There are terribly few reliable farm management studies which appraise the inputs of farmers (financial, technical, labor), outputs and production, the seasonality of the process, and management practices and decision-making. Without this knowledge, extension and technical research are severely emasculated. In the institutions which train officers for agricultural extension, research, and administrative tasks, there is therefore a severely restricted ability to make such officers aware of the basic nature of the farm systems they are supposed to be helping.

There are many reasons for this lack of attention to the economics of farming. Perhaps the most important has been the almost exclusively technical orientation of agricultural developers—the economics and sociology of farming, historically and until very recently, have been virtually ignored. There has also been the chronic shortage of qualified personnel which has led, among other things, to the devising of rather blanket policies for improvement covering wide areas. Because of differences between farm systems within such areas, and differences in size and capabilities of farm systems within such areas, and differences in size and capabilities of farms in any one system, only a few farms may in fact be influenced by such policies. In any

case the preoccupation with the development of crops for export, as well as the shortage of staff, has meant that the larger farms have received most of the extension and research attention: the majority of farmers, who are on smaller holdings, have had little economic research done on them.

Combined with the scarcity of trained people, the typical organization of agricultural staff has also often precluded a proper appraisal of farms and their constraints. The lowest level extension workers, those in immediate contact with the farmers, have been undereducated and undertrained, and each has hundreds of farms to deal with. They are usually not competent to appraise the problems of even the few farmers they may be in touch with. But even if they were, communications within agricultural departments and agencies have normally been downward, not upward. The more senior officers with university training, who have often not had sufficient field experience and established rapport with farmers, issue directives and the lower echelons attempt to carry them out—the flow is downward. Yet it is these senior extension and field officers who are advising research stations on the work which needs doing to improve agriculture (the economics of technical research is discussed at point No. 3 below).

2. *The eonomics of incentives of the farmer —how the farmer views his own development problems.* Not unrelated to the first research item above, this is basically the need to view the process of development through the eyes of the farm household—to look out from the center of our model. As one examines the cumulatively growing maze of planning documentation, of schemes, programs, projects, etc., all designed by agencies and departments to raise agricultural output, and all very expensive to formulate, one is constantly struck with the growing gulf between ambitions and efforts, on the one

hand, and the meager results, on the other. Policy-makers, politicians, planners, and administrators, domestic and foreign, are attacking the problems or bottlenecks *as they see them.*

But that is rarely how the farmer sees them. I personally have been amazed, almost everywhere, at how differently the farmer and the official view the same problem or set of problems. Most efforts at agricultural development have experienced highly limited, or very slow, success, or failed entirely, because the farmer and his family could not relate the effort to their own aspirations, their own farm's resources, or their own sense of economic viability. We need to devise farm systems which are economically attractive, which are capable of being learned fairly easily, which do not conflict too seriously with the farmer's other economic and social obligations and objectives, which are not incompatible or inconsistent with his own resources (particularly labor and cash), and which have sufficient properly trained staff to support them.

There is another dimension to the question of incentives. For a variety of reasons, some farmers and communities are "riper" for development than others. The political and social, as well as economic, priorities for development are established by a nation's senior body, so that particular areas, crops, and social groups are allocated their development resources. But when more local programs are studied, it is usually the case that development resources, particularly skilled manpower, are not sufficient to attack the problems of every village and every family. So where does one allocate these scarce resources?

Caeteris paribus, they should go to those communities, villages, or farms which are the most ready to use them, those which will, *in fact,* combine them with their own resources to get the most substantial and the most rapid increases in output. We badly need methodologies of rapid survey and appraisal which will tell us which farmers or villages are the most prepared to innovate and change. This is the combined task of many social scientists—historically only the agriculturalist has been involved, and there is a wealth of failure to indicate that what might be technically possible is not necessarily "humanly" possible. To the best of my knowledge, very little work of this kind has been done, at least in a manner which may be used by those responsible for allocating development resources. A number of researchers are now working on this problem in parts of West Africa and South America.

I believe it must involve, among other things, a proper sampling of households to ferret out and appraise the "frustration gap." The typical rural household at any point of time has needs for a certain level and composition of income. It obtains these from a variety of sources. The following list would cover many of the most important needs and opportunities for income earning for the typical rural household, though there will be local variations:

I. *Needs*
  A. *Real (physical)*
    1. food for the family in residence
    2. food to send to absent members
    3. shelter
    4. tools and equipment
  B. *Cash*
    1. tax money
    2. school fees
    3. to buy that amount of subsistence food not produced on own farm
    4. other necessities for living (utensils, cloth, etc.)

II. *Possible sources of income*
    1. food produced on own farm, including livestock products

2. tools, equipment, shelter, services produced on own farm
3. sale of food crops for cash, or live-stock products
4. sale of crops produced expressly for markets (usually export)
5. migrant farming
6. seasonal wage labor—local
7. seasonal wage labor—at a distance
8. extended migration to wage labor (year or more)
9. trading and commerce of all kinds

Over time, the pressure of the family's population on their farm is going to expand minimum food and other needs in a fairly predictable manner. Or one may measure at the village, regional, or national level.

Family (or village, or national) popula-

tion roughly doubles in thirty years; hence, food and other basic requirements also double. It will probably be the case, how-ever, that the family will not be able to grow all their own food, so that over this thirty-year period the volume of cash in-come earned will have to increase.

It will be normal, however, for the fam-ily (village, region) to desire a rising stand-ard of living. If the alternatives for earning and acquiring this income are available and used, so that the family (village, region) actually acquires what it wants, then regard-less of rate of increase in the curve of felt income needs, there is no frustration gap. The rate of increase in the propensity to seek out the means to raise farm produc-tivity tends to follow the rate of increase in felt income needs. Because of the relatively

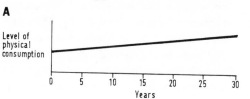

A

Level of physical consumption

Years

Needs for basic subsistence rising proportional to population growth

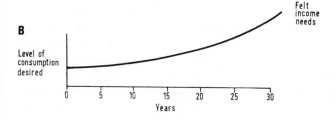

B

Level of consumption desired

Years

Felt income needs

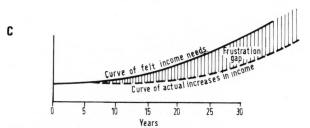

C

Curve of felt income needs

Frustration gap

Curve of actual increases in income

Years

Fig. 5-2. RELATIONSHIPS BETWEEN LEVELS OF CONSUMPTION AND INCOME

restricted possibilities of increasing incomes, the family or community "ripest" for development at any point of time is that with the largest "frustration gap," regardless of the level of income at which the gap occurs. It is possible, or even likely, that the gap is greatest among those who have already experienced some degree of development. Should that gap get too large, of course, for enough people, political unrest and other social problems arise. If it is very small, on the other hand, as it still is in many communities, then no amount of persuasion or pressure will induce a family or group to adopt new production systems, even if the suggested new items are otherwise suitable. Many livestock societies in the Middle East and Africa, for example, tend to be in this category. Development policy for them should thus emphasize the raising of their aspirations, as well as having new and effective production systems available for them to adopt.

It is also useful to remember that, as far as my own experience is concerned, the typical rural householder (and more certainly his son) prefers his nonfarming alternatives to increase his income to his farming. As long as wage labor or trading or whatever are alternatives he may adopt to solve his income needs of the moment, he will usually prefer them to going through all the strain of learning and adopting a more intensive agricultural system. And I don't blame him. This appears particularly true in sub-Saharan Africa. One of the increasingly important pressures to improve farming, in fact, in many parts of the world, is the relative decline in wage labor and other income-earning opportunities—young men are thus forced to earn their income from farming.

3. *The economics of technical research for agricultural development.* Technical research has two main functions. One is to provide an understanding of the complicated physical environment. The second task is to evolve the means by which a farmer or herder, in any particular situation, may improve his productivity on a sustained basis. New inputs and systems must be capable of being adopted into the existing and varied farming systems with their particular constraints. They must also be economically secure and attractive.

There is no space here to discuss technical research in detail. It must be pointed out, however, that there is an incredibly long list of attempted agricultural projects and schemes that have failed because not enough was known about soils, water supplies, or other physical factors. Not that more data should be collected indiscriminately; that is expensive. But each project or scheme for development covers a specific area with its own combination of physical ingredients which must be spelled out clearly. Considerable success, however, has been achieved in some parts of the underdeveloped world in the selection and hybridization of improved varieties for export, in pest and disease control, and, in a few places, in fertilizers.

But, generally speaking, technical research has *not* provided answers to the problems of the farmer. There has been an excessive technical bias and oversimplification, and little work has been done on farm *systems* as a whole, including food crops. This is partly because the technical researcher usually knows little about the farm system he is trying to improve, some reasons for which have been discussed above.

It is true that technical "solutions" have been found to many problems. Most of these "solutions," however, have not been or cannot be adopted by the farmer, much to the frustration of the research or the extension officer who promptly labels the farmer as "lazy" or some such. That is because the technical "solution" is neither feasible nor economic from the point of view of the farmer. That is, the innovation must be capable of being fitted into the existing farm system, given the constraints of seasonality, labor, cash, etc. in any particular case. The technical "solution" must also have the economic and financial appeal that will motivate the farmer to adopt it. For both these reasons, particularly this latter, most suggestions and innovations coming from research stations are *not* adopted by the general run of farmers for whom they were designed (though a few may do so). It is just not true, therefore, that there is a vast warehouse of technology and science just waiting for proper extension and demonstration before it may be applied. If that were true, we would have much more progress than we have.

There are many aspects of the solution of this problem. The economist would view it in several parts: the need for a thorough knowledge of the economics of the existing systems; the transmission of that knowledge through extension to research officers; an appreciation of the economics of the innovation; and sufficient testing of recommendations under *actual* farm conditions to determine the practicability of the recommendation. This latter is a particularly weak link in the chain.

The "Project" Approach

I should like to conclude this essay with consideration of yet another approach. It is important to operational economists and should be at least mentioned in a background paper of this kind. For lack of a better term, it may be referred to as the "project" approach.

As a general principle, already mentioned in other connections, a nation's policy-makers are interested in maximizing the return to the economy of their investment of development resources. The development plan

is an attempt to collate such a package of activities. Of the many scores of activities in which funds and skilled manpower may be so invested, how do you choose that particular combination which maximizes returns to the economy?

What is needed is the identification of a possible set of development activities, and the computing of a rate of return on each of them. For each candidate for investment, an integrated bundle of information is needed describing the technical, economic, financial, organizational, and implementation aspects of that specific activity. Investors, domestic and/or external, may then appraise the costs and benefits of the particular scheme, and rank the various possible investments in terms of their usefulness or contribution to the economy. As one examines development plans, particularly for the agricultural sector, it is apparent time and time again that the schemes and activities are so often strung together as nonintegrated entities with little background evaluation of the costs and benefits of each to the economy. Production is increased, after all, in a specific place, with a particular combination of people and institutions doing a specific combination of things. Each scheme or project has identifiable parameters in space and time, and in people and other resources. A project economist wants to make sure that what is done will raise the output fastest.

There is a severe shortage of project economists to conduct this work. One may theorize about these economies, and may make yet more lists (as I have done in this paper) of what should be done to raise output to combat population growth. But what counts is what happens—performance. Viable projects must be multiplied by the score instead of the all too usual dissipation of such a large share of development resources. Rapid economic development is only possible when we level our lances at the proper windmills.

The Potential Contribution of Geographers

Geographers and development economists may therefore collaborate to help with the practical production problem in a number of ways, though they may be summarized quickly. Comments were made earlier on the weak theoretical contributions of economists—theoretical systems developed by geographers are apparently slimmer still, at least to the moment.

Geographers should describe basic relationships in space and time. To help development, they can combine the physical and ecological with some knowledge of agriculture and economics to describe in detail, through extensive field work, the milieux in which development activities and projects will take place. If accurate and comprehensive, this information then becomes a critical input for planners, economists, and others who need such data for proper analysis of what should be done, where, and when.

In the context under discussion in this seminar, in other words, I view the contribution of the geographer to the analysis and the solution of the problem of population "pressure" as a "service" contribution; perhaps it is the most important contribution. Decisions are not made by geographers in underdeveloped countries: they are made by politicians and economists. One thus detects, I think, a certain sense of frustration among geographers—we all like to be boss, even just sometimes.

But geographers could be much more effective than at present were they to learn the language of politics and economics more thoroughly—some have, of course. But most have not; their contributions somehow are not accepted or are somehow not read sufficiently often by decision-makers. The bulk of the literature provided by geographers on low-output nations is consumed by other geographers.

In sum, geographers *can* help developers; a few have done so. But many more should work in ministries in low-output nations—development is not an academic exercise.

6. THE ADJUSTMENT OF RURAL POPULATION TO DIMINISHING LAND RESOURCES

John Fraser Hart

The relationship between rural population and land resources is exceedingly complex. Although they are commonly bandied about, it is extremely difficult to formulate precise, operational definitions of such terms as "environmental potential," "degradation of habitat," "population-resources equilibrium," "population pressure," "critical population density," "overpopulation," "underemployment," and "population mobility-migration." Terms such as these, despite their widespread popularity, defy definition even at the local or regional scale, and they appear to be almost completely unmanageable when the entire world is considered.

Nevertheless, I believe it is axiomatic that a given piece of ground can support a given number of people under a given set of technical, economic, political, social, cultural, and psychological conditions without any serious deterioration of the ground itself. This is the concept of an optimum population, which I find quite useful in attempting to unravel the relationships between the rural population and the resources of the land which it inhabits. I could be just as happy, however, with the notion of a "comfortable" population; that is, a population of such a size that it could live in peace, without stress, and (in theory, at least) in perpetuity, with the resources available to it.

The actual size of such a comfortable population, quite patently, would vary enormously from place to place. In 1963 Japan had a rural population density of more than 850/km² of cultivated land (Kiuchi, p. 484), and densities in the Philippines in 1960 ranged as high as 907/km² at cultivated land on the island of Cebu (Simkins, p. 265); in both areas it appears that the people were adequately, if not well, fed. At the other extreme, *chitemene* systems of agriculture can safely support only 1.5 to 3.9/km² on the plateau of northern and central Zambia (Kay, p. 368).

Paradoxically, similar densities, 1.6 to 4 rural farm persons per km², would probably represent overpopulation in 1967 in the heart of the U.S. Corn Belt, one of the richest and most productive agricultural areas in the world, where cash grain farmers estimate that corn yields of 60 bushels to the acre only cover their costs of production, and where yields of 125 bushels per acre are the rule and not the exception. In order to make a "decent" living by cash grain farming in this area, the farmers feel that they must have at least 600 acres, which means a rural farm population density of only three or four persons per square mile (1.1–1.5/km²). Furthermore, many of these farmers are "underemployed" between the date of fall harvest and spring plowing, and some of them spend their winter months in Florida.

Our concern here, however, is not with the actual numbers of rural persons who can comfortably subsist on the resources available from a given piece of ground. We are much more interested in understanding what happens when the carrying capacity of any rural area is exceeded. When this occurs, when a rural area has more inhabitants than it can comfortably support, it appears that the people who live in the area have three possible courses of action: first, colonization; second, intensification; and third, devastation or emigration. Although all three courses of action are unlikely to be available to the people of any given area which is overpopulated, it is quite apparent, from the papers which have been collected into this volume, that each has been chosen by various groups of people in various parts of the world in recent years. Let us examine each of them in turn.

Colonization

Although it is generally assumed that most of the habitable parts of the earth have long since been occupied by groups of men, this volume provides several examples of the spread of settlement into new areas in quite recent years. In the Philippines, for example, Simkins found that increases in production of the more common food crops since World War II have come more from extensions of acreage than from enhanced yields on land already in use; and Sandner concludes that colonization of new lands has offered some relief for population pressures in Costa Rica over the last few decades. And even in India, before Independence, the Karnal district of the Punjab had "cultural waste lands" into which land-hungry migrants flocked when political conditions changed (Gosal, p. 459).

Political conditions are not the only type of institutional barrier that may inhibit colonization of apparently available land. In some countries of Middle America, for example, a certain type of land may be used quite intensively, whereas similar land across the border in an adjoining country may remain almost completely unused. Nothing in the experience of potential colonists qualifies them to cope with its different physical environment. A system of land tenure which concentrates holdings in the hands of a few wealthy, and possibly disinterested, owners may also pose major barriers to colonization.

A rather specialized form of colonization occurs when the development of irrigation or drainage works makes previously uncultivable land available for agricultural settlement. Rościszewski says that the construction of the Aswan High Dam, for example, will increase the agricultural area of Egypt by about 40 per cent, although this gain will be neutralized by current population increase. The development of irrigation works can also provide relief from population pressure through agricultural intensification, rather than through colonization, if it permits farmers to make more effective use of land which is already under cultivation.

Although agricultural colonization of new lands may help to reduce population pressures, it may also have undesirable side effects. The colonists, especially if they are drawn from different groups or areas, may be deculturalized, and the resultant lack of an adequate social structure may result in an inability of the group to organize for economic betterment, or to utilize available agricultural extension services effectively.

Intensification

Perhaps the most common course of action recommended to alleviate the problems of rural overpopulation is to make more intensive use of the land already under cultivation (*Gosal, Rościszewski, Sandner*). Food production can be increased, sometimes in spectacular fashion, by the use of fertilizers and insecticides, by the introduction of new crops and improved seeds, by shifting from low- to high-yielding crops, by multiple cropping, by the use of such improved techniques as irrigation and contour plowing; in short, simply by taking advantage of the knowledge, skills, and techniques which are already in use by farmers in many parts of the world.

Mrs. Boserup concludes that the problem of food supply in developing countries is less one of technical feasibility than of the rapidity with which the technically feasible can become actual practice. She has prepared such an excellent prospectus concerning the possibilities of alleviating population pressures by the intensifiation of food production that it would be gratuitous to attempt to add to it.

There may be difficulties, of course. Increased food production will require an increase in the capital invested per agricultural worker. The change from an extensive to an intensive system will require more man-hours of labor per unit of output. Manpower may pose problems, for the specialists needed to make the plans and put them into effect may not be available in adequate numbers. The best educated and most enterprising rural youths may be reluctant to pursue agricultural careers. The government will need to play a more active role in agricultural planning. And tenure reforms must be an integral part of such planning, lest existing tenure arrangements thwart changes in land use.

Relief of rural population pressure by agricultural intensification often runs afoul of immensely complex and difficult problems of land tenure. It is commonly assumed, for example, that communal tenure systems impose serious constraints on development and intensification; and agrarian reform, perhaps with changes in the settlement pattern to permit more efficient use of the land, is often postulated as a necessary precondition for modernization. Conversely, however, agricultural improvement and intensification, if they reduce the number of workers required to produce the same amount of food, may even increase population pressures under a "minifundia" land tenure system in which many small farmers depend upon opportunities for seasonal employment on large estates.

In addition to the difficulties associated with changes in land tenure systems, there are many other serious obstacles to agricultural intensification in the developing countries of the world. For example, Porter argues that many of the agricultural techniques of mid-latitude farming cannot be justified in the tropics on economic grounds, because the value added to crop production per acre by such improvements is commonly less than the cost of the improvements. Furthermore, it is quite likely that the social and psychological obstacles may be just as important as those which are economic. Mrs. Boserup comments on the fact that Chinese advisers in Africa were amazed to discover the unused possibilities of paddy production there; perhaps their amazement was inversely proportional to their knowledge of African dietary habits.

McLoughlin reminds us that many technical "solutions" to farm problems have not actually been adopted by farmers, because the so-called solution failed to make any sense from the point of view of the practising farmer. McLoughlin argues that agricultural development is dependent upon full knowledge and understanding of three factors: first, the exact nature and rationale of the existing farming system; second, the methods, tools, systems, services, and institutions that could be used to improve it; and third, the means of motivating farmers to adopt the new techniques.

Devastation or Migration

The third course of action which can be taken by the people of an overpopulated rural area is to destroy its resources, or to leave it; if all the resources of an area are destroyed, of course, then the people must leave it. In other words, migration inevitably follows devastation, but devastation need not necessarily accompany migration.

At first blush the term "devastation" might seem unduly strong; but I submit that such is not the case, for some or all of the resources of many rural areas have indeed been destroyed as a result of overpopulation. For example, Kay points out that each individual resource has a critical population density above which that resource will become scarce; increasing pressure above this level leads to increasing scarcity and the resource may be eliminated altogether. Vogt cites the specific example of the Mexican state of Oaxaca, where deforestation and erosion have produced regions so dead that one can get nothing useful from them, and a great part of the population has no alternative but to emigrate.

Lest this be considered exceptional, let it be said at once that a careful review of the regional papers contained in this volume produces a sad litany of resources devastated: abandoned coffee plantations in Brazil (*Bonasewicz*); declining soil fertility in Jamaica and in Cameroon (*C. G. Clarke, J. I. Clarke*); waterlogging of soils in the Punjab (*Gosal*); land deterioration in Zambia (*Kay*); erosion problems in Nigeria (*Mabogunje*); increased soil alkalinity in Egypt (*Rościszewski*); soil impoverishment and erosion in Costa Rica (*Sandner*); and lowered soil productivity on the Middle Ganga Plain (*Sen Gupta*). There can be no doubt that one of the major effects of overpopulation is the destruction of resources.

Turning to migration, it is a truism that one of the best ways to relieve overpopulation in any given area is to have some of the inhabitants seek employment in another area. This is not always possible, of course, but this volume contains examples of migration from such widely diverse places as Brazil (*Bonasewicz*), Cameroon (*J. I. Clarke*), the Punjab (*Gosal*), Japan (*Kiuchi*), Nigeria (*Mabogunje, Mortimore*), Egypt (*Rościszewski*), Costa Rica (*Sandner*), and the Philippines (*Simkins*).

Migration may be seasonal, temporary, or permanent. Where most of the migrants are males, as is often the case, migration can produce a relict population consisting predominantly of women, children, and old people, thereby creating serious shortages of agricultural labor, and further reducing agricultural productivity. Mabogunje suggests that the movement of too many rural people to cities can create serious inflation in food prices if too few people are left on the land to maintain adequate food production. He believes that many cities in the developing countries of West Africa have been highly subsidized by the rural economy; urban workers leave their families in rural areas, do not have to feed them from their earnings, and sometimes even receive food from them. The ownership of rural land provides a form of social insurance, for the city worker can return to it when he is unemployed, ill, or too old to work.

Conversely, of course, if urban workers remit cash and goods to their families, the return flow can stimulate progress in the rural area. But how long can the cities of developing countries continue to absorb and assimilate the rapidly growing population that results from the growing imbalance of migration from rural to urban areas? Is rural-to-urban migration merely transferring the problems of the countryside to the "overpopulated metropolis"?

But what happens in areas of rural overpopulation where emigration is impossible? Is this the case in which death, rather than migration, becomes the prime regulator of population numbers? Miss Sen Gupta, in her analysis of population and resource development in India, appears to assume that emigration is the only means for solving the problem of rural overpopulation in that country, for she devotes virtually all of her attention to the capacity which various regions have for diverting rural population to urban/industrial centers. As McLoughlin points out, however, a major obstacle facing

India, as well as other countries which seek to solve problems of rural overpopulation by the development of industrial magnets which will attract people from the countryside, is the fact that industrial expansion will depend, in considerable degree, on significant increases in rural income to provide markets for the products of industry.

Summary

Under a given set of technical, economic, political, social, cultural, and psychological conditions a given piece of ground can support a given number of people without undue stress. Adjustments of some kind are necessary when this number is exceeded. The adjustment might take the form of colonization of new areas, it might take the form of intensification of agricultural practices, it might take the form of emigration of part of the people to seek employment in other areas, or it might take the form of over-use of resources and their eventual destruction.

7. PRESENT AND POTENTIAL FOOD PRODUCTION IN DEVELOPING COUNTRIES

Ester Boserup

Technical Potentialities for Additional Food Production

In the recent past, some developing countries achieved spectacular progress in food production by the use of fertilizer for food crops and by the introduction of improved seeds, of which the first was hybrid maize. Moreover, in many countries a shift took place from the cultivation of low-yielding cereals to that of high-yielding food crops such as rice, maize, cassava, sugar, and potatoes. In most developing countries, there is scope for much more progress through these methods. Yields of food crops remain at low levels because little or no chemical fertilized is applied, and improved seeds are used on only a small part of the sown area. Likewise, there is much scope for accelerating the substitution of high-yielding types of food crops for low-yielding types.

The dramatic increase of crop yields caused by the use of fertilizer and improved seeds has focused attention on these particular ways of increasing food production, and other possibilities have tended to be overlooked. In fact, taking the developing world as a whole, it is true to say that the largest potential for increased food production is in the replacement of extensive systems of land use by more intensive ones, rather than in the achievement of higher yields for a given crop or in the substitution of one crop for another.

It may be useful to begin the discussion of the potential for more intensive use of land for food production by a systematic grouping of the main systems of land use (3). If the land used for nonfood crops and for nonagricultural purposes is disregarded, the main systems of land use are as follows, listed by increasing degree of intensity:

(a) cultivable land in completely uninhabited regions;

(b) land used only for the collection of vegetable foods and for hunting;

(c) land used only for grazing by domestic animals;

(d) land used in long-fallow agriculture (sometimes called shifting cultivation);

(e) land used in short-fallow rotations with grazing on fallow land;

(f) land used for annual cropping without fallow;

(g) land cropped twice a year, without fallow;

(h) land cropped three times or more annually, without fallow.

Many sparsely populated developing countries, as for example in parts of Africa, still have huge areas under the first four types (a, b, c, d) of extensive land use listed above. More densely populated developing countries, among them those of the Indian subcontinent, have relatively little land under the first groups and much under groups (e) and (f). In the most densely populated developing countries, such as Egypt and Eastern China, a large share of the cultivated land is under type (g) and in Japan a considerable share of the cultivated land is under type (h).

It is not possible to tell precisely how much of the land in developing countries is under one or other of these systems of land utilization. The classifications found in international statistics of land use are "Eurocentric." For instance, "bush land used in long fallow rotations," the predominant type of land use in many developing countries, finds no place in international statistics; it is included, or rather hidden, under broader headings such as "arable land," "forest land," or "wasteland" (7).

To be useful in the analysis of food potentials, statistics of land use should distinguish five categories, viz. shifting cultivation with long and medium periods of fallow for regeneration of fertility; land in short-fallow rotations; land cropped annually; and land under multi-cropping. Preferably there should be a distinction between rain-fed and irrigated land within each of these groups. Some of the basic information needed for such a classification is available in specialized literature of various types; but more field surveys and a more systematic use of existing information brought up to date at regular intervals would improve the basis for estimates of the potential for additional food production.

The first, spontaneous reaction of tribal or peasant families to population growth within their community is to look for additional land to cultivate by the traditional methods. If no such land is available they have to use the land at their disposal more intensively, i.e. to move one or more steps in the list above. Thus, people who have been collecting more food than they produced may see the amount collected per head decline when their numbers are increasing and this will induce them to produce more. People who have been cultivating their land, for instance, with two years of cultivation after eight years of fallow may change, say, to three years of cultivation after six years of fallow. Peasants who used a short-fallow rotation may put some of their land under annual cultivation,

and peasants who previously took one crop a year may begin to sow successive crops on some of their land.

Such intensification of land use may mean that the land gets too little time for recovery, so that yields decline. If the land under more intensive use is sloping, erosion may result, and the reduction of falllow and pasture areas may entail weakened draft animals, and hence poor land preparation and reduced yields.

Since antiquity, several methods have been known whereby such deterioration of land and animals can be avoided: (i) the natural regeneration of the land during the periods of fallow can be replaced by various other methods of fertilization; (ii) sloping land can be terraced; and (iii) instead of grazing and browsing, the animals can be fed from cultivated fodder. In recent decades, technical and scientific progress have much enhanced the efficiency of these methods and thereby increased the possibilities of raising food production under population pressure.

FERTILIZATION AS A FACTOR IN INTENSIVE LAND USE

Where extensive types of long-fallow rotations are used, the burning of the natural vegetation on the ground before sowing may provide sufficient fertilization. With short-fallow, or no fallow, one or more of the following types of fertilization must be used: (1) vegetable or mineral matter collected from surrounding land, to be spread on the cultivated area; (2) manuring by droppings from grazing animals or by the spreading of composts with animal manure; (3) manuring by night-soil, household waste, and crop residue; (4) the use of leguminous crops in the rotation; (5) industrial fertilizer.

In regions where multi-cropping is practised without the help of industrial fertilizer,

Population density	Rain-fed land Humid	Dry	Irrigated land
A	wheat/fallow	grazing only	no land irrigated
B	wheat/fallow	wheat/fallow	no land irrigated
C	wheat/fallow	wheat/fallow	wheat/fallow
D	wheat/fallow	wheat/fallow	wheat/fodder
E	wheat/fodder	wheat/fallow	wheat/fodder
F	wheat/fodder	wheat/fallow	double-cropping

several of the other methods are usually applied simultaneously. Nevertheless, it may be impossible to find enough fertilizer of various kinds to have more than a minor share of the land under multi-cropping, especially where animal manure is used for fuel. The use of chemical fertilizers removes this limitation to the expansion of the area under multi-cropping, thereby increasing the food potential considerably in densely populated developing countries.

Progress in soil chemistry and biology are steadily enlarging the potential for food production by making it possible to use land which was previously considered useless and to obtain high yields from land which used to be regarded as poor. With scientific progress, ideas as to what land should be considered good or bad, cultivable or incultivable, are steadily changing. At one time, land in the tropics was considered unsuitable for more intensive cultivation other than that by long-fallow techniques. Now the problem is seen as that of finding the suitable methods for intensive land use in particular tropical regions. It is a problem which is far from solved for all tropical regions, but intensive land use is spreading in many parts.

IRRIGATION AS A FACTOR IN
INTENSIVE LAND USE

In dry regions the soil may not contain sufficient moisture to allow a crop each year without irrigation. In such regions popula-

tion pressure promotes on one hand the more intensive use of rain-fed land and on the other the spread of irrigation. A schematic illustration of this gradual spread of more intensive land utilization in a dry region is given below. For instance, crop rotations may change with increasing population, as shown in table above.

In the end, nearly all humid and dry land may be brought under irrigation. In Egypt virtually all land sown seems to be under perennial irrigation, with about two-thirds of it double-cropped. In other parts of the Near East, where population densities are much lower than in Egypt, there is a long way to go before the intensity of land use becomes comparable with that of Egypt. Most of the irrigated land in the Near East is still under a wheat/fallow rotation, and, in addition, parts of the region have extensive humid rain-fed areas under wheat/fallow rotations. However, the potential for further expansion of the area under irrigation is much larger than in Egypt (11).

The scope for irrigation has been widened in recent years by technological innovations and in the related activities of terracing and levelling of land. Subterranean water can be brought up from deeper layers; perennial flow irrigation can be introduced in regions where this would have been impossible or extremely costly with traditional techniques, and sometimes water can be saved and salinity and water-logging avoided by the use of spraying techniques instead of flow irrigation. Modern equipment makes it possible to re-shape sloping land and thus control erosion and prevent the silting up of dams.

FODDER PRODUCTION

The successive stages of land use in a dry region listed above may also serve to illustrate the potentialities for fodder supply with growing population densities in North Africa and West Asia. The transition from population density A to B turns permanent grazing land into cultivated under a wheat/fallow rotation. This reduces the fodder potential. But the introduction of irrigated land with a wheat/fallow rotation at stage C enlarges the potential, and so do the succeeding changes from wheat/fallow to wheat/fodder rotations in irrigated and humid land and the final change to double-cropping in irrigated land, if some of the additional crops are fodder crops. If there is less demand for fodder, the crops replacing fallow may be leguminous or other crops for human consumption. If a more rapid increase of crops for human consumption is needed, the draft animals may be replaced by tractors. Draft animals are a heavy drain on land resources in dry regions, because each animal can be used only during a short period of the year if the crops are to benefit from the best growing season, and can therefore be utilized for only a small area.

Both in regions with a dry season and in regions with a cold season, the more rapid operations made possible by using tractors instead of animals can help to make room for more than one crop annually. Widespread tractorization was the basis of the recent change from two to three crops per annum in Japan. Also biological research, producing fast-growing crops, has contributed to increase the potential for multicropping.

Although modern techniques have widened the potential for food production in very densely populated regions, the potentialities are, of course, much larger in more sparsely populated regions. In the Indian subcontinent, population density is very high in some districts, but in others fairly extensive types of land use predominate. Even in the most densely populated districts, multicropping is less widespread than in Egypt or the Far East, and in some of the less densely populated parts of the Indian subcontinent there is much scope for additional irrigation, and for more intensive use of rain-fed land. Systematic fodder production for domestic animals is still the exception rather than the rule, and pasture improvement is extremely rare. Little chemical fertilizer is used on food crops, and crop yields can be much improved.

In most of Africa, population is still so sparse that the grazing of natural pastures and long-fallow agriculture in rain-fed land are the predominant systems of land use for food production. But present high rates of population growth make it necessary to find alternatives to the traditional systems, lest the land deteriorate because of reduction of the regeneration periods between the crops. There remain huge untapped food potentials in Africa. River valleys and swamps in Africa—and in Latin America—are as suitable for paddy production as the Asian ones. Chinese advisers in Africa were amazed to discover the unused possibilities of paddy production in that continent. In actual fact, however, there is small reason for amazement; these African potentialities remained largely untapped because the sparse population could be fed without considerable capital investment in land improvement and without the addition to the daily work load which irrigation would entail.

Developing countries, within which there are some very sparsely or completely uninhabited regions, sometimes choose to make the sudden transition from the most extensive to intensive types of land utilization by means of settlement schemes for such regions. This has been done not only in sparsely populated countries in Africa and Latin America, but also in more densely populated countries like Viet Nam and Ceylon, which have seen their potentialities for food production suddenly enlarged by the eradication of malaria from regions which used to be regarded as uninhabitable for settlers from outside. Also veterinary progress has enlarged the food potential, for instance in regions of Africa where the risk of trypanosomiasis had hitherto prevented the rearing of cattle.

The widespread concern about the population explosion in developing countries has given much stimulus to systematic agricultural research. This has already widened the potential for food production, as mentioned above; but many results of recent research are still in the pipeline, and the number of scientists working with these problems is steadily increasing. In fact, the problem of food supply in developing countries is less one of technical feasibility than of the rapidity with which the technically possible can become actual practice. More precisely, the problem is whether it will be possible, in the period until birth control can markedly slow down rates of population growth, to sustain annual rates of growth of food production which are as high as, or preferably significantly higher than, the rates at which population is growing. The main factors which need to be analyzed in order to answer this question can be grouped under three headings: the capital requirements for agriculture; the ability to organize this investment, i.e. agricultural planning; and the strength of the political and social obstacles to such capital investment. These problems will be dealt with in the following sections.

Capital Requirements for Expanded Food Production

As population increases in a given country, the labor force available for agricultural production expands at roughly the same rate and, of course, the area of land per head declines. These changes, naturally, raise the demand for the third factor of production, capital. Production of food for the increasing population requires an increase in the amount of capital (particularly in the public sector), not only in step with the increase of the labor force in agriculture, but beyond that an increase of the amount of capital per head of agricultural worker so as to compensate for the declining area of land at his disposal (including fallow and grazing land). If the purpose is not only to produce food for the increasing population, urban as well as rural, but also to improve nutritional standards, the amount of capital per worker in agriculture must increase even more steeply.

Nobody will object to the statement that the feeding of an increasing population from a given area requires an increase in the amount of capital. It is less generally realized that demand for agricultural labor may also be increasing. In discussion about possibilities of food production many take for granted that the existing agricultural labor force in developing countries is more than sufficient to produce even a rapidly increasing output.

Two factors help to explain this belief: (1) the large amount of seasonal unemployment in agriculture in many developing countries and the short working hours in some regions of long-fallow cultivation are taken as sufficient proof of the existence of a *general* labor surplus, supposed to be readily available and sufficient for large-scale expansion of agricultural output; (2) as mentioned above, attention is most often focused on the need and the scope for raising crop yields rather than on the transition to more intensive land use—in the sense of more frequent cropping of a given piece of land. This means that labor requirements per unit of additional output are underestimated, since an increase in the area sown each year requires a roughly proportionate increase in the input of labor, while little additional labor is needed in order to apply chemical fertilizer or improved seeds, though additional labor will be needed to harvest a larger crop.

Often, the change from extensive to intensive systems of land use brought about by the pressure of population requires, in addition to the increase in capital per worker, an increase in hours of labor per unit of output. Under long-fallow systems, tribal populations may be able to produce their food with a small input of labor per family, a very large land area (including fallow) per family, and virtually no capital. When they change to more intensive use of the land, they need much less land per family and they need to invest considerably in land improvements, in additional implements, etc.; but they also need to work more hours per year in order to obtain the same amount of food per family as before. Available information about labor input in the production of food with long-fallow methods suggests that a family of man, wife, and small children may typically use around 1000 hours of work per year to produce their food, most of this work being performed by the women (5). Peasant families producing food by intensive systems of agriculture, but without mechanized equipment, must work many more hours per year in order to produce the necessary food for subsistence, especially if they must also produce fodder for their draft animals. Hours of work per family spent on food production

may be 3000 to 5000 per annum in regions with labor-intensive systems of production (4). Part of this labor is spent on the maintenance and renewal of the capital investment in irrigation canals, bunds, and terraces.

In view of these large differences between labor input in extensive and intensive systems of agriculture, we cannot exclude the possibility that the realization of the potential for food production under rapid increase of population may sometimes be prevented by an insufficient supply of labor. This, however, occurs in special cases and more generally the limiting factor is the supply of capital.

For the expansion of food production in response to the increase of population, capital investment is required in the following: (i) land improvement; (ii) equipment; (iii) infra-structure; and (iv) knowledge.

LAND IMPROVEMENT

In this category heavy investment is required in the clearing of land for permanent cultivation, as compared with the more superficial clearing for shifting cultivation; in leveling, terracing, draining, and bunding of land; in the digging of wells and of irrigation ditches. Major irrigation works and other land improvements undertaken by public authorities on public land are usually classified as infra-structure investment. Land improvement as here defined may be done by the cultivator and his labor force with traditional techniques, or it may be organized by landlords, cooperatives, or public authorities, using either traditional techniques or modern mechanical equipment.

In the past, traditional techniques of land improvement have been used successfully under various types of organization in communities with growing populations. But with the high rates of population growth now prevailing it would seem desirable to use mechanized equipment for land improvement to a much larger extent than is usual in developing countries. This would make it possible to accelerate the transition to intensive land use and thus to achieve a more rapid increase of employment opportunities for *current* agricultural operations and of food production.

EQUIPMENT AND MATERIALS

In addition to the equipment for land improvement mentioned above, more intensive land use requires additional equipment for current operations, either of the traditional type (hand tools, plows, and draft animals) or mechanized equipment. In densely populated regions, irrigation equipment for use on farms is an important item. Also for this item a choice is possible between traditional and modern equipment, such as between the *shaduf* and the diesel pump.

Many economists advise against the use of mechanized equipment for current agricultural operations in developing countries, their attitude being motivated by the fear of creating unemployment. They overlook that some types of machinery, such as pumps for watering, may create additional employment because they permit irrigation on land which otherwise would have remained unirrigated. Likewise, the use of tractors may create additional employment by facilitating multicropping, as already mentioned; in some regions, for instance in parts of the Near East, it is the number of draft animals and the grazing area required for them that effectively limits the sown area (11). Therefore, it is important that decisions on mechanization in agriculture be made with an open mind, and should be dependent on specific local conditions. A dogmatic denunciation of the use of mechanized equipment may prevent a fuller development of the potential for food production in developing countries.

INFRA-STRUCTURE

This category includes, among other things, major irrigation works and public works designed to prevent erosion in catchment areas, floods, and the silting up of dams. Investment in these accounts for a large share of total investment in agriculture in regions with dense population dependent on irrigated agriculture, and many developing countries have invested heavily in this way in recent decades (7).

Development of marketing facilities, provision of grain stores, feeder roads, and other transport investment in settlement areas may conveniently be included in infrastructure investment for agriculture. Some investment of this nature, in particular feeder roads and other transport improvement, may require large amounts of capital in cases where settlements are established in remote regions without any existing facilities. The true costs per additional unit of output may turn out to be extremely high in new settlements based upon capital-intensive irrigation schemes which are so located.

KNOWLEDGE

It seems natural, for our purpose, to define investment in "human capital" in agriculture rather broadly, so as to include not only the creation of physical assets, such as agriculture schools and research establishments, but also costs of operating such establishments, as well as current expenditure for extension and advisory services. The needs for these developments emerge when population pressure on food resources makes it necessary to change from the traditional methods of cultivation to systems of more intensive land use. It seems pertinent therefore to regard them as investments needed for the introduction of new systems of agriculture.

The classification of agricultural services as investment in agriculture serves to remind us that in a number of developing countries there has been, in the years after independence, a decline in the existing fund of "human capital" in the form of knowledge of agriculture. Many foreigners employed in agricultural services left without being replaced by similar numbers of the country's own nationals, with similar qualifications as teachers, technicians, or administrators. Where expatriate experts are employed, their service now tends to be for limited periods on contract, so that they are unable to build up a fund of experience, and continuity in development is broken when they are replaced.

Attention is often drawn to the contrast between rapid progress in agriculture in industrialized countries in recent decades and the slow progress in the developing countries, and the corresponding contrast between "burdensome surpluses" on one side and difficulties of financing imports on the other. In considering this widening "food gap" in developing countries, it must be remembered that far more investment (per unit area and per worker in agriculture) has been undertaken in the industrialized countries than in the majority of the developing countries; and that, for instance, the marketing facilities developed in developing countries were usually limited to nonfood crops. The way to avoid further widening of the "food gap" between industrialized and developing countries is, therefore, to invest more in the agricultural sectors of developing countries and to invest less in subsidized high-cost food production in industrialized countries. A first step might be to channel a drastically increased share of foreign aid to the agricultural sector in the developing countries.

Apart from the need to invest more in the agricultural sector and in ancillary facilities and services, including marketing facilities, there is also need for much larger investments in industries producing for agriculture—fertilizer, other chemicals, and equipment—and

in industries processing agricultural produce.

AGRICULTURAL PLANNING

In the past, the adjustment of food production to higher population densities was brought about most often through the spontaneous action of cultivators and of tribal or village authorities. Under the far more rapid increase of population now prevailing in developing countries, agricultural change needs to be more radical and accelerated than in the past. In particular, governments in developing countries are coming to play a more active role in agricultural planning than most colonial or national governments in these countries used to play in the past. The government's role can no longer be limited to the traditional one of financing and organizing major infra-structural investments. The government will have to take the initiative in village planning, provide the cultivator with plans for the intensification of land use adapted to local conditions, and supply the necessary credits and some sort of incentive to undertake the investment. This may involve, for instance, support of food prices or the granting of subsidies to some particularly desirable inputs.

The problems which must be solved by agricultural planning may be discussed under four headings: (i) choice of the regions for the development of intensive land use; (ii) choice between short-term and long-term investment; (iii) coordination between investment and incentive policies; (iv) changes in land tenure related to the changes in land use. A few comments on each of these problems are offered below.

THE CHOICE OF REGIONS FOR DEVELOPMENT

The first problem is to decide whether efforts should be spread evenly over a large area or be concentrated, at least to begin with, in a few places where conditions for more intensive agriculture appear to be particularly promising. Of course, the answer to this question must differ in countries with uniform climate and soil from those with wide regional disparities in conditions for intensive agriculture.

If failures are to be avoided, the choice of development regions must be preceded by systematic studies of the potentialities for food production in the different parts of the country in question. For this, large numbers of specialists of various types are needed, and such personnel are available in few if any of the developing countries. In the next few decades more and more developing countries will discover the need for systematic research into their agricultural potentialities, and the demand for agricultural planning will increase accordingly. Up to a certain point the specialist required may be available under existing programs of technical assistance; but the supply is likely to be exhausted in the relatively near future, unless the problem of training of agricultural experts is tackled vigorously and without delay.

THE CHOICE BETWEEN SHORT-TERM AND
LONG-TERM INVESTMENT

Some types of investment in agriculture yield results in the form of larger output a few years after the investment decision is implemented, while other types of investment in agriculture contribute to larger output only several decades after the investment plan was first initiated. An example of the latter type of investment are the capital-intensive irrigation projects supplemented by settlement schemes, on which some developing countries are concentrating most of their efforts in the agricultural sector. Such schemes usually take between one and two decades before the first crops are available from the land to which a controlled supply of water has been made available, and it may take half a century before the whole area is bearing crops. The concentration of

agricultural investment on this type of development is an important factor which helps to explain the slow growth of food production in some developing countries where large sums have been invested in agriculture in recent years.

The preference for capital-intensive irrigated agriculture and for settlement in "new villages," and the neglect of investment in minor irrigation works and in other land improvements in "old villages," is a legacy from the colonial period. The idea of creating new agricultural units appealed to the colonial administrator, who usually desired to intervene as little as possible with the traditional way of life of the indigenous population. Furthermore, the need for the development of food production in that period was primarily a need to provide food for the growing urban centers, and this could be done by means of surplus production in "new villages." Less concern was felt about the development of food production and incomes in the "old villages," where population at that time was increasing less rapidly and sometimes was stagnating.

A change of attitude in favor of the expansion of food production in "old villages" occurred in many areas before the end of the colonial period; and at present governments in many developing countries feel the need for other types of investment than in settlement schemes. The two types of development, however, require different types of technicians, and therefore the new policy is likely to come up against difficulties in the supply of adequate manpower.

COORDINATION OF INVESTMENT
WITH INCENTIVE POLICIES

Most cultivators in developing countries produce crops for sale in addition to producing food for their own use, and many produce food surpluses by employing hired labor. These cultivators will take up intensive systems of land use only if they can expect what they regard as a sufficient return on expenditure for land improvement and other investment. Therefore, governments may have little success with supplying infrastructure investment, credits, and extension services unless the relationship between prices of inputs (including the cost of employing hired labor) and of outputs are such that they encourage new farming methods. The utilization of the capacity of irrigation facilities often remains low, because governments fail to provide the incentive for growing irrigated crops for which costs per unit of output may be higher than for crops grown by extensive methods.

In other cases food production may fail to expand, in spite of incentive prices or subsidization of inputs, because insufficient investment has been made in marketing facilities for food crops, in food-processing plants, or in the production of agricultural inputs. For instance, if investment or import policies hold down the supply of fertilizer so that it must be distributed by some kind of rationing, the subsidization of its price is a sheer waste of public money and can have no incentive effect. In India, fertilizer is subsidized but often unavailable in the required quantities in the villages.

CHANGE OF LAND TENURE RELATED TO
CHANGE OF LAND USE

The systems of land tenure in developing countries are closely connected with systems of land use. Therefore, changes in land use are often thwarted by existing tenure arrangements (3: Chaps. 9-12). For instance, long-fallow cultivators have a right to clear land in areas belonging to their community. When long-fallow agriculture is replaced by a system with cultivation of permanent fields, it is necessary to change to another system of tenure, which gives the cultivator more permanent rights to the land he is cul-

tivating. Under land use systems based on the grazing of fallow land, some of the cultivators, or some noncultivating members of the village community, enjoy the right to graze animals on the fallow area for a certain part of the year. In that case, the substitution of a more intensive system for the old one requires the abolition of the grazing rights. In densely populated regions the introduction of multi-cropping may be impossible without a change of the customary system of rent; for instance, when custom requires that the land owners be paid a certain share of each crop, such as is the case in many parts of India. If, then, the cost of the second crop is higher per unit of output than the cost of the first crop, there may be insufficient incentive for multi-cropping unless the customary rent system is replaced by a system of fixed annual rent.

Because of this interdependence of land use systems and land tenure systems, tenure reforms must be an integrated part of agricultural planning. The first step in planning local food production must be to choose a region for development and to determine the appropriate system of land use and the type of crops to be grown. The next step is to find out what changes of land tenure and what types of investment are necessary to bring about the intensification of production. The third step would be a decision about the ways and means to convince the cultivator of the advantages to be gained from carrying out the desired changes. If any one of these steps is neglected, the system of land use will fail to change in the desired direction and the planned additions to output will not materialize.

The tenure reforms which are required in order to facilitate the change from extensive to intensive systems of land use are not necessarily identical with the kind of change the cultivators demand in periods of population pressure. When the number of members in his family is increasing, the first reaction of the cultivator will be to look for more land to cultivate with the traditional methods. Hence, in periods of rising rural population there are likely to be demands for the transfer of land from large to small holdings. To avoid this, governments would have to take prompt action to promote changes to systems of more intensive land use.

A redistribution of land from larger to smaller holdings can raise food production and create more employment only to the extent that it may induce the adoption of a more intensive pattern of land use. On the other hand, if more intensive land use is introduced in the larger holdings without a preceding redistribution of land, the increase of employment thus obtained will make redistribution seem less urgent. If governments, for political or other reasons, hesitate to provide sufficient incentive for more intensive land use in larger holdings using hired labor, a vicious circle may develop: the lack of employment opportunities creates strong demand for expropriation of land from larger holdings. The owners of such holdings feel uncertain of their future rights of ownership and therefore hesitate to invest in agriculture. Thus, when the government finally takes action to encourage more intensive land use, the attempts may be unsuccessful; the pattern of land use then remains extensive, and employment opportunities become more and more inadequate in relation to the increasing supply of labor. The result is growing political tension and declining living standards in rural areas.

Political and Social Obstacles to the Utilization of the Potential for Food Production

Many developing countries have quite recently advanced from colonial status to independence. This change of status unavoidably gave a stimulus to administrative and other investment in the new capitals and in other large towns. In addition, many independent governments regarded the establishment of industry as a requirement of highest priority. In these circumstances, as might be expected, most of the domestic investment resources and the major part of foreign aid have been devoted to purposes other than the expansion of food production. Moreover, in some cases the easy terms on which food aid could be obtained acted as a disincentive to either public or private investment in domestic food production. Political and social considerations induced governments to supply the urban population with cheap imported food, rather than raise food prices in order to encourage a more intensive use of the national potential for production.

Governments were not alone in considering food production as less important than industry or other urban activities. The more enterprising members of rural youth in all developing countries, including a large proportion of the literate population of rural origin, have been drawn toward city life with its more attractive employment opportunities in administration or in new industries. The migration from the villages of the most enterprising and best educated young people has done much to delay agricultural change.

Young people at higher levels of education have also tended to regard agriculture as a less desirable occupation. In some developing countries, the few small agricultural schools have difficulty in finding pupils, or else they manage to attract mainly those who have been unable to get access to more desired types of higher education. Even those who have been trained in such institutions afterwards apply for and obtain urban jobs unrelated to agriculture.

While there is growing awareness among

governments in developing countries of the need to devote more resources to the expansion of food production, there is much less sign, if any, of a change of attitude among the literates in the villages and the applicants for higher education. The difference in living conditions in cities and rural areas in developing countries is so wide that very attractive incomes and careers would have to be offered in agriculture and agricultural services in order to attract sufficient numbers of qualified candidates. In other words, very large income differentials would have to be accepted between government officials posted in the villages and educated farm managers on one hand and the ordinary cultivators on the other. This may be unacceptable for political and social reasons, and thus the lack of qualified manpower is likely to be a serious obstacle to the development of the potential for food production.

Improvement of Food Standards

The need for expansion of food production in developing countries is based partly upon the growth of population and partly on the unsatisfactory levels of nutrition. In some developing countries calorie intake is deficient for a considerable proportion of the population; in many more countries the intake of animal protein is very low. As long as per capita incomes remain low the per capita demand for animal food will also remain small, at least in densely populated countries where animal food is expensive as compared with vegetable food.

In recent years much research has been done for the development of cheap vegetable substitutes for animal proteins, based on different crops including maize, groundnuts, soybeans, and pulses. Such substitutes are industrially produced in some developing countries and are used for school meals or sold through ordinary commercial channels. By promoting their use, improvements in nutritional levels can be achieved in developing countries which are unable to secure a rapid increase of per capita incomes.

A similar need to promote the use of suitable vegetable substitutes for animal food may exist in those developing countries which succeed in raising per capita incomes. Experience has shown that when developing countries succeed in raising per capita incomes, a stage is reached where the demand for animal food is increasing rapidly. Some types of domestic animals are quick breeders, and output can be rapidly expanded if fodder is available. But the transformation of fodder into animal food involves a considerable loss of calories, and a rapid expansion of animal production based upon home-grown fodder is possible only if crop productions can be increased rapidly. Therefore, many governments which cannot afford to use foreign exchange for large-scale purchases of fodder or animal food, will have to find ways of preventing a major increase in the consumption of animal food. For this purpose, the use of vegetable substitutes may have to be encouraged while; at the same time, measures are taken to restrain the general switch of consumption from vegetable to animal food.

Conclusion

The preceding analysis of the potential for food production suggests the conclusion that in most developing countries competing demands for scarce capital resources, and the lack of qualified agricultural planners, farm managers, and advisers, are major impediments to the utilization of technical potentialities. Therefore, even in countries where technical potentialities for additional food production are considerable, the rate of increase of agricultural incomes may remain relatively slow in the next decade.

This may not prevent rapid economic development in those few developing countries which have particularly rich nonagricultural resources. For instance, countries with rich oil resources or other mineral resources can use foreign exchange earned from nonagricultural production to purchase the required food supplies in countries where the supply elasticity of food is high. In such countries a rapid rate of growth in the nonagricultural sectors may compensate for a slow rate of growth in the agricultural sector.

Also developing countries with less favorable conditions for an expansion of exports may be forced to import part of their food supplies until they succeed in stepping up food production or reducing birth rates or both. In such countries the need to use foreign exchange for major imports limits the scope for importing capital equipment. Therefore, the nonagricultural sectors cannot grow at a rate sufficiently high to compensate for a low rate of growth of the agricultural sector which employs a large proportion of total population in nearly all developing countries. Thus, in countries of this type, the over-all rate of growth is likely to remain fairly low. In such cases food aid may have constructive effects, if it can be supplied on terms that induce farmers and governments in the recipient countries to increase their own efforts. This implies that the price structure in the country which is receiving food aid must be inducive to expansion of food production; and it implies moreover that food aid must be supplemented with other types of aid, aimed at promoting home production of food.

REFERENCES

(1) W. Allan: *The African Husbandman* (Edinburgh, 1965).
(2) K. M. Barbour and R. M. Prothero, eds.: Essays on African Population (London, 1961).
(3) E. Boserup: The Conditions of Agricultural Growth: the Economics of Agrarian Change under Population Pressure (London, 1965).
(4) J. L. Buck: Land Utilization in China (Shanghai, 1957).
(5) C. Clark and M. R. Haswell: The Economics of Subsistence Agriculture (London, 1964).
(6) C. Clark: Population Growth and Land Use (London, 1967).
(7) C. Clark: The Economics of Irrigation (London, 1967).
(8) C. Eicher and L. Witt, eds.: Agriculture in Economic Development (New York, 1964).
(9) Food and Agricultural Organization: Production Statistics. Table 1 (Annual).
(10) Food and Agricultural Organization: The State of Food and Agriculture (Rome, 1967).
(11) Food and Agricultural Organization: Indicative World Plan for Agricultural Development. Near East: Sub-Regional Study No. 1. (Rome, 1966).
(12) P. Gourou: The Tropical World (London, 1961).
(13) Organization for Economic Co-operation and Development: The Food Problems of Developing Countries (Paris, 1968).

(14) O. Göran: Population Control and Economic Development (Paris, 1967).

(15) J. Phillips: The Development of Agriculture and Forestry in the Tropics (London, 1961).

(16) T. Schultze: Transforming Traditional Agriculture (New Haven, 1964).

(17) T. Schultze: Economic Crises in World Agriculture (Ann Arbor, 1965).

(18) T. Schultze: What Ails World Agriculture? *Bulletin of Atomic Scientists,* Vol. 24, 1968, pp. 28-35.

(19) P. de Schlippe: Shifting Cultivation in Africa (London, 1956).

(20) L. D. Stamp: A History of Land Use in Arid Regions (Paris, 1961).

(21) W. Thomas, ed.: Man's Role in Changing the Face of the Earth (Chicago, 1956).

(22) United Nations: World Population Conference 1965. Vols. I-IV (New York, 1967).

8. A TYPOLOGY OF POPULATION PRESSURE ON RESOURCES IN WEST AFRICA

Akin. L. Mabogunje

One of the most striking facts about West Africa is that in a continent of generally sparse population, it is a relatively densely settled area. The region occupies 5,200,000 km² and had a population of 93 million in 1963. This gives an average density of about 16/km², compared with 9 for Northern Africa, 7 for Southern Africa, 13 for Eastern Africa, and 5 for Central Africa (24: 43). The fundamental reason for this is that over a large part of West Africa there is sufficient heat and water to facilitate plant growth and agricultural production. West Africa lies between the equator and the Tropic of Cancer, and throughout the year temperatures are perpetually above 21°C. Rainfall, however, is less uniformly distributed. In general the coastal areas in the south have the highest rainfall—over 2500 mm. This decreases progressively inland, but even the northernmost parts of the region receive as much as 250 mm. Thus, the vegetation pattern varies from the dense rain forest of the south through both wet and dry savanna farther to the north.

Throughout West Africa a favorable environment allows man to make a comfortable living either by agriculture or by animal husbandry. Yet, in spite of this, the proved capacity of West African land to support population is far from impressive. The population density of 16/km², which is remarkable for Africa, pales into insignificance when compared with densities in Europe or Asia. Part of the reason is the persistence of agriculture based on bush-fallow over large parts of the area. This implies that, in the absence of manuring or fertilizing techniques, for every hectare of land used, some four, five, or more must be kept in reserve for the farmer to fall back on when he has exhausted the fertility of that under use. It is a system in which equilibrium requires a low density of population per unit area and a very low rate of natural increase.

Prior to the twentieth century, many events combined to maintain this equilibrium. The low state of medical knowledge, generally poor sanitation, underdeveloped transportation, weakness of trade relations, and, in particular, frequent instability in political relations leading to warfare, enslavement, or death, all meant that the high birth rate of the population was matched by an equally high death rate. Indeed, according to Wilcox of the League of Nations, the population of Africa remained fairly constant at 100 million through the latter half of the nineteenth century. However, Carr-Saunders believes a more realistic pattern would indicate a decline in total population from 100 million in 1650 to 90 million in 1800, when the population slowly started to grow again (6: 42). These figures give a population density for the continent of no more than 3.4/km² until virtually the twentieth century.

In spite of this generally low over-all density, there were areas in West Africa which by the nineteenth century had emerged as major centers of human concentrations, with densities of greater than 40/km². A map of population distribution shows these areas as falling within two broad east-west belts (5: 165), a coastal belt which includes in particular the Ibo and the Yoruba areas of Nigeria as well as such smaller concentrations as the Mende of Sierra Leone, the Fula domain on the

114

Fouta Djalon, and the Wolof-Serer country in Senegal. The second belt is inland and includes in particular the Hausa country around Kano and along the Rima River, and the Mossi country around Ouagadougou.

In all of these areas, the crucial factor making for high population densities was the security against destructive internal strife or external aggression. Among the Yoruba, the Hausa, the Mossi, and the Wolof, this security was achieved as a result of a highly complex political organization which recognizes a hierarchy of chiefs responsible to a monarch. Among the Ibos, it appears that the isolation provided by the forest environment was a major factor of protection against external aggression.

Everywhere in West Africa, sixty years of French and British colonial administration have radically changed environmental conditions. The establishment of the *Paix Française* or the *Pax Britannica* brought an end to the slave trade and provided peace and security, under which economic activities could be more vigorously pursued. Greater production of food and the relative ease of transportation from areas of surplus to areas of deficit meant the end of famine in many places. Better nourishment provided greater resistance to diseases. Modern medical services and improved sanitation further reduced the chances of indiscriminate death. The result has been a considerable decrease in the death rate from about 50 to under 30 per thousand persons, while the birth rate has remained fairly constant at between 45 and 55 per thousand. With an annual natural rate of increase of more than 20 per thousand, the population of West Africa rose from an estimated 48 million in 1930 to 93 million in 1963. This is one of the fastest growth rates in the world, and implies that the population can virtually double itself within thirty-five years.

A rapid rate of population increase has

been noticed in most underdeveloped countries. In these areas no corresponding economic growth is being achieved so that there is considerable apprehension that the population may soon outstrip the resources necessary to support it. Such a situation would seem to confirm the gloomy predictions of Thomas Malthus, and indeed neo-Malthusians everywhere are predicting dire consequences for uncontrolled population increase in the underdeveloped countries. While some of their arguments have little relevance for the extensive underpopulated areas of West Africa, they do acquire some significance in the traditional centers of high densities, where one suspects that the pressure of population on resources is reaching far beyond the critical limits. In these areas, overpopulation is manifested in the deterioration of the environment, the collapse of traditional agricultural systems, and massive emigration of people.

This phenomenon of overpopulation or the pressure of population on resources is, however, a complex one which does not admit of easy definition. The operational definition, based on the simple idea of high density or high ratio of population to land, ignores the more vital variable of the standard of living or social well-being which the people involved expect to derive from their resources. Thus, resources which may be adequate for "decent living" in one instance may be grossly inadequate in another, that is, one community may be able to support a relatively high density with its resources while another, were it to reach the same density, would show evidence of overpopulation and substantial emigration.

The Factor of "Expectations" in Population Pressure

The "expectations" of a community is thus perhaps the most crucial factor in the understanding of population pressure on resources. This variable itself is not easy to define although the two conditions which encourage a high level of expectations can be identified:

(a) easy communication of new ideas of "high living," either directly by demonstration or indirectly through education;

(b) existence, within reach, of the purchasing power necessary for the practical adoption of these ideas.

Various activities of the colonial administration helped to raise "expectations" throughout West Africa, although the level varies from community to community. The most important of these activities was education, including not only formal instruction but also exposure to newspapers, the cinema, radio, and television. In both the former British and French territories, formal schooling was for a long time carried on only by Christian missionaries. In the former British colonies, Freetown, founded in 1792, was the springboard for much of the educational work of the missionaries. Freetown provided a training ground for freed slaves who, grateful for their deliverance by the British Royal Naval Squadron, which had intercepted a number of slave ships, were only too happy to learn "the white-man's ways." In the succeeding decades, many of them returned to their homes in present-day Ghana and Nigeria to join efforts with missionaries from Europe, carrying new ideas into the very interior of the country. In the former French West African territories, St. Louis, and later Dakar, played much the same role as Freetown. From the early nineteenth century, pioneering work in education was carried out by various religious orders and by a handful of lay teachers brought out from France under government contract. From this base, they expanded to other coastal towns in Senegal, Guinea, the Ivory Coast, and Dahomey. The educational activities of these missionaries were most concentrated in the southern parts of the region. Their progress inland was checked, apart from any other reason, by the greater importance of Islam among the interior population. More than this, in Nigeria, progress was positively restrained by the British colonial administration in their bid to reassure the Fulani emirs of northern Nigeria of their nonproselytizing mission.

The result is that in West Africa today the degree of education and enlightenment, and therefore of social and economic expectations, decreases sharply as one goes inland from the coast. This fact is clearly brought out in Table 8-1, which shows the propor-

TABLE 8-1   PERCENTAGE OF CHILDREN OF SCHOOL AGE AT SCHOOL IN WEST AFRICA

Coastal States or Regions	1953	1959
Senegal	17.9	34.4
Ivory Coast	15.1	37.2
Togo	35.1	54.5
Dahomey	23.7	35.7
Western Nigeria	—	59.4
Eastern Nigeria	—	89.5
Southern Ghana	—	86.0 (1960)
Inland States or Regions		
Mauritania	5.3	9.6
Mali	6.6	10.6
Upper Volta	4.7	10.3
Niger	2.5	6.1
Northern Nigeria	5.4	7.2
Northern Ghana	—	18.5 (1960)

Source: *Report on the Social Situation in the Associated Countries of the European Economic Community,* European Economic Community, Sept. 1960;
Ghana: *Report of the 1960 Census,* vol. III, Accra, 1960;
Nigeria: *Western Nigeria Statistical Bulletin,* vol. 6, No. 122, Ibadan, June-Dec., 1964; *Statistical Digest of Eastern Nigeria,* No. 24, Enugu, 1965; and the *Northern Nigeria Statistical Yearbook,* Kaduna, 1964.

tion of school age children actually in school in different parts of the region. The calculation of school age is based on the UNESCO standard practice of regarding this section of the population as equal to 15 per cent of total population. Given the relatively youthful population of most West African countries, this proportion is more likely to be nearer 20 per cent than 15, in which case the percentages given are even slightly in excess of reality.

Missionaries throughout Africa clearly recognized that it was not enough to teach new ideas; they had to provide people the wherewithal to carry them out. One of these men put it lucidly in these words:

> Our designs and hopes in regard to Africa are not simply to bring as many individuals as possible to the knowledge of Christ. We desire to establish the Gospel in the hearts and minds and social life of the people, so that truth and righteousness may remain and flourish among them, without the instrumentality of foreign missionaries. This cannot be done without civilisation. To establish the Gospel among any people, they must have Bibles and therefore must have the art to make them or the money to buy them. They must read the Bible and this implies instruction [3:321].

With such a program, it was no wonder that as soon as missionaries were established in a community, their major concerns were to find a marketable commodity and to teach some industrial skill. For example, a Dr. Irving was sent out to Nigeria in 1853 by the Church Missionary Society of London to study the marketable resources of the country—cotton, gums, indigo, dyewood—and to direct the attention of the emigrants and the Christian converts toward such resources (2: 81). And one heard in 1851 the Rev. Mr. Crowther at Abeokuta had encouraged his congregation to collect some 250 kg of lint cotton for ex-

port to London (7). The project flourished and only five years later, the amount of lint cotton exported from this area had risen to 4444 kg.

In the succeeding decades, this promotion of "legitimate commerce," in place of emphasis on slaves, led to a remarkable transformation in the economy of West Africa. Traditional crops such as palm oil, groundnuts, and cotton acquired new significance as commodities of trade, and crops such as cocoa, coffee, tea, soya beans, and benniseeds were introduced and came to dominate the landscape in large parts of West Africa. There was everywhere remarkable increase in the variety and volume of commodities exported. Correspondingly, there was a marked rise in the value of exports which provided the wherewithal for buying an increasing range of imported manufactured foods. Table 8-2 typifies the general pattern of growth of exports and imports.

TABLE 8-2   GROWTH OF EXPORTS AND IMPORTS IN NIGERIA (IN U.S. $)

	Export	Import
1908	7,440,000	7,440,000
1929	42,240,000	31,680,000
1938	22,320,000	20,640,000
1948	130,000,000	100,560,000
1958	325,680,000	401,040,000

The consumption of imported manufactured goods brought a new dimension to the standard and way of living of the people. The possession of nontraditional gadgets and equipment, such as bicycles, sewing machines, phonographs, radios, television, and the automobile, became a major symbol of social distinction, and economic expectations came to be defined in terms of the ability to accumulate a wide variety of material goods. And it was clear that education not only introduced people to their existence but also provided the means whereby they could earn the income to purchase them.

As with the pattern of educational progress, the production for export and, therefore, the acquisition of purchasing power showed a sharp decrease from the coastal areas inland. Indeed, the French distinguished in their former West African territories between an "external sector" and an "internal sector" (18: 188). The external sector was that generally forested area of West Africa within 160 to 200 km of the coast where most of the production for export, more than 80 per cent of the total purchasing power and most of the development in trade, transportation, and health was concentrated. The internal sector lay inland, mainly in the grassland zone. Here, because of transport costs, the primary producer not only received low returns for his products but paid higher prices for all imported articles.

In general, the combination of low levels of education, low production for export, and low import consumption causes social and economic expectations in the interior to remain low. The subsistence sector of the economy is still dominant and the desire or need for extra income relatively limited. By contrast, in the coastal areas, the greater importance of education, export production, and import consumption serves to raise expectations well above those of subsistence, and also to provide strong motivation for greater exertion in economic activities.

Theoretical Typology of "Population Pressure"

This discussion of the nature of expectations in West Africa sets the stage for examining, on a theoretical plane, various types of "population pressure." It emphasizes that instead of being a product of interaction between two variables—resource (land) and population—the phenomenon should be conceived of as the result of three: resource (land), population, and expectations. For the purpose of our conceptual analysis, each variable can be regarded as existing in either a high (H) or a low (L) state, and, for any given area, the three can occur in any combination. By the law of permutation, this will result in a total of eight possible situations. Table 8-3 lists these, and shows that a condition of population pressure on resources

TABLE 8-3   THEORETICAL SITUATIONS OF
POPULATION PRESSURE

Variables Situation	Resources	Population	Expectation
1	H	H	H
2	H	H	L
3	H	L	H
4	H	L	L
5*	L	L	H
6*	L	H	H
7*	L	H	L
8	L	L	L

can exist in any one of the three situations marked 5*, 6* and 7*. These may be described as follows: (a) When resources and population are low but expectations are high; (b) when resources are low but population and expectations are high; (c) when resources and expectations are low but population is high. In West Africa, each of these is clearly typified and can be illustrated with reference to the Egba of Western Nigeria, the Ibo of Eastern Nigeria, and the Mossi of Upper Volta.

THE EGBA OF WESTERN NIGERIA
The Egba of Western Nigeria are a subgroup of the Yoruba who today occupy an area of 5420 km^2 and in 1963 numbered 630,000. Thus, the population density is only about 120/km^2, which is much lower than the 136 km^2 for the region as a whole. The

background to the population situation in Egbaland, however, goes back to the early nineteenth century, when the Egba occupied a much larger area (14: 16). About 1817, neighboring Yoruba groups attacked the Egba. As a result, most of their towns and villages were destroyed, much of their land was lost, and for a time they were allowed to occupy only a restricted part of their former territory. Within this limited area, they founded in 1830 the new town of Abeokuta, which by the 1850's had a population estimated at about 100,000 (4: 33). Hostilities continued intermittently for most of the nineteenth century, and the Egba were forced to encircle Abeokuta with military outposts in order to delimit a zone for safe farming. This zone was fixed on the west by the Ogun River, and on the north, northeast, and southeast by the outposts of Aiyetoro, Oshielle, and Oba respectively. Partly because only a limited amount of land was available, there was great competition for land within this zone. Each family making a claim on farmland often settled on it directly to safeguard that claim. Settlements in the zone today, therefore, consist of numerous hamlets—as many as one or two per square kilometer—of usually no more than 100 inhabitants each.

One effect of the movement into the restricted area was that it made the 1830 settlers an original land-owning group. Although communal ownership of land was still recognized in theory, in practice every head of household at the time became an individual land owner. In fact, for many years afterwards, the right of alienation, which is the final test of ownership, remained with individuals rather than the community. When, therefore, a new system, which placed economic rather than social value on land was introduced, people were fully freed of the encumbrances of communal ownership and could traffic in land as they wished.

This development followed closely on the arrival of Christian missionaries and their numerous converts from Sierra Leone in 1840. The converts, or Sierra Leone immigrants as they were commonly known, were mostly Egba who had been sold into slavery as a result of the hostilities in the early part of the century. While sojourning in Sierra Leone after being freed, they had been given a liberal education by the missionaries, which included encouragement to undertake commercial ventures with an eye to profit (11: 213-23). In 1838, the crew of a coastal trading vessel purchased by one of the converts recognized Lagos as the harbor from which they had been exported. In the succeeding years, therefore, thousands of them returned from Sierra Leone to Lagos, Badagry, and Abeokuta.

In Abeokuta these immigrants continued their economic activities. Since they had no land of their own, they encouraged local people to sell so that as early as 1858 transactions in land were commonplace in Egbaland. Indeed, by 1903 the effect on the community as a whole was believed to be so deleterious that the colonial administration passed an Order-in-Council to prohibit sale of land (17: 264). But the order was ineffective and a new one was passed in 1913. The reaction of the Egba to these attempts at checking what had now become a fact of life is shown in a petition of 1922 signed by 800 of them requesting permission for the unrestricted sale, mortgage, or lease of property and land. The petitioners, in fact, claimed, inter alia, that "from time immemorial it had been the privilege of any Egba to deal with his house or land in any way he liked. He could mortgage, lease or sell it to anybody he liked irrespective of race or colour." Such claims, although recognizing current pactices, were clearly in breach of tradition.

The impact of the Sierra Leone immigrants was not limited to the new value they gave to land. They were also among the chief beneficiaries of educational activities being undertaken by the missionaries. The effect of this became clearly demonstrable in the growing importance of the converts in the trade of the country. Indeed, the observation of the British Consul in Lagos in 1861, that "the progess in civilisation is much too fast to please the native chiefs who could not compete either in mercantile or agricultural pursuits with the emigrants from Sierra Leone, Brazil and Cuba," was equally true for Abeokuta (2: 163), where there were very few important traders who were independent of missionary influences. Thus the Egba not only had practical examples of the new way of life but opportunities to partake of it much earlier than other groups in Nigeria. In succeeding decades, Western education made tremendous strides among them. Indeed, by 1963 they had, after the Ijebu, the highest rate of school attendance (83 per cent) in Western Nigeria.

All this meant that even before the end of the nineteenth century the paltry income from cultivating land within the closely settled zone around Abeokuta could no longer satisfy an increasing proportion of the rural population. Although densities were at the time no more than 40-60/km², the population pressure on the land began to be felt. By the early 1900's, the Egbas began to emigrate in large numbers to both rural and urban areas. A large proportion simply moved out into the forested areas to the east and southeast, where for the previous seventy years fear of attack from hostile neighbors had effectively discouraged settlement. These areas were found most suitable for cocoa cultivation, and in the two decades succeeding 1910 large numbers of new villages were established there.

Part of the emigrating group went to Lagos, where the enlightenment to which they had been exposed in Abeokuta was much more pronounced. As early as 1867, Egba who had been converted to Christianity were moving to Lagos to escape envious persecution by local chiefs. In the following decades they continued to come in large numbers, so that by 1931 people from Abeokuta Province were the second largest group from any of the Yoruba provinces. Table 8-4 shows that their number continued to increase in Lagos up to 1950, by which time they had become numerically the most important group although their rela-

TABLE 8-4   PROVINCIAL ORIGINS OF YORUBA IMMIGRANTS TO LAGOS

Province	Total Number		%	
	1931	1950	1931	1950
Colony	3,604	8,610	8	10
Abeokuta	11,765	20,242	26	24
Ijebu	6,968	19,566	13	23
Ondo	2,408	6,277	5	7
Oyo	13,350	17,786	29	21
Ilorin	7,716	12,561	19	15
Total Yoruba Immigrants	45,811	85,042	100	100
Total Population of Lagos	126,108	230,256		

Source: *Census of Lagos, 1950,* Government Printer, 1952.

tive importance showed a decline from 26 to 24 per cent.

Today there is ample evidence that the zone around Abeokuta is an area where population pressure on resources has been high. Years of intensive cultivation has considerably reduced the fertility of the soil, so that, apart from the wild oil palms, only the less demanding cassava crop—along with a little maize and cocoyam—can be grown. Everywhere there is evidence of population loss and settlement desertion. In many hamlets and villages, numerous houses are in various stages of dilapidation; in formerly large villages public buildings, particularly churches and mosques which were begun on a grand scale, have either been discontinued or completed on a more modest basis. Some hamlets were deserted entirely, their sites overgrown by bush.

Yet even though settlements were deserted, most people did not relinquish their claims to land. Some continued to cultivate land both in the closely settled zone and in the newly developed forested areas. In the first they grew food crops, in the latter they planted cocoa. Others, especially those migrating to the cities, made arrangements whereby local relatives used the land in exchange for 50 per cent of the proceeds of harvesting the oil-palm fruits. Only in a few cases was the right to use the land completely given up in favor of the relatives left behind.

It is clear that population pressure on resources in Egba Division is more the result of rising expectations than of excess population on the land. The emigrant to new cocoa lands who continues to farm in the closely settled zone is clearly attempting to increase his realizable income. In the same way, the farmer who was allowed access to the land and the oil-palms of his emigrating relations now has a greater scope for additional income. In a sense, then, this type of population pressure can be conceived of as belonging to the normal process of economic development, involving greater use of resources and a higher per capita income. This, however, was possible because the group involved had available unused land or extra resources waiting only to be developed with time.

THE IBO OF EASTERN NIGERIA

Unlike the Egba, the Ibo typologically represent a group with a poor resource base but with very high population and expectations. They are found in the forested region of southeastern Nigeria. Over most of this area rainfall varies from 3750 mm in the south to 1250 mm in the north. Physiographically, the country shows two basic units: a western cuesta flanked on the east by scarps running north to south, and the eastern basins of the Cross and other smaller rivers. The crucial factor in the environment is provided by the post-Jurassic sandstone rocks found over most of the area. Soils derived from these rocks, known as red earths, are very sandy and porous, and lose fertility rapidly under cultivation, becoming increasingly acid. In terms of resources, therefore, it is this poor soil condition that underlines much in the population problems of Iboland.

The origin of the Ibo in this area is not known, but it is clear that within the fastnesses of their forest environment they developed no institution above village level (12: 3). The basic unit of organization is a compound, housing a man, his wives, their young children, and perhaps one or two close relatives. The compound also forms the hub of an almost concentric system of land use. Immediately surrounding the hub is what is usually called the compound land, an area of permanent cultivation where cocoyams predominate, but all types of crops, including yams, vegetables, plantain, oil-palm, raffia palm, and coconut, are grown.

The only crop excluded is cassava, one that is both less demanding in its physical requirements and less desirable in its qualities. Permanent cultivation is maintained through the use of animal manure and household refuse. The compound land usually extends little beyond 800 meters from the hub, and is generally owned on an individual basis.

Beyond the compound land lies the farm proper, an area of bush-fallow cultivation where a rotational cycle of seven years of fallow to one year of cultivation has been suggested as the optimum (24: 36). Until recently yam was the principal staple grown, usually in a mixed cropping with maize, melon, okra, and pepper, but in response to population pressure cassava has become even more important than yam. Oil-palm grows wild in fallows. Although the outer agricultural zone is generally treated with the compound area as family property, on occasion communal control is established over it. Apart from these two basic divisions of compound land and the farm proper, there are the palm groves which are common village property and rarely exceed 1.5 hectares, and wasteland, such as swamps, juju groves, and eroded areas.

The Ibo country appears to have always been liable to overpopulation. In pre-European days its effect was mitigated by losses, especially through the slave trade. It has been estimated, for instance, that in the period 1801-20 some 370,000 Ibo were sold into slavery (1: 38). The British pacification of the Ibo country and the establishment of orderly government took place only in the early decades of this century, but their effect on the population position has been phenomenal. The total Ibo population jumped from about three million in 1921 to nearly ten million in 1963, all within an area of no more than 52,000 km². The pressure of population on resources was accentuated by the fact that over the same period the Ibo were making rapid strides in education and the acquisition of various skills. Material deprivation in their homeland served to strengthen their determination to succeed, and this in turn has raised the level of expectations among them. As Table 8-1 has shown, Eastern Nigeria today has the highest level in West Africa of school-age children actually in school.

But the physical odds against human success were really great, for within Iboland a large population displays a very irregular pattern of distribution. Basically the pattern reveals a belt of very high density running northwest to southeast and averaging more than 240/km², which is flanked on all sides by areas with not more than 120/km². Within the high density belt in Okigwi, Orlu, and Awka, densities rise to more than 400/km². For an economy based on rain-farming without irrigation, these densities are clearly excessive and their effects are evident everywhere. The sandy soils show remarkable instability under the impact of frequent cultivation (21: 46). Gully erosion of staggering dimensions is noticeable in many places, but especially along the scarp of the Awka-Orlu Uplands and the Nsukka-Okigwi escarpment. One such gully near the villages of Agulu, Nanka, and Oko in Awka Division is about 450 meters wide and 100 meters deep (10: 33-34). Indeed it has been suggested that within the Awka area alone, gully erosion has claimed more than 1,265 hectares of farmland or 2.5 per cent of the land (22: 5).

The impact of the pressure of population on resources has social significance as well. The demand of so many for so little land has led everywhere to extreme fragmentation of holdings. In many areas the average holding per person is now no more than 0.2 hectares. The pressure has also encouraged the individualization of holdings and the breakdown of both familial and communal control. A concomitant of this development has been frequent land disputes between individuals and groups, sometimes leading to fatal incidents.

With the continuing fragmentation of land, the fallow period has been drastically reduced from an optimum of seven years after one year of cultivation to two years' fallow after two years of cultivation. The result has been a loss of soil fertility followed by a gradual decrease in productivity. Less fertile soils encouraged the supercession of yam, the traditional staple, by the recently introduced, but inferior, cassava. It is said to be a hardier crop and gives an average yield of about 11,350 kg per hectare even in degraded or depleted soils, which is far in excess of the 6600 per hectare credited to yam. But low productivity has meant a considerably reduced income for the majority of the farmers, and many have had to seek a variety of other occupations to meet such financial obligations as the annual flat-rate tax of $3.00. Sometimes, extra income is needed to buy food for the long hunger season between harvests.

Yet rural indebtedness remains rife in the Ibo countryside and has encouraged the rise of a class of speculative land operators. Pressed for funds, many farmers have used their land as security for loans from richer members of the community. Failure to pay back the loan means, of course, virtual loss of the land, and the creation of a growing class of landless farmers. One finds in the overpopulated area of Iboland today the anomalous situation of individuals owning more than 80 hectares of land. A few, in fact, are said to own as many as 400. Such individuals lease out part of their holdings to farmers desperately in need of extra land to produce a little more food for their families. But such is the scarcity value of land in this area that not only size, but also length of fallow period commands a price.

Thus, a holding of about 0.4 hectares which has been under fallow for only one year is leased for a season for no more than $0.60. If it has been in fallow for four years, the price may be as high as $2.50.

Many of the landless farmers have become laborers offering their services to the richer, land-owning group. Some are allowed to remain on their land but in a dependent status. Others who have not lost their land still must look for new or additional sources of livelihood simply because their holdings are too small to support them. The mass exodus of people from the overpopulated areas of Iboland has been one of the most striking phenomena of the present century. In a sample survey of ten randomly chosen families in Abriba in 1963, it was found that of a total of 177 people, as many as 116 (or nearly 70 per cent) had migrated (20: 21). Similarly, in Oko village (Awka Division), in spite of a rapid increase in population between 1939 and 1949, the number of taxpayers fell from 909 to 734 during the same period. Thus, by 1966 estimates showed that as many as two million Ibos were to be found in Northern Nigeria and a million and a half in other parts of the country. Yet there is evidence that a good number of migrants move away only temporarily, or even on a seasonal basis. The destinations of most of these people are less densely settled areas in the Cross River Basin. Recently, school boys who spend their vacations earning extra income to help pay school fees have added to the numbers of seasonal migrants.

Throughout Nigeria, whether in city or rural area, the Ibo migrant has made significant achievements and invaluable contributions to the economic life of the country. More than this, his activities have helped to raise the standard of living of the many who have not left the security of their homeland in Eastern Nigeria.

THE MOSSI OF UPPER VOLTA

In many ways the Mossi contrast sharply with the Ibo. Living in an area equally poor and with an excessive population density, the Mossi have not shown an equally avid urge to raise their standard of living. Also, unlike the Ibo, the Mossi are a culturally well-knit community, some of whom as early as the eleventh century were organized into a kingdom, which established its capital at Ouagadougou in the fifteenth century. Another Mossi kingdom, Yatenga, had its capital at Ouahigouya from the twelfth century. The monarch, or Mogho-Naba, of the former ruled the country through governors who were appointed to each of the five provinces. Each province comprised a number of districts under appointive chiefs whose major task was to collect regular taxes and special imposts. The districts in turn were made up of numerous villages whose affairs were administered by local leaders.

In spite of their advanced cultural organization, the Mossi played a comparatively limited role in the great historical events of the Sudan. Their kingdom seems to have served as a buffer, protecting the smaller, weaker states to the south from exposure to northern tribes and cultures (19: 78). Even the impact of Islam was only slight and sporadic among them. The antipathy or indifference of these people to foreign influence seems to have carried through to the modern period. Table 8-1 shows that even today Upper Volta has one of the lowest proportions in West Africa of school-age children actually in school. Nonetheless, as pointed out earlier, the country's landlocked situation and distance from the coast have been in part responsible for its backwardness in the present century.

The implication is that for most Mossi the desired standard of living remains fixed at only slightly higher than the traditional level of subsistence. But the environment can barely provide more, given the present population densities and the traditional technology. The two basic elements of this environment are the relatively dry climate and the wide occurrence of infertile lateritic soils. Much of the Mossi territory lies within the Sahel-Sudan savanna belt, where rainfall ranges between 725 and 1125 mm. It comes mainly within a five-month period from May to September, so that for a large part of the year the area is very dry. The dryness is further emphasized by the impermeable character of the Pre-Cambrian rocks, which encourage rapid run-off and sudden floods.

The Mossi numbered roughly 2.3 million in 1965 and occupy an area of about 67,600 km². This gives an average density of nearly 36/km² which for the dry savanna of West Africa is rather high. It has been suggested that the basis for this high density is the security against external threat and the internal stability provided by the Mogho-Naba dynasties both in Ougadougou and Ouahigouya since the medieval period. The period of French colonialism continued this trend although many people perished through the French system of forced labor. In addition, French colonial efforts in sanitation and medicine were not spectacular and although crude birth rates remained as high as 49 per thousand, death rates were more than 31 per thousand. (15: 77). The annual rate of growth has been only about 1.6 per cent compared with, for instance, 3.5 in the Ivory Coast and 3.0 in Guinea.

This demographic information, however, does not give an adequate impression of the degree of population pressure on the land. Two factors, in particular, point out that the situation among the Mossi is more serious than suggested. First, unproductive lateritic soils reduce some cultivable areas by as much as two-thirds. Izard-Heritier noted in her study of the Mossi of Yatenga that on the basis of over-all land space, each inhabitant could have as much as 3.4 hectares, but in terms of cultivable area, no more than 1.2 hectares (13: 10). The second factor relates to the social organization of the Mossi which places great importance on hierarchical ordering. Members of higher orders enjoy numerous privileges and rights denied to the populace. Thus, in a Mossi village, the chief has the largest unit of land which is cultivated by the free labor of his subjects. Also, within a family, at the death of the father the eldest son takes the larger, better holdings while the rest is shared among his brothers in order of seniority. These inequalities in distribution of cultivable land only help to aggravate local pressure of population on resources.

The typical unit of Mossi settlement is the village. As in the Ibo country, the cultivated area shows basic division between compound land under permanent cultivation and the farm proper subject to rotational fallow. The farm proper, however, is subdivided in two parts: on one half, Fulani herdsmen have been encouraged to pasture their cattle. The manure provides a natural fertilizer which helps to minimize the worst effects of a shortened fallow period; but in spite of this the Mossi area has perhaps the lowest yield per hectare of millet and sorghum in the savanna region of former French West Africa. In 1957, for instance, the average yield was as high as 580 per hectare in Mali and 480 kg per hectare in Niger, but less than 400 kg per hectare in most parts of the Mossi country.

The effect of population pressure on resources is shown in numerous other ways. As in the Ibo country, the most obvious has been in the transformation of the vegetal cover. The need for more and more agricultural land has led to the virtual elimination of trees with the exception of the baobab and shea-butter, which have been specially preserved for their economic value. The intense utilization of the land which

such vegetal destruction represents has led in many places to severe soil erosion and loss of valuable agricultural land.

Because of the more developed social control and organization among the Mossi and the generally low level of social and economic expectations, the impact of population pressure on resources has not been as overwhelming and provocative of far-reaching social changes as among the Ibos. It is true that one of its most notable effects has been the annual mass emigration of Mossi young men, especially between the ages of 16 and 30, to Ghana and the Ivory Coast. It has been estimated that between 50,000 and 100,000 Mossi workers, virtually all of them young males, emigrate to the coffee and cocoa plantations of the Ivory Coast alone (23: 375). But most of them return to Upper Volta after harvests and only a very small proportion migrate permanently.

One reason for this is that the Mossi migrant has little to offer at his destination and shows very little incentive or ability to learn new ways. In an investigation of 9518 Mossi returning from Ghana in 1954, it was found that more than 85 per cent of them had been laborers on farms or in the forests (8: 31-37). In other words, the Mossi migrant was not turning his back on his overcrowded homeland in order to seek a better life elsewhere; he was going away only for a short time to earn a little extra money to help meet local obligations or to show off that "he too had been to Kumasi." Moal pointed out that the average amount brought back each time by migrants who had spent a period working in Ghana or the Ivory Coast was usually between 5000 and 10,000 francs, that is between $20.00 and $40.00 (16: 256). But most of the money soon disappeared in presents to the chiefs and elders, and the migrants were rapidly reabsorbed into the traditional surroundings. Apart from providing an opportunity to buy a bicycle or a few articles of clothing, emigration does not seem to have any material effect on the standard of living of the Mossi.

Quite to the contrary, the annual exodus of the young and active creates a number of social and economic problems. It has been a major cause of disruption of family life and has tended to increase the rate of abduction of young girls, seduction of other people's wives, and divorce. It has also led to a demographic disequilibrium in which most communities have a preponderance of children and aged people. In a number of cases this has seriously affected the amount of land cultivated as well as the entire agricultural economy of a community. Moal mentions that in the canton of Manga in the Cercle of Ouagadougou, emigration was so intense in one year that much land was left under fallow and acute food shortage was experienced the following year (16: 253).

Conclusion

The three groups studied above have one thing in common—the low level of their resource base. But it is clear that the extent to which pressure on this base is felt is a function of population density but more so of the level of expectations. Indeed, on the basis of expectations it is possible to make two generalizations about pressure of population on resources. The first is that where population pressure is felt or aggravated because of a high level of expectations, a situation is created which may constitute a wholesome response to the need for economic advancement. This type of situation may lead to three developments. First, it may lead to a fuller utilization of resources whereby new and formerly unusable land is brought under cultivation through the adoption of new crops or new techniques of production. Secondly, it may encourage permanent mi-

gration from some of the overpopulated rural areas, either to new agricultural lands, to cities, or to other parts of the country. The permanence of this loss means that more land is available to those left behind. Finally, it may stimulate some fundamental changes in social and economic attitudes to such issues as ownership of the land, emigration, acquisition of new skills, wealth, and competition.

The second generalization is that where population pressure on resources is simply that of sheer number without a heightening of expectations, one finds a tendency toward a break-down of socioeconomic conditions. There is usually little effective reduction of population since, in the absence of high economic expectations, there is a disposition to meet the challenge through a lowering of living standards. The migration of young men is usually seasonal and involves no renunciation of the rights left behind. In such a situation there is a growing inefficiency in the use of resources as the deterioration of the environment calls for a greater output of labor. Lastly, little positive change is evidenced in social and economic attitudes, except perhaps bewilderment and despair at the disruption of family life and the growing estrangement of the youthful from the aged population.

In West Africa, population pressure on resources has been shown to be a complex phenomenon. Given an average density of 16/km², West Africa in general does not suffer from overpopulation, but there are pockets, such as those identified in this paper, where the pressure of population on resources is high. It has been shown that an increase in social and economic expectations could be a major factor in the alleviation of the situation. Modern Western education and external trade help to detemine the level to be reached, and create conditions which facilitate the solution of the problem. For, as

Evans puts it, "it is the essence of Western education to reject all that tends to hold the human spirit in bondage and this can be as much a rejection of low social and economic circumstances maintaining a depressed standard of living as of political overlordship. In different ways both seek to enslave the human spirit and to deny those aspirations toward the good life which are implicit in Western culture" (9: 315). From this point of view, therefore, the vigorous commitment of most West African governments to the rapid provision of modern educational opportunities in their countries constitutes the greatest reassurance against the neo-Malthusian prospect of an area where population is fast outstripping the resources that support it.

REFERENCES

(1) John Adams: Sketches Taken during Ten Voyages to Africa, between the Years 1786 and 1800 (London, 1822).

(2) J. F. A. Ajayi: Christian Missions in Nigeria, 1841-91 (London, 1965).

(3) T. J. Bowen: Missionary Labours and Adventures in Central Africa (Charleston, 1857).

(4) R. Campbell: A Pilgrimage to my Motherland, 1859-60 (New York, 1861).

(5) R. J. H. Church: West Africa: a Study of the Environment and of Man's Use of it (London, 1966).

(6) A. M. Carr-Saunders: World Population (London, 1964).

(7) Rev. S. A. Crowther: Letter of May 9, 1851, *Church Missionary Society Archives,* CA2/031, 1851.

(8) R. B. Davidson: Migrant Labour in the Gold Coast (Achimota, 1954).

(9) P. C. C. Evans: Western Education and Rural Productivity in Tropical Africa, *Africa,* Vol. 32, No. 4, 1962, pp. 313-23.

(10) B. Floyd: Soil Erosion and Deterioration in Eastern Nigeria, *Nigerian Geographical Journal,* Vol. 8, No. 1, 1965, pp. 33-44.

(11) C. H. Fyfe: The Life and Times of John Ezzidio, *Sierra Leone Studies,* Vol. 4, 1955, pp. 213-23.

(12) M. M. Green: Igbo Village Affairs (London, 1964).

(13) F. Izard-Heritier and Michel Izard: Les Mossi du Yatenga (Upper Volta, 1959).

(14) S. Johnson: The History of the Yorubas (London, 1921).

(15) B. Kayser: La Démographie de l'Afrique Occidentale et Centrale, *Les Cahiers d'Outre-Mer,* Vol. 18, No. 69, 1965, pp. 73-86.

(16) G. Le Moal: Les Migrations de Mains-d'Oeuvre Voltaique, *Sixth International West African Conference, São Tomé, 1956,* Vol. 5, 1959, pp. 247-60.

(17) A. L. Mabogunje: Some Comments on Land Tenure in Egba Division, Western Nigeria, *Africa,* Vol. 31, No. 3, 1961, pp. 258-69.

(18) J. Richard-Molard: Afrique Occidentale Française (Paris, 1956).

(19) G. P. Murdock: Africa, Its Peoples and Their Culture History (New York, 1959).

(20) N. I. Ndukew: Migration Agriculture and Trade in Abriba Town (unpublished ms., Dept. of Geography, University of Ibadan, 1964).

(21) G. E. K. Ofomota: Factors of Soil Erosion in the Enugu Area of Nigeria, *Nigerian Geographical Journal,* Vol. 8, No. 1, 1965, pp. 45-59.

(22) A. I. Onwueke: Awka Upland Region: The Land of Migrant Farmers (unpublished ms., Dept. of Geography, University of Ibadan, 1966).

(23) E. P. Skinner: Labour Migration and its Relationship to Socio-Cultural Change in Mossi Society, *Africa,* Vol. 30, No. 4, 1960, pp. 375-401.

(24) L. D. Stamp: Land Utilisation and Soil Erosion in Nigeria, *Geographical Review,* Vol. 28, No. 1, 1938, pp. 32-45.

(25) United Nations, Statistical Yearbook (New York, 1965).

9. POPULATION, SOCIETY, AND THE ALLOCATION OF RESOURCES

H. C. Brookfield

A field so wide as that embraced by my title can scarcely be tackled entire. There is a large theoretical literature, especially in the fields of economics and anthropology, that has a bearing on the question; empirically, the subject could be tackled either diachronically as a study of changes in society that have accompanied population growth, or synchronically by comparing societies similar in certain respects but dissimilar in their degree of population pressure. It would be safer to select one of these approaches and to follow it through to the exclusion of the other; at the risk of falling between stools, however, I propose to try to adopt elements of both, not pretending exhaustively to cover the whole field of either. Though it leads to theoretical discussion, my approach is essentially empirical, and what I propose to do is to invert the question by asking how social and political institutions in different cultures are employed to facilitate the management of resource use under different levels of PPR. Further to simplify, I shall not try to draw evidence from complex industrial societies, and though I pass to societies that are politically and economically centralized, shall begin with societies that some might term "primitive" or "archaic," and of which the 17th Report of the U.N. Population Division had this to say:

> Ancient institutions cannot cope with the resulting population increase [from a decline in the death rate], nor, as a general rule, with rapid economic progress since they are adapted to stationary or slowly developing conditions [53: 282],

while Pierre George, after dismissing hunters and gatherers and "closed" societies of shifting cultivators from our field of useful interest, went on:

> It would be an error of perspective, and—more serious than that—of judgment, to deal with the pre-industrial societies of tropical Africa or East Asia from the point of view of their traditional institutions [survivances], rather than that of their role in the modern world. The object of our investigation makes this clear. The numerical relationship between people and utilized land, or between men and natural resources, and the demographic prospects of such populations do not depend on their traditional economic organization, but rather on the methods of production and distribution in the internal market, and more especially on the degree to which their economies are penetrated by the exogenous, world-wide economic system (28: 79-80).

My evidence is drawn mainly from societies in the Western Pacific and western Indian Ocean areas, including parts of Southeast Asia and Africa—areas in which I am, for the most part, able to supplement my gleanings with some personal knowledge. I try to view these societies, as a geographer, as man-environment systems—open, and indivisible, but capable of entry at any point for purpose of analysis. I suggest that the group of social and political institutions governing access to resources and the distribution of the products of work may usefully be taken as such a point of entry. My governing hypothesis is that these sets of institutions operate in such a way—or are structured in such a way—as to accommodate some measure of demographic variation, but that major variation creates stresses which may call forth modifications in the institutions; conversely, major modifications such as the innovation of political centralization, or colonial rule, or structural changes in the form of economic organization, will greatly affect the capacity of the system to support demographic variation. There is nothing very new in this, except perhaps in the suggestion that from comparative and cross-cultural study of allocation of the means of livelihood within societies might be squeezed useful indices of PPR.

Throughout, I am trying to avoid two pitfalls; first of setting up a continuum and then concluding that it exists; second of anthropomorphizing social and political institutions into things that act, whereas in reality they are but means adopted by men to achieve their ends. In view of the approach adopted, it will not be easy to avoid these errors, and in lieu of repeated caveats and circumlocutions sprinkled throughout the text, I must ask the reader to bear this single notice of intent in mind, and to avoid being misled by verbal shorthand that might otherwise suggest the contrary. The first of these pitfalls is encountered at once, for some ordering of material is necessary, so I begin with societies that lack centralized political institutions, then later turn to examine some of the concomitants of centralization.

Societies Without Centralized Political Institutions

In the absence of centralized authority, control over resources must rest with the local community, and the peaceful or warlike interaction of such local communities, supplemented by such arrangements as exist for exchange, reciprocity, and redistribution (45: 250-56) and transfer of resources between individuals. Taking "land" to mean the complex of resources to which all need access, allocation is commonly achieved by defining this access in terms of some princi-ple of either locality or descent, or both together. We can often speak of "landed groups" and of the "territories" of such groups. Abstracting slightly, we may view these local bounded areas within man-environment systems either as the land area thus delimited plus the persons with access to it, or as a defined group of persons plus the land to which they have access. Since transmission of land rights is based on kinship in most societies, membership in landed groups may be most readily defined in terms of some kinship principle. A wide variety is possible, among which the unilineal principle—whether patrilineal or matrilineal—is the simplest conceptually, but also the most restrictive in terms of the persons entitled to rights. Wider kinship principles of grouping, incorporating patrilateral and matrilateral kin, lead readily to dual and multiple membership of groups. For convenience, all of the first set of societies here discussed are patrilineal in principle though, as we shall see, rights are not so sharply limited in practice.

Two main variables occur within patrilineal systems. The first depends on the marriage rules. In most societies marriage is possible anywhere outside of a limited range of kin, and may thus be permissible within a patrilineally defined descent group. In other societies, all coeval members of a patrilineage are classificatory brothers and sisters, and may marry only outside the group. The second variable is related to the disposition of landed-group territory: it may be in one discrete block, or it may be partly or wholly dispersed among the territorial blocks of other landed groups. In the former case, the patrilineal descent group normally lives together as a "local group," while in the latter the local group (usually a village) is commonly composed of members of several patrilineal groups. The interaction of these two variables will affect the geographical distribution of the cognatic and affinal kin of each individual, and of their land.

Strict adherence to patrilineal or agnatic transmission of rights in a fixed territorial unit would speedily create problems due to varying growth rates in adjacent groups. This is a situation that may be accommodated by varying the territorial boundaries—a solution that presents increasing difficulty the more permanent are the improvements to land made by cultivation—and/or by means of a flexible interpretation of the rules governing land rights. Most commonly, individual kin and affines outside a unilineal descent group may be permitted or invited to use a group's land, either on a temporary basis as visitors or on a permanent basis by becoming notionally absorbed into the donor group. Since a descent group requires some notion of a unifying genealogy, this absorption of non-agnates may result in revision of the conceptual genealogy.

Such a situation prevailed in the tiny volcanic island of Tikopia just east of the Solomon Islands group, occupied by people of Polynesian origin. When first studied by an anthropologist in 1929, the Tikopians held their land in dispersed and interdigitated blocks held by patrilineal descent groups; however, married women brought to their family estate a dowry of land from their natal-group blocks for lifetime use, and loans were made between relatives. In a distinct area used only for short-term crops it was possible for anyone to work land without seeking permission of the holders. The various patrilineages were grouped into four major clans, all dispersed, the chiefs of which exercised some conservationist authority for the whole island, each over a particular crop. With an acute awareness of PPR, forms of population restraint had long been practised, by means of coitus interruptus, delayed marriage and permanent bachelorhood, abortion, infanticide, and even suicide.

Even so, it has twice in remembered history been necessary to resort to civil war in which the losers were either exterminated or else driven to almost certain death at sea (23; 24: passim). Within so tightly organized a community, social pressures could be highly effective in the enforcement of population-limitation measures held to be necessary by all: such were in fact quite common in the pre-Christian Pacific.

In recent years missions and government have suppressed some of the checks, and, despite some emigration, population rose from 1300 in 1929 to 1750 in 1952. Though the introduction of money and imported foodstuffs eased the situation, natural calamity compounded the effect of rising population in creating stress within the man-environment system. Cropping patterns have changed, fallow periods have been shortened, land boundaries are far more exactly marked out and maintained, and disputes are more frequent. The giving of land in dowry has ceased altogether; land transfers to relatives outside the defined, agnatic territorial group have diminished in frequency, and access to resources has become far more rigidly defined (11: passim; 25: passim; 50).

Some writers have claimed to recognize a similar response to land shortage among the densely settled populations of the highlands of central New Guinea, and elsewhere in the world. A theoretical argument concerning the effect of PPR on social and territorial organization has developed, and shows no signs of early resolution. Meggitt goes so far as to offer as a general proposition that

> where the members of a homogenous society distinguish in any consistent fashion between agnates and other relatives, the degree to which social groups are structured in terms of agnatic descent and patrilocality varies with the pressure on available agrarian resources [42: 266].

Others have cast doubt on this rigid cause-and-effect hypothesis: in a high-density area of the central New Guinea highlands, Brookfield and Brown noted that:

> although individuals and groups guard their land interests against intrusion, especially in the more valued areas, several mechanisms exist whereby the land poor can obtain land, both individually and in groups. These mechanisms provide a flexibility in land holding which the rules of ownership would seem to prevent [15: 125].

In discussing this seeming disagreement it is important first to establish the limits of difference, second to examine the actual quantitative bases for comparison. Within the highlands of Australian New Guinea, all populations have an ideology of grouping by patrilineal descent, and all have a segmentary system of social organization through which smaller groups nest into larger. Arable land is, however, individually held, and there is continual to-ing and fro-ing of individuals who either live temporarily with, or more permanently join, other cognates and affines outside the territory of their own agnatic group.

The discussion has perhaps been confused by failure to distinguish adequately between the two concepts of group and territory; between the defined group of persons plus the land in which they have rights—the descent groups—on the one hand, and the delimited land area plus the persons with access to it—the territorial group—on the other hand. It may be helpful briefly to examine the evidence from three societies: Bena, Enga, and Chimbu, with this in mind.

The Korofeigu-Bena live in a grassland environment that suffers fairly regular seasonal drought. They occupy precisely delimited and compactly shaped group territories at a density around 27/km². Under their relatively intensive agricultural system, this low density requires them to occupy only a small part of their territory at any one time; individual rights are not maintained in the long-fallowed areas since so long a time elapses between use and re-use of the same tract of group territory. Members of agnatic groups collectively hold the group reserve, but individuals hold the plots they are currently using. The descent group and the territorial group are sets of persons with only overlapping membership. Of a total population of 232 in Nupasafa clan territory, there are 30 active adult men, of whom only 20 are known to be agnatic members of the descent group; all the others have come from other groups, some to live uxorilocally with their wives, others because their mothers are Nupasafa, some using more remote cognatic and affinal connections. Taking the whole male population of Nupasafa clan territory, of all ages, 70 per cent would be classed as agnates (36: 166). The affiliated men have equal rights in land and in most other respects with natal members of the landed group. Thus of the *territorial* landed group, 33 per cent are immigrants. Of the *descent* landed group, that is all men who are genealogically members of Nupasafa clan, 43 per cent live and farm in the territories of other groups (34: 145-75; 36: passim).

Mae-Enga live more than 400 m. higher than the Korofeigu-Bena, in an area with little rainfall seasonality but liable to cold nights which limit the rate of growth of crops. They also occupy precisely delimited clan territories at a density of about 96/km². Their agricultural system depends on the making of mulched mounds in semi-permanent fields; a sharp distinction exists between the mounded sweet-potato fields and the impermanent mixed-gardens, made for the most part on sloping land of inferior quality (54). Enga live in dispersed family house clusters close to the permanent fields; they are grouped into clans and subclans which collectively recognize territory.

Descent group and territorial group are far more closely equated in the Enga mind than among the Bena. Outsiders are accepted only as guests with limited rights; though they may pass gradually from being outsiders to being quasi-agnates, their descendants being incorporated into the notional genealogy as full agnates, uncertainty over land rights dogs even the second-generation immigrant. Meggitt argues that this reluctance to admit outsiders arises from an awareness of PPR, and that the Enga themselves see the situation in these terms. It also seems, however, that dislike of divided loyalties is significant in a situation of intense inter-group competition, for

> People can never be sure of the intentions of an attached member of their parish, and the agnatic members are reluctant to grant him equal status in the group. They reserve the right to evict him when they choose. If they do expel him, he must return to his natal clan, whatever may be his chances of regaining his father's land [43: 35].

A number of writers have found Meggitt's rigidly patrilineal Enga hard to believe by comparison with the structural looseness of surrounding societies, and even his data have been reinterpreted to show quantitatively that the differences are exaggerated. McArthur finds only 65 per cent of males in Kara clan of Mae-Enga to be full agnates, a value slightly but not significantly *lower* than that cited by Langness for the flexible Korofeigu-Bena (40: 284). Barnes concludes that Enga practice cumulative affiliation which they rationalize by stress on agnation, and hence are in fact much less rigid structuralists than they or Meggitt suppose.

We have already noted the evidence of flexibility in Chimbu, the third society here considered, with a population more densely

settled than the Mae-Enga. In fact the proportion of agnates among the men of six Naregu-Chimbu subclans is 79 per cent, while agnates plus accepted quasi-agnates together number about 90 per cent, which is the same proportion as Meggitt finds for a group of Enga clans (15: 14; 43: 10). But Chimbu readily welcome outsiders, and offer accepted quasi-agnates full and equal rights with agnates: the leading man of one of the more land-poor of Naregu-Chimbu subclans, with a crude density of 160/km^2, is himself a quasi-agnate. Almost 60 per cent of the men in a group of subclans in Naregu-Chimbu made at least one residential move between subclan territories during the years 1958-65 (15: 140). Naregu-Chimbu live at an altitude intermediate between that of Mae-Enga and Korofeigu-Bena, and suffer little risk of either drought or deleterious cold; the average population density of this part of Chimbu is 138/km^2, and the agricultural system is less fixed in location of fields than that of the Enga. It is little wonder therefore that a number of writers have concluded that Meggitt failed to establish his Tikopian hypothesis on this comparison.

However, discussion has been confused not merely by inadequate distinction between agnation and patriolocality and between descent and territorial concepts of the landed group, but also by its one-dimensional reliance simply on population density. Meggitt makes a serious attempt to overcome the fact of higher Chimbu density, both by observing that while Chimbu population clusters are very closely settled, there are also vacant areas not paralleled in Enga, and by suggesting that Enga sweet potato yields are appreciably lower. This latter suggestion is weakened by recent data which show that in the relevant middle altitudes Enga sweet potato yields are only about 10 per cent below those of Chimbu, while at higher altitudes Enga methods offer the better yields; however, the same data source shows that Enga population is increasing at a fairly rapid rate, while that of Chimbu is hardly more than static (17: passim). This growth could be more relevant than any considerations of comparative density.

After all, attitudes toward immigrants, and flexibility or looseness in practical interpretation of very similar rules of land tenure and transmission are behavioral matters, and there is no necessary reason to seek deterministic or even normative correlations that should fully explain them. The fact that Enga attitudes are different from those of Chimbu and Bena is demonstrated beyond doubt by Meggitt's evidence, as is the fact that Enga are more acutely perceptive of rising land shortage (43: 45). Meggitt certainly fails to distinguish between shortage of terrace land suited for the semi-permanent mound fields, and relative abundance of sloping land used for impermanent mixed gardens: the latter is much more readily lent (54). It is the improved, mounded in-field close to the houses that is jealously guarded, and this especially because of the need to look forward to the next generation (43: 45). It is a perception of a whole system, not merely of a sense of crowding, that leads Enga to behave as they do.

A closer comparison of the same sort may be found within one society of lowland New Guinea, where Lea (37: 157) offers the following quantitative comparison between two villages among yam-growing shifting-cultivators, the Abelam:

		Village A	Village B
Crude population density	(km²)	50	106
Cultivable land per head	(ha)	1.4	0.6
Area cultivated per head	(ha)	0.06	0.04
Yam harvest per head per day	(kg)	3.4	2.0
Average length of fallow period	(Years)	17	10
Pigs and piglets kept	(Number)	109	5

He also finds that in village B agricultural practices are more slovenly, quarrels are more frequent, and land is less freely lent than in village A. In village A 69 per cent of gardens are operated by a person other than the landholder; in village B only 36 per cent. Body weight of individuals is lower, the ceremonial cycle has been abandoned, the fallow is more invaded by grass—in all these and other respects there is evidence of stress in village B, stress that seems to be related to PPR.

But again population growth is more rapid in village B and its region than in and around village A. Village B has had a much more unfortunate post-contact experience with government and mission, leading to a demoralization only partly related to PPR. There is perception of PPR, and land-holders' restriction of freedom of access to resources may be related to this awareness; it is, however, also related to a cessation of the ceremonial exchanges in which a wide range of interpersonal and intergroup relations is recognized and formalized; this in turn is related to a complex of causes among which the strength of PPR cannot be identified with certainty.

Among the Arusha of Mt. Meru in Tanzania, awareness of PPR in modern times has had effects quite contrary to the demoralization of Abelam village B. Instead the most crowded of Arusha have turned most thoroughly to the production of coffee as a cash crop for market, and to the support of a market-trading system under which they buy a proportion of their foodstuffs. At the same time the allocation of parts of the family or lineage estate to sons has become difficult, resulting in the pioneering of new land on the fringes by the sons, the consequent weakening of family bonds, but at the same time the development of wider alignments in the segmentary lineage system (31: 268-71; 30: 13-16). The Chimbu of New Guinea have also turned to coffee and a market economy, while in pre-contact times and to a limited extent also today, families and fragmentary groups driven out of the territorial areas by war or other pressures have formed new and sometimes compound groups on the fringes, still recognizing kinship with territorial groups remaining in the former home areas: in Enga similarly such colonies facilitate a process of chain migration from the more densely settled areas to the pioneer fringes.

It might be helpful to sum up this phase of the argument: among these several societies of homogenous type and acephalous organization, there are a number of ways in which PPR is both perceived by the people to exist, and may also be recognized to exist by outside observers. Yet responses are very different. At the production level, there seems to be an actual decline in technology and yields in Abelam village B, shortening of fallow in Tikopia, possibly an elaboration of the use of mulched mounds in Enga, entry into a readily absorbed cash crop in Chimbu and Arusha. All must and do retain flexibility in permitting the members of the society access to resources, but while some perhaps increase the rate of temporary land transfer between territorial landed groups, others seek to restrict such transfer and to limit long-term recruitment of outsiders into the descent land group. In Abelam there is also evidence that might suggest reduction of transfer between territorial landed groups, but we cannot be certain from the data whether this is also true of Enga and Tikopia.

But the difficulty with one-dimensional hypotheses such as that which we have been discussing, or even that of Boserup who argues that population growth is a revolutionary force in bringing about agricultural change (10: 56-59), is that they neglect or threaten to neglect other relevant factors. In the Enga-Chimbu comparison there are at least three other variables that might be taken into account: the permanent Enga infield, close to the house cluster, has no exact parallel in Chimbu, and it could be fixity of land use as much as shortage of land as a whole that is the operative consideration; Enga population is growing more rapidly than that of Chimbu, hence awareness of the needs of the rising generation may be more keenly felt, especially in a situation where agriculture is in part fixed in location; Chimbu combine into larger political groups than Enga, and form tribes composed of a number of clans, so that the range of persons in a relationship of collaboration is wider for any Chimbu individual, and there is thus more scope for flexibility.

One could go on, but it is clear first that no simple hypothesis is sufficient, and second that there are alternative responses for a population faced with perception of PPR. But these are simple truths not limited to homogeneous societies: we must look further.

Differentiation Within Uncentralized Societies

Though Tikopia has its chiefs, and while powerful men and insignificant men certainly exist in all these societies, there is generally a lack of class differentiation.

While we must be careful to avoid any suggestion that differentiation emerges in response to PPR, it is nonetheless clear that a rigid adherence to rule in the transmission of rights to resources would result in differentiation if continued; some groups, and some individuals, would amass a much more than proportionate share, and could use this by exploiting the disadvantaged, and by obtaining wealth from the surplus production by means of trade.

Even within the highlands of central New Guinea, one society has advanced some way along this path. The Kapauku of the West Irian mountains have an essentially similar subsistence base to the Bena, Chimbu, and Enga, but in an environment where the best land is a man-made creation of drainage and mounding on the fringes of swamps. All land is individually owned, but there are great inequalities; and the land hungry have to be highly mobile in their efforts to seek rights through cognatic or affinal ties, or from related or unrelated land-rich men to whom they become attached in a client relationship. The economy is monetized with cowrie-shell currency, and there is extensive trade in pigs and valuables both within Kapauku and with adjacent peoples. Land may be sold, leased, or rented against payment in shell currency (46; 47: passim). Money, amassed by the land-rich men, is also a means to power.

Differentiation is more marked in the mountains of Luzon, Philippines, where there is also very marked differentiation in arable land. Irrigated terraces for rice, sometimes used for dry crops in winter, are made almost wherever there is water to supply them; dry-fields dependent wholly on rainfall are impermanent in location. Though rice is the preferred food, sweet potatoes grown on the dry-fields and on terraces in winter supply most of the diet. For many generations it has been possible to make only marginal additions to the supply of irrigated pond-fields in the more closely occupied areas such as central Ifugao, though pond-field irrigation has extended into other parts of the Luzon mountains only in modern times. Much labor is required to construct and maintain the pond-fields, and all are individually owned. Impermanent dry-fields, on the other hand, are not subject to continuing ownership of the site by individuals, and access to land for making such fields is achieved through membership in a territorial group. Pond-fields are valuable property, and in each district have come mainly into the hands of a minority, though few holdings exceed a hectare. Rice was formerly used as currency in buying and selling pond-fields, but money is now used, and some pond-fields are now worth several thousand pesos.

In Ifugao, three distinct classes of persons emerged: the wealthy, the middle class with just enough pond-fields for their own use, and the poor who can obtain access to pond-fields only as tenants of the wealthy. Servants and some slaves were also recruited from among the poor. In the drier western areas of the Luzon mountains, wealth is also reckoned in cattle, and the poor would care for the cattle of the wealthy against a share of the proceeds from sale, as the Kapauku do with pigs. Ultimately, the system depended on trading contacts with the adjacent lowlands, which provide the wealthy with an outlet for their surplus rice and cattle. In modern times, other avenues of earning money have appeared through mining and urban work, and the dependence of the poor on the wealthy has diminished greatly. Nonetheless, there remains a considerable seasonal migration of labor within the mountains (3; 4: passim).

In these examples, the emergence of differentiation within the system seems to arise from a combination of circumstances that includes shortage of available land, a high labor input in improved land which leads to fixity of individualized land rights more rigid than in a less intensive system, and trading outlets whereby surplus production can be converted into wealth. Explanation has to call on elements drawn from different parts of a whole system, and it is certainly not sufficient to rest on population growth alone. Durkheim's view that "the division of labor varies in direct ratio with the volume and density of societies" (22: 262) is at best a partial explanation, of essentially the same order as generalizations about "hydraulic" societies or the "standard-of-living" effect that should check population growth. All are refined forms of determinism, refined in suggesting a process, but deterministic in their presumption of a single-path cause-and-effect relationship. But changes in the "volume and density" of societies are important, and the concomitants of such changes need now to be more fully explored.

The Concomitants of Centralization of Political Power

On *prima facie* grounds we might expect situations such as those discussed above to vary in a number of ways following the emergence or external imposition of centralized political authority. There would now be a superordinate authority in land matters; division of labor would be facilitated and labor could be mobilized on a larger scale; redistribution through the central authority would dominate over reciprocity, but at the same time the scope for market exchange would be greatly widened; scope for differentials in wealth would also be enlarged. Conversely, we should expect the local descent and territorial groups to become of reduced significance, and mechanisms formerly employed to even out differentials in population pressure to be replaced or supplemented by larger-scale movements and mobilization of resources.

By no means all of these may occur, and all can develop to some degree without any political centralization at all. Widening of the span of political co-operation can occur in acephalous societies through migration and colonization on the fringes, as we have seen in the case of the Arusha. In Chimbu, political groups are larger than elsewhere in the New Guinea highlands, and take the form of political associations of clans that may have no notion of genealogical relationship. This increase in the "volume" of society may be related to "density"; certainly it is the absence of any opportunity to widen the span of society in isolated Tikopia which makes the problem of PPR there particularly intractable, and is inimical to flexibility.

Nor is centralization necessary for the evolution of market trading: centralization does not arise among the Kapauku; in the Berber highlands of Morocco market trade spread over quite wide areas without political centralization (9: 198-99); the same occurred on a smaller scale in inter-tropical Africa and in the Pacific. Division of labor can arise without centralization, whether by the emergence of differentials or by means of a religiously sanctioned caste system. But while all this is true, and emphasizes the fact that changes due to centralization are changes in degree rather than of kind, the fact remains that once a central authority is created with wide powers, the hitherto narrow limits placed on such trends are removed a very great way.

The relationship of political centralization to PPR is obscure, even though such a relationship is sometimes assumed without strong supporting evidence. Gluckman suggests in passing that PPR was a factor in the sudden formation of the Zulu state from among a population of cultivators and pastoralists organized in localized, exogamous, patrilineal descent groups in the late eighteenth century. About 1775, new methods of warfare and the raising of regiments from former age-classes led to the domination of some tribal chiefs, and in short order to the dominance of a single ruler. Local reorganization followed as the descent groups were dispersed and remustered into locality groups under appointed headmen; but except for the redistributive taxation necessary to support the army and royal house, no immediate economic revolution resulted: there seems little reason to involve PPR in the interpretation (29: 25). A more general inquiry failed to find any positive correlation between population density and the presence of centralized political institutions in a sample of African societies (26: 7). Most generally, the local emergence of political centralization can be traced to some external stimulus or stimuli from an area with long-established central institutions, though closer inquiry would probably reveal preconditions for acceptance of the innovation.

From our present point of view, a particularly interesting example of political centralization is presented by the Mérina of central Madagascar, for this seems to have had quite minimal external stimulus in the critical, initial period, yet is reasonably well documented from the recording of oral tradition by nineteenth-century observers. The Mérina probably represent the last wave of migrants of Malay origin into Madagascar, and spread over the central plateaus between about the tenth and eighteenth centuries, clearing the forest for the cultivation of irrigated rice in the valleys; they also grew yams and taro, acquired sweet potato at some uncertain date, and acquired manioc and maize certainly after the sixteenth century. These latter crops were grown on dryfields. From the pre-existing population they

acquired notions of cattle as wealth, and their animals were pastured on the seasonally dry grasslands that replaced the formerly extensive forests.

Initially it seems that Mérina were organized in territorial groups, recognizing double descent—in either male or female line—and with most marriages taking place within the local community: only parallel cousins were prohibited partners. Locality would thus be the main principle of initial clustering, and dominance of endogamy would preserve the genealogical identity of the local community (*fokon'olona*). As villages grew large, they would divide and new villages would then notionally be linked by descent from the sons or daughters of a single ancestor (19: 24ff). Villages were fortified, and hilltop sites were preferred; large common tombs would be close to the center of each.

As population increased, Imérina (the country) expanded by displacing or absorbing the former inhabitants, often bringing these latter into slavery. Society became differentiated into three classes, whose members were largely endogamous: nobles, commoners, and slaves. Differentiation further elaborated as some commoners were enslaved after defeat in warfare or as punishment, while a chiefly class developed from among the nobles, gathering a number of village-groups (*fokon'olona*) into fiefs under lords. The authority of these lords extended to control over access to resources. Thus the "founding ancestor" of one *fokon'olona* was said to have prohibited the cultivation of long-lived plants such as manioc (*sic.,* but improbable) near the village, since such long occupation of the soil would deprive some people of access to land (19: 200). As the territorial power of some lords widened in span in the eighteenth century, it became possible to mobilize larger bodies of slaves to begin extensive drainage works in the swamps of the Tananarive plain. But this did not get far, for there was fierce warfare between rival lords. This period of conflict was abruptly terminated in 1787 by a revolution leading to the victory of Andrianampoinimérina, founder of the unitary state.

The population of Imérina in 1787 is quite unknown. There was occasional famine and some poverty among the free population, and it is probable that local land shortage was felt, though this was in large measure due to the dislocations wrought by the wars. There was some market trade at fixed localities on fixed days (21: 105), and there were already some permanent settlements of a higher order than villages. In the main, each fortified village or *fokon'olona* would command some seasonally irrigable land in the valleys, but main sustenance probably depended on the dry-fields around the village; the country was already almost wholly deforested.

Andrianampoinimérina ruled initially only over the central group of valleys around the Tananarive plain. It was his object to create a stable base for the state, and to this end he set his hand to the reorganization of almost every aspecet of the Imérina man-environment system. He improved the basis for subsistence by extensive drainage works, mainly in the Tananarive plain, to facilitate second cropping and a great extension of rice cultivation. In order to mobilize the necessary labor, he created central political institutions, and to support these established new markets and encouraged the supply of produce to support urban populations. The poor were encouraged to sell in the markets, even if they had nothing to offer but cooked manioc, in order to gain at least some purchasing power (21: 108). Tananarive was built up as the highest-order central place, where the king resided, and whence radiated his 70 royal messengers who ensured liaison between central government and the districts (20: 124). These districts replaced the former chiefly fiefs, and the power of the chiefs was reduced by treating independent *fokon'olona* equally with nobles' estates in land matters. *Fokon'olona* boundaries were demarcated, and the local communities were grouped on a half-district basis for new forms of ceremony, and also for obligatory communal work. Half-districts were allocated tasks in competition with the other half, and the loser was required to pay money to the winner (19: 68). By these and other means the autarky of the *fokon'-olona* was broken down at the same time as its security was built up, and circulation of goods and money was increased. Within *fokon'olona* land was reallocated, and the king's authority became absolute in land matters.

This reorganization was achieved largely through a series of personal decrees, announced verbally at Tananarive usually on market days, for there was no writing. The king's speeches were memorized for transmission to the districts, and became part of a body of verbal tradition which was largely recorded during the nineteenth century, being perhaps embellished somewhat in the course of transmission and recording. Two examples exhibit an absolute ruler's philosophy of government in relation to land and population in a manner seldom equaled in any place or time:

> "I remind you, Mérina, that the soil of this country belongs to me as does the power. I shall therefore give you land, not having enough cattle or money to distribute among you. You will live on the parcels that I shall assign to you, but the land remains mine, as does the authority. I shall divide the land into *hetra* [taxable allotments] on the basis of one *hetra* per man; each of my subjects will thus have resources sufficient to satisfy his needs, be he humble or powerful; since I shall have assured him of the means of existence on conditions equal to those of his neighbors, he

must in consequence serve me. It is not possible for me, the king, to allocate to you measures of rice, nor to visit everyone to assure myself that he lacks nothing. I thus establish you in the source of well-being, in the irrigated land of which I am sole master, so that you may find the means to feed yourselves and the strength wherewith to serve me." [Translated from 19: 50]

And at another time:

"Rice is my ally and my friend: without it I cannot feed you who, thanks to me, are a great people. . . . Therefore I will not tolerate disputes over water which must flow freely, for rich and poor alike. . . . I have enlarged and pacified my kingdom, and now wish to see the land cultivated with care and improved, so that the enemy of famine will no longer threaten us, so that all my subjects may live well, and population can increase. Lords and chiefs must see to this, and I shall hold them responsible for inaction on the part of their people; I shall punish those convicted of negligence. Land not used by its holders will be put to use, on temporary title, by whosoever wishes to cultivate it." [Translated from 18: 119]

It seems that land allocation applied only to irrigated rice land of which the area was greatly increased by means of public works. The sizes of *hetra* do not seem to have been equal, varying according to one source from 0.04 to 0.4 *ha* (Standing, cited in 19: 50). Whether or not it was so at the outset, holdings became fragmented, and a few years ago in Tananarive District there was an average of 2.3 parcels per land-holder, the total holdings varying in size from 1.15 *ha* in the country areas to as little as 0.23 *ha* close to the city (18: 121): the peri-urban area received large quantities of manure from the city, greatly increasing its productivity.

Andrianampoinimérina also raised an army with which he conquered outlying areas of Mérina settlement, and extended his authority into the densely populated Vakinankaratra and Betsileo country of similar culture and occupancy to the south, though here there was rather less active social reorganization. After his death in 1810 the Imérina state continued to expand, to cover most of Madagascar by mid-century. At the center there was active modernization with the aid of missionaries and European advisers, but the state became both more centralized and more tyrannical; the *fokon'olona* on which Andrianampoinimérina had relied for the base of his structure lost much of their independence, and differentials of wealth multiplied. Some of the improvements were neglected, even in the Tananarive plain. Soon after French conquest in 1895, some 200,000 slaves were emancipated (49: 260); many large holdings were then broken up into share-cropping sections worked mainly by former slaves under *métayage*. Emigration from the central areas of Imérina and Betsileo, which had begun under the monarchy, now became massive, so that nearly a quarter of the population of Mérina and Betsileo origin now lives elsewhere in the island (18: 128).

This emigration is often supposed to be based on PPR in the central highlands, yet it seems that population was declining at the time of French conquest and rapid increase in any major part of Madagascar is only a recent phenomenon. Chevalier vigorously challenges the view that emigration from the central highlands was prompted by PPR, pointing to the absence of grinding poverty either among the migrants or those left behind, and to the large undeveloped areas—some of them irrigable—in the heart of the country between Tananarive and Antsirabe (18: 122-30). I covered much the same ground as Chevalier at the end of a drought, and wonder if he does not overstate his case. Small differences in level greatly affect irrigation potential, and except for some large tracts that would demand major works, not many water sources seem to lie unused. Also where soil-moisture conditions are favorable, as in the heads of valleys on the granites around Tananarive, or more widely on the basalts around Antsirabe, not much dry land seems unoccupied. Because of the large areas of dry grassland used only for cattle, crude densities by District are low, seldom exceeding 30/km² except close to the towns. However, Tananarive Province as a whole had agricultural densities of about 1020/km² on rice land, and 610/km² on all land growing food crops in 1961. Comparable figures for Fianarantsoa Province (Betsileo) were about 780/km² on rice land and 510/km² on all food crop land (calculated from data in 35: 83). These are high values.

Tananarive city, with 300,000 inhabitants, is overwhelmingly Mérina in population: adding the city population to the emigrants, not more than half the descendants of the original population and their slaves remain on the land in Imérina. These townward and outward migrations may or may not be related to PPR in their origin, but they have certainly permitted substantial population growth without leading to stress and to serious PPR. Further, the growth of Tananarive as a primate city of Madagascar has increased population capacity in the surrounding rural area which supplies the city with foodstuffs. This dynamic equilibrium is now threatened by accelerated population growth, but in the Malagasy state as a whole the problem remains that of underproduction rather than overpopulation.

Imérina has some of the characteristics of a theoretical Isolated State, especially in the early years, and we can evaluate the effects of political centralization almost in isolation. The centralization and reorganization of the economic base, decisively accelerated by Andrianampoinimérina with unusual attention to the ramifications of a whole man-environment system, and the concomitant enlargement of political space, created opportunities for the support of a greatly increased population. In the heartland of Madagascar, political centralization with economic diversification and rural-urban differentiation was in the long run the most effective force in permitting the support of higher densities. Increase in the "volume and density" of society certainly occurred, and with it progressive division of labor and use of land, but it is the integration of the system that permitted differentiation to occur so rapidly and decisively; PPR may have provided one precondition for this integration, but it is not easy to see how it can be regarded as a cause of the innovations.

"Survivances" and "Organization Moderne": The Limits of "Involution"

More common than the Imérina experience has been the direct impact of an external world-wide economic and political system on a local system through colonialism. This has created not an integrated transformation of a system, but the imposition of an industrial sector alongside and impinging on an agricultural sector in the manner of the "dual society." This situation, first analyzed in strongly negative terms by Boeke, has since given rise to an extensive theoretical literature (32: 274-344; 44: passim). The classic ground of sociological, economic, financial, and technological dualism is Indonesia, and especially Java, around which some of the most important contributions to this discussion have been made.

This is not the place to take issue with some assumptions of dual economy theory, in particular the assumptions not only of Boeke but also of later writers, such as Hagen, on the role of motivation in the agricultural sector; Higgins deals with these fairly effectively, but his own substitution of technological dualism may also overdraw the sectoral contrast. Two aspects of dual economy theory are of particular concern here: first, the supposed effect of industrial investment in launching population explosions; second, the consequent damping effect on incentive to substitute capital for labor in the agricultural sector, or to vary the technical coefficients and so improve labor-productivity in the industrial sector.

JAVA

In Java the population explosion began early in the nineteenth century in the central and east-central parts of the island where sugar plantations were first established and the "culture system" was first put into operation; it spread over the rest of the island and into other parts of Indonesia along with the expanding intrusion of the industrial sector. The policy of the Dutch was to avoid disrupting the culture of the native people, but rather to use this culture by calling contributions of cash crops from the agricultural sector to feed the trade generated initially in the industrial sector; to pry salable products out of the Javanese economy without modifying the structure of the rural society. The effect was to create a dependence on money, and to facilitate major population expansion, perhaps by varying diet, perhaps by creating means of spreading consumption more evenly over the year, perhaps by improving the trading network by which food could be distributed, perhaps from response to rising demand for labor, perhaps from causes not understood. The expansion was at just about such a rate as to ensure that while per hectare production of both food and cash crops increased greatly, per capita production remained about static right through into modern times.

All this was done as capital input went mainly into the industrial sector, and the expansion of production in the agricultural sector depended more and more exclusively on increasing inputs of labor. Thus we have in rural Java the remarkable social response to rising PPR which Geertz terms "agricultural involution." The social system was not disrupted or torn apart; rather it was steadily driven in on itself. This was possible because the foundation of the system was the terraced pond-field, an ecosystem of great stability, and with a remarkably elastic response to additional inputs of labor. Sugar, grown in rotation with rice on the terraces, seems positively to have improved soil conditions for rice, but does not have the same capacity to absorb additional labor remuneratively. As a consequence the internal arrangements for spreading access to resources, which should fade under the impact of political centralization, in fact became more elaborate in Java. Corporate land-holding, normally weak or absent in areas of permanent cultivation, was here strengthened by the dominance of the companies over the peasant: by constant reallocation of land the companies could plan sugar cultivation in economic units, while individuals still had access to wet pond-fields for rice (27: 47-123).

The social effect of agricultural involution was thus to mesh the work and land arrangements of the village ever more closely as population increased, so that:

> the productive system . . . developed . . . therefore, into a dense web of finely spun work rights and work responsibilities spread, like the reticulate veins of the hand, through the whole body of the village land. A man will let out a part of his one hectare to a tenant —or to two or three—while at the same time seeking tenancies on the lands of other men, thus balancing his obligation to give work (to his relatives, to his dependents, or even to his close friends

and neighbors) against his own subsistence requirements. . . . In share tenancy the ever-driven wet-rice village found the means by which to divide its growing economic pie into a greater number of traditionally fixed pieces and so to hold its enormous population at a comparatively very homogenous, if grim, level of living [27: 99-100].

The elasticity of the ecological system thus facillitated "flexibility within fixity" in the allocation of rights to resources; though average productivity of a unit of labor declined, marginal productivity continued to remain above zero, and elaboration of interpersonal relationships of mutual aid and indebtedness continued to keep the whole system viable. Integration into a wider economy was a part of this process, indeed the principal cause, but in Java integration led to differentiation only between sectors; differentiation within the agricultural sector was squeezed down by the equalization of poverty.

In 1930 the sugar market collapsed, and for nearly 40 years Java has been subjected to an unending series of upheavals and disasters. It seems involution has continued, deepened, and spread, and that despite changes of ownership and personnel, dualism has also persisted (27: 124-43). But there has also been abundant evidence of stress, in the burgeoning population of the towns, the economic hyperinflation coupled with the scarcity of rice, and perhaps in the savagery against communists and Chinese that followed the attempted coup of 1965. Population densities now exceed 500/km² over a widening area of rural Java and locally exceed 2000/km², and there is mounting evidence of saturation in the most crowded districts where increase cannot be accommodated by any amount of agricultural involution.

The Javanese situation arises from a particular combination of external innovations upon an existing man-environment system characterized by unusual ecological stability and elasticity of return to labor. But the form of response is not unique to Java, nor to similar ecological situations. Involution implies an elaboration of existing mechanisms governing access to resources in order to accommodate a greater number of persons within the system, without revolutionary changes in economic production and organization. Given this wider interpretation, we can also recognize elements of involution among the acephalous and homogenous societies discussed earlier in the paper, though it is clear that this is by no means the only response. We can also recognize involution in a society which is wholly neolocal, which has come into being in a hitherto unoccupied area as a consequence of colonial development, but which nonetheless has evolved mechanisms governing access to resources which arise in part from the areas of origin of the immigrant populations, but have developed in the context of a monetized system depending on cash agriculture and wage labor.

MAURITIUS

Mauritius, in the western Indian Ocean, was initially populated largely with the aid of slaves bought on the Madagascar coast, and within 130 years of the beginning of permanent settlement in 1735, cultivation had already extended roughly to limits it did not surpass until after 1960; crude population density had already reached nearly 200/km². A cane-sugar plantation system evolved in the late eighteenth century and flourished in the early nineteenth century, using slave labor; when slavery was abolished in 1833 the plantations were able to import indentured labor from India and continued with little structural change until the 1880's. Thereafter indentured migration halted, and many plantations were partly or wholly fragmented into small holdings. To-day about 70 per cent of cultivated land is still owned by companies and estates, though a major part of this is worked by tenants and share-farmers. The rural population is over-whelmingly Hindu-Indian, though in some areas there is also a significant Muslim-Indian minority. The *Creoles*, mixed-blood descendants of the slaves, free-coloreds and other pre-1833 elements, participate little in the sugar industry, but are active in fishing, in subsidiary agricultural enterprises, and also in towns (7; 13; 14; 41; 55).

All land is thus held under registered title, and access to work is significant to a much greater number of Mauritians than is access to land. The present organization of Mauritian rural society, through which this access is largely achieved, reflects both In-dian origins, transmitted through the planta-tion labor-lines to the straggling *morcelle-ment* villages, and also the money economy that has been dominant in Mauritius from the outset.

The Mauritian village is frequently only an aggregation of scattered houses linked together by lanes and paths, and generally with a core along a motorable road; most villages are served by bus, and hence linked with the group of towns in the northwest of the island whence the bus services radiate. Villages are often internally differentiated between different communities—Hindu and Muslim, sects and castes of Hindus, northern and southern Indians speaking different lan-guages, small numbers of *Creoles* and Chi-nese. The last-named group are almost in-variably shopkeepers, and some shops are also run by Indians; shopkeepers operate on a rolling-debt system known as *roule-ment*, and most of the clientele is perma-nently in debt to the shopkeeper. The shop-keeper in turn is in a *roulement* relationship with the merchants, wholesalers, and large money-lenders in the towns.

Most villagers depend either wholly or mainly on wage employment on the estates. This is organized through a job-contractor or *sirdar*, who receives the pay from the estates, and generally advances it to his workers, who are thus in a *roulement* rela-tionship toward him, and he in turn to the estate. The work force organized by a *sirdar* is generally drawn from among his own kinsmen, affines, neighbors, members of the same caste or of the same community group or *baitka*. Also in the village may be Indian small planters who also serve as middlemen in financial transactions, and offer loans for weddings and feasts, for capital to run small-holdings, and similar needs, especially to their own share-cropping tenantry, and again often on a *roulement* basis. Mutual indebted-ness thus extends throughout the village, be-tween widely scattered kin and affines in different villages, and between the villages and the towns: its ramifications run verti-cally and laterally through almost the whole dimension of the Mauritian economy (5, 6, 7).

The system of mutual support is struc-tured in a number of ways. The first level is that of ethnic group and religion, and here elements of dualism remain present. Most of the larger sugar estates, and the principal commercial houses with their ex-tensive subsidiary enterprises remain in the hands of European families, themselves closely linked to one another cognatically and affinally, and with financial connections extending outside Mauritius. Formerly this small population sector, which controlled the sugar industry, overseas commerce, and finance, also staffed most senior positions in the civil service not occupied by expatriates, and exercised great influence on govern-ment. Over a period of at least 90 years, but with rapid recent acceleration, this once exclusive land, money, and power sector has been invaded and undermined in many ways. There are now substantial Indian holdings in the estate and manufacturing side of the sugar industry, in commerce and finance (the latter especially, but not exclusively Muslim), and in the course of constitutional changes that began in 1947 and led to independence in 1968, political power and patronage have passed mainly into Indian hands. Prolonged periods of depression in the sugar industry brought many Europeans financially into the hands of Indian moneylenders, and the former sharp economic dualism has been deeply eroded.

Retail trade is dominated by the Chinese almost throughout the island, but especially in rural areas. Not only commercial, but also kin links run outward from the compact Chinese quarter in the capital, Port Louis, to all parts of the island. Certain aspects of the island-wide economy are dominated by tight "rings" of well-organized operators: Gujarati and Muslim financiers, a ring of Muslims butchers and meat-traders, and so on. At the village level castes remain endogamous, and in addition most Hindus practise the village-exogamy that most brought from northern India: kinship and affinal links thus become spread across the island, and are very widely reckoned. These relationships are of great importance in obtaining work at all levels, and the same general principles of mutual aid, which operate at village level for recruitment to the cane-gangs, operate also on an island-wide basis for recruitment of semi-educated young men in commerce and the civil service. Not surprisingly, the same practices have extended into politics in modern times. But kin and affinal links are not the whole story: there is also the intricate web of financial indebtedness that cross-cuts all groups, operating through a financial hierarchy that binds together the economy of the whole island.

This intricate system developed during a long period following the cessation of massive immigration in the 1880's, during which population growth was slow and the available work force fluctuated only within quite narrow limits, without much or any expansion (12: 114-16, 33: 4). Money was scarce, and there have been periods of extreme hardship as during the 1930's when the average wage of a male laborer fell to U.S. $0.10 per day. However, work was fairly readily available, and there were fairly regular seasonal shortages of labor during the cane-crushing season. The individual villager or town-dweller (who quite often worked in rural occupations) thus had some measure of freedom and mobility (6: 214). This was horizontal mobility, for vertical mobility was limited by the control exercised by particular ethnic and other groups over recruitment into certain fields of employment. Thus the European Franco-Mauritians saw to it that almost all higher managerial and technical positions in the sugar industry were filled by members of their own group (8: 50), and the light-colored *gens-de-couleur* exercised a similar if less tight control over most responsible and skilled positions in government and the professions. This sort of control broke down somewhat during a period of prosperity and general expansion that followed the Second World War, when urbanization was accelerated, and the general area around the towns received many migrants wishing to participate in new employment possibilities (14).

This seeming opening toward widened economic freedom in employment was, however, short-lived. Population began to grow very much more rapidly than hitherto after 1945 from a complex of causes, of which the most important was the dramatic reduction in the death rate brought about by the total elimination of malaria. After 1958, and with much greater impact in the 1960's, the population of working age began to increase very rapidly (52: 55ff). The potential work force is now growing by some 6000 per annum and at a rising rate. Even allowing for the fact that the economically active proportion of both males and females is unusually low in Mauritius, it is expected that the potential work-force will rise from 187,400 in 1962 to 270,000 in 1972. Overall population density, presently about 400/km^2 is expected to reach 800/km^2 during the later 1980's (1: 52-56). The 1962 population density on cultivated land was already 752/km^2, and despite increases in the extent of cultivated land by the development of the high country for tea, and some extension of irrigation, will certainly surpass 1000/km^2 in less than a generation.

Prospects of expanding employment at a sufficient rate are slight. The sugar industry employs about 30 per cent of the active work-force, and its level of employment has been almost static for many years: improvements in production have had to be made with an eye to reducing costs and increasing efficiency in line with overseas competitors, and have been achieved almost wholly by increasing the input of capital, while labor input per ton of output has declined. Other agricultural activities are small employers, and some subsist only with the aid of subsidies; others, such as the production of potatoes and dairy produce, might be expanded by action to control imports, but only at the price of an increase in the cost of living. Major efforts have been made since 1960 to expand industrial employment, but the limited capacity of the local market is a deterrent to investment, and though the spread of small factories is impressive, its total effect on employment is not great. Commerce and services have tended to grow with population, while Government itself is a major employer and unquestionably employs personnel to a level not warranted by the demands of efficiency: even the extensive output of government publications—a boon to the re-

search worker—reflects this overemployment in Government.

In a survey conducted during the intercrop season of 1958, it was shown that 15 per cent of the economically active population was unemployed: at this time there was probably still reasonably full employment during the crop season, for the level of employment in a whole range of activities fluctuates with the fluctuation in the sugar industry. The involuted system of mutual aid in seeking work continued to operate as numbers rose, but encountered the sharp limits to employment capacity of the major industry, and began to fail. The cost of outdoor relief employment had been growing steadily for a number of years, and in 1963 public assistance became the largest single head of Government expenditure. By the middle 1960's, Government was employing "relief workers" in large and growing numbers, and using them on public works including clearance of high ground for timber and tea, but also such surprising projects as a freeway across the island. Over 40,000 were in this sort of relief employment by 1967.

Since it is no longer possible for all men to find work through the customary channels, Government has had to intervene on a larger scale, both by comprehensive planning and by direct employment of surplus labor. But the scope for use of such labor is limited, and intergroup conflict for access to work has begun seriously to emerge. Riots in 1968 were generated partly by conflict between groups over access to work in the Port Louis docks; the achievement of independence in 1968 with an Indian-dominated government—albeit within a multi-racial Labour Party—has accelerated already heavy emigration of the Franco-Mauritians and the *gens-de-couleur:* since relaxation of Australian immigration controls in 1967 Australia has become the principal outlet for these people, many of whom are skilled and well educated. In Government service, non-Indians express the certainty that the top jobs will soon go exclusively to Indians. Pressures to change the personnel at the top in the sugar industry can be forecast with certainty, whatever the reaction of Government.

Political independence creates a new dimension in an island micro-state that may be disintegrative:

> After independence, when there is no longer any recourse to Whitehall and the overseas servants have left, the political decisions are left squarely with those who have known each other since childhood [56: 34].

In a plural society suffering keen and growing competition for access to the means of livelihood, and with little prospect of developing new economic activities on a sufficient scale, there is serious risk that sectional interests will be favored to the detriment of those whose loyalties are divided; like outsiders among the Enga, or Chinese in Indonesia, the mainly non-Indian opposition who voted for continued association with Britain, rather than independence, at the 1967 election, might find themselves squeezed out as the dominant group seeks to obtain a larger share of the economic pie. In Mauritius there has not been overmuch encouragement for the opposition to hope otherwise: faced with a declining per-capita income and a mounting body of unemployed voters, politicians vulnerable to local and group pressures too close to be escaped have not dared to propose draconian action to cope with the national problem, such as a change in diet from ever-more-costly imported rice to locally grown root crops, or penal taxes on large families to encourage the slowly growing birth-control movement. There seems to be a kind of euphoria, an expectation that external aid in some form will save the day. Meanwhile, certain politicians have encouraged the electorate to believe that this is just another of the cyclic bad periods that the island has experienced in the past. Even the 1962 census, and other ominous documents, remain unpublished.

Toward a Synthesis

In Java and Mauritius, we find the "survivances" to be extraordinarily effective in coping with rising PPR up to a certain level. In Java the labor-elasticity of the wet-rice system permitted the support at a minimal level of grinding poverty of very high population densities in a homogenous rural society. In Mauritius the system of mutual indebtedness through *roulement* has certainly continued to involute; but mutual aid in obtaining access to work has run foul of labor-inelasticity in the principal industry. In each case the problem was ultimately shifted to the center of the state, by massive drift to the towns and other migration in Java, by the need to employ some 20 per cent of the work force on relief in Mauritius. The larger territorial space of Indonesia offered some leeway; the maintenance of a large standing army perhaps offered more, and this army has ultimately become the effective Government. In Mauritius, conflict over work and the democratic processes themselves in a small island are likely to throw increasing political influence into the hands of the unemployed, and whatever leaders they will follow.

There are common processes at work in the man-environment systems of all this wide and contrasted range of societies. If we consider them as whole systems, among which increasing population is a major disturbance of the steady state, and focus attention more on equifinal process than on empirical uniqueness, these common processes become clearer. The variables emphasized in this discussion have included: territorial space, labor-elasticity of the production system, dualism as a limiting factor, mechanism for restricting access to resources, differentiation within the society, the effects of integration and centralization. Some of these may be grouped. Integration and centralization widen territorial space, except where this is physically limited; dualism may be an externally imposed form of differentiation, but it is linked with the internal differentiation of the society; flexibility and restriction are essentially alternative paths; labor-elasticity of the production system is both effect and cause of other variables.

Can we find any simplistic way through all this maze? Is there any means by which we can approach more closely an operative measure of PPR in relation here to society, rather than to environment? If we could identify any society in which *all* institutional means of coping with the volume of numbers had failed, leading to anarchy and chaos, it might be easier to answer this question in the affirmative, but this is not so. Tikopia had a fine balance between numbers and resources in the pre-colonial situation, but the checks seem to have been maintained successfully for a long time; colonial rule has created new outlets for emigration and has brought new means of subsistence; increase in numbers has caused Tikopians to turn to restriction of access to resources, but this may be conditioned by the fact that other means of livelihood, not necessarily on the island, are now available. In Java and Mauritius redistribution of people and resources through the central state has thus far been able to take over from the level at which internal "flexibility within fixity" has become inadequate to cope with rising population. Enga awareness of PPR causes them to act restrictively, yet there is evidence that much the same sort of flexibility as we find in Chimbu and Bena in fact continues in operation; further, we cannot be

sure that this restrictive outlook stems only from PPR, and not also from other causes. We can empirically identify levels within a society at which existing means have proved inadequate, and have precipitated change; we can even identify at least one case where this realization has led to hopelessness, rather than innovation. But anything we might call "social breakdown" cannot anywhere be identified from this cause. Elements of flexibility continue everywhere.

In common with several of the writers quoted, I have sometimes used "flexibility" as a shorthand for "mechanisms for flexible distribution of access to resources," and have used "restriction" as the converse of these—the mechanisms that could or should lead to fixity in access to resources. We have seen repeatedly the existence of "flexibility within fixity," "flexibility that the rules would seem to prevent," means by which "land not used by its holders may be put to use, on temporary title, by whosoever wishes to cultivate it."

Flexibility can be attained in many ways, but essentially by means that are summed up in Polanyi's threefold classification of economic systems: reciprocity, redistribution, and exchange, here extended into a wider area of operation. Reciprocal flexibility is the normal mode in homogenous, acephalous societies such as Tikopia, Bena, Chimbu, and Enga, but is also the mode in rural Java and in job-seeking in Mauritius. Redistributive flexibility arises from political centralization, and is seen *par excellence in* Andrianampoinimérina's Imérina and at least in theory in the Marxist scheme of things. It happened in the "New Deal," in development finance for colonies by such organizations as the Commonwealth Development and Welfare Fund or *Fonds d'Investissements pour le Développement-Economique et Social d'Outre-Mer;* on a larger scale in all foreign aid programs; it has been adopted in Mauritius, and attenuated elements of redistributive flexibility can also be found in the conservationist and other functions of the clan chiefs in Tikopia. In another sense of redistribution, the creation of networks, markets, and town facilitates the redistribution both of goods and of population under the auspices of the state. Flexibility through exchange is achieved through relationships between landlord and tenant, by the buying and selling of land, and by the employment of labor. *Roulement* in Mauritius is flexibility achieved through the exchange economy but having elements of both reciprocity and redistribution through the central finance institutions as well.

By contrast, restriction is achieved through all forms of ownership and control of resources, whether by individuals or defined groups of individuals. It is also achieved between groups of measures to restrict either migration, or the access to fields of work and enterprise controlled by particular defined groups, be these territorial or vested with control over some non-territorial part of the whole economy. Restriction is present in all the societies discussed, whether in the discouragement of outsiders in Enga clans and Tikopian lineages, in the exclusion of the Javanese peasant from the controlling sectors of the economic system in which they were required to participate, in the Franco-Mauritian control over the key positions in the sugar industry and at numerous other levels in the Mauritian system, in the control exercised by Mérina chiefs and nobles over certain *fokon'olona* which the flexibility decrees of Andrianampoinimérina were designed to reduce. It is found, too, in the practices of organized labor, the immigration policies of very many countries, and in all forms of monopoly and monopsony.

Abstracting "flexibility" and "restriction" from the varied means of their operation, then, we might be able to set up two opposing continua, or a "flexibility-restriction" matrix, within which societies might be placed at any point in time. Though any form of quantification, however approximate and however purely ordinal, involves great uncertainty in this highly subjective field, the difficulties are not notably greater than those inherent in the "behavioral matrix" recently proposed (48). Very tentatively, such a "flexibility-restriction" matrix is illustrated from the data here presented in

Figure 9-1, and might be found to be of some service both in generalizing the response of society to PPR and also the relation of population numbers and growth to the actual operation of the social and political institutions of a society.

With this matrix, tentative and perhaps tendentious though it is, I conclude. It is essentially an empirical device, but also a device for the summation of a range of empirical evidence within a theoretical framework. Doubtless it could be greatly improved by use of measures that would reduce its subjectivity; but it might serve to focus attention on the importance of social and political institutions in the whole system that is affected by such changes as rising population, or the urge to economic development.

I conclude here because there is no real conclusion to this argument. I have perhaps demonstrated in the field of PPR what Lewis says for the field of economic development, that

> institutions promote or restrict growth according to the protection they afford to effort, according to the opportunities they provide for specialization and according to the freedom of maneouvre they permit (38: 7).

Perhaps I might also have helped to demonstrate that PPR is seldom a wholly independent variable, that it is but one of a whole group of forces operating on any so-

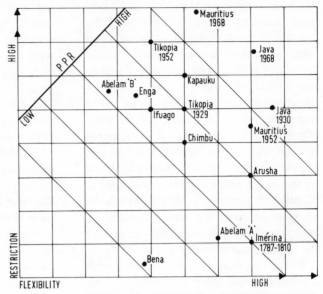

Fig. 9-1. RESTRICTION-FLEXIBILITY MATRIX
(For explanation, see p. 149 in text.)

ciety. Perhaps it is not even this, but merely an expression of a condition that is but the resultant of a whole group of forces at any point in time, a group that includes population growth, but also all innovations, culture, technology, and perception of resources and needs. Seen as a resultant, it would be helpful if we could identify it in precise terms, but to understand it we must understand the forces that create it, and which interact on each other through it. Social and political institutions are among these forces. But as for what the resultant PPR itself is, maybe we might paraphrase an African member of the now defunct parliament of the former Federation of Rhodesia and Nyasaland who said: "Where is this thing? [he spoke of racial partnership]; we have been searching all through the thick bush to know exactly where it lies."

REFERENCES

(1) Edith Adams: Evaluation of Demographic Data and Future Population Growth in Mauritius: 1962-1987 (New York, United Nations, 1966).

(2) J. A. Barnes: Agnation among the Enga: a Review Article, *Oceania*, Vol. 38, 1967, pp. 33-43.

(3) R. F. Barton: Ifugao Law, *University of California Publications in American Archaeology and Ethnology*, Vol. 15, 1919, pp. 1-186.

(4) R. F. Barton: Ifugao Economics, *University of California Publications in Archaeology and Ethnology*, Vol. 15, 1922, pp. 385-446.

(5) B. Benedict: Factionalism in Mauritian Villages, *British Journal of Sociology*, Vol. 8, 1957, pp. 328-42.

(6) B. Benedict: Cash and Credit in Mauritius, *South African Journal of Economics,* Vol. 26, 1958, pp. 213-21.

(7) B. Benedict: Indians in a Plural Society: a Report on Mauritius, *Colonial Research Studies No. 34* (London, Colonial Office, 1961).

(8) B. Benedict, ed.: Problems of Smaller Territories (London, 1967).

(9) F. Benet: Explosive Markets: the Berber Highlands, in: K. Polanyi, C. M. Arensberg, and H. W. Pearson, eds.: Trade and Market in the Early Empires: Economies in History and Theory (Glencoe, Ill., 1957), pp. 188-217.

(10) E. Boserup: The Conditions of Agricultural Growth: the Economics of Agrarian Change under Population Pressure (London, 1965).

(11) W. D. Borrie, R. Firth, and J. Spillius: The Population of Tikopia, 1929 and 1952, *Population Studies,* Vol. 10, 1957, pp. 229-52.

(12) H. C. Brookfield: Mauritius: Demographic Upsurge and Prospect, *Population Studies,* Vol. 11, 1957, pp. 102-22.

(13) H. C. Brookfield: Pluralism and Geography in Mauritius, *Geographical Studies,* Vol. 5, 1958, pp. 3-19.

(14) H. C. Brookfield: Population Distribution in Mauritius: an Inquiry into the Determinants of Distribution in a Tropical Sugar Island, *Journal of Tropical Geography,* Vol. 13, 1959, pp. 1-22.

(15) H. C. Brookfield and Paula Brown: Struggle for Land: Agriculture and Group Territories among the Chimbu of the New Guinea Highlands (Melbourne, 1963).

(16) P. Brown and H. C. Brookfield: Chimbu Settlement and Residence: a Study of Patterns, Trends and Idiosyncracy, *Pacific Viewpoint,* Vol. 8, 1967, pp. 119-51.

(17) Bureau of Statistics: Territory of Papua and New Guinea. Report on Intensive Agricultural Surveys in the Chimbu Survey Area 1962-64, *and* Report on Intensive Agricultural Surveys in the Wabag Subdistrict 1962-64 (Konedobu, 1967), mimeographed.

(18) L. Chevalier: Madagascar: Populations et Ressources, *I.N.E.D. Travaux et Documents No. 15* (Paris, 1952).

(19) G. Condominas: Fokon'olona et Collectivités Rurales en Imérina (Paris, 1960).

(20) H. Deschamps: *Histoire de Madagascar* (Paris, 1960).

(21) G. Donque: Le Zoma de Tananarive: Etude Géographique d'un Marché Urbain (Première Partie), *Madagascar: Revue de Géographie,* No. 7, 1965, pp. 93-227.

(22) E. Durkheim: The Division of Labor in Society (Glencoe, Ill., 1947).

(23) R. Firth: We, the Tikopia (London, 1936).

(24) R. Firth: Primitive Polynesian Economy (London, 1939).

(25) R. Firth: Social Change in Tikopia (London, 1959).

(26) M. Fortes and E. E. Evans-Pritchard, eds.: African Political Systems (London, 1940).

(27) C. Geertz: Agricultural Involution: the Process of Ecological Change in Indonesia (Berkeley and Los Angeles, 1963).

(28) P. George: Introduction à l'Etude Géographique de la Population du Monde, *I.N.E.D. Travaux et Documents No. 14* (Paris, 1951).

(29) M. Gluckman: The Kingdom of the Zulu in South Africa, in: M. Fortes and E. E. Evans-Pritchard, eds.: African Political Systems (London, 1940), pp. 25-55.

(30) R. F. Gray: Introduction, in: R. F. Gray and P. H. Gulliver, eds.: The Family Estate in Africa: Studies in the Role of Property in Family Structure and Lineage Continuity (London, 1964), pp. 1-33.

(31) P. H. Gulliver: The Evolution of Arusha Trade, in: P. Bohannan and G. Dalton, eds.: Markets in Africa (Evanston, 1963), pp. 250-84.

(32) B. Higgins: Economic Development: Principles, Problems, and Policies (London and New York, 1959).

(33) W. A. B. Hopkin: Policy for Economic Development in Mauritius: Objectives and Principles, *Mauritius Legislative Council Sessional Paper No. 6 of 1966* (Port Louis, 1965).

(34) Diana R. Howlett: A Decade of Change in the Goroka Valley, New Guinea: Land Use and Development in the 1950s (Ph.D. dissertation, Australian National University, 1962), multilithed.

(35) H. Humbert and G. Cours-Darne: Notice de la Carte Madagascar: Carte Internationale du Tapis Végétal et des Conditions Écologiques à 1:1,000,000, *Extrait des Travaux de la Section Scientifique et l'Institut Française de Pondichéry, Hors Serie No. 6* (Pondichéry, 1965).

(36) L. L. Langness: Some Problems in the Conceptualization of Highlands Social Structures, *American Anthropologist*, Vol. 66, *Special Number, New Guinea, the Central Highlands*, pp. 162-82.

(37) D. A. M. Lea: Abelam Land and Sustenance: Swidden Horticulture in an Area of High Population Density, Maprik, New Guinea (Ph.D. dissertation, Australian National University, 1964), multilithed.

(38) W. A. Lewis: The Theory of Economic Growth (London, 1955).

(39) A. Maude: Population, Land and Livelihood in Tonga (Ph.D. dissertation, Australian National University, 1965), multilithed.

(40) M. McArthur: Analysis of the Genealogy of a Mae-Enga Clan, *Oceania*, Vol. 37, 1967, pp. 281-85.

(41) J. E. Meade et al. The Economic and Social Structure of Mauritius, *Mauritius Legislative Council, Sessional Paper No. 7 of 1961* (London, 1961).

(42) M. J. Meggitt: The Enga of the New Guinea Highlands, *Oceania*, Vol. 28, 1958, pp. 253-330.

(43) M. J. Meggitt: The Lineage System of the Mae Enga of New Guinea (Edinburgh, 1965).

(44) H. Myint: The Economics of Developing Countries (London, 1964).

(45) K. Polanyi: The Economy as Instituted Process, in: K. Polanyi, C. M. Arensberg, and H. W. Pearson, eds.: Trade and Market in the Early Empires: Economies in History and Theory (Glencoe, Ill., 1957), pp. 243-70.

(46) L. Pospisil: Kapauku Papuans and their Law, *Yale University Publications in Anthropology No. 54* (New Haven, 1958).

(47) L. Pospisil: Kapauku Papuan Economy, *Yale University Publications in Anthropology No. 69* (New Haven, 1963).

(48) A. Pred: Behavior and Location: Foundations for a Geographic and Dynamic Location Theory, Part I, *Lund Studies in Geography, Ser. B., Human Geography,* No. 27, 1967.

(49) C. Robequain: Madagascar et les Bases Dispersées de l'Union Française (Paris, 1958).

(50) J. Spillius: Natural Disaster and Political Crisis in a Polynesian Society, *Human Relations,* Vol. 10, 1957, pp. 3-28.

(51) F. Standing: The Tribal Division of the Hova Malagasy, *Antananarivo Annual,* No. 11, 1887, pp. 354-66.

(52) R. M. Titmuss, B. Abel-Smith, and T. Lynes: Social Policies and Population Growth in Mauritius, *Mauritius Legislative Council Sessional Paper No. 6 of 1960* (London, 1961).

(53) United Nations, Department of Social Affairs, Population Division: The Determinants and Consequences of Population Trends: a Summary of the Findings of Studies on the Relationship between Population Change and Economic and Social Systems, *Population Studies,* No. 17 (New York, United Nations, 1953).

(54) E. W. Waddell: The Dynamics of a New Guinea Highlands Agricultural System (Paper delivered at the Fortieth Congress of the Australian and New Zealand Association for the Advancement of Science, 1968), mimeographed.

(55) H. J. Walker: Overpopulation in Mauritius: a Survey, *Geographical Review,* Vol. 54, 1964, pp. 243-48.

(56) D. P. J. Wood: The Smaller Territories: Some Political Considerations, in: B. Benedict, ed.: Problems of Smaller Territories (London, 1967), pp. 23-34.

We have no reservations in stressing the importance of the physical environment in any study of population pressure on resources. This is so not only directly where physical resources are involved, but also to varying degrees indirectly in any consideration of social resources. In the developing world particularly the physical environment is an inescapable fact of life.

Geographers, caught in a flight from unreasonable physical determinism with which their discipline has been associated in the past, have tended to underplay the importance of the environment in population-resource relationships. Far too little attention has been given to it as a vital factor, and often there has been a failure to recognize, let alone an attempt to understand, its complexity. The variables which should be considered in an attempt to reach understanding are many, and it is true that a paucity of data may inhibit their analysis.

Geographers have not been as neglectful of the physical environment as scholars from other disciplines involved in planning for development. Economists, whose decisions are eminently important to this field, are especially prone to give scant attention to environmental factors in their theories and models. We would point out the dangers of thinking in terms of countries with "uniform soils and climate" (*Boserup*). Such generalizations have no validity in fact at whatever scale they are applied, and they are likely to lead to disaster if employed in practice. It is better to think in terms of "the incomprehensible complexity of the environment" (*Vogt*), making every endeavor to reach the maximum understanding. *Vogt* stresses that "every piece of land is unique," and warns against the dangers of identifying one area too closely with another. While the value of valid comparisons and useful analogies cannot be denied, there is evidence to demonstrate that experience cannot always be directly transposed from one area to another because *similar* environmental conditions *seem* to exist in each. The need to understand basic aspects of the environment for planning for development is recognized in the work of a non-geographer like *McLoughlin*. He describes himself as "an operational economist," and his views are conditioned by considerable and varied field experience which too few economists possess.

The potential of the physical environment is discussed by *Tricart* and *Porter*. *Tricart* questions the concept of physical potential in the strict sense. He emphasizes the need to assess the balance between positive and negative aspects of the environment, which present respectively bases and limitations for development. These, he argues, can only be determined in the socio-political context in which development is to take place. Physical as well as human features can be utilized as resources for development only if there is an effective will as well as the means to effect this transla-

154

tion. The emphasis is somewhat different in *Porter's* exploration of the potential of the environment with reference to Africa; though he is concerned not with deterministic influences but with the man-use opportunities the environment may offer. He indicates several strategies for the study and assessment of environmental potential—bio-physical, agro-meteorological, ecological, and agro-economic. Of these he suggests that the ecological approach might be initiated immediately and is the one likely to involve the least cost. The complexity of assessment is emphasized, and attention drawn to the desirability of interdisciplinary work in making it.

The view of *Tricart* and *Porter* that the dimensions of environmental potential are as much culturally as physically determined is underlined and illustrated in other papers. Landscape change and evolution, which result from the exploitation of potential, may be understood from a study of the interaction of physical and cultural processes working through time as well as space (*Webb*). These produce markedly different results in differing physical regions, each with its particular problems. Exploitation of the potential of the physical environment may be achieved by methods of *extraction* and of *adaptation* (*Kay*). The former methods are most common in the least developed economies, while the latter prevails among the most developed. As well as being important in assessing the state of existing population-resource relationships, the mode of exploitation may have particular bearing upon whether the basic elements of the physical environment are being deteriorated, maintained, or even being improved, as a result of human use. Moreover, many economies in the developing world involve "polyfunctional behavior" in their exploitation of the potential of the physical environment. These economies are based upon both extraction and adaptation, with the emphases varying not only between one economy and another but also within economies at different times. Failure to take these variations into account may lead to inaccurate assessments of both the quantity and quality of resources.

The tendency to take a limited view of the ways in which the environment may be used has produced a concentration of attention upon agricultural production. Probably this shortcoming is due in part to interpretations largely derived from agriculture as it is now practiced in the more developed parts of the world—an example of unsatisfactory direct transfer of experience. To be useful the transfer should be made with historical perspective, which gives careful consideration to the growth patterns of economies in developed areas.

Tricart points out that it is difficult to clearly identify particular stages in the development of population-resource relationships, since the majority of the factors involved are relative and not absolute. This is a recurring theme in the essays in this volume. In developing countries, in economies directly dependent upon exploitation of the environment (through extraction and/or adaptation), the range of understanding and expertise is limited; and it is possible for a critical stage to be reached before there are any clear signs of deterioration in the environmental base. *De Planhol* draws attention to the difficulties of making such an assessment in mountain environments, and suggests that the evidence may come more clearly from changes in the ways people live (e.g. changes in pastoral movements and the departure of some members of communities as seasonal laborers). If, when such stages are reached, the pressures continue, the best that can be hoped for is a situation of relative economic and social stagnation (*Tricart*), and, as *Kay* puts it, some "progress must be made in order to stand still." The continued maintenance of such situations can be only at the expense of the environment, and will eventually lead to permanent deterioration. Opinion on this will clearly vary with experience and attitude. The conservationist viewpoint is expressed by *Vogt,* while *McLoughlin* (in discussion) argued the need to destroy existing resources in order to achieve development, on the assumption, of course, that such destructive activity would be adequately planned and executed. *Vogt* writes of a situation in Central America that is "deteriorating rather than developing" with a trend that may be irreversible, though *Sandner* questioned this extreme view in a later discussion.

It can be pointed out from past experience that other factors have intervened to prevent extreme deterioration in the environment. However, these have often involved only the transfer of problems, or the development of new problems elsewhere. Such situations are considered in the next group of papers which deal with migrations and urban growth. It is doubtful if there is scope for such transfers and changes to continue indefinitely, for this would inevitably lead to rapid and permanent degradation of the physical base.

In all these approaches there is no suggestion that there should be a return to environmental determinism. But we do plead the need for environmental realism. Geographers would be failing in a task clearly theirs, if they did not press more strongly the importance of the physical environment as a dependent and an independent variable in population-resource relationships. In developing countries, as elsewhere, while the physical environment is permissive, offering potential and possibilities of manipulation, it is also all-pervasive and its influences are inescapable. The physical environment has been underrated in the past; it may be ignored only at peril at the present and in the future.

10. PHYSICAL ENVIRONMENT AND POPULATION PRESSURE

J. Tricart

Overpopulation can be defined as a function of the relationships between man and environment. These relationships are found in every human society and are, in turn, a function of its social organization, including its political and economic structures, and its level of technical and cultural development. Viewed schematically, three types of situations can occur:

(*a*) *The society promotes a technical-cultural development whereby the environment is more intensively utilized and no deterioration occurs.* It is capable of expanding quantitatively, offering ever greater facilities to all of its members (increased standard of living combined with a demographic growth). This is the situation realized in the "advanced" countries (western and central Europe, North America, and the Soviet Union).

(*b*) *The society is characterized by stagnation or so slow a development that one may consider it quasi-stagnation.* Technical-cultural development is very slow; production means and techniques undergo no significant changes; the ways of using the environment do not change; demographic expansion is possible only by using more space; war, famines, and epidemics bring the population back to a certain level after every period of expansion; and the average population densities fluctuate with time around a certain value that does not greatly change.

(*c*) *The society promotes a development which dangerously exploits the environment, bringing about its deterioration.* One of the best indices for this is a drop in agricultural unit yields, regardless of a reduction in arable territory as related to total agricultural space. The imbalance thus created may stem from too rapid a relative demographic expansion, or from a speculative economy that seeks to remove too many resources from the environment.

In the first case (a), the demographic expansion possible within certain limits is compatible with progress, including a higher standard of living. There exists a certain margin of tolerance. Within this margin, a more rapid increase in population is possible, even desirable. This demographic increase may in fact stimulate growth. Let us consider the example of France since about 1880. The holocaust of 1914-18 caused an inadequacy in demographic growth, which acted as a brake on development. The reaction was pro-natalist policy. In spite of increased growth rates, France absorbed the return of the French from North Africa (more than a million persons) with no difficulty. One may, then, even speak of *underpopulation*. On the basis of this example and within the above general scheme, underpopulation may be defined as a situation in which a more rapid demographic increase leads to acceleration of socioeconomic development (rise in the GNP and the average living standard). Of course, this can involve only an over-all estimate, covering a nation or region endowed with some autonomy. But it can even include failures in partial adjustments. This is the case in France with the immigration of foreign workers seeking jobs relinquished by the French. A situation of this sort, combined with a growth in the GNP,[1] is perhaps one of the most characteristic features of underpopulation.

1. The term **GNP** is used in preference to "living standard" because it permits an estimate of total national economic growth. In stratified societies, living standards may develop in a divergent manner, and vary considerably among

157

The Underpopulated Societies

In societies characterized by underpopulation, pressure on resources as a result of the increasing economic interdependence of the world makes itself felt in terms of unused potentials, unequal development as a result of international exchanges of wealth, and insufficient resources.

(a) *The unused potentials.* As the economic interdependence of the world becomes closer, few resources remained unused. For example, any mineral deposit capable of being worked profitably today is either used or held in reserve. The gold prospector now belongs to the folklore of the nineteenth century. Increases in known reserves of certain mineral products, such as oil, result from the development of exploration techniques, and are not related to the demographic conditions of the countries in which discoveries are being made. Have not certain important deposits been discovered during the course of the last few years in developed, densely populated countries, such as the natural gas of Groningen (Netherlands)?

Potential resources represent a residual state of affairs. In the field of mining, where the labor factor is secondary, the close economic interdependence of the world permits resources to remain untouched only in exceptional cases, i.e. when a sufficiently strong political power can hold them in reserve, or more often, when large companies are interested in keeping them to themselves. But modern mines are heavily mechanized, and there are therefore few direct demographic repercussions. The colonial type of mineral exploitation for the purpose of exporting raw materials is generally not capable of sig-

nificantly modifying demographic pressure. Even in the exceptionally favorable case of the Mauritanian iron mines, where major employment has been generated, the jobs created represent at most one or two years of the demographic surplus. Considered more important is the supply of raw materials to the industrialized countries, thanks to which they can assure their own growth and avoid overpopulation.

By contrast, renewable potentials in agriculture, forests, and pastures remain in certain parts of the world. Political constraints during the past fifty years have reduced demographic interdependencies. Whereas in the second half of the nineteenth century massive migrations from Europe settled and exploited vast agricultural spaces in Siberia, Australasia, and America, thus diminishing the agricultural-forest-pastoral potential (even in sparsely populated regions like the northern forests of Canada and Siberia), these migrations virtually stopped following World War I. Potential resources are today being exploited primarily *within* national boundaries. Gabon, for example, remains empty while a short distance away are the dense population centers of Nigeria. Thus, reserves do remain. Some of them have been given over to concessions whose effects are analogous to those of the mining concessions. Plantations have been created for the purpose of massive exports of tropical products, including quality woods. Although reliance on local labor is greater than in the mines, the economic and demographic consequences are similar. One policy at present is to limit a labor force that becomes too demanding to suit the beneficiaries of a concession (for example, the United Fruit Company plantations in Panama). What happens is that plantations are transformed, under the cover of land reform, if possible, into small farms which continue to sell all products according to previous agreements. The

---

groups as the function of power relations. In France, for example, the living standards of the elderly have not only remained static but have actually fallen in recent years.

company thus maintains specialization of crops and market monopoly, while lessening the risks. Although growth in the employed work force may result, a rise in the standard of living is improbable, and the problem of demographic pressure cannot be considered solved. Such a development, controlled by modifications in the balance of power between large foreign concessions and the local working class, ultimately leads to an increasing depletion of empty land. On the other hand, reserves remain, of necessity, in empty regions, and even have a tendency to multiply in Tropical America (Guianas, Amazonia, Colombia).

The halt in the creation of plantations, because of land reform or nationalization movements, poses complicated problems of internal colonization for countries with vacant lands. These "reserves" are generally difficult to put into use by spontaneous colonization. When the latter develops, it customarily adopts inadequate techniques, ending with the formation of ephemeral pioneering frontiers as a result of the squandering of resources. This is the case in the western Ivory Coast, in Marajo in Brazil, and on the lower Andean slopes overlooking Lake Maracaibo in Venezuela. Most frequently, these areas do not have at their disposal the instruments needed to promote rational colonization (i.e., the difficulties encountered by S.U.D.E.N.E. in Brazil, in its efforts to promote colonization on the borders of Amazonia). The ultimate result is a deterioration of the environment, sometimes accompanied by a demographic regression.

(*b*) *The role of international exchanges of wealth.* Because of the growing imbalance of the terms of trade, economic interdependence on a world scale becomes both the cause and the effect of unequal development, producing a process of absolute retrogression which tends to snowball. Today growth in world commerce leads to an increase in demographic pressure on resources in underdeveloped countries and a decrease in industrialized countries. Industrialized countries are able to supply themselves with raw materials and goods at favorable costs and to export industrial products at advantageous prices. As a result, they are able to maintain a dense population unrelated to local resources, and thus become centers of immigration for the people of the Third World (i.e., Puerto Ricans in New York, West Indians in London and Paris, North Africans in France, Turks, Greeks and Yugoslavs in Germany and Switzerland, and Chinese in Hong Kong). Meanwhile, the demographic pressure on resources in underdeveloped countries steadily increases. One wonders whether such a situation can last. A sudden change in the terms of world exchange could transform underpopulated, industrialized countries into overpopulated countries; it would be felt first in small territories that supply few raw materials and food products (Northwestern Europe). In the United States and even to a greater extent in the U.S.S.R., the complementarity among regions would make it easier to avoid a crisis.

The confusion which this imbalance produces in underdeveloped countries is reflected in the pursuit by certain of their leaders of the myth of industrialization. A poorly conceived industrial system can fetter development by bringing about increased technical and financial dependence on foreign countries, without creating sufficient jobs to alleviate demographic pressure, lowering the cost of manufactured products, or raising the standard of living.

(*c*) *Insufficiency of certain resources.* This particular type of pressure on resources has already appeared in certain underpopulated industrialized countries. Destined to increase, it even now imposes restrictions on development.

For example, the American Megalopolis,

the Parisian agglomeration, the Lorraine metallurgical region, the Ruhr, the Netherlands, and Belgium, for several years now have experienced increasingly frequent spells of water scarcity and are additionally troubled by problems of contamination. A dry summer can force a reduction in industrial activity as well as restrictions on water supplies for personal consumption.

Modern techniques have made it possible to multiply recycling stages after purification or to envision the desalinization of sea water. But water thus obtained is not always suitable for all uses: purified sewage water may be bacteriologically clean, but it may retain a certain unattractive taste; and desalinized water is usually too costly for most uses. Moreover, the depletion of the water supply has increased its cost. And, with the need to mobilize new resources, the price of water has become an important factor in the cost equation, often involving competition. In the Seine Basin, for example, supplementary irrigation, so necessary for agricultural development and more intensive exploitation of the land, is severely restricted because a large part of the flow is needed for urban supplies, industry, navigation, and for carrying sewage. A program of reservoirs designed to increase the minimum-level flow is now being studied. Comparative studies on limitations resulting from insufficient water resources (i.e. Kuwait or Curaçao) are very much needed.

The Countries in Equilibrium (Stagnation)

An endemic phenomenon rarely encountered today—stagnant societies—still persists in a few isolated spots (Yemen before the fall of the Imam, villages in New Guinea, parts of Amazonia, and certain of the Polynesian islands). Prior to the Industrial Revolution, however, societies such as these, characterized by slow, limited technical progress, pre-

vailed throughout the world. The residual situations which they produced often became the points of departure for the dangerous exploitation of the environment which characterizes many overpopulated or overexploited societies.

For a country in equilibrium, maintenance of equilibrium is a condition for its survival since its technical means are limited and possibilities for modification are slight. The study of the major breakdowns of such equilibria in the past would be a particularly fruitful subject for study, one which historians have thus far seriously neglected. Societies in equilibria imply a mediocre vitality, a slow development, hence little flexibility in the face of technical progress. They exist within a context of some technological permanence, and are thus particularly vulnerable to the modern world, which, by contrast, is characterized by a veritable explosion of new techniques.

Because they developed prior to the economic interdependence of the world and under conditions where changes were limited, the essential aim of each society was the self-support of cells of small quantitative significance. The restraints applied to the commerce in grain, the basic food crop in prerevolutionary France, are quite characteristic of such a situation. The relations between populations and resources therefore become established within the boundaries of limited regions, defined by the range of transportation of the period.

This partitioning, derived from limited technical knowledge but maintained by social organization and political power, restricted the scope of areas affected by imbalances, but also made them more dangerous by preventing compensatory phenomena. Local famines, especially those resulting in epidemics, periodically decimated the population. During the colonial period, when the British sought to transform India, they constructed a network of railroads. New areas were opened and it became possible to combat famines effectively. This was the simplest solution, one which avoided immediate change in the social and political structures. In the Ivory Coast economic liberalism also hastened action on transportation, which enabled a large part of the country ultimately to pass from a subsistence economy, to a commercialized, indeed speculative economy.

All traditional societies achieve a certain equilibrium between population and resource, an equilibrium without which they could not survive. The structure of this equilibrium is a function of the techniques that are perfected or adopted by each of these societies, and of the degree to which they are adequate to the environment. Each equilibrium permits a certain demographic pressure on the territory used. The only significant data are therefore net densities per hectare cultivated, fished, foraged, or pastured. The gross densities have scarcely any meaning. Demographic expansion within the framework of this equilibrium can occur only by utilizing unused reserves or by replacing one type of land utilization with another. In West Africa, for example, farmers in the Sahel zone of southeastern Mauritania have been replaced by shepherds, probably at the cost of a reduction in population density. Conversely, farmers have penetrated into the mesophilic forests and have there replaced people who lived by means of hunting and gathering, with a consequent increase in density. Although our knowledge is still fragmentary and in a state of flux, such modifications are becoming increasingly evident.

Although we are generally aware of the existence of a limit on population pressure beyond which these equilibria cannot persist, the inverse and complementary aspect of the problem is often neglected. In effect, the majority of these equilibria cannot maintain themselves except when a minimum population density is reached.

Let us take an example cited in the remarkably penetrating paper by Mr. Kay. The traditional forest fallow system in Africa implies long rotational cycles if the forest is to be able to reconstitute itself, not only to supply humus to the soil but to preserve the biological resources important for food and handicrafts. When traditional precautions are taken (such as preservation of tall trees to assure some shade and to serve as seed bearers) in the Ivory Coast and Guinea forests, a minimum of 15 years of fallow is required if the equilibrium is to be safeguarded. If, in order to simplify the calculation, we assume 17 years of fallow, and 3 of cultivation, only 15 per cent of the agricultural space can bear crops in any given year. This fact sets the maximum population compatible with maintenance of equilibrium. We thus obtain an upper limit. But there is also a lower limit. We can demonstrate this in Latin America with the Venezuelan *conuco,* a system encountered under other names in all forested regions (with low populations and exploited by former slaves or cross-breeds) from Brazil to Guatemala. This system operates under the same physical-geographic conditions as in Africa and is subject to the same forces, despite the fact that the relief is generally more pronounced. But while cultural and technical levels are the same, the social context is very different. The strong social restraints of African villages do not exist because here there are no villages. Thus, African customs favoring reconstitution of the forest are eliminated. In the context of the low population density in regions that are initially almost empty, the forest fallow system has degenerated. Everything that can be is cut and burned, without any thought of sparing shade trees or seed-bearers. Cultivation is carried on as long as possible, until the soil is completely exhausted or badly eroded—then the plot is permanently abandoned. Mediocre secondary forest does not tempt the squatter, who prefers new patches of forest, thought to be virgin, but which are actually climactic in nature. The insufficient demographic pressure ultimately leads to the replacement of the forest fallow system by a nomadic culture, by the destructive pioneer frontier. When, as is the case at present in much of Latin America, the growth of the population leads to a rapid disappearance of climatic vegetal formations, it becomes necessary to reclaim secondary formations that offer far fewer subsistence possibilities. Impoverished soils deteriorate more quickly and give lower yields, thus accelerating their abandonment and accentuating the imbalance, and subsidiary products from hunting and gathering become increasingly sparse and less varied.

A denser initial colonization, leading to the assignment of limited and delineated spaces to each human group, would have favored the transplanting of the forest fallow system, and the consequent protection of the population-resource equilibrium. The degenerate system of the nomadic culture, in the absence of a social structure, created an imbalance and caused the available resources to be inferior to those derived from the forest fallow system.

Another example, in a quite different context, is the Mediterranean region of France during the seventeenth, eighteenth and beginning of the nineteenth centuries. There, under conditions of high demographic pressure, numerous slopes were divided into cultivated terraces, separated by dry stone walls. The parcels of land, which became smaller as the slope steepened, could be worked only by hand, and access to them was limited in most cases to pack animals. Such conditions are no longer compatible with the social-economic context; and with a few exceptions, such as the area of flower-growing near Grasse, these territories have been abandoned. But their arrangement was remarkably adapted to the morpho-climatic condition of the region, which was characterized by a compact formation of the slopes due to drainage on marls, argillaceous sands, and clays. The terraces, by forcing the water to infiltrate, prevented drainage. When persistent rains occurred, the water saturated the earth, accumulated behind the walls, then slowly filtered across the dry stones. The geomorphologic stability was practically assured.

Today spontaneous vegetation has recolonized the terraces. The earth, which is no longer worked, is settling and the walls have become clogged and impermeable, retaining water instead of allowing it to filter. Sometimes, where the substrata contain underground levels, reeds and other marshy plants appear spontaneously on the abandoned terraces. Walls crumble and these breaks are the points of departure for small ravines. Sometimes the water retained by the clogged walls even allows mud flows to begin. In Menton, these have caused damage to the land and even claimed victims. Although the population of the region as a whole has increased greatly through urbanization, rural areas have experienced a reduction in demographic pressure which has manifested itself in the serious deterioration of the physical environment.

The traditional equilibria between man and environment are thus characterized by a specific net population density, a veritable bifurcation: too low a density leads to the degeneration of the man-land relationship. Conversely, too much pressure generates breaks in the equilibria, a situation which we shall now examine.

The Overpopulated or Overexploited Regions

Excess pressure of population upon resources, or, if you prefer, overpopulation, stems from two different sources: (a) Excessive population density and (b) The desire to mobilize rapidly the existing resources within the context of a speculative economy. This is the *Raubwirtschaft* or "robber economy," so well known in pioneer frontier zones. It ruins the soils, as it did in the coffee zone of Brazil, or in the prairies of North America. The stripping of ore-bearing deposits is much the same phenomenon. Pursued when general economic conditions are favorable, this type of economy extracts maximum profits from empty areas with no concern for the future. Only the fact of increasing scarcity of vacant land is limiting this exploitative practice.

In both cases, excessive pressure on resources results from inadequate production techniques. The demographic repercussions and the economic end differ. In the pioneering zone, flows of immigrants supply strangers whose purpose is to extract quick profits from the riches of an empty, untouched country. When capital is invested, it must realize a maximum yield; and this is what prevents the employment of satisfactory techniques. For example, in the forested regions southwest of Lake Maracaibo, the level lands were monopolized by wealthy owners as soon as malaria had been wiped out and communication routes opened up the region. The lands are now covered with grass, so that they can ultimately support plantations of sugar cane, banana, oil palms, coconuts, and probably even hevea rubber. Currently, animal husbandry is profitably carried on within ranches varying from 100 to 1,000 hectares. But this nonetheless represents an extensive occupation of the soil, with low labor density and relatively low economic yield. Its justification lies in its speculative advantages; rapid returns on capital and minimal investments.

For a farm of 100 hectares, correctly managed, animal husbandry offers net returns of 12 to 15 per cent of the capital at the end of two to three years. Crops would not yield more, despite a rate of investment four to five times higher. But in areas put into production 10 to 15 years ago, a decline in yield is already being noticed, one which does not fail to be disturbing. Moreover, this capitalistic type of animal husbandry, financed by the middle class, is associated with the exploitation of Andean or Colombian peasant labor. It is they, in fact, who do the clearing, carry out the burning, and work the land for two or three years as tenant farmers. These migrant laborers come from a region with strong demographic pressure where they cannot settle on lands suitable for cultivation. They tend to install themselves on the steep lower slopes of the Andes which do not tempt speculators. This is land which should be left wooded or devoted to animal husbandry.

The pioneer frontiers make it possible to reduce demographic pressure in regions of emigration; but the very conditions of their existence exclude the possibility of resorting to rational development techniques. At the end of a more or less prolonged period, the land is left exhausted and incapable of high yields. In the state of São Paulo and in Val Paraiba, Brazil, lands once planted in coffee are incapable of supporting anything but mediocre pastures or eucalyptus brush. Even after several decades of rest, the soils will require fertilization and irrigation in order to support coffee plantations again. Similarly, the grain exploitation of the American prairies produced the dangerous erosion and frequent ruin of the soils which became most evident during the Depression.

In Venezuela, Andean peasants have spontaneously colonized the Motatan Delta since 1952. Cultivation on burned land has now completed the elimination of the forest which now covers no more than 6 per cent of the central portion of the delta. The secondary brush is being attacked and the yields are much lower. Thus a tendency for the inhabitants to emigrate again is being noted. Only locally has a more stable type of agriculture, with simple fallow practices, developed. It is essential to emphasize that this pioneer region is witnessing a cultural regression: more than 50 per cent of the peasants who are practicing the *conuco* system and using the digging stick have declared that they know the techniques of plow culture, but no longer practice it. This despite the fact that cattle are being raised by the *hacendados* of the region, and they could quite easily maintain a few themselves, as draft animals, if for no other purposes.

One can compare frontier zones in which speculative crops are being quickly developed for high returns. For example, among the Wolofs in Senegal, peanuts have enjoyed rapid success since the colonial power and commercial companies combined their efforts to cultivate the crop around 1880. Continued planting, however, has led to forcing a return to the forest fallow system. It has also created a need for seasonal foreign labor. Increased revenues in the area have to a large extent been offset by the need to import foods; thus growers have received much less profit from this commercial cultivation than have the middlemen. The standard of living has not risen as rapidly as monetary returns, because of the amounts withdrawn by the tertiary sector. But in the absence of new cultivation techniques, extracted yields have exceeded the possibilities of the environment, and a serious deterioration of the soils has taken place, accompanied by major wind erosion. After only fifty years, the region of Louga, one of the first to turn to the cultivation of peanuts, had lost a good part of its population and supplied a large flow of immigrants to the pioneering regions of eastern Senegal.

Pioneering regions and those with speculative cultivation consequently have many features in common. Both have an organization whose purpose is to rapidly mobilize latent agricultural riches, using techniques that involve a minimum of investment and that usually bring about a rapid degradation of the environment. Nomadic cultivation on burned-out lands is a primitive form of this.

Demographic pressure ultimately leads to analogous results. Progress in medicine can be spread at a far lower cost and with far less effort than new development techniques. This explains the present widespread situation in the Third World: a rapid growth in population, necessitating a search for more abundant food resources by means of traditional agricultural methods. The very serious imbalance which results from this search takes the form of overpopulation. A large part of the population is underemployed, reduced to concealed unemployment. Many of the peasants of the Third World average no more than one hundred days of work per year. Simultaneously, soils deteriorate and yields begin to drop, especially as a result of fallow system. A vicious circle is begun: the drop in yields reduces the period of fallow which in turn triggers the exploitation of greater areas and the cultivation of excessively steep slopes. Intense erosion generally accompanies the agronomic deterioration of the soils and all too often assumes irreversible forms. In those regions where demographic pressure is greatest and techniques remain unchanged, the food situation becomes increasingly severe not only because of the larger number of mouths to feed, but also because of the drop in yields, and, after all the reserves of the land have been used, a reduction in aggregate harvest.

Much too frequently, demographic pressure increases as the result of a wider exposure to the outside world, which arouses new desires and at the same time creates favorable conditions for the adoption of speculative cultivation. This increases pressure upon resources since it contributes to the development of the tertiary sector and consequently to the continuation of unfavorable terms of trade between agricultural and industrial products on a worldwide level. It is not uncommon to find that among groups living under similar physical conditions and exerting the same pressure on resources, those that remain within a self-sufficient economy enjoy better nutritional conditions than communities practicing extensive commercial cultivation.

Problem of Population-Resources Equilibrium

The three types of situations that we have briefly analyzed make it possible to define the nature of demographic pressure on resources, or, still better, the *population-resources equilibrium*. Whereas too numerous a population ultimately leads to a depletion of resources, too small a population not only can impede the development of but may also cause a certain deterioration in the environment. There is no question that the greater danger by far results from an excessive demographic pressure on resources, but the contrary case helps us to understand the true nature of the population-resources equilibrium.

First, it is necessary to define the nature of "resources." As emphasized by V. V. Pokshishevskii and P. Gourou, and as we have indicated above, the concept of resources is inseparable from the level of technical development. For our Neolithic ancestors, iron was not a resource because they were ignorant of metallurgy. The development of hybrid corn has modified the extent of the area in which the cultivation of the plant is possible. But the resource concept is not only a function of a given stage in technical development. It also depends on the economic context and the idea of *value*.

Thus there exist *marginal resources* whose exploitation is possible only under a certain circumstance, for example, mines with so high a cost factor that they are worked only when market prices allow, or certain items that are cultivated only when the use of imports is limited. This was the case during World War II in Great Britain and France. Socialist countries often begin to work ore-bearing deposits previously disdained. Tariff unification in Europe may bring about a reclassification of resources in 10 or 20 years. It is not impossible to imagine that increased demographic pressure may in turn cause our notion of "resource" to evolve independently of other factors. The two terms of the relationship "population pressure on resources" are not strictly independent one from the other; on the contrary, they partially react upon each other. Thus it seems more accurate to speak of the population-resources equilibrium.

The term "resources" is ambiguous from another viewpoint. The distinction between renewable and nonrenewable resources is quite fluid and not always clear. Mining products, for example, are nonrenewable but they are not necessarily being exhausted. The progress of geologic exploration and extraction techniques often makes it possible to discover new reserves at the same rate at which deposits are being exploited, or even to move ahead. This area benefits from technical efforts of exceptional scope; and progress in the physical sciences will ultimately make it possible to put any problem concerning our supply of mining products into terms of energy. As long as sufficient energy is available, the various metals in the earth's crust can be extracted from it—even if their concentration is very low. Another example: can a soil capable of being eroded be considered a renewable resource? Imbalances can produce irreversible developments which affect the capabilities of soils for agricultural production, the plant cover, and even the climate. The presumably renewable resources deteriorate and cease to renew themselves. Strictly speaking, a resource is renewable only when certain equilibrium conditions, comparable to the climax of biogeographers, can be permanently realized.

Considerations such as these have led us to insist on a concept that seems more adequate, that of the *limitations and bases* of development. Limitations are the special features of regional conditions which offer obstacles to development. They are equivalent to what city-planners call constraints, and are physical in nature as well as socioeconomic: i.e., mountainous terrain, excessively dry climate, chemically infertile soils, areas subject to flooding, insufficient population, endemic diseases, insufficient technical level of the labor force, lack of capital, inadequate or costly transportation. These limitations usually are relative and can be overcome by means of adequate measures: i.e., techniques for improving the physical environment (irrigation, drainage, agronomic practices adapted to the climate and soils); new methods of development (new crops or varieties better adapted to local conditions, industrialization); improved economic and social policies (changes in social and economic structure, development of capital and investments, loans, and adequate foreign aid); demographic policy (technical training, population transfers). The use of fertilizer, for example, may diminish or suppress the danger of erosion under certain conditions. Thus in the region of Machiques in Zulia, Venezuela, we have described the severe risk of erosion on slopes of more than one degree occupied by mediocre pastures on argillaceous sandy formations. Under the usual conditions, these pastures yield about 3.85 tons of forage per hectare. Yet experimentation with the application of fertilizers on one-hectare plots has succeeded

in raising the yield to more than 22 tons. With this denser kind of pasture, the danger of erosion is largely eliminated from the slopes. Socioeconomic limitations are determined by the character of the society at a given moment in its development; they are a function of this development and are therefore bound to change.

The bases are the positive elements in the balance, in contrast to the negative *limitations*. They are the characteristics that can serve as the foundation for developmental policy in given socioeconomic and technical situations. Like the limitations, they are varied in nature and include physical and human elements. A forest region capable of being exploited rationally in advance of agricultural development is a good example of a developmental base. When the trees are cut and the vegetation is set aflame in order to clear the land, the base is destroyed and the forest becomes a limitation, requiring additional labor input, with no return. An abundant population may be either a limitation to development or one of its bases, depending on predetermined goals. Thus developmental bases are relative and are determined by local and temporary conditions. A limiting feature may, on the contrary, become a base under certain conditions. In the tenth century, the Rhine Delta, marshy and subject to flooding from the ocean during storms, posed serious limitations for utilization. In the course of centuries, the tenacious efforts of the Dutch and the Flemish profoundly modified natural conditions. Damming and drainage transformed the delta into a highly productive agricultural region.

As a function of each social situation, including its economic structure and stage of technical development, various regional geographic characteristics can be divided into limitations and bases for development. As long as a situation reflects little change, evolving slowly in a linear way, a balance is maintained—a state of equilibrium or quasi-equilibrium. In the past it has been realized most markedly within a context of very slow development of technology. In Europe, for example, from the fifteenth to eighteenth centuries, agricultural techniques changed little; and they imposed a certain limit on rural population density. Population size fluctuated in time as a function of wars. During periods of decline, lands were abandoned; during periods of growth, ground was cleared or recleared. Thus, under conditions of slow technical development, demographic oscillations manifest themselves as variations in the amount of agricultural land. These areal variations allowed demographic pressure on resources to change little.

On the other hand, a definite demographic increase took place in Western and Central Europe during the eighteenth century. First, there was a maximum expansion of lands, including the development of marginal areas. Then came a breakdown in the equilibrium, and a phase of overpopulation, which manifested itself most notably in a deterioration of the environment. The mid-eighteenth century was a period of intense man-made erosion in northeastern Fance. The soils, impoverished and kept diffuse through plowing, were easily scraped off by stream action. Ravines even appeared in some places. However, the introduction of new techniques put an end to the crisis. The decisive factor in this reversal was the introduction of the potato, which requires greater care in cultivation, and is beneficial to the soil; and of pastures of clover and alfalfa, which protect the soil against erosion, aid in nitrogen fixation, and encourage the development of livestock industry. Animal husbandry, which supplied the manure indispensable to soil maintenance and which had been imperiled by demographic pressure requiring extension of tillage developed anew. Increased quantities of manure and the effects of leguminous plants

were sufficient to re-establish the equilibrium. Increased productivity allowed the rural population to grow for another century without modification of techniques and without lowering living standards.

Mrs. Boserup's communication quite clearly demonstrates the importance of technical modifications in agriculture if a society is to feed and, above all, employ a larger population under better conditions. Grandiose and expensive projects are not the most effective means. A generalized program, conducted by the peasants themselves, is indispensable, and the larger undertakings must be limited to cases where conditions warrant them. Let me cite the costly irrigated perimeter around Cenizo in Venezuela. Here a number of peasants continue to practice dry cultivation despite knowledge of the techniques of canal irrigation, proper direction, and a supply of cadres. In the Punjab, on the other hand, a region with traditional irrigation, Mr. Gosal reports a doubling of the population, thanks to the irrigation of argillaceous lands which the traditional argriculture could not utilize.

Techniques therefore determine the population-resources equilibrium to a very large extent. In the past, the slow development of techniques went hand in hand with a generally slow demographic growth. The weakness of communications among different communities contributed to this state of affairs. Stagnation or slight demographic expansion was also, in turn, an unfavorable factor for the development of techniques. This situation has gradually modified since the sixteenth century. The increase in mobility during the period of major geographical explorations allowed the introduction of new plants into many areas of the world: corn and potatoes to Europe; corn, cassava, and the peanut to tropical Africa; sugar cane and cotton to America. Some of these plants were introduced as speculative cultivation, the base first of the mercantile economy, and then of capitalism.

One cannot, however, project the pattern of the modifications Europe experienced in the nineteenth century during the beginning of the Technical Era upon present-day underdeveloped countries. In effect, the imbalance produced in Europe between population and resources was more easily overcome, thanks to massive emigration to America and other new countries. Between 1840 and 1914, each of the European countries experienced a wave of emigration, which reduced the acuteness of the problem. Now such movements are no longer possible; and a changeover in technology has to be achieved under the pressure of immobile populations. Perhaps birth control will eventually provide a palliative.

The present period—the 1960's—is characterized by general imbalance, one of whose major features is underdevelopment. It assumes three main forms:

(1) A commercialized economy that is rapidly conquering the world, one that requires relatively small investments (improvement of transportation, facilities for packaging and storage), and little emphasis on the introduction of new production techniques. It easily attaches itself to traditional production systems and the imbalances which it generates appear only after the passage of time (50 years of degradation of the American prairie or the region of Louga in Senegal, for example). In underdeveloped countries this commercialized economy has assumed the form of plantations—an economy which is increasingly juxtaposed to traditional exploitation, bringing about a rapid modification therein. In fact, one of its strengths is its generation of new appetites. First of all, it transforms the producer into a consumer. Commercial trade has always begun by displaying cheaper wares to undercut local products. Because of the inequality

of international trade, this commerce ultimately drains the farmers, principally those in underdeveloped countries. The development of wants and consequent indebtedness to the tradesman encourage increased production of salable commodities and, as a result, a more intense pressure on resources. The demands of commerce ultimately lead to a general transfer of revenues from the countryside to the cities, and at the end of the cycle, to the more developed countries. The development of a commercial economy, without improvement in techniques allowing an increase in aggregate production, manifests itself as a population-resource imbalance which takes the form of a debased nutrition and often a depletion of the environment.

(2) A demographic growth produced by the introduction of new public health measures. As is the case of the commercialized economy, this requires minimal investment. To save a man by means of vaccination or antibiotic costs hundreds of times less than the modern equipment and agricultural land required to support this man. Consequently, there has been no corresponding modification of production techniques. People are saved from disease without being assured of their food for the next day. They are admitted to hospitals, where they are cared for and snatched from the jaws of death, to which they are condemned by undernourishment the day that they are cured and leave the hospital! Anyone who visits the Third World is familiar with this tragedy. Demographic growth and the limited mobility of the people are reducing to an ever greater degree the possibilities for expanding the exploited territory and, as a result, for maintaining more population without modification of techniques or depletion of the environment. Thus, the dreaded process of absolute retrogression is triggered in most underdeveloped countries: the incipient

down-grading of the environment is at first translated into declines in yield, at the very time when the demographic burden requires increased yields. These declines further increase the pressure of population upon resources; this sets in motion an irreversible deterioration, which has the effect of multiplying the limitations and restricting the usable space. What areas have been slashed by ravines and lost to agriculture? How many plains have become marshy because of water courses becoming more torrential and because of alluvial deposits from stripped-down, poorly cultivated slopes?

(3) The failure of a society to adapt to the increasingly rapid progress of technology. Limitations which accentuate the population-resource imbalance by causing the exploitation of resources to stagnate in the face of an expanding population are frequently social in nature. The assimilation of new techniques is difficult and slow. They require knowledge and experience if they are to tap increased resources from the environment without degrading it. For example, it is easy to import tractors and learn to drive them. To manufacture them, and above all, to maintain them, care for them, manage them is rather more difficult. But to obtain the best yield by integrating them harmoniously into the agricultural production system is still more difficult. In the Soviet Union, for example, for a long time plowing was done in the direction of the slope in order to save fuel and to fulfill bureaucratic standards. Yet increased erosion resulting from this practice was entirely neglected. We shall say nothing about the mystique of the plow in French colonial policy and of the mistakes resulting from it in moist tropical regions. In North Africa, since independence, there has been a significant amount of unemployment, increased by the departure of the French and the breaking of colonial ties. The available labor force was to be used for conservation work, in imitation of the United States. Work crews in Morocco and Tunisia were given the job of building hundreds of kilometers of banks. But banks are frequently not suited to the geomorphological conditions, and hold back water on argillaceous slopes, which then begin to slide. Mud flows caused by the banks blocked roads and endangered villages, especially in the Riff. Insufficient knowledge of the geographic environment thus caused a poor utilization of techniques and inhibited the advance to a higher equilibrium. Since then, Tunisia has created a Department of Geomorphology which, with the aid of the Center of Applied Geography, provides advice on the protection and conservation of soils and waters.

The coherent measures required by a sound technical development policy are rarely promoted and applied systematically in the underdeveloped countries. A good knowledge of man and of the environment, systematic experiments conducted for an adequate period, and good, generalized professional training are basic requirements. Without them, the technological transformation, a question of life or death, cannot be realized under favorable conditions. Finally, the introduction of a commercial economy and the increase in demographic pressure generate social tensions that weaken the cohesion of the societies in question and limit their possibilities for action. How many archaic social systems oppose technical change, from the castes of India to the *latifundia* of Latin America? The development of a speculative economy customarily generates increased social inequalities and concentrates the major portion of the wealth in the hands of an urban middle class, who do not make the investments necessary for the growth of production. How much of the commercial profits realized in the Third World are deposited in the banks of New York or Switzerland?

An increase in social and political tensions accelerates this flight of capital, and there, too, absolute retrogression comes about. In many underdeveloped countries, it is possible to demonstrate disinvestment as far as means of production are concerned!

A serious error, for which the international organizations are largely responsible, has been to encourage investments, with expenditures of capital, without attaching sufficient importance to labor force utilization and training. This is the case particularly of almost all soil and water conservation and restoration work, for which biological methods are almost always preferable to mechanical methods. This sort of work has little chance of succeeding and surviving unless it is well received by the peasants who must assure its maintenance. It requires training and psychological conditioning, even a kind of mystique, closely tied to political action. Many plans can be realized almost without capital, by using underemployed labor.

At present, rapid technical development in most countries allows us to envision a new population-resource equilibrium with a higher demographic burden than that of the traditional equilibria. This is particularly possible in agricultural matters, largely because agricultural production uses the most labor. The easiest solution to adopt is the introduction of either selected or new varieties of plants that better accommodate themselves to the limitations of the environment. The increased peanut production in Senegal is a recent example of the former. The introduction of new plants or breeding animals is a more delicate operation, although it took place spontaneously and on a very large scale during the period of the major explorations. Currently it is necessary for such a plant to be introduced not only into the cultivating system and to be compatible with the techniques on which the latter is based, but also into the social structure and into the working calendar. The introduction of coffee and cacao plantations in the Ivory Coast, for example, has meant the disruption of traditional social structures. Likewise, the industrial use of palm oil collides with very strict social limitations in the traditional system of owning and using land. At this level, a thorough knowledge of the limitations and bases of development becomes necessary. This is true to an even greater degree when one thinks in terms of modifying actual production techniques. This, in fact, cannot be done without qualitative changes in the labor force or socioeconomic modifications. In France, for example, the suppression of the fallow system, following the adoption of leguminous plants and of a system of weeding at the end of the eighteenth century, produced an acute social crisis in the country, a crisis that was one aspect of the changes that produced the Revolution.

The passage from one equilibrium to another with a different structure is precarious and always accompanied by serious tensions. This is what we are now observing on a worldwide scale in the underdeveloped countries, where such a transformation is made inevitable by the upsurge in expectations produced by the development of a commercial economy and by demographic expansion. Many restraining factors, primarily social in nature, oppose this transformation and, by delaying it, accentuate the population-resource imbalance. The longer these constraints operate, the further deteriorating effects will extend, compromising the possibilities of moving on to a new equilibrium based on a higher technical level.

Conclusion

A certain degree of demographic pressure is necessary for man to seek to improve the utilization of his resources. Every time a human group expands and migrates toward empty lands, the law of least effort causes it to abandon its more advanced practices and return to primitive ones. But, on the other hand, a demographic expansion more rapid than the advance in techniques, especially when it is combined with increased demands, ultimately leads to an over-exploitation of resources, to the creation of imbalances which may generate an irreversible deterioration.

We are therefore faced by a dilemma. A certain margin of tolerance between stagnation and excessive pressure is available to us. It is quite clear that this margin will not be the same everywhere, varying with social and economic conditions, on the one hand, and with the physical characteristics of the environment, on the other. Certain environments are more tolerant than others (for example, temperate maritime climates in contrast with semi-arid climates exposed to violent irregular rains; level regions in contrast to those with steep slopes). To examine how human factors and physical limitations combine to determine this margin of tolerance is an indispensable and specifically geographic task.

11. WHAT EVER HAPPENED TO KRILIUM?

William Vogt

Par son existence même, l'être, vivant modifie le milieu dans lequel il évolue.
J. Duche

At the outset it is important, I think, to discuss briefly what I am talking about in the framework of the theme of this meeting —the geography of population pressure on physical and social resources. I assume *human* populations are of primary concern though many other populations, including *Anopheles albimanus,* other insects, various soil organisms, isopods, and two or three rats play important operational roles in the ecosystems of Mexico and Central America, the area assigned to me.

It is essential to recognize that the term "man" is necessarily an open-ended one if man is to be considered in an operational sense, as he must be if his multifarious activities are to be understood in relation to his environment. A noted economist is alleged to have said (42: 63) that "if land were farmed as well as the Dutch farmers work their acres today . . . the world would now support 28 billion persons at one of the best diets known." Leaving aside, for the moment, the productive quality of the Dutch polders versus the tropical laterites, and the fact that the Dutch annually import millions of pounds of non-fat milk solids and fish proteins to produce veal and broilers, there is a vast gap between the behavior of the North Sea farmer and the peasant on the steep slopes of Tlaxcala, or of Santa Ana in El Salvador. "Man" as a taxon gives little idea of what human populations *do* in their environments (13: 378).

The Hollander is one of the world's best educated people; in Central America only about 2 per cent of the population go beyond primary school and 1 per cent beyond secondary school (39: 23), and the quality of higher education rarely, if ever, equals that of the Universities of Leyden and Utrecht.

The chromatograph and microscope have been called "extensions of the human nervous system"; the automobile and bulldozer could be considered extensions of man's musculature. In 1960, 35,000,000 Mexicans had 808,000 motor vehicles in their country of 1,900,000 km²; Los Angeles, alone, had more than 2.1 cars per acre. Mexico, at this density, would have over 1000 million cars. The Mexicans, unlike the Los Angelesians, are not "walking about in nearly 9000 tons of carbon monoxide a day, 1180 tons of hydrocarbons, 330 tons of oxides of nitrogen, and a sizable tonnage of aldehydes, sulphur compounds, acids, ammonia, lead, and other poisonous substances" (18: 52). Even in their bronchial cilia, the Mexicans and Central Americans presumably differ significantly from Californians.

The Panamerican Highway through Mexico and Central America is one of the most destructive single accomplishments of man. It has opened up hundreds of thousands of square miles of land unsuitable for agriculture to exploitation that has resulted in vast downgrading and destruction of forests, soil erosion, and disruption of the hydrologic cycle. Internal-combustion man and digging-stick man (both of whom are present in Central America) shape their environments in different ways at different rates.

The populations of these middle American countries are predominantly rural, with Mexico being the most urbanized: In 1960, 30 per cent of its people lived in communities of 20,000 or more, 18 per cent in El Salva-

172

dor, 12 per cent in Honduras, 23 per cent in Nicaragua, and 24 per cent in Costa Rica (29: 14). Movement to larger towns is, however, accelerating.

Population Projections

Human populations and their habitats, despite their variability, share certain probabilities that may justify comparisons and—given current patterns of human behavior—projections.

The first of these projections has to do with population sizes. For these I have used the rather conservative estimates of Dr. Carmen A. Miró (29: 11) because of her broad treatment of Latin America, rather than those of Ing. Jorge Arias (39: 7) which seem perhaps more realistic, so as to understate my case. Almost any statistic should be considered an approximation, if only because of lack of facilities for data collection and analysis. The figures presented here, however, are good enough approximations as a basis for discussion, if one bears in mind the fact that they could perhaps be revised 10 per cent or more in either direction; and as Roger Revelle suggests (23: 32), demographers have tended to underestimate population growth.

Miró gives the following populations and natural increase rates; the 1999 projections are based on the latter.

Population (millions)

	1965	NIR	1999
Mexico	41,400,000	34.5	122,700,000
Guatemala	4,340,000	32	11,890,000
Honduras	2,180,000	30	5,614,000
El Salvador	2,850,000	38.9	8,410,000
Costa Rica	1,420,000	41.6	5,220,000
Nicaragua	1,660,000	33	4,692,000
Total	53,934,000		158,526,000

Natural increase, the difference between birth and death rates, may change during the next thirty-two years, though for cultural reasons birth control pobably will not make substantial progress and, at least for a time, birth rates may continue to rise with improvements in maternal health and the control of sterility-inducing infections such as gonorrhea. Besides more than 40 per cent 28: 576) of the area's population are under 15 years of age, which means that the number of breeders will increase heavily in the near future.

Many of the data for the Central American Common Market (CACM) countries discussed in this paper come from a meeting held in El Salvador and Guatemala in October 1965 and summarized in (39).

Food Shortages and Malnutrition

Although there is a generally accepted nutritional standard of about 2600 calories, of which 70 gms are proteins, the *Instituto de Nutrición de Centro América y Panamá* (INCAP) sets 56 gms of protein as a daily acceptable minimum.

For the area under discussion this would have required 144.4 trillion calories per day in 1965, including more than 3 million kilos of protein using the INCAP standard; by 1999, the total will have risen to 413.4 trillion calories of which some 8.8 million kilos should be protein. But these estimates involve so many variables, such as methods of preparation and quality of food, distribution, and preservation, that it is difficult to evaluate them fully.

One of the best nutritional measures is the cost of feeding a family of six which, for the CACM countries, is calculated by INCAP as $2 per day. The Sub-Committee for Agricultural Economic Development, meeting in San José, Costa Rica, October-November 1964, estimated that for CACM countries the per capita income of the 64 per cent of the people living by agriculture was $43 per year (including subsistence farming products), whereas, simply for an adequate diet, INCAP estimated that about $125 would be required.

In Guatemala, in a study made in the Pediatrics Department of the city's General Hospital, it was established that "about 80 per cent of the children showed evidence of nutritional deficiencies." (39: 9)

According to the Minister of Public Health of El Salvador (39: 17), "Malnutrition is the underlying cause, apparently the most important one, of the high mortality of children from 1 to 5 years." In 1962 almost one-half of all deaths in Central America fell within this age bracket.

In El Salvador, according to Dr. Alejandro Marroquín of the University of El Salvador, "There are many towns in which people eat meat only one day a year—that dedicated to the village's saint." (38: 6)

The agricultural production index for Central America, averaged for the period 1952-55, had risen nearly one-third by 1964-65, but the production of *foodstuffs* had actually decreased. In El Salvador, both the population and agricultural production increased by about 50 per cent, yet food production dropped about 15 per cent (39: 13-14).

Frequent assertions that Mexico has "closed the food gap" are unhappily not true (15: 24; 36; 70), despite the fact that Mexico exports meat, shrimp, cotton, sugar, rum, tequila, fruit, and garden truck. Flores, using a slightly smaller family size—5.248—than INCAP, calculates that in the 1950's 15 per cent of the nation was lacking between 15 and 21 per cent in per capita calories (15). In 1958, she estimates, 65 per cent of the income of urban dwellers and 85 per cent of that of rural workers went for food— even at the inadequate dietary levels. In

1961, "Five leading Mexican nutritionists established . . . that the most serious social challenge facing our government is the enormous problem of malnutrition among the broad masses of the people" (8: 53). A report prepared by the *Banco de Mexico* predicts serious food shortages by 1975, and states that in Puebla (far from the most backward part of the country) in 1960, 40 per cent of the population "never ate eggs, fish, meat or milk" (16). According to a recent article in *The Economist:* "The Mexicans themselves believe that 15 per cent of the population goes hungry and possibly 60 per cent is undernourished . . ." (32: 684). In 1963, maize, Mexico's most important food, was produced at the rate of 38 bushels per hectare; the United States' production averaged 168 bushels (10: 38). In 1966, Mexico was producing about 83 bushels of wheat per hectare compared with the 185 produced by Dutch farmers.

Production per hectare has been falling over much of Central America. For example, both maize and rice had sharp drops between 1950-51 and 1963-64 (39: 46-47). One does not really need statistical evidence in this area; he has only to look at the fields, where the ravages of erosion are obvious, where the size of the corn stalks at the top of a slope frequently will be half the size, or even less, of those at the bottom. In Guatemala, "At no point between Guatemala City and Quetzaltenango is one very distant from eroded land. Along the river Samala, long sections of the hillside, whose angle of repose has been changed by the destruction of vegetation, have collapsed upon the valley floor" (35: 7). Dr. Paul C. Standley, one of the botanists best informed about Central America, stated: "In the valley of Siji woody plants have been exterminated, so that at present the only available fuel is grass roots. Tortillas are not made because they require too much fuel; instead the people subsist on *tamalitos blancos,* which need less fuel for their preparation.

". . . erosion is a menace in all the volcanic part of Guatemala. Perhaps the most vivid illustration of complete deforestation is seen on the steep slopes of the beautiful Volcano of Agua, facing Antigua, where hardly a tree remains, and deep *barrancas* have been gouged down the slopes . . ." (27: 18).

An ecosystem, at times compared to a net or a spider web, extends over the surface of the earth, and from the soil into the atmosphere, which not only supplies such nutrients as carbon and nitrogen but through such forces as wind and evaporation, may have a dominant influence on habitats for plants and animals. It is in reality four-dimensional. Nutrients, as will be discussed later, cycle from the soil through plants and animals back to the soil (in some cases only to be washed to sea and trapped for long periods). The fourth dimension is time.

Dr. C. V. Plath, FAO officer assigned to the *Instituto Interamericano de Ciencias Agricolas,* states: "one of the lamentable characteristics of the underdeveloped areas is the lack of information on physical and social conditions. Unfortunately, Central America is not an exception and there is in existence very little trustworthy information on the region. . . . It is unfortunate that the five-year development plans of the Central American countries were made before an Atlas, now in the process of completion, was developed. . . . Generally the information on the socio-economic productivity of human activity is even more fragmentary, out-of-date, and less trustworthy than the information on physical resources." The recent series of index maps published by the Pan American Union (21) gives a fair idea of the vast gaps in our knowledge. It is almost an Atlas of Ignorance. In 1965, Guatemala was only beginning its first cadastral survey.

Productivity of the Mexican-Central American Ecosystem

The food of a population may be taken as a clue to the innate productivity of the environment, the quality of applied technology, and the effectiveness of agricultural research. Obviously, when a malnourished population may be expected to increase 200 per cent within three decades, there would seem to be reason for concern. Food—and water—are the least common denominator in any society; they are in a sense the emergent part of the iceberg.

The production of food is affected by many factors, but the available constellation of soil, water, and favorable climate, is indispensable. (Hydroponic gardening is too expensive for more than very limited development, and the practical utilization of algae and synthetics derived from petrochemicals is so far in the future that these sources of food will probably have little effect on the 6 or 7 billion people who will populate the earth by the end of the century.) A closer look at the soil and water resources of Mexico and Central America is in order.

Recent Mexican statistics reveal the following (6: 6): of the nation's 1,964,000 km², only 36 per cent has a slope of less than 10 per cent, the same proportion 10-25 per cent, and 28 per cent more than 25 per cent slope. The steep areas account, of course, for much of the widespread erosion in Mexico, although even a 3 per cent slope may erode badly under tropical downpours.

About 52 per cent of the land (following the classification of the Ministry of Water Resources) is arid, 31 semi-arid, 11 semi-humid, and 6 humid. Twenty-eight per cent consist of noneroded soils or those with merely incipient erosion, 21 per cent are moderately eroded (irrigated, or level grazing land), 43 per cent have accelerated erosion, and 8 per cent are "totally" eroded or nonproductive land. Thirty million hectares are considered cultivable, of which 15 million are currently under cultivation. (In the 1960 census some 28 million hectares are unaccounted for.)

Tamayo (7: 22) estimates 30 million hectares cultivable, 92 million grazing land, 43 million in forest, and 31.4 "useless."

In Central America Dr. Plath estimates that out of a total area of 423,411 km², some 53,000 or 12 per cent are suitable for intensive use and "will give high yields when modern agricultural techniques are applied." Yet one-third of this area consists of slopes requiring special soil conservation treatment which in Central America the land rarely gets. He assigns 97,000 km² or 23 per cent to "extensive uses with moderate yields, applying modern methods of production . . ." (39: 54).

"It is on these lands," he states, "that one finds many of the small and medium sized farms [including] much of the existing subsistence agriculture. . . . Despite the fact that the great part (90 per cent) of these lands possess slopes that require soil conservation practices, they are capable of producing much more when traditional methods are replaced by modern methods even though they are simple." The remaining 65 per cent he reserves for forests (including those needed to control the hydrologic cycle) and light grazing (39: 54).

In view of Dr. Plath's insistence on "modern methods," it might be noted that in 1967, El Salvador earmarked 8 per cent of its total government budget for agriculture; Guatemala, 1.9; Nicaragua, 3.9; Costa Rica, 2; and Mexico, 1.2. These are not exactly liberal amounts to cover conservation, research, and extension work, to mention three pertinent fields.

Dr. Gerardo Budowski, a forester and ecologist from the *Instituto Interamericano de Ciencias Agricolas,* recently estimated that in Central America (including Panama), slightly less than 8 per cent of the land was ecologically suitable for agriculture—a bit more than 16 million hectares in countries occupied by about 14 million people. He cautions particularly against colonization of humid tropical areas—estimated at about 181,000 km²: "Many economists and planners like to show these great areas on the Central American maps, indicating that they have a great future once they have been made healthy and opened up with roads. . . . The truth is that there is little justification for an optimistic view. The experience of colonization in other countries with similar life zones demonstrates that only when there is a favorable topography can one hope for success in agriculture and cattle raising. It is very rare to encounter large areas with such favorable characteristics. For very good reasons, man has avoided this zone in the majority of cases."

This is a fact that has long been known to students of the tropical earth, though the understanding has not generally percolated upward to the bureaucratic levels where policies—and projections—are made.

What might be called the transient character of tropical soils, with their thin humus layer and extreme vulnerability to leaching, has been especially well set forth by Pierre Gourou, of the Collège de France, and by P. W. Richards.

"For climatic reasons tropical soils are poor and tend to become poorer quickly. This would not be so bad if the soil remained in its place and kept a friable structure favorable to agriculture. But tropical soils are threatened with erosion and laterization. . . . Soil erosion . . . in tropical regions . . . assumes a very violent form. . . . Tropical soils are poor in humus. Even in the forest humus blackens the soil to a depth of only a few inches. In dense forests the quantity of organic matter is considerable and has been estimated in Yangambi in Belgian Congo at between twenty and twenty-five tons . . . per annum per acre. But in these forests the deposits do not enrich the soil, for they are offset by equivalent losses, with the result that the soil contains at most 1.8 per cent of humus, whilst fertile soil in temperate regions often contains more than 10 per cent." (17: 16-19; 24: 205; see also 4: 75ff)

Licenciado Rodolfo Brena Torres, Governor of the Mexican State of Oaxaca, wrote in a personal communication: "The problem of the land is acute here. Lack of foresight started the destruction of the forests that covered the state in the XVIIIth Century; the lands stripped of their vegetation were eroded by wind and rain, leaving this desolate landscape, sad to look at and even sadder from the economic aspect—since there remain regions so dead that one can get nothing useful from them. The population increase makes the situation more distressing and in the face of the impossibility, for a great part of the population, to satisfy here the necessities of existence, it has no alternative but to emigrate to other places, at times on a temporary basis as when the *braceros* [migrant farm workers] go to work in the United States, or at other times to settle in Mexico City or neighboring states" (38: 6).

Professor C. A. Donis, of the Institut Agronomique de l'Etat, Gembloux, Belgium, speaking recently out of a wealth of experience in Africa, said: "Safe estimates, provided shag [shifting agriculture] is practiced in a regular diffused pattern, should fix the cultivable percentage at rarely above 75 per cent and the minimum length of fallow rarely shorter than 12 years. Above 25/km², degradation of soils and vegetation should occur" (14: 34, 31). He also stated, "When

the slope of the ground is anything but gentle, and some authors note that the process starts with 3 per cent slope, surface erosion of a more serious type sets in, the topsoil is removed, silting up the valleys, soil fertility is gone and grass savanna installed." There is, of course, in the area under discussion, a very small percentage of land of less than 3 per cent slope.

Many writers have commented on the soundness of "shag" as an adjustment to the low fertility of tropical soils—a sound adjustment when populations are small. As someone has said, farmers rotate their land instead of rotating their crops—yet they are recognizing the inadequacy of this process more and more as mounting population pressures require a shortening of rotations.

According to Dr. Jorge Arias, of the University of San Carlos de Guatemala, the CACM countries have the following densities, which far exceed Donis's "safe estimates" (39: 4).

Country	*Inhabitants per km² of cultivated land (farm land, permanent crops, meadows, pastures)*
Guatemala	135.9
El Salvador	148.6
Honduras	79.6
Nicaragua	88.1
Costa Rica	81.7

Of course, there is sustained agriculture, rather than shag, in some parts of Central America and Mexico. As Budowski points out, "Large areas of fresh volcanic soils have been farmed in Mexico and Central America for centuries without adding fertilizers or using refined conservation techniques. . . . Indians, when organized in communities with a certain degree of self-government, often had a good knowledge of ecological balance. . . . Good examples can be found north of the steep Cuchumatanes Mountains in Guatemala, or in that same country the preservation of natural forested areas very close to population centers where cuttings or encroachments are regulated by a special council chosen among elderly people. . . . The above picture is sharply in contrast with other areas where opening of new roads leads invariably to the clearing of prevailing forest in a relatively short time and often subsequent destruction of the productivity of the land" (13: 146-48). And he states elsewhere, "Shifting cultivation, formerly restricted to drier or colder areas, is moving into this area [wet tropics] because of increasing population pressure" (11: 240). As Tosi and Voertman estimate (34: 194), "Two formations—*tropical moist* and *subtropical wet forest*—occupy approximately 54 per cent of the land area of Central America yet contain only about 10 per cent of the population."

Functional Complexity of the Ecosystem

I would like to discuss here the almost incomprehensible complexity of the environment and a disagreement with our sapient organizer who refers to "the simple facts." The facts are never simple! Failure to recognize this is very much part of what Dr. Zelinsky has called the "folk wisdom of the literate." Professor Gourou surely had this in mind, in part, when he sagely observed, "man has interpreted the environment in terms of his techniques" (33: 346).

It is extremely difficult to achieve a reasonably sound understanding of man—the organism-as-a-whole in his environment-as-a-whole—without including the idea of "function."

> The notion of "function" has played a very great role in the development of modern science and is structurally and semantically fundamental. This notion was apparently first introduced into mathematical literature by Descartes. Leibnitz introduced the term itself. The notion of a "function" is based on that of the *variable*. In mathematics variable is used as an ∞-valued [infinite-valued] symbol that can represent *any one* of a series of numerical elements. . . .
>
> A rough definition of a function is simple: y is said to be a function of x, if, when x is given, y is determined. Let us start with a simple mathematical illustration: $y = x + 3$. If we select the value 1 for x, our $y = 1 + 3 = 4$. If we select $x = 2$, then $y = 2 + 3 = 5$.
>
> In general y is determined when we fulfill all the indicated *operations* upon the variable x, and so get the final result of this operation. In symbols, $y = f(x)$, which is read, y equals function of x, or y equals f of x . . . .
>
> The notion of a "function xy has been generalized by Bertrand Russell to the very important notion of a "propositional function." . . . By a propositional function, I mean an ∞-valued statement, containing one or more variables, such that when single values are assigned to these variables the expression becomes in principle a *one-valued* proposition. The ∞-valued character of propositional functions seems essential, because we may have a one-valued descriptive function with variables, or a one-valued expression formulating a semantic relational law expressed in variable terms, etc., yet these would be propositions. . . .
>
> An important characteristic of a propositional function, for instance, "x is black," is that such a statement is neither true nor false, but ambiguous. It is useless to discuss the truth or falsehood of propositional functions, since the term true or false cannot be applied to them. But if a definite single value is assigned to the variable x, then the propositional function becomes the proposition which may be true or false. For instance, if we assign to x the value "coal," and say "coal is black," the infinite valued propositional function has become a one-valued true proposition (20: 134-36).

Ecology, classically defined as the relationship of an organism to its environment, might be more adequately described as the four-dimensional interrelationships of the environment-as-a-whole, including the organism-as-a-whole. This means that it is chiefly concerned with variables, that most of these are dependent variables, and that they must, therefore, be regarded as functions. Just as the organism-as-a-whole is different from the sum of its parts, so is the environment-as-a-whole. . . .

We live in and depend on a *physical* world that supplies not only the basic needs of our survival but the surplus wealth that, operated on by human thinking and skills, makes possible what we consider a high standard of living. Basic to our physical survival are adequate supplies of carbohydrates, fats, proteins, vitamins, etc.; often extremely complex substances, and these are primarily drawn from the soil.

Besides our food we must have, in virtually every part of the globe, adequate housing and this, again, has frequently been drawn from the soil in the form of lumber if only as the wattles supporting adobe walls. . . .

Water is an equal necessity with food; since, deprived of water, a human organism dies much more rapidly than when it is deprived of food, perhaps water should be considered more important than food. Water is required not only for drinking, but for agriculture, manufacturing, sanitation, power, etc., and as the standard of living increases, the per capita use of water necessarily goes up at a geometric rate. . . .

The various elements making up our productive world—soil, water, forests and grasslands—seem relatively simple. . . . In fact, however, each one of them is a dependent variable and is frequently part of a structure that could be described only by an extremely complex equation, were it possible to describe it mathematically.

Soils, for example, are functions—that is to say, the results of interactions—of the parent material or rock from which they are derived; of insolation—a particularly powerful influence in the tropics; chemical action of air and rain; of slope—some soils have a higher angle of repose than others; temperature, in reference to absolute amounts, range, and distribution throughout the year; of water in relation to total precipitation, its distribution throughout the year, and the amount deposited in brief periods of time; of wind, as an evaporative and erosive force; fire, caused by friction, lightning or man; or plants, as they condition the soil through their successions and as they protect it against erosion; of the animals that live in and condition the soils—protozoans, isopods, insects, earthworms, and of larger burrowing forms, plus grazing animals that may destroy plant cover and initiate erosion with their cutting hooves; of time; etc. [37: 7-9].

As a result of these functional interactions, every piece of land is literally unique —one of a kind that is different at any moment in time. There are, of course, greater and lesser degrees of similarity, but the identification of one piece of land with another is false to fact.

There are certain demands this land must fulfill, which it should not be necessary to spell out here, but which are obviously ignored by government administrators, and even by geographers and economists who think in economic rather than geographic or ecologic parameters. For example, Simon Teitel, a Latin American economist with the U.N., writing in *The New York Times,* May 2, 1967, stated, in connection with economic development of Latin America" . . . considerations about disrupting the environment . . . are hardly relevant."

Dr. Raymond F. Dasmann of The Conservation Foundation has written in a recent unpublished manuscript,

> The dependence of life upon solar energy is complete. This includes not only the dependence on sunlight in supplying warmth and illumination to the earth's

surface, but also on its role in providing energy contained in food and in the fuels that are burned to operate our industrial civilization. . . .

Energy captured by green plants becomes available to higher organisms in an ecosystem, and is said to flow throughout the various energy levels, or trophic levels, of a *food chain*. A food chain consists of a series of organisms, one feeding upon the other. Because of the inefficiency in energy transfer, and loss of energy at each transfer in the manner to be described below, food chains are usually short.

In the transfer of energy from green plants to herbivores that consume green plants, most of the energy stored by the plants is lost through dispersal as heat in the processes of digestion and metabolism, or through elimination as undigested waste. The energy actually stored in the tissues of a herbivore usually represents only a small percentage of the energy originally available in its food. Thus the hog, a relatively efficient energy converter, will supply in its tissues only 20 per cent of the energy in the corn that the hog feeds upon. When carnivores feed upon herbivores there is still another loss of energy, and most of the energy contained within the tissues of herbivores does not appear as energy stored within the body of the carnivore. Thus, in any ecosystem, the amount of energy available to a species that fed exclusively upon other carnivores would be quite small compared to that originally available in green plants.

The inefficiencies of energy transfer within an ecosystem are examples of a long recognized physical law, the second law of thermodynamics, which states, in effect, that in any spontaneous transformation of energy some will inevitably be lost to the system, dispersed as unavailable heat energy. It is a law that humans have learned to live with. In overpopulated areas, few can afford the luxury of energy transferred from green plants through herbivores. Plant foods must be consumed directly by man to achieve the caloric intake needed to sustain life. Quality of diet, the luxury of

feeding upon meat-animals or fish, must be sacrificed to caloric quantity. However, while caloric quantity may be adequate to sustain life for a short period, a sacrifice in food quality results in serious consequences to health, reproduction, vigor, growth, and other metabolic processes. Protein hunger is far more widespread in the world than caloric hunger. . . .

Despite the massive consumption of energy in industrialized societies, all societies must meet the basic food energy requirements of man through dependence upon *the annual storage of energy by green plants. The flow of energy through natural or modified food chains remains the process most vital to continued human occupancy of the earth.* . . .

Energy and water flow along food chains in every ecosystem. Water, in its movement from soil to plant to animal also brings with it the chemical nutrients on which life depends. These are in limited supply in every ecosystem. . . . The continuation of life in an ecosystem . . . depends upon the continuous turnover and exchange of nutrients, and a minimum net loss of nutrients to the system. . . .

A great variety of . . . chemical elements must be present in the soil for plant growth to occur. It is not enough, however, for them to be present, they must be present in available form which usually means either dissolved in water in the soil solution, or loosely attached to clay or humus particles within the soil. . . .

Tropical forest soils developed under high rainfall regimes are often heavily leached and oxidized. They contain an excess of iron and aluminum salts but a deficiency of other elements. Most of the nutrients are tied up within the living matter of the ecosystem of plant and animal life. As soon as these nutrients are released through death and decay, they are picked up again by plants and returned to the system. If vegetation is cleared and burned, nutrients once contained within it are released in quantity to the soil; but since the soil lacks absorbing clay particles to hold the nutrients near the soil surface, they are quickly leached away by rainfall. The parent soil, because of leaching and oxidation is in itself relatively sterile and consequently unable to sustain an extractive form of agricultural use for long. Relatively high production may follow the initial clearing, but it cannot be long sustained. The soils respond poorly to fertilizers since they lack the structural compounds that will hold and make available to crop lands the elements supplied.

These processes, it should be noted, are physical phenomena, operating in an environment that had come to terms with itself long before the arrival of the human race.

Human Impact upon the Ecosystem

The impact of man, who has probably not been present in Central America much more than 10,000 years, was relatively insignificant for millennia. True, he modified the vegetation and perhaps the landforms through resultant erosion, by fire, but this effect was local. Cook and Simpson estimate the population of Central Mexico (geographically, though not ecologically, tropical) at about 10 million in 1519 (12: 46) and Barón Castro that of El Salvador as 130,000 (6 per km²) in 1524 (5: 124). The late George Vaillant suggested that conflict, revolt, and crop failure contributed to the downfall of Teotihuacán, and that the crop failure was largely the result of deforestation, erosion, and consequent disruption of the hydrologic cycle (36: 169-70). The decay of the Mayan "empire" has been postulated on more or less the same mismanagement of the land (33: 695); but there seems to have been no widespread disruption of the structure of the land in Mexico and Central America before the arrival of the European. The process that was set in train in the sixteenth century has continued to the present day, accelerating at an exponential rate that is even steeper than the curve of population growth.

One of the earliest "technological improvements" was the introduction, by the Spaniards, of horses, cattle, sheep, and goats. Simpson reports apparently serious overgrazing as early as 1595. "The yearly burning of sheep pastures noted by Father Ponce destroyed forest and brush cover and prevented its replacement, as Gourou observes of the African veld . . . . Overgrazing and burning, in a land of long dry seasons and torrential summer precipitation, contributed, probably to a disastrous degree, to the erosion pattern characteristic of old sheep land of the central plateau. All the regions where sheep were most heavily introduced in the sixteenth century have today vast and dismal stretches of semidesert badlands. . . ." (26: 22-23)

The innovation of the steel plow and draft animals of course speeded the destruction of steep slopes, in anticipation of the tractor and bulldozer.

One of the most dynamic factors in this ecosystem is the rainfall pattern. The highly variable Central American rainfall distribution has recently been reviewed by Portig (22: 68-90). In annual amounts it ranges from 6.5 meters in San Juan del Norte, Nicaragua, to less than 500 mm in Zacapa, Guatemala. From El Salvador there is a record of 600 mm in half an hour (9: 66) and *The New York Times* recently reported, from Honduras, 760 mm in one night. Parts of Baja California have less than 200 mm in a year (31: 43), and Portig reports as little as 11 mm in three months in Guatemala City. Deficient rainfall means, of course, low productivity except where irrigation is possible. The heavy rainfall, especially in the intense tropical *aguaceros* or "cloudbursts," creates severe flooding and erosion hazards.

The devegetation of the uplands, accelerating the erosion, is widely aggravated by the need for fuel. Mexico is more fortunate than Central America in having petroleum resources, but the distribution facilities are poor. *Carbón vegetal* and *Leña* or firewood are very widely used by country folk; the need for these has been one of the major hazards to national parks. It is estimated that in Central America 60 per cent of the energy is derived from *"combustibles vegetales,"* 9 per cent from electricity, and the remainder from petroleum (39: 65). It is reported that in El Salvador deforestation has proceeded to the point where people are forced to buy wood from the coastal mangroves, though it is less satisfactory and more expensive.

So many nostrums, salves, poultices, tranquilizers, and amphetamines are being prescribed for "developing" countries that it is impossible to list all of them. One of the most dangerous may be the new pesticides that are deluging Mexico and Central America. Woodwell and others have recently elucidated the "biological magnification" of the effect of DDT and related chlorinated hydrocarbons passing through the soil into the ecosystem. There seems to be no specific analysis for Central America, but Babione reports from the area,

> The geographical location of high levels of persistent malaria transmission and high DDT resistance are almost identical. . . . Almost without exception, they are precisely the same areas where cotton cultivation is carried on intensively, or has been at some time recently. . . . From the first of August to the end of February or even March, the cotton fields are sprayed at least once a week by aircraft using various insecticidal mixtures. DDT is one of the most common ingredients of the cocktail used . . . the larvae also live in DDT contaminated water. . . . Resistence to DDT has appeared in A. albimanus in rice-growing areas in Nicaragua and the Dominican Republic where aircraft dispersal . . . is used [1: 76-77].

The impact of such a poison on the four-dimensional ecosystem has, of course, not even begun to be comprehended.

Dementia Economica

Space limits discussion to only two other factors. The first, a product of the human nervous system, largely developed under the benign climatic conditions and relief of Northwestern Europe, I am inclined to call *Dementia economica*. It consists, in part, of substituting limited symbols—such as dollars, *pesos, colones, lempiras,* and *quetzales*—for such reality as topsoil, fertility, soil metabolism, available water, protein, and the complex interdependencies within the ecosystem —including man. The commonly used symbols are quite correctly labeled "currency," presumably in recognition of their temporary value despite attempts to stabilize them. Our modern alchemists are even discussing the creation of something that would have astounded their medieval predecessors: "paper gold." Mexico (to cite merely one example) boasts of a rising Gross National Product (measured in *pesos*), while per capita protein for her people (measured as a median or mode, *not* as a mean) almost certainly decreases along with her available and indispensable topsoil and water. For soil conservation she annually appropriates fifty cents per square mile!

Self-deception appears unique to the human race; it alone has been able to survive (though still a very young species) despite dedication to superstitions, religion, flag-waving, economics, and recently marijuana and LSD. (One is tempted to suggest that opiates are the religion of the people.) The new high priests of economics are powerful indeed; their influence spreads far beyond that of the devotees who plucked out living human hearts in obeisance to Quetzalcoatl. The new hierarchy tears out the heart of the land, in the name of development, as it fosters the sowing of such row crops as cotton and tobacco which may be exchanged in the far-off market-place for pieces of the currency, while the masses of people are short of food and forced to produce their carbohydrates on mini-plots of inferior land. This again results in part from economic reasoning: the level and fertile land, such as alluvia, can produce more pieces of the "currency" when it is used for cash crops and for grazing—often by meat animals for export. In Central America 80 per cent of agricultural producers are crowded into 12 per cent of land, often areas that because of slope should never be farmed, and which bring poor yields; 0.3 per cent of the producers have 33 per cent of the land, including much of the best (25: 7) and economically, at least in the short term, the most productive. Until those who manage the land base their thinking on the physical processes—the environmental metabolism—taking place in the land itself (including water movement and biotic processes), there can be little hope of maintaining long-range productivity. Since each piece of land is unique, the transference of techniques from one ecological zone to another is often disastrous. What I have come to think of as "Iowa thinking" has been responsible for the destruction of millions of acres in the tropics.

The Futility of Instant Gimmickry

The "developers" have recently discovered that hundreds of millions of people do not have enough to eat. As usual, they are largely seeking a one-shot solution—fertilizer—which brings me back to the title of this paper.

On December 30, 1951, *New York Times* science writer William A. Laurence reported from the meeting of the American Association for the Advancement of Science

a synthetic chemical that converts nonproductive into productive soil in a matter of hours instead of the years or generations required by present methods. . . .

The chemical, named Krilium, is not a fertilizer. It is a soil conditioner. . . .

Extensive tests carried out during the last three years by the Monsanto Chemical Company and by approximately eighty soil scientists [*sic*] in various sections of the United States indicate that the new chemical . . . will mark the beginning of a revolutionary era in agriculture. . . .

The development was announced . . . by Dr. Charles A. Thomas, president of Monsanto; Dr. C. A. Hochwalt, vice-president in charge of research and development, and by a group of scientists from Monsanto and other institutions. . . .

Scientists attending the symposium expressed the view that the new synthetic soil conditioner might prove to be an even more powerful weapon against communism than the atomic bomb, since communism thrives among peoples who live on soils that no longer produce enough food to support their increasing population. . . .

Early skepticism was expressed by Blanco Macías, and Krilium, in the ensuing years, has seemed to vanish except for an occasional sour comment such as that of Ing. Agr. F. Suarez de Castro (30: 26).

In view of the recent burgeoning of suggestions (even by economists) that the food crisis must be solved through the massive use of fertilizers, I asked the Monsanto Company what had happened to Krilium. Their reply, on February 27, 1967, was that "Krilium is no longer a commercial product and, essentially, in a nutshell we had a product which was technically a success and commercially and economically a failure."

Our developers are putting on a big push for fertilizer production, even forcing some governments such as India to expand production of fertilizer (which, itself, may be an environmental pollutant) though we often have less than rudimentary understanding of the environments in which it will be used. "Herdt and Meller have shown that the response of rice yields to 20 and 40 pounds of nitrogen in India is only about two-thirds that in the U.S. Further, when used at rates of about 50 pounds, nitrogen reduces yields in India, whereas in the U.S. the crops continued to respond to nitrogen up to 120 pounds per acre" (3: 42). The research to establish sound fertilizing procedures (even disregarding, as most agronomists have, the ecology of the soil) can only be developed through years of research that, in the countries under discussion, has hardly been begun. Hernandez estimates that, at the very least, ten years of research will be needed to begin to learn how to manage the soil of southeastern Mexico.

In Mexico and Central America, man has intruded into an ecosystem that evolved without him and his technology. Into this ecosystem he has injected many techniques —perhaps the most disruptive being death control that swiftly pyramids human numbers—that have had almost incalculable effects in the four dimensions of his environment. These pressures are nearly everywhere destructive.

These countries are, on the whole, deteriorating rather than developing. It is not at all certain, given the power and complexity of the forces involved, that the direction of the trend is reversible. And they, unhappily, are more or less typical of much of the "developing" world.

REFERENCES

(1) R. D. Babione: Epidemiology of Malaria Eradication in Central America, *American Journal of Public Health,* Jan. 1966, pp. 76-77.

(2) G. Bachelier: La Vie Animale dans les Sols (Paris, 1963).

(3) Kenneth L. Bachman: Can We Produce Enough Food? in: World Population and Food Supplies, 1980 (American Society of Agronomy, 1965), p. 42.

(4) Pierre Birot: Le Cycle d'Erosion sous les Different Climats (Rio de Janeiro, 1960).

(5) Rodolfo Barón Castro: La Población de El Salvador (Madrid, 1942).

(6) Ing. Agr. Gonzalo Blanco Macías: *Tierra,* March 1952, pp. 161-63.

(7) Gonzalo Blanco Macías and Guillermo Ramírez Cervantes: La Conservación del Suelo y el Agua en México (Mexico, 1966).

(8) George Borgstrom: The Hungry Planet (New York, 1965).

(9) W. C. Bourne, T. W. McKinley, C. P. Stevens, and Mario Pacheco: Preliminary Survey of Conservation Possibilities in El Salvador (San Salvador, 1946).

(10) Lester R. Brown: Increasing World Food Output (Washington, 1965).

(11) Gerardo Budowski: The Choice and Classification of Natural Habitats in Need of Preservation in Central America, *Turrialba,* Vol. 15, No. 3, 1965, p. 240.

(12) Sherburne F. Cook and L. B. Simpson: The Population of Central Mexico in the Sixteenth Century, *Ibero-Americana,* 31, 1948.

(13) F. Fraser Darling and John Milton, eds.: Future Environments of North America (New York, 1966).

(14) Proceedings of Duke University Tropical Forestry Symposium (Durham, 1965).

(15) Ana María Flores: La Magnitud del Hambre en México (Mexico, 1961).

(16) J. C. Goulden: Dilemma in Mexico, *Wall Street Journal,* Sept. 12, 1966.

(17) Pierre Gourou: The Tropical World (London, 1953).

(18) Lewis Herber: Crisis in Our Cities (Englewood Cliffs, 1965).

(19) Efraím Hernandez X: Les Recursos Naturales del Sureste y Su Aprovechimiento, *Chapingo, Epoca II,* Vol. II, No. 6, Chapingo, Mexico, 1962, p. 54.

(20) Alfred Korzybski: Science and Sanity (Lakeville, Conn., 1933).

(21) Pan American Union: Index of Aerial Photographic Coverage and Mapping of Topography and Natural Resources (Washington, 1965).

(22) W. H. Portig: Central American Rainfall, *Geographic Review,* Vol. 55, Jan. 1965, pp. 68-90.

(23) Prospects of the World Food Supply, a Symposium (Washington, D.C., 1966).

(24) P. W. Richards: The Tropical Rain Forest (Cambridge, 1952).

(25) ROCAP Guatemala: CAPTO Circular A-80, Department of State (Washington, 1964).

(26) Lesley Byrd Simpson: Exploitation of Land in Central Mexico in the Sixteenth Century, *Ibero-Americana,* 36, 1952.

(27) Paul C. Standley: The Forests of Guatemala, *Tropical Woods,* No. 67, 1941, p. 3.

(28) R. W. Steel: Geography and the Developing World, *The Advancement of Science,* March 1967, pp. 566-82.

(29) J. Mayone Stycos and Jorge Arias, eds.: Population Dilemma in Latin America (Washington, 1966).

(30) Ing. Agr. Fernando Suarez de Castro: Conferencias, Fundación Shell (Caracas, 1966).

(31) Jorge L. Tamayo: Geografía General de México, *Tomo II* (Mexico, 1949).

(32) *The Economist,* 13 May 1967, ccxxiii, 6455, p. 684.

(33) William L. Thomas, ed.: Man's Role in Changing the Face of the Earth (Chicago, 1956).

(34) Joseph A. Tosi, Jr. and Robert F. Voertman: Some Environmental Factors in the Economic Development of the Tropics, *Economic Geography,* Vol. 40, No. 3, 1964, pp. 189-205.

(35) William Vogt: Report on Activities of the Conservation Section,

Division of Agricultural Cooperation, Pan American Union, 1943-1946 (Washington, 1947).

(36) William Vogt: Road to Survival (New York, 1948).

(37) William Vogt: On Structure and Survival, *General Semantics Bulletin,* Nos. 10 & 11, 1953.

(38) William Vogt: Comments on a Brief Reconnaisance of Resource Use, Progress and Conservation Needs in Some Latin American Countries (New York, 1963).

(39) William Vogt, ed.: La Conservación Humana en Centro América (Guatemala, C.A., 1966).

(40) George M. Woodwell: Toxic Substances and Ecological Cycles, *Scientific American,* Vol. 216, No. 4, 1967, pp. 24-31.

(41) George M. Woodwell, Charles F. Wurster, Jr., and Peter A. Isaacson: DDT Residues in an East Coast Estuary: a Case of Biological Concentration of a Persistent Insecticide, *Science,* Vol. 156, No. 3776, pp. 821-24.

(42) Anthony Zimmerman: Catholic Viewpoint on Overpopulation (New York, 1961).

12. THE CONCEPT OF ENVIRONMENTAL POTENTIAL AS EXEMPLIFIED BY TROPICAL AFRICAN RESEARCH

Philip W. Porter

If the world were simple, geography wouldn't be any fun. The world, however, exhibits immense complexities, which pose a continuing challenge to man in his attempts to understand the environment and his relations with it. The student who attempts to assess the potential of land for agricultural purposes must first face up to three dilemmas.

The Dilemma of Scale

A map of environmental potential, like any map, must be drawn at a scale. Information drawn at a large scale may be useful to a farmer, but not permit us to make any general statements about environment. On the other hand, synthetic statements on potentialities of the environment, while they usually have a pedagogic value, are at such a scale of generalization—both cartographic and factual—that the farmer or agricultural planner cannot base specific decisions on them.

The environment in which real people plow fields, tend cattle, and collect wild fruits is far removed from our ecological or agroclimatic description of it. The farmer's fields are near him, he operates at a 1:1 scale with his universe. Ecological and agro-meteorological discussions, such as the ones examined in this paper, are carried on at scales which in the extremes are as small as 1:100,000,000. Like all scientists, the environmental scientist seeks to discover lawful generalizations concerning the world he observes. Ecologists (agricultural economists, agrometeorologists, range management specialists, etc.), however, are mostly in government employ, and thus are torn between finding answers that will satisfy specific problems (such as, at what rate can a block of land be stocked with cattle without deterioration to the vegetative cover), and finding answers that have the virtue of generality. It is these two domains (specificity and generality) which ecologists, agronomists, and geographers find it difficult to unite. We know that all environments have varying potentials; we generally know what uses are suitable for a particular piece of land; we know a good deal about the environmental parameters that give rise to these different potentials; but we still have difficulty in moving directly from the physical causes of environmental character to prescriptions for suitable uses of the environment.

Efforts to generalize agricultural potential at the continental or world scale are commonly dissatisfying. Attempts to provide a sweeping universal model for the measurement of agricultural potential, based on meteorological data, tend to be greatly oversimplified and at times naive (8; 22; 86; 95). More sophisticated analyses tend to be overcomplex. For example, Phillips's presentation of bioclimatic regions is based on vegetation communities—climaxes and plant succession (103), and is thus ecological rather than meteorological in concept.

The ecological map is not a scientific explanation of the environment in the sense that the biophysical processes are fully accounted for. An ecologist takes vegetation as it comes, accounts for its present state through an examination of climate and soils, with particular recourse to the history of fire and previous cutting, cultivation, or grazing, and establishes the probable plant succession for an area. Phillips's method of presentation, which uses climax or bioclimatic regions, leads the reader into a fearful maze of detail with a key of no less than 154 coded letters. Thus at the most general level —that of the bioclimatic region—we orient ourselves with "HSFESL: Related to HFEL; Cx with much SV." This we learn to translate as: humid-subhumid forest, on the eastern and southern lowlands of Africa—related to humid forest of the eastern lowlands of Africa, a vegetation climax with much secondary vegetation due to various forms of disturbance (cultivation, grazing, and browsing by livestock, burning of vegetation). The complexities of this shorthand make large portions of Phillips's valuable book virtually unreadable.

The Dilemma of Complexity

We have already seen that an assessment of environmental potential in terms meaningful to the farmer or herdsman involves many variables. Recognition of this fact is contained in Jacques Cochemé's recent discussions of the FAO/UNESCO/WMO agroclimatic survey of the semi-arid parts of West Africa (28; 29). His analysis of a broad zone in West Africa (4,000 km long, from the Atlantic to the Sudan border, and 800 km wide between desert and forest) includes the following topics: rainfall—variability, seasonal variation, intensity; availability of water—potential evapotranspiration, water budget, periods of availability of water, annual variability; light and heat—radiation, temperature, photoperiodism and dry matter production. Some common crops of the area such as millet, sorghum, maize, cowpea, groundnuts, and cotton are also discussed.

Implicit in the notion of "potential or optimal use" is the idea that land so used could support a certain density of population at a particular level. It would be useful to be able to specify optimal use as the group of crops that should be grown in an area. But the scale at which such statements become meaningful is very nearly topographic, and of a low order of generality. The growth cycle of even a single food crop such as millet, which in the West African study was 60 to 200 days, may exhibit a great range. Varietal differences in a crop are enormous, with some varieties being adapted only to a narrow range of ecotypes. Thus exchange of crops between areas of similar climates, with moist humid periods of identical length, may be unsuccessful. An example is provided by Cochemé:

"A sorghum found well adapted to the conditions at Bambey in Senegal, and with a photoperiodically fixed date of heading, might give disappointing yields at places with the same annual rainfall further east. At those places the moist and humid periods, though of the same duration, would begin and end earlier than in West Senegal. Also, since they are further south, owing to the dipping of the isohyets, flower initiation would be photoperiodically retarded. Heading would therefore occur significantly later than at Bambey and well after the end of the humid period" (29: 8). Many food grasses are known to be extremely sensitive to photo period. For example, "with sugar cane, a difference in day length of 10 minutes is sufficient to induce or prevent flowering" (35: 67).

Cochemé resists any temptation to translate the separate analyses of his report into a synthetic presentation of agroclimatic types. It is important that we understand the reasons behind his forbearance.

It is realized that in a region where a given set of conditions prevail, this sameness is reflected in the vegetation which integrates these conditions, and consequently also in the land usage. This leads to subdivision of an area into natural or agroclimatic regions and subregions. Such concepts are common usage and, though often formulated rather loosely, they are not without utility for the exchange of information for teaching and for scientists and planners first approaching the problem from outside. . . .

To be directly effective in guiding local agricultural policy a fineness of detail and a thoroughness of consideration of all the factors involved is needed, of a kind which cannot be provided by one single integrated system of classification.

For each specific need of agricultural exploitation, the climate parameters and indices used in this study may require to be separated into classes with different limits. When different parameters have to be considered in association, the number of combinations is multiplied. In the end, as many systems of climate classification suggest themselves as there are distinct requirements. [29: 10]

The foregoing statement contains one of the most important lessons I have learned in searching the literature on methods of assessing environmental potential in tropical Africa. Geographers are numbered among the few who still like to think of themselves as universal men, people able to see a complex problem whole. This is an egoism that the world can little afford. The object of environmental assessment is to discover optimal land uses which are compatible both with nature and society. If such optimal uses may be discovered by extending our senses and our ability to reason through electronic means, then we should not hesitate to do so. Geographers, by habit, want to see results summarized in map form. We tend to feel that the electronic storage of data robs us of our sight, whereas computer generation of maps to many different specifications actually restores our eyesight and enhances it many times over. As Cochemé says:

The main advantage of organizing a set of several continuous variables into a fixed system of classes is that it becomes more accessible to the limited powers of the human memory. With the presentday use of electronic storage of information, this advantage has disappeared. Regrouping of the parameters into classes appropriate to the problem in hand can be done for the asking. [29:10]

Cochemé notes that the study of agroclimatology is hampered by a lack of agronomic data. The greatest need is for information on crop yields and biological events such as flowering. Those of us who do field work in geography could be of great service in supplying such information.

The Dilemma of Scientific Truth

We know, or at least we are persuaded, that the various patterns of behavior in plants and animals are the result of processes which ultimately could be reduced to physical statements. I am not sure that the agrometeorologist who seeks a physically coherent explanation of, say, the radiation balance and rates of evapotranspiration, or the ecologist who seeks a reasoned explanation of a vegetation assemblage are truly in scientific pursuit of the relationship of the plant with its milieu. If mean monthly temperatures predict, they will be used; if *Cryptosepalum pseudotaxus* forest indicates land that has good soil and will give good millet yields, it may be treated as an ecologic type. There are, I suppose, scientists who seek a sort of ultimate understanding of the behavior of plants and animals at the molecular or atomic level. We are even disposed to believe that the truths they find will in due course be relevant to society. On the other hand, it must be noted that the lowliest tiller of the soil has his own corpus of truth based on hard-won experience. The agricultural planner, too, commands a body of knowledge of a sort that says "to do X will result in Y"; but these are more immediate truths. The reason why X produces Y may be of no interest. Thus, there are many sorts of truth, and a number of investigative points along a continuum of ever increasing complexity at which we may commence our search. There is also the hard truth that the potential of an environment is as often "The people won't stand for it," as it is "The land cannot withstand such use" (36). The question remains, at what points in the continuum of inquiry does one search for the necessary truths, keeping in mind the need for immediate effective application of findings (especially in areas of population pressure), as well as the long term desire to obtain general theoretical understanding of biophysical processes?

THE DIMENSIONS OF ENVIRONMENTAL POTENTIAL

The phenomena that impinge on the possibilities within the environment and the men who use it are as broad as knowledge itself. Problems of disease and human psychology are surely relevant to the study of pressure of population on physical and social resources, yet we set them aside here as being topics more appropriately dealt with by competent specialists. The dimensions we will consider in this section are as follows: (1) human nutritional requirements, (2) the maintenance of soil fertility, (3) concepts of the normal surplus and subsistence risk, (4) land tenure, and (5) level of organization—relation of agriculture to other sectors of the economy.

The reader will see that in four out of five cases we have, in a sense, turned the question of potential upside down, electing to look at the question of environmental po-

tential from the point of view of the land itself. The question is not how well endowed is the land, but how well endowed are the people (technologically, socially, politically) who live on it?

A map of land-use merely describes a pattern, it does not explain it. Explanation of land-use necessarily involves all the expectations, technology, and labor of the people who use the land. We need to know the timing and spacing of labor, the inputs of capital; we need, in short, man-use maps too (14: 118; 26).

Human Nutritional Needs

Some years ago the FAO in committee reports established recommended minimum nutritional standards for both calorie and protein requirements (45; 46). Their suggested minima vary according to sex, age, body weight, work level, and climate (temperature), with special values for pregnant women and lactating mothers. Using the values for the "reference man"—an adult, aged 25, weighing about 143 lbs (65 kg), we find that 2900 to 3050 calories/day would be required for a man living in the warmer parts of tropical Africa. The caloric needs of children are much less (e.g., aged 1-3 years, 1200 calories/day; aged 7-9 years, 1900 calories/day); for women the need is less (2100-2200 calories/day), except during pregnancy or when nursing young (3000 calories/day).

Taking into account the age and sex pyramid typical of tropical African countries, and the proportion of women who are pregnant or nursing at any given time, the average recommended calorie requirement would be about 2150/day. Judged against that standard the countries of East and West Africa generally come off fairly well (Table 12-1) (47).

The African diet, however, is shown to be

TABLE 12-1   ESTIMATED FOOD SUPPLIES FOR
HUMAN CONSUMPTION IN CALORIES AND
PROTEINS (PER CAPUT PER DAY)

Countries	Calories	Proteins (grams)	Animal Proteins (grams)
East Africa			
Ethiopia	2215	64	16
Kenya	2240	63	12
Tanganyika	2175	59	8
West Africa			
Cameroon	2500	65	17
Chad	2540	85	14
Ghana	2605*	45	9
Guinea	2400	50	4
Liberia	2540*	47	4
Mali	2170	69	11
Nigeria**	2100	59	7
Togo	2645***	59	15
Upper Volta	1850	61	5

* = Probably overestimated
**= Provisional estimate
*** = Certainly overestimated
Source: 47:23.

markedly deficient in the supply of proteins, particularly those of high nutritive value such as milk, meat, and eggs. The recommended daily intake of proteins of high nutritive value for the "reference man" or woman is 23 grams; for infants it is 2 grams for every kilogram of weight; for a person reaching puberty the rate might be 35 to 40 grams; and for nursing mothers it should be 30 grams. Again, taking into account the variables mentioned above, the mean daily requirement of protein of high quality in tropical African countries would be about 26 grams. Since the publication of revised nutritional standards by FAO in 1957 (46), however, the quantity of animal proteins considered necessary in a diet has been reduced to about 20 per cent. Total daily protein intake should be from 65 to 70 grams, of which about 14 should be of high quality. Table 12-1 shows that people in many countries of East and West Africa consume far

less high quality protein per day than the recommended minimum. While protein of a lower quality is provided by cereals and legumes, even the addition of these sources to total intake is often not sufficient to meet total daily requirements, particularly in the tropical forest environments (47: 24).

Carbohydrates tend to predominate in the diets, accounting for 60 to 85 per cent of caloric intake. The total need for calories appears to be met in these countries, but there are seasonal, regional, age, sex, and socioeconomic differences. Children may obtain only 60 to 70 per cent of their requirement. In the forest where the staple is yam or cassava, the daily per capita intake of animal protein may be only 1 to 3 grams.

What does it take in cropped fields and livestock to provide these recommended dietary minima, which are set at a level calculated to maintain a person's good health, not merely to keep the person alive? This depends on the nutritive value of a crop, its yield per acre, the way it is prepared, and so forth. Brown gives the following estimate of food requirements for an African family unit, which he says ranges generally between 6 and 10 members, with a mean of 8 (or 6.66 adult equivalents): for agriculturalists: 1270 kg of cereal, 545 kg of legumes, some stock products; for pure pastoralists: the blood, meat, and milk from 60-70 stock units (18).

The cereal and legumes would apparently supply each person with 1750 calories and 46 grams of protein daily. The remaining 400 calories would be obtained from meat, milk, and the fruits and garden relishes used in cooking (64). There would be a slight deficiency in high quality protein unless meat (or its equivalent in milk or eggs) were consumed at the rate of about 14 grams per day. This standard diet, with certain variations, may now be used to assess the population carrying capacity of particular productive systems, whether they be subsistence economies or schemes for mechanized farming.

Casting food requirements in terms of caloric and protein needs only grossly simplifies a complex pattern of nutritional needs. Not considered are vitamins (especially A and C and the complex of B vitamins), minerals, or trace elements that may be important to good health. In tropical Africa the most prevalent deficiency diseases are often traced to a lack of vitamins and other elements listed (20).

Again, in computing food requirements only, we ignore other needs in the family economy—fuel, fiber, building materials, household furnishings, and implements. This serves to re-emphasize the point that assessment of environmental potential is complicated by cultural considerations, and meaningful only if defined in terms of a given level of living.

The Maintenance of Soil Fertility

Vegetative cover has two important consequences for agriculture. First, by its constant supply of litter to the ground it permits the build-up of organic matter in the soil—a process which is very rapid both in the forest soils and the grassland soils of tropical areas. Second, the growth of plants leads to the accumulation and immobilization of minerals, which become available to cultivated plants when vegetation is cut and burned. Left to itself vegetative cover will reach an equilibrium in the cycling of nutrients and soil will reach an equilibrium in the rate at which litter added to the forest or grassland floor is decomposed.

When a farmer cuts vegetation, he terminates this equilibrium very abruptly. When the land is cropped, organic levels in the soil decline and mineral nutrients are no longer immobilized, but exported to the granary or lost through leaching and erosion. In most areas of African agriculture, the decrease in the level of organic matter is very rapid, "especially of those fractions which are important for ensuring a constant supply of nutrients (nitrogen and phosphorus) to the growing plant" (78: 53). With lowered yields, a farmer abandons the land to fallow and makes a farm elsewhere.

Some sort of crop fallowing sequence can be found in every part of tropical Africa, carried out on soils ranging from exceedingly fertile to those little better than pure sand. Consequently, the rate at which soils recover to a usable level varies greatly. There is also great variation in yield per hectare of cropland, as well as the number of times a field may be used before it is returned to fallow. The yield per hectare, the cropping cycle, and the fallow cycle together set population limits to forms of agriculture based on rudimentary tools—axe, cutlass, hoe, and fire. There are calculable optimal population limits or densities which can be sustained at given technological levels without deterioration of the environment. It has been calculated that the Congo forest can support densities of $30/km^2$, while the upper limit of support in some of the drier parts of Zambia may be less than $1/km^2$.

When population increases to the point at which land must be cropped more frequently, the following cycle is set in motion: the fallow period is reduced; yields decline rapidly; larger areas are planted; fallow periods are further reduced. Fields which have lain fallow for only part of the normal recovery period will perform less well when cropped. Organic matter may build up sufficiently, but the amount of mineral nutrients will decrease considerably with the burning of vegetation. Pressure to shorten the fallow cycle thus has built into it a multiplier effect, since both area cropped and frequency of cropping are increased.

The role of fire in promoting transient soil fertility is sometimes not fully appreciated. It has been found that wetting dry soil results in a sudden flush of nitrate and decomposition of organic matter. During a dry season, microbial activity is low and little humus decomposition takes place. The drier the soil, the greater the amount of nutrient suddenly released from the humus with the first rains (11). Fire, in a sense, intensifies the dry season in some areas and virtually provides one in moist forest areas where rains may cease only briefly. A fire has four effects on the soil. It raises soil temperatures, which results in the decomposition of organic matter in the upper layer—releasing mineral nutrients; it provides charcoal (worked into the soil by termites) which affects pH levels; it influences runoff; and, finally, it releases the mineral nutrients immobilized in the vegetation. The flush of nutrients is immediate with the rains, and declines quite rapidly as they progress. It is not surprising, therefore, that in many African cultures farmers are keenly alive to the need to plant early. The practice of mixed planting makes sense when viewed in the context of a sudden peak in soil fertility.

Just to emphasize the crucial importance of the ephemeral fertility accompanying the first rains, we cite Dowker's calculation of the depressing effects on yields that result from delay in sowing (Table 12-2). Using the average of these tests, which were conducted during three consecutive years, we find that the average grain loss per day of delay in planting was 5.2 per cent, or about 54 kg. To plant a week late was equivalent to taking a one-third reduction in yield. The causes of this decline lie partly in water shortages that appear as the season advances; in large part, however, they relate to the rapid decrease of nutrients as the rainy season progresses. Gwynne has suggested that the difference results in part from variations in root behavior. Crops developing in a relatively dry soil early in the season may put out extensive root systems, taking advantage of the ephemeral presence of large quantities of phosphorus and other minerals. Late-planted crops developing in moist or saturated soils build less extensive root systems, and are more vulnerable to drought, should it occur later in the season (M. Gwynne, personal communication).

Nutrient balance and cycling in tropical

TABLE 12-2   YIELD OF TABORAN MAIZE AS RELATED TO
TIME OF PLANTING

Year	Seasonal Rainfall (mm)	Time of Planting	Yield of Grain kg/hectare	Mean Reduction in Yield per Day (%)
Nov. 1959–60	210	Dry	1979	—
		4 days after rain	1558	5.3
		7 days after rain	1170	5.9
Nov. 1960–61	291	Dry	1526	—
		6 days after rain	954	6.3
April 1962	311	Dry	4580	—
		6 days after rain	3284	4.7

Source: (40)

plants will one day be understood. When exact budgets of soil and vegetation associations can be prepared, it will be possible to fit crop-fallow systems into them with great precision. For the present, however, we must make do with less exact findings. It appears that forest soil in fallow rebuilds to an equilibrium level of organic matter in only four or five years. The rate at which mineral nutrients are immobilized in the leaves, branches, and trunks of trees is slower; but the level reached after only 5 years is from half to three-quarters of that reached after 18 years (78: 63). Laudelout suggests that in the Congo a fallow in excess of 15 years will not add substantially to the fertility of the soil; indeed, there are several reasons why it should last no longer than 15 years (78: 107). Fallow periods in areas of sparse woodland, such as the *miombo* lands of Zambia discussed by Trapnell and Clothier, may have to be much longer, because of the poverty of the soil, the slow rate at which minerals are immobilized, and because of the wood demands of the *citemene* form of agriculture. In the latter, branches are lopped from the trees, stacked into high brush piles, and burned—thereby concentrating the nutrients in a small area (126: 22). It is worth noting that *citemene* agriculture requires only two tools—the axe and fire. The timing and intensity of the burn are exceedingly important. A late burn, just prior to the onset of the rains most enhances the transient fertility in the soil, provided the fire does not get out of hand. The fire should not burn so fiercely that it incinerates the organic layer. The most favorable burn incinerates the surface litter, with temperatures reaching about 120°C to depths of 5 cm (78: 102).

Whatever the soil-vegetation association of an area, there is a frequency with which it may be used, whether for farming or for grazing livestock, that will keep the soil in good heart. Modern techniques such as the use of "mineral and organic fertilizers, contour plowing, crop rotation, green manures, synthetic herbicides, utilization of higher yielding and disease-resistant varieties and complicated machinery" may add time to the fallow period, but at a price (78: 3). The value added to crop production per hectare by such improvements is commonly less than the cost of the improvements; and in consequence many of the agricultural techniques of mid-latitude farming cannot be justified in the tropics on economic grounds. It is apparent that cultivation based on long fallows will be with us in tropical Africa for a good many years to come.

The Normal Surplus and Subsistence Risk

Many observers of African subsistence economies have noted the tendency of farmers to overproduce their food requirements in most years. MacDonald, in calculating food requirements and land use acreages in Uganda, found considerable over-production, that "wastage of food is inevitable and is likely to be much higher than realized" (81: 155). An example of crop yields over a number of years shows why a farmer commonly overproduces his family requirements.

The farmer will plant about 4 hectares year after year, because even in a bad season he will obtain enough to feed his family. In Ukambani, Kenya, two rainy periods permit the Kamba farmers to crop twice and thus to plant out half of the required land at a time. The yield aspect is complicated by interplanting, which is customary with the Kamba.

In most years there is extra maize—to use for initiation festivities and to show hospitality to friends, or to sell to pay school fees, buy cattle, and so forth. It is possible that the frequency with which beer is brewed in some cultures is related to this surplus.

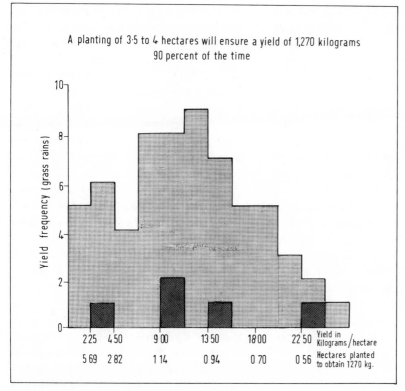

A planting of 3·5 to 4 hectares will ensure a yield of 1,270 kilograms
90 percent of the time

Fig. 12-1. MAIZE YIELDS AND PLANTING REQUIREMENTS FOR A FAMILY OF EIGHT.
(Diagram based on yield data from Katumani Experimental Station, Machakos (dark shade); supplemented by estimates of yields between 1904 and 1962 for grass rains, Kitui Boma, using Glover's regression for maize yields (light shade). Data must be considered approximate for yields under traditional technology. The values are somewhat higher than general yields at Kitui Boma.)

Though such maize-millet beers are nutritious, a person gains less protein and fewer calories from them than he would if the grain were eaten as a porridge. A feature of many African farming systems is a communal work party which clears fields, weeds, or helps to harvest a man's crop—payment being in beer and sometimes food. Work parties may be difficult to promote if there is no prospect of beer when the task is completed. Thus a period of food shortage can jeopardize the prospects of a crop in the following season—another instance of a multiplier effect.

William Allan calls the feature of over-production in subsistence farming "the normal surplus" (3: 35-48). This important concept underlines two things: (1) food wastage, viewed from a standpoint of abstract economics, is built into the agrarian system; (2) farmers clearly recognize that growing crops is a risky business. This recognition of subsistence risk is evidenced in a host of ways, which allow a farmer to hedge his bets against the vagaries of nature. Among the overt actions designed to reduce risk are dispersion of fields, use of multiple environments, dispersion (exchange) of livestock, exchange of granaries, marrying a second wife from a village with a harvest season different from the village of the first wife, planting famine crops, interplanting of crops, early planting, care in weeding to reduce transpiration and reduce soil moisture depletion, irrigation and terracing, and manuring (104).

To return to the diagram (Fig. 12-1), it can be seen that if population pressure builds to the point at which the farmer can no longer crop a fully rested 10 acres, then he is immediately more vulnerable to the uncertainties of the weather and depressed crop yields. It should be noted that the introduction of cash crops has the same effect as increasing population pressure for it serves to decrease the fallow period and increase land pressure. The production of surplus food and its subsequent waste through indifferent harvesting, poor storage techniques, and so forth, are important considerations in the assessment of the pressure of population on resources.[2]

Land Tenure

Man, no less than nature, is involved in subsistence economies. Land use, as we noted earlier, implies man use. All societies have institutions through which such things as property, land, water, labor, trade, etc. are regulated. That the institutional structures vary enormously from culture to culture is too well known to require comment. Any anthropologist worth his salt discovers in his work with the people of a particular culture that the concepts of land tenure have subtleties that, like certain French expressions, cannot be successfully rendered in English. We learn that ownership is best thought of as "being with" the land (10: 5; 33). Or we learn that an individual has the "right of contiguity" to the fields of his brothers, though

2. In connection with storage problems the reader is referred to the following review articles: 66, 115.

the right does not apply to any particular

piece of ground (12: 13). It is like the right of my youngest daughter to sit next to her mother, regardless of where we dine.

Rights are often hierarchical, "estates of administration" in Sheddick's terminology, in which the farmer has the right of continuous use, the chief of his village the right of reallocation should the land fall idle or the man die and so forth (Sheddick). A congeries of rights surrounds the use of land—covering improvements (such as terracing, irrigation, the planting of fruit trees or cash crops), stubble grazing by neighboring stock, access to water, and collecting of wild fruits and fire wood.

The form of land tenure, however, is by no means a good predictor of whether a community will be receptive to agricultural innovations. Furthemore, whatever the system of tenure, the right in all African societies of the individual to use land for growing crops and grazing his stock is simply not open to question. Whether land is owned individually, held in the name of a local chief, or the possession of a royal paramount chief, the man at the bottom of the scale can always claim the right to cultivate. So long as there is no pressure on the land and no great involvement in the world economy, tenurial matters are not issues of great moment.

Three phenomena appear to have a strong effect on land tenure—population pressure, the introduction of cash crops, and labor migration. When population pressure makes land a scarce commodity, poor land is brought into cultivation and good land tends to become fragmented, as the sons of a parent insist on their fair share of the family farm. This leads very quickly to uneconomic farming practices since the separate parcels cannot be managed or improved as a unit. Land values are likely to increase; and if land becomes a saleable item, the door is open for speculation. The courts and tribal councils become jammed with cases involving boundary disputes between neighbors and inheritance suits among brothers. The uncertainties of tenure attending land fragmentation and litigation can have a dampening effect on land prices. A large increase in land values was experienced in Kikuyu country, Kenya, when farms became consolidated and registered, and a purchaser's land title became more secure.

Where a cash crop is introduced, the individual growing the crop almost inevitably comes to think of it as his own. Even if the land is not alienable from the group, his "improvements" are, he argues. In a society where inheritance is through the maternal line, this leads to serious difficulties for a man. In many societies the permanent alienation of land is essentially an antisocial act. A man renounces his brothers and his kin, the moral values of his culture, in setting aside land which only he may use and which he may sell to whom he chooses. The most progressive African farmer I have ever met —one whose operation on 6 hectares netted him approximately $1400 per year, plus a rich and varied subsistence diet for him, his two wives, their 15 children, and two hired men—had taken the unusual step, having patiently amalgamated his farm from a number of separate parcels, of buying out his father and his brothers, so that no one could come to him and say: "Look, I haven't enough land; can you let me have the field down by the road?" Few people are capable of renouncing their traditional obligations to their fellow man so completely. I have often wondered what the neighbors and kinsmen of this successful farmer really thought of him.

Land is virtually the only security the African farmer has, aside from the institutions of mutual aid—family, clan, age grades —that assure him sources of help. It is not surprising, then, that individuals who migrate from their homeland, sometimes thousands of miles, to work in mines, factories,

and on farms, are reluctant to sever ties with home and relinquish their rights in land. The artificial life in the mining compound and factory is full of insecurity and anxiety; and an exceedingly high labor turnover has been noted for African employment in this sector of the economy. "Home is the place where, when you go there, they have to take you in." A man with no land to return home to is rootless indeed.

The continued ownership of land by men who have migrated to centers of labor demand intensifies the land fragmentation that may have induced them to migrate in the first place. An area which combines the fissional forces of population pressure and absent migrant laborers with the fusioning forces of cash crops—which commonly tend to be grown by farmers who have consolidated and planned their holding—offers remarkably complex land-use patterns. The populous western hill country of Ukambani is such an area. With coffee as a cash crop, severe land fragmentation, population densities at the section level reaching 600/km² and half the young men off to Nairobi, where many of them are unemployed, this area presents all the problems we have been discussing, even if it does not provide their solutions (105: Cpt. 4).

Level of Organization—Relation of Agriculture to Other Sectors of the Economy

It has been argued that one of the fruits of colonialism was the stabilization of population distribution, tribal domains, and economic systems—aspects of African geography which previously had been fluid (3: 335). While this overstates the case, it is true that population movements and changes in land allocation took place with the knowledge and under the legal constraints of the colonial government. Further, the infrastructure of administration, railroads, roads, and often European settlement and agricultural production, led to the superimposition of a system capable of dealing with and even preventing periodic crop failures, outbreaks of locusts and army worms, and epidemics among both stock and man.

The issue of agricultural improvement is not the provision of the greatest amount of food by the most economical methods. If this were so, game-ranching would replace pastoralism in large semi-arid areas. Actual operations in Rhodesia on a 50,000-acre ranch have shown that a return of $7 per hectare can be obtained with a working expenditure of less than $7000 a year. A typical game cropping quota for this ranch for one year is 1000 impala, 500 duiker, 100 grysbok, 20 bushbuck, 150 zebra, 30 kudu, 20 sable, 5 eland, 8 wildebeeste, 10 hippo, 100 haros, and 50 guinea fowl. Due care is taken to preserve enough females so that young stock will replace those cropped (90). Talbot and Talbot have shown that the carrying capacity for wild ungulates in savanna country is about 2.5 to 3 hectares per beast, and in bush country it is about 5.5 per beast. This far exceeds the rate at which typical *Bos indicus* cattle can be grazed without endangering the land (79).

Game-ranching requires little labor. Had Britain's celebrated effort at the mechanized production of groundnuts in East Africa succeeded, it too would have required relatively little labor. The reason for citing these two examples of food production on a large scale is to stress the fact that the need in Africa is not so much to increase food production, as it is to provide a decent livelihood and security for every family. This cannot be done simply by drawing off large numbers of individuals from the farms, to relieve the population pressure in rural areas. One sometimes hears of an overpopulated area, where fields are gullied, holdings are

fragmented, and the people poor and undernourished, referred to as a "rural slum." Betterment schemes which aim at enclosure, registry of land, introduction of cash crops and modern farming techniques have, I think, much in common with urban renewal projects in the United States, for they very often displace a portion of the people whom the scheme is intended to serve. "Urban removal," as the slum dweller wryly described it, applies equally to many rural development schemes, which must provide land for those displaced from their fields and for those who, in an era of land fragmentation, have migrated to towns and become landless (3: 380; 75: 12).

Sir Philip Mitchell, a former governor of Kenya, concluded in the early 1950's that the production of primary cash crops for export in East Africa had reached a peak, was on the decline, and that, "far from there being possibility of its substantial increase, populations working under this system are going to find increasing difficulty in supporting themselves even at the present level" (3: 390; 43: 45). This view may appear unduly pessimistic in the light of what has happened in the past ten years in East Africa; yet it remains true that in producing coffee, tobacco, palm oil, pyrethrum, tea, or cotton for export, the African farmer is at the mercies of a world market in which glut and depressed prices are commonplace. Competition from farmers in other countries and from synthetic sources places him in a disadvantageous position; and it is the task of government marketing boards and international commodity commissions to try to stabilize the market and assure the farmer a regular income.

It is apparent that one objective of agricultural development should be to drain off excess population and put it to productive use elsewhere in the economy; yet the non-agricultural sector of the economy accommodates only a small part of the immense influx to urban areas. The ranks of the unemployed in many African cities are constantly increased by the arrival of people from rural areas. A long period during which governments deliberately encourage a large portion of the population to remain in farming seems likely. Allan notes the interdependencies of the agricultural and the nonagricultural sectors of African economies locked in a cycle of non-development from which it is difficult to escape. "The market for manufactured goods among a population, consisting largely of subsistence and semi-subsistence cultivators and petty commodity producers is far too small to encourage industrial development. There can be no significant increase in purchasing power without a very large increase or agricultural output. Yet general and substantial increase in agricultural productivity and prosperity depends on the development of the non-agricultural sectors, the creation of jobs for the rural surplus, and the consequent generation of expanding markets for farm products" (3: 464).

INDUCED AGRICULTURAL SYSTEMS

A word about "induced systems" of agricultural production might be appropriately interpolated at this point. The literature is strewn with the post mortem analyses of schemes and reassessments of long-term governmental development policies. Every variety of scheme has been tried (50). Discussion and critical evaluations of many of the schemes tried in tropical Africa are given by Allan, Phillips, and Harrison Church (3: 392-460; 103: 330-66; 62: 1-48). Some, like Richard-Toll in Senegal and the Groundnut Scheme in Tanganyika, have been highly mechanized.[3] Others, notably the *paysannat*

farming in the Congo, have had an element of compulsion (7: 65). Group farming and yeoman farming have been attempted with varying success, with reward rather than compulsion being the means whereby high standards of land management are maintained (1; 2; 38; 87; 88; 91; 123). The plantation as a form of agricultural enterprise also merits consideration, for while it often involves private capital and interests, it provides examples of organization, production, and population-carrying capacities that are worthy of study. The social and economic conditions of laborers on plantations are sometimes poor, but this is not necessarily inherent in the system itself (33). We referred earlier to game-ranching as a means of producing meat in great quantity at low cost. Grazing schemes for pastoral or semi-pastoral people were tried in a big way in Kenya in the 1950's and early 1960's (1; 19; 131). These induced systems of land management have varying carrying capacities, but they generally incorporate specific measures designed to intensify land use and to increase production. This is as true of grazing schemes and the *paysannat* shifting cultivation of forest *couloirs,* which both carry low densities, as it is of high-density, cash-crop, yeoman-farmer schemes in Kikuyu country. One thing is certain, where these schemes have survived they support people at a higher economic level than formerly, and on an environmentally sustaining basis. In many instances, the population densities are substantially higher than those which the traditional economy could have supported on an environmentally sustaining basis.

Figure 12-2 illustrates this point. It shows the "severity" of overpopulation for the lo-

---

3. See (62) and (134), 38 pages that made history. The scheme went ahead despite doubts raised at the time by competent critics (49,

85). As Seabrook says, "Nearly all the vociferous critics were heard only after failure had become apparent, and the amount of wisdom after the event was prodigious" (117: 90).

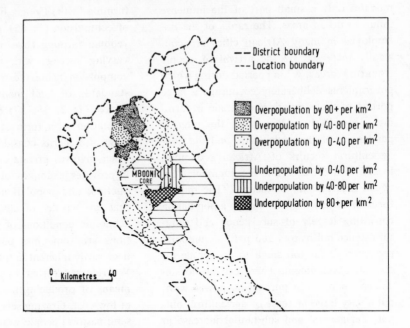

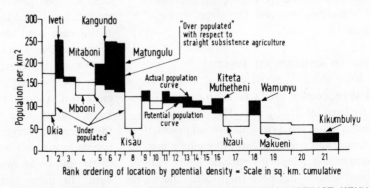

Fig. 12-2.   A. POPULATION PRESSURE IN MACHAKOS DISTRICT, KENYA:
PRESSURE ON STRAIGHT SUBSISTENCE AGRICULTURE
B. ACTUAL AND "POTENTIAL" POPULATION DENSITIES IN
MACHAKOS DISTRICT, UKAMBANI, KENYA

cations of Machakos District in Ukambani.
The carrying capacity of each location was
calculated on the basis of measured yields
collected as part of the FAO World Census
of Agriculture 1960. Yields were measured
for ecologic zones as well as administrative

areas. The year 1960 was not a good year for
agriculture in Ukambani. Yields were only
mediocre here; they probably represent the
threshold value of planted acreage. Two crop
seasons were involved, except at the highest
elevations. Crops for which data were avail-

able were maize, pulses, bulrush millet, and sorghum. The crop which gave the highest yield for a given season and ecologic zone was selected as the one we would have people plant. The crop yield for each ecologic type was multiplied by the area of the ecologic type found in each location. The summed yields in a location for all ecologic types were then modified in accordance with customary fallow systems and by deducting the portion of land that was non-arable. The remaining yield divided by a per capita/annum food requirement value (similar to the one described on p. 191) gave the number of people in the location that could live there, basing their subsistence on the traditional technology. This figure divided by area gives the carrying capacity/km^2 for the location; and a look at actual population densities establishes what sort of "population pressure" exists.

It is clear that some locations greatly exceed the limit imposed by the traditional economy. How then do the people survive? One answer is the cultivation of coffee, another is intensive methods of farming, using terraces, manure, grass leys, grade stock, fodder, herbicides and insecticides. The areas that stand out as overpopulated (Iveti, Kangundo, Matungulu, and Mitaboni) are areas of great cash crop development. The areas of notable underpopulation (Okia and Kisau), near the Mbooni core from whence people have traditionally moved, are explained partly by the great environmental risk that farmers experience in this lower area, and partly from the history of land degradation that occurred in the mid-1940's, a legacy still to be seen in the gullied slopes and in the vegetation of the area (105).

The point of this exercise has been to show that what is population pressure in one system (the traditional Kamba method of farming) is not necessarily population pressure under another (yeoman farming with cash crops). Population pressure is there, to

be sure, but its magnitude is not what is suggested by the diagram, which is based on densities that could be supported by a subsistence economy.

Ester Boserup, in her illuminating and stimulating book, *The Conditions of Agricultural Growth,* argues that where the pressure of population on resources is sustained and slow, man finds it in himself to work harder, to intensify his use of the land, and to make a given piece of land serve him both well and often (14). This will be true where land has the inherent qualities that permit continued improvement and intensification of use. Many densely peopled parts of tropical Africa appear to have gone through a cycle or evolutionary sequence similar to the one she suggests. As we noted earlier, the "Scramble for Africa" tended to stabilize the ethnic map of the continent and the geographical association of peoples, economic systems, and land. A result of this has been the rapid increase of population and a sudden and intense build-up in land pressure, rather than a slow sustained pressure, such as Mrs. Boserup postulates as instrumental in effecting agricultural intensification. The responses in land use have been erratic and volatile—characterized by migration, land fragmentation, moves to marginal areas unsuited to the agricultural system, and attendant land devastation, social upheavals (Mau Mau being one example), and a variety of attempts to re-establish a balance in land use—schemes which have had both good and indifferent results. Further, in view of the poor envionmental base over much of tropical Africa, it seems unlikely that the process of intensification could evolve in response to slow, sustained population pressure except in the more favored parts. In semi-arid areas the process of intensification might move from a "forest" to bush fallow system and not progress beyond, for any further shortening of the fallow rotation would overstep inherent environmental limits, lead to land deterioration and a lowered carrying capacity.

Conclusion

Population geographers are not going to solve the problems we have been discussing in this section. We can help a good deal in describing and even in explaining population pressure on physical and social resources; but it lies with local administrators and farmers and herdsmen to effect changes in the relationship with the environment.

At this point there should be a long essay on the importance of the values and attitudes held by the people of different African cultures. What are the views of people on work, leisure, community esteem, wealth, property, and dignity? We should know the answers to such questions as: "What is the best thing that can happen to a man? What is it in life that is truly worthwhile? Whom can a man trust?" In the responses to these questions are the answers to many questions concerning proposed developments. The assessment of the potentialities of the environment is incomplete, and potentially meaningless, if not accompanied by an analysis of the society which will exploit that potential.

METHODS OF ASSESSING ENVIRONMENTAL POTENTIAL

As we have seen, there are many dimensions to the assessment of environmental potential. There is more to it than soil fertility and rainfall. It involves human nutritional requirements and land tenure; it involves extant systems of production, the world market, and the psychology of man. What strategies have been used by those who have sought to assess environmental potential? How successful have they been?

In examining the literature on environmental assessment, one finds that the studies examined group themselves under four general headings—agrometeorology, ecology, agricultural economics, and soil-plant physiology—and are restricted to tropical Africa. Because surveys address a set of related problems, the lines between the several approaches are quite often indistinct.

The Agrometeorological Approach

We should point out that the terms "carrying capacity" and "environmental potential" have differing but kindred meanings. Carrying capacity is specific and suggests an optimal density of some sort—people per square kilometer, livestock per hectare—while environmental potential has a more general frame of reference. In this more general context most agrometeorological studies concern themselves with the performance of crops in the matrix of biophysical elements which affect plant growth. The question of the optimal matching of crops with environments is surely one of environmental potential; but the manner in which agroclimatic studies are presented sometimes obscures this fact. That is, we are shown general analyses of meteorological aspects, followed by specific analysis of crops. It only adds up to "environmental potential' in the sense of how many people could be supported by an optimal allocation of crops if the reader or the governmental administrator takes the trouble to correlate the information himself.

"Knowledge of the quantity of water consumed by natural [plant] cover constitutes an indispensable stage in the analysis of the internal relations of the soil-climate-vegetation complex. The study of these relations assumes a fundamental character, for it is these which regulate the ecologic conditions on which depend essentially the rhythm of plant growth and a large part of human activity" (42: 88). This statement from the humid steamy forest of Yangambi, Congo is echoed in Salisbury, Muguga, Kano, Bambey, Bingerville, in fact throughout tropical Africa, wherever research into the processes which govern plant growth are investigated. Studies of energy and water balance in recent years have been prodigious (97; 98). The work of H. L. Penman has had great influence, and much research has been done in the Congo (Kinshasa) at INÉAC—Institut National pour l'Étude Agronomique du Congo (9; 41; 42; 111). It is also useful to cite the work of physicists in East Africa—Pereira, Glover, McCulloch, and Sansom, taking particular note of the catchment area studies published as a special issue of the East African Agricultural and Forestry Journal[4] (55; 82; 99; 100; 101; 113). The search has been for instrumentation which will give a valid but inexpensive means of determining water need. Other work, some of it following Penman, has been done in Central Africa (66; 107).

Water balance studies attempt an accounting of the flux of energy and water through time. Records must be kept of radiation, both direct and indirect; energy loss through back radiation and use in vaporization of water and heating the air; moisture income; moisture and heat storage in soil; moisture loss through evaporation; runoff and seepage. The matter of wind, turbulence, and the vapor gradient of the air over the plant surface complicates the picture. An important object of these studies is to find out how much water crops need and when.

Although the rationale of the subject is familiar to geographers, one phase of energy/water balance studies does warrant further comment. It concerns seasonal vari-

4. Forthcoming maps of East Africa showing potential evapotranspiration (according to the Penman equation) have been compiled by T. Woodhead (Tanzania and Kenya) and D. A. Rijks and W. G. Owen (Uganda).

ability, especially that of rainfall, for the other terms usually considered—wind, saturation deficit, temperature, and radiation—are remarkably consistent from year to year. As might be expected, rainfall variability comes in for the greatest amount of scrutiny in areas where man is most affected. East Africa, Zambia, Rhodesia, Sudan, and the Sahel/Saharan margin have been the object of much investigation with a variety of approaches being used (40; 44; 53; 54; 56; 57; 72; 73; 112; 127).

The French work I have not searched thoroughly, although the work of ORSTOM and the Service de l'Hydraulique de l'AOF should be cited together with a number of separate studies (28; 29; 37)—articles by Rodier, Damieau, Roche, Dubreuil and Bouchardeau and Cachan, Cachan and Duval, and Schoch. In the former British West African territories, one thinks of the work of several people (51; 59; 122; 133).

The point of studying rainfall variability takes us back to Figure 12-1 which shows the maize yields a farmer could expect from an acre of cropland. The study of rainfall variability as related to water need for agronomically significant seasons is a study of the risks a farmer takes in his subsistence activities. Not all of the studies cited take transpiration requirements into account, but those by Manning and Dagg (34; 84) do. Their presentations are prototypes of the sort that should be carried out for large portions of Tropical Africa. The importance of their work cannot be overemphasized. Dagg in particular gives attention to soil moisture availability and the varying transpiration rates which characterize plants in early leaf, in full leaf, and so forth. The risks inherent in planting a given crop in a marginal environment can be assessed with precision, and, if necessary, a quick-maturing or drought-resistant variety may be obtained, often through selective field trials.

These agrometeorological studies constitute an assessment of environmental potential which the development planner can use in improving levels of living and in calculating limits to the number of people that should live in an area.

The Ecological Approach

"The principle upon the strength of which the Ecological Survey of Northern Rhodesia was proposed was that the natural vegetation of an undeveloped country, properly understood in relation to soil and other environmental factors, and classified in consistency with them, should provide the most efficient simple guide to its agricultural and forest potentialities" (126: ix). Thus begins the Report of the Ecological Survey by Trapnell and Clothier on work begun in 1932; from it has developed a school of ecologic thought and method whose influence has been worldwide.

This approach has been used extensively in East and Central Africa; and it is worthwhile to give a short description of the field techniques employed, as well as the results obtained. The survey of Uganda had, in Langdale-Brown's words, three objects: "1. To achieve a census of the botanical resources, it was desirable to map units on as many features of the vegetation as possible. 2. In order that the units might be used as a measure of the environment, it was necessary that they should occur over a limited range of habitat conditions. 3. The proposed application of this survey to vegetation management and conservation made it necessary to use natural successional units. The use of successional units is also fundamental to the assessment of agricultural potential" (76: 10; 77).

In the Uganda survey, three years were allotted to the field mapping phase, covering the non-forested parts of the country—the forests having been already adequately inventoried. "A previous survey of a typical savanna area . . . showed that plant communities distinguished by their most abundant species, subordinate species and physiognomy occur in definite habitats, are valid as units of succession, are easily recognized in the field and have the advantage of being distinguishable on 1:30,000 vertical aerial photographs" (76: 10; 30). A traverse technique which Trapnell used in his 1937 study was combined with the technique of the Zurich-Montpelier school (15).

"Observations were made on both sides of traverse lines which were routed along roads, motorable tracks and footpaths. The distances between apparent changes in the vegetation were noted, together with details of the salient features of the communities: species present and their cover-abundance, physiognomy (with height and percentage aerial cover of the different strata), soil type, topography and drainage conditions" (76: 10).

The vegetative stands were then grouped on the basis of probable climax, floristic characteristics, physiognomy, and drainage conditions. The object was to define homogeneous regions. Finally, the details of the various traverses were plotted on a base map at a scale of 1:250,000 resulting "in a skeleton map showing the distribution of plant communities close to the traverse lines" (76: 12). Vertical photographs and photo mosaics were then used to fill in the detail between the traverse lines. In all, over 16,000 km of traverse were plotted on the map with an average density of 1.6 km of traverse territory per 10.2 km² of territory. The survey does not end with the map, for there is a full discussion of plant succession, climax, and the effects of fire and cultivation. There are also discussions of present land use, availability of land for extension of agriculture and irrigation, range resources, and maps and text relating to land use potential.[5]

Langdale-Brown's conclusions on environmental potential, like those of most ecological surveys, are qualitative and contain no explicit reference to carrying capacity. There is good reason for this. "The problem of how a certain area should be used is a complex one involving social and economic factors as well as the factors of the physical environment. . . . If we limit our assessments of land capability to present productivity we shall not move far from subsistence agriculture. . . . However, while the units distinguished in ecological and soil surveys are related to land potential, it is impossible to draw conclusions about their potential on *a priori* grounds; thus it is necessary to correlate these units with performance data" (77: 94).

Environmental potential changes with technology, and any ecological area can be used in a variety of ways depending on specific economic and social conditions. Langdale-Brown argues that ecological survey is based on reconnaissance and is a first step toward land use planning, which should include subsequent study—detailed soil survey, collection of meterological data, and agronomic trials to establish the utilization limits in each ecologic zone (77: 94-95).

A number of ecoogical surveys resembling the one under discussion have been carried out. Some are less detailed in environmental assessment, but give a fuller treatment of the agricultural and social systems found in the zone surveyed. In East Africa, surveys by Brown, Gulliver, Humphrey, Morrison, Pratt,

Greenway and Gwynne, and Trapnell may be cited[6] (17; 39; 60; 68; 69; 89; 106). In Central Africa many studies have been carried out either by the Departments of Agriculture or under the auspices of the Rhodes-Livingstone Institute (3; 4; 48; 58; 70; 71; 102; 108; 116; 124; 125; 135).

A wealth of Belgian ecological work has been produced by INÉAC, much of it reported in the three massive tomes of the Comptes Rendus de la Conference Africaine des Sols held at Goma in 1948.[7] However, the only really detailed, yet theoretical, discussions I have come across in French on overpopulation in relation to carying capacity are by Tondeur and Henry[8] (30: 2325-2352; 65).

The French do not seem to include the

5. Mention should be made of the two companion series to the vegetation survey. Series 1— *Soils,* Memoirs of the Research Division, Department of Agriculture, has reports by E. M. Chenery, C. D. Ollier, J. F. Harrop, S. A. Radwanski, and J. G. Wilson, while Series 3—*The System of Agriculture Practiced in Uganda,* Memoirs of the Research Division, Department of Agriculture, has five reports by D. J. Parsons.

6. An example in Kenya of calculation of population carrying capacity is furnished in (68: 1-15). The same pamphlet contains another article pertinent to the question of population pressure and land tenure (69: 17-60). C. G. Trapnell will soon complete an ecological survey covering the southwest highlands of Kenya, an area of some 109,000 km[2] which contains all the high potential parts of the country as described in (39). The Land Resources Division of the D.O.S. has also recently carried out agro-ecologic surveys in the Gambia, Botswana, Western Cameroon, Malawi, Nigeria, Guinea, Uganda, and Tanzania.

7. Published as (30); see especially Section 3, Les Systèmes de Culture dans Leurs Rapports avec la Conservation des Sols, pp. 1403-1980, and Section 5, Etudes Economiques et Sociales dans Leurs Rapports avec le Problème de la Conservation des Sols, pp. 2119-2485.

8. G. Tondeur (30: 2325-2352) offers a careful and exceedingly pessimistic appraisal of possibilities in Rwanda, Burundi, and eastern Kivu Province [Congo (Kinshasha)]; and J. Henry (65) describes the Belgian rationale for introducing a policy of *cultures obligatoires* to regularize shifting cultivation, permit individual land holding where appropriate, encourage the growth of cash crops, and generally keep the agricultural economy operating on a sustained basis that would not be detrimental to the environment. The organization of the *paysannats,* and background on communal and individual systems of land allotments are contained in (52) and (83).

ecological approach in their arsenal of techniques of environmental assessment. At least my search of French work did not turn up any studies of an ecological genre. French West African work appears to treat microclimatology, hydrology, or agricultural economics. The bulletins of the Centre Recherches Agronomiques of Bingerville (Ivory Coast) and Bambey (Sénégal) are comprised of agronomic studies (but see La Protection des Sols [121; 129]).

In most instances the ecological reports do not carry their conclusions to the point of specifying the carrying capacity of their ecologic regions (Trapnell's 1943 report [125] being an exception); and it remained for an agricultural officer, faced with the need to make some hard decisions about a rapidly deteriorating reserve, to do the straightforward calculations necessary to compute carying capacities for subsistence agriculture.

A widely known technique for calculating carrying capacity is that of William Allan (4: 20-65). His approach, developed in the 1930's in Northern Rhodesia and published as *Studies in African Land Usage in Northern Rhodesia,* involves three sets of information—the percentage of cultivable land, the Land-Use Factor, and the Cultivation Factor (3; 4). The cultivable land is land that can be cultivated by traditional methods. The Land-Use Factor expresses the relationship between duration of cultivation and duration of fallow. A field used for crops in alternate years has a Land-Use Factor of 2; a field cropped once and left fallow for 15 years has a cultivation factor of 16. Allan recognizes six land categories on the basis of the Land-Use Factor: permanent cultivation land, semi-permanent land, recurrent cultivation land, shifting cultivation land, partial cultivation land, and uncultivable or waste land. The affinities between this classification and the sequence described by Boserup are close

and of much comparative interest (14: 15-16). The Cultivation Factor is the acreage planted per capita per annum, a figure which reflects the "normal surplus" aspect discussed earlier.

An example follows: an area is 48 per cent cultivable; the Land-Use Factor is 3 (i.e. two years fallow for one year cultivation); the Cultivation Factor is 0.8 (i.e. 0.8 acres [0.31 hectares] are planted per capita per annum). We substitute in the formula (slightly modified):

$$\text{C.P.D.} = 640/(100 \text{ L.U.} \times \text{C/P})$$

where: L.U. = Land-Use Factor
$$= 640/(100 \, (3) \times 0.8/48)$$
C = Cultivation
$$= 128 \text{ people per mi}^2$$
$$(50/\text{km}^2)$$
P = Cultivable Percentage
(range 0 to 100)

and C.P.D. = Critical Population Density

According to this formula, a density exceeding $50/\text{km}^2$ will lead to an encroachment on fallow land before it has recovered and to land degradation and lowered yields; thus 50 is the Critical Population Density. The use of the notion of "normal surplus" neatly avoids any need to calculate crop yields per acre. Further, it asks no questions about the level of living normal to the population. The use of "normal surplus" acreages is the strength of Allan's method when calculating population carrying capacities of subsistence economies; it is its weakness when applied to systems of agriculture which are involved in cash crops and the money economy.

CONCLUSION

It is virtually impossible to envisage integration of all the separate analyses of meteorological parameters into one great formula whose outcome = Potential. We quoted Cochemé earlier on this point. The agrometeorological methods which seem to push our understanding of user/environment links farthest involve mapping probabilities of water needs being met by rainfall for specific seasons and crops under known constraints of varying E_t (transpiration) rates, rooting depths, and soil moisture-holding capacities (34). But this is a far cry from an integrated measure of environmental potential.

Proponents of the ecological approach argue that they employ the great integrating mechanism which processes all the facts of soil, drainage, insolation, and rainfall, and comes up with an expression of environmental potential—the vegetation in the landscape. Their assessment of potential can be converted into specific population-carrying capacities, provided one knows the percentage of land cultivable, the ratio of cropped to fallow land, and the amount of land required annually to feed a person. This assessment applies, however, only to subsistence forms of agriculture, and when changes in farming technique and cash crops are introduced, the issues of potential and carrying capacity become clouded, at which point simple calculations will no longer do.

THE SOIL-PLANT PHYSIOLOGIC APPROACH AND THE AGRICULTURAL ECONOMICS APPROACH
What of the other approaches to environmental assessment? We mentioned that there was a soil-plant physiologic approach. In a way this approach combines the quantitative aspect of the energy and water balance method—with its careful measurements and system of budgeted accounts—with the biological aspects of ecology. The aim in part is to understand the cycle of minerals as they move into plants and back to the soil. It is a sort of dynamic biochemistry which studies both the equilibrium of a vegetative cover

and the soil beneath it through time and the effects of disrupting that equilibrium through fire, grazing, cutting, or cultivation. The literature on this type of approach is voluminous, but marginal to our problem for it deals generally with non-food plants. The *Journal of Ecology, Ecological Monographs, Ecology,* and various journals devoted to plant physiology such as *Plant and Soil* contain examples of this approach. It is probably the mode of analysis that gives the fullest answer to questions of plant-carrying capacity, but its method is intensive, time-consuming and commonly of restricted applicability.[9] In a world where land-use decisions have to be reached more quickly, it is likely that other ways of investigation will have to be adopted.

The soil-plant physiologic approach is at one end of a continuum—it discovers real answers to the biophysical processes in soils and vegetation. Farther along the continuum scale, we might place the energy-water balance approach, which tends to use data on plant behavior without much concern about the processes producing the behavior. Still farther along the scale we come to ecology, which observes and interpets the outcome of a complex set of interactions, without much attention to the separate components. At each stage in our movement along this continuum, the presence of man intrudes more forcibly. Would it be unfair to place agricultural economics at the other end of this continuum? Would it be unfair to claim that the agricultural economist starts with the character of the environment taken as given?

An example which proves the rule of agricultural economics, yet illustrates it too, is provided by an excellent two-volume study, *An Agricultural Survey of Southern Rhodesia* (6; 132). The first volume is an

9. Bibliographic references leading one to studies in soil-plant physiology are given in (78: 54-57, 73-74).

Agro-Ecologic Survey; the second an Agro-Economic Survey. All the topics one would expect in Volume 1 are there: physiography, climate, soil, vegetation, the whole culminating in a delineation of "natural" regions and sub-regions, with discussion of their potential.

I find it instructive that the same hesitancy to specify carrying capacities, the same reluctance to be explicit about environmental potential seizes Vincent and Thomas, the authors of Volume 1, just as it did the ecologist, Langdale-Brown, and the agrometeorologist, Cochemé. "With so many variables to contend with, it is evident that if an *ad hoc* exercise were indulged in to determine potential, a great many speculative conclusions could be reached, which, though imposing, would have little or no practical value. . . . For these reasons, no attempt has been made to forecast possible production" (132: 105). The agricultural economist in the second volume, however, is able to specify by what margin the various African reserves are overpopulated, and thus there is some recognition of carrying capacities and potential. The bankrupt philosophy this inadvertently reveals regarding the governmental view of economic development of the African reserves is of interest here.

The economic approach to agricultural development is well illustrated by Clayton's work in Nyeri District, Kenya, which employs linear programming as a means of assessing which mix of crops, agricultural techniques, and labor input maximizes profits—a maximization that can be viewed in several ways: income-capita, income-manhour of labor, or income-acre (25; 26; 27). In the 1963 study, he analyses six real farms and farm families. We take as an example one farm of 2.8 hectares in Kairia sublocation on the boundary of the Kikuyu Grass-High Bracken zones. The farmer can devote full time to the farm (200 manhours per month), while his two wives and a mother can each contribute 3 hours per day. The total monthly labor supply is 425 manhours, or the equivalent of 2.13 people. For this farm, Clayton proposed 18 plans which varied the following parameters: all hand labor, use of hired tractor; use of owned tractor; use of hired labor; varying acreages of potatoes, maize, grass ley (with milk production), fallow, and two cash crops; coffee (with mulch) and tea; cropping restrictions (constraints of good management to maintain soil fertility).

Table 12-3 summarizes four plans, each of which optimizes some aspect of the agricultural enterprise.

These alternative plans show that the scarce item in the system is not land but labor. The productivity of the land is doubled by hiring additional laborers. It is obvious that the farmer and his family will earn a higher income and have more leisure time if hired labor can be had at a rate of 2.00 Shs. per day (about 3.5 U.S. cents per hour). Plans differing only in their use of hand labor and tractor show that there is little economic advantage to be gained in mechanization. The use of hired labor does supply a job and an income for landless people, but there is a social cost. It creates an economic gap and encourages a widening social gulf between landless and land-owners, something which is generally antithetical to the social norms of tribal culture. Analyses of the sort done by Clayton provide a basis for examining alternate modes of development. We note that agricultural production is only increased if more labor is expended. This process swallows leisure time, a "cost" of agricultural development which some are willing to pay, and others are not.

The main trouble with attempts to define carrying capacity is that we can seldom isolate the dependent variable—the system of exploitation of the environment. Allan's

TABLE 12-3   ECONOMIC CHARACTERISTICS OF A COFFEE-TEA ALTERNATIVE
FOR A FARM IN SOUTH NYERI, KENYA

Plan*	Description	Net income	Income/ capita	Income/ hectare	Income/hr. worked** a.	b.	c.	Leisure time retained***
2	Hired tractor with no cropping restrictions. Dairying with coffee.	£206	£96.9	£85.0	Shs.1.14	—	Shs.*1.14*	32%
7	Owned 2-wheel tractor with tea and coffee.	£254	£*119.5*	£105.0	Shs.1.04	—	Shs.1.04	9%
17	Hand-labor with a total labor force of 5 adults. Tea = 4.7 acres, coffee = 1.0 acres.	£*412*	£82.4	£170.3	Shs.4.13	Shs.0.25	Shs.1.12	62%
18	Hired tractor with a total labor force of 5 adults. Tea = 4.7 acres, coffee = 1.0 acres.	£*412*	£82.4	£170.3	Shs.*4.26*	Shs.0.25	Shs.*1.14*	*64%*

* Only those plans which maximize some aspect are shown in the table. The maximizing figures are italicized.
** a—refers to the immediate family.
   b—refers to hired help paid a standard wage of Shs.0.25/hr.
   c—shows the income/hr. for the total labor input, allowing no wage differentials between the immediate family and the hired labor.
*** Clayton includes a term called "unused labor". In a sense this is leisure time. The family labor input available for a year is 5,300 hours; the table shows what percent of this is *not* expended under each plan.

method, reviewed earlier, is useful only if there is an implicit assumption that the traditional agricultural system of group X is not going to be tampered with. No modern African government would adopt such a regressive policy position; to do so would be tantamount to accepting a policy of economic stagnation.

A summary of the impressions gained from literature on environmental assessment might be as follows: (1) an ecologic survey is the most economical first step; (2) for those large areas of tropical Africa with only marginal potential for advanced agriculture, this may be the only sort of agricultural

survey warranted (excepting, perhaps, hydrological investigations; (3) the planning of agriculture in areas of higher potential must be done on an *ad hoc* basis; and (4) problems of environmental assessment are so complex that they require full interdisciplinary cooperation. The data provided by agrometeorologic surveys and detailed soil surveys, combined with the sort of farm planning that can be done by local administrators and agricultural economists, form a basis on which an intelligent assessment of environmental potential may be made. There may be many elements of classical Greek tragedy in the unfolding story of population pressure on physical and social resources in tropical Africa; but one that is assuredly *not* in the script is a *deus ex machina* in the form of some marvellous formula that will assess environmental potential and sort out the problems of population pressure. The solutions to these mundane problems lie closer at hand.

REFERENCES

(1) African Land Development (Nairobi, 1962).

(2) Agricultural Policy in the Federation of Rhodesia and Nyasaland (Salisbury, 1958).

(3) William Allan: Studies in African Land Usage in Northern Rhodesia, Rhodes-Livingstone Papers, No. 15, 1949.

(4) William Allan: The African Husbandman (Edinburgh, 1965).

(5) W. Allan, Max Gluckman, D. U. Peters, and C. G. Trapnell: Land Holding and Land Usage among the Plateau Tonga of Mazabuka District, Rhodes-Livingstone Papers, No. 14, 1948.

(6) R. Anderson: An Agricultural Survey of Southern Rhodesia, Part II. Agro-Economic Survey (Salisbury, 1960).

(7) H. Beguin: La Mise en Valeur Agricole du Sud-Est du Kasi, *Série Scientifique,* No. 88, INÉAC, 1960, pp. 1-263.

(8) M. K. Bennett: An Agroclimatic Mapping of Africa (Stanford, 1962).

(9) Étienne A. Bernard: Le Determinisme de l'Evaporation dans la Nature—Étude des Aspects Géophysique et Écologique du Problème dans le Cadre du Bilan Énergétique, *Série Scientifique,* No. 68, INÉAC, 1956, pp. 1-162.

(10) Daniel Biebuyck, ed.: African Agrarian Systems (London, 1963).

(11) H. F. Birch: Humus Decomposition and Soil Nitrogen, *Record of Research,* East African Agriculture and Forestry Research Organization, 1957, pp. 22-24.

(12) Paul Bohannan: Land, Tenure, and Land-Tenure, in: Daniel Biebuyck, ed.: African Agrarian Systems (London, 1963), pp. 101-14.

(13) Paul Bohannan: Land Use, Land Tenure and Land Reform, in: Melville J. Herskovits and Mitchell Harwitz, eds.: Economic Transition in Africa (Evanston, 1964).

(14) Ester Boserup: The Conditions of Agricultural Growth (London, 1965).

(15) J. Braun-Blanquet: Pflanzensoziologie (Vienna, 1951).

(16) H. C. Brookfield and Paula Brown: Struggle for Land (Melbourne, 1963).

(17) L. H. Brown: The Development of the Semi-Arid Areas of Kenya (Nairobi, Ministry of Agriculture, 1963).

(18) Leslie H. Brown: An Assessment of Some Development Schemes in Africa in the Light of Human Needs, in: *The Ecology of Man in the Tropical Environment. Proceedings and Papers,* International Union

for the Conservation of Nature and Natural Resources, No. 4, 1964, pp. 280-87.

(19) R. H. Brown: A Survey of Grazing Schemes Operating in Kenya (Nairobi, Department of Veterinary Services, 1959).

(20) R. A. Bullock: Population Geography and Development Planning, A Paper Presented at the 1966 Symposium of the East African Academy (Makerere, 1967).

(21) A. H. Bunting: Some Problems of Agricultural Climatology in Tropical Africa, *Geography,* Vol. 46, 1961, pp. 283-94.

(22) Juan J. Burgos: World Trends in Agroclimatic Surveys, Symposium on Methods in Agroclimatology (Reading, 1966).

(23) P. Cachan: Signification Écologique des Variations Microclimatiques Verticales dans la Forêt Sempervirente de Basse Côte d'Ivoire, *Annales Fac. Sci., Université de Dakar,* Vol. 8, 1963, pp. 89-155.

(24) P. Cachan and J. Duval: Variations Microclimatiques Verticale et Saisonnières dans la Forêt Sempervirente de Basse Côte d'Ivoire, *Annales. Fac. Sci., Université de Dakar,* Vol. 8, 1963, pp. 5-87.

(25) E. S. Clayton: Labour Use and Farm Planning in Kenya, *Empire Journal of Experimental Agriculture,* Vol. 28, No. 110, 1960, pp. 83-93.

(26) Eric Clayton: Economic Planning in Peasant Agriculture (Wye College, Ashford, 1963).

(27) E. S. Clayton: Agrarian Development in Peasant Economies—Some Lessons from Kenya (London, 1964).

(28) Jacques Cochemé: FAO/UNESCO/WMO Agroclimatology Survey of a Semi-Arid South of the Sahara, *Nature and Resources,* Vol. 2, No. 4, 1966, pp. 1-10.

(29) Jacques Cochemé: FAO/UNESCO/WMO Agroclimatology Survey of a Semi-Arid Area in West Africa South of the Sahara. Symposium on Methods in Agroclimatology (Reading, 1966).

(30) Comptes Rendus de la Conference Africaine des Sols, *Bulletin Agricole du Congo Belge,* Vol. 40, Nos. 1-4, 1949, pp. 1-2557.

(31) E. M. Chenery: An Introduction to the Soils of the Uganda Protectorate, Memoirs of the Research Division, Series 1: Soils, No. 1, 1960.

(32) Conference Inter Africaine sur l'Hydrologie, CCTA, Publication No. 66, 1961, articles by J. Rodier, G. Damiéau, M. Roche and P. Dubreuil, and A. Bouchardeau.

(33) P. P. Courtenay: Plantation Agriculture (London, 1965).

(34) M. Dagg: A Rational Approach to the Selection of Crops for Areas of Marginal Rainfall in East Africa, *East African Agricultural and Forestry Journal,* Vol. 30, No. 3, 1965, pp. 296-300.

(35) William Davies and C. L. Skidmore, ed.: Tropical Pastures, (London, 1966).

(36) R. P. Dore: Climate and Agriculture—The Intervening Social Variable, Symposium on Methods in Agroclimatology (Reading, 1966).

(37) G. A. Delorme: Répartition et Durée des Précipitations en Afrique Occidentale (Paris, 1963).

(38) Department of Settlement: Annual Reports, (Nairobi, 1963 et seq.).

(39) Directorate of Overseas Surveys: Annual Report (London, 1966).

(40) B. D. Dowker: A Note on the Reduction in Yield of Taboran Maize by Late Planting, *East African Agricultural and Forestry Journal,* Vol. 30, No. 1, 1964, pp. 33-34.

(41) G. Dupriez: Le Réseau d' Écoclimatologie de l'INÉAC, *Bulletin d'Information de l'INÉAC,* Vol. 8, No. 5, 1959, pp. 283-301.

(42) G. L. Dupriez: L'Évaporation et les Besoins en Eau des Différentes Cultures dans la Région de Mvuazi (Bas-Congo), *Série Scientifique,* No. 106, INÉAC, 1964, pp. 1-104.

(43) East African Royal Commission 1953-1955 Report (London, 1955).

(44) A. C. Evans: A Study of Crop Production in Relation to Rainfall Reliability, *East African Agricultural Journal,* Vol. 20, 1955, pp. 263-67.

(45) Food and Agricultural Organization: Calorie Requirements, F.A.O. Nutritional Studies, No. 15 (Rome, 1957).

(46) Food and Agricultural Organization: Protein Requirements, F.A.O. Nutritional Studies, No. 16 (Rome, 1957).

(47) Food and Agricultural Organization Africa Survey: Report on the Possibilities of African Rural Development in Relation to Economic and Social Growth (Rome, 1962).

(48) Barry N. Floyd: Changing Patterns of African Land Use in Southern Rhodesia, *Rhodes-Livingstone Journal,* No. 25, 1959, pp. 20-39.

(49) S. Herbert Frankel: *The Times,* Oct. 4 and 5, 1950.

(50) Ruth S. Freitag: Agricultural Development Schemes in Sub-Saharan Africa—A Bibliography (Washington, 1963).

(51) B. J. Garnier: Measuring Potential Evapo-Transpiration in Nigeria, *Publications in Climatology,* Vol. 7, No. 2, 1954, pp. 140-76.

(52) G. Geortay: Organisation de l'Agriculture Congolaise dans les Paysannats, *Bulletin d'Information de l'INÉAC,* Vol. 10, No. 1, 1961, pp. 1-15.

(53) J. Glover: The Relationship between Total Seasonal Rainfall and Yield of Maize in the Kenya Highlands, *Journal of Agricultural Science,* Vol. 49, No. 3, 1957, pp. 285-90.

(54) J. Glover and M. D. Gwynne: Light Rainfall and Plant Survival in East Africa, I. Maize, *Journal of Ecology,* Vol. 50, No. 1, 1962, pp. 111-18.

(55) J. Glover and J. S. G. McCulloch: The Empirical Relation between Solar Radiation and Hours of Bright Sunshine in the High Altitude Tropics, *Quarterly Journal of the Royal Meteorological Society,* Vol. 84, No. 359, 1958, pp. 56-60.

(56) J. Glover, P. Robinson and J. P. Henderson: Provisional Maps of the Reliability of Annual Rainfall in East Africa, *Quarterly Journal of*

the *Royal Meteorological Society,* Vol. 80, 1954, pp. 602-9.

(57) P. E. Glover, J. Glover and M. D. Gwynne: Light Rainfall and Plant Survival in East Africa, II. Dry Grassland Vegetation, *Journal of Ecology,* Vol. 50, No. 1, 1962, pp. 199-206.

(58) Max Gluckman: African Land Tenure, *Rhodes-Livingstone Journal,* No. 3, 1945, pp. 1-12.

(59) S. Gregory: Rainfall over Sierra Leone. Research Paper No. 2, Department of Geography, University of Liverpool, 1965, 58 pp.

(60) P. H. Gulliver: The Population of the Arusha Chiefdom—A High Density Area in East Africa, *Rhodes-Livingstone Journal,* No. 28, 1960, pp. 1-21.

(61) R. J. Harrison Church: Problems and Development of the Dry Zone of West Africa, *Geographical Journal,* Vol. 127, No. 2, 1961, pp. 197-204.

(62) R. J. Harrison Church: Observations on Large Scale Irrigation Development in Africa, *Agricultural Economics Bulletin for Africa,* No. 4, 1963, pp. 1-48.

(63) J. F. Harrop: The Soils of the Western Province of Uganda, Memoirs of the Research Division, Series 1: Soils, No. 6, 1960.

(64) Heinz Nutritional Data (Pittsburgh, 1964).

(65) J. Henry: Les Bases Théoretiques des Essais de Paysannat Indigène. Entre Pris par l'INÉAC au Congo Belge, *Contribution à l'Étude du Problème de l'Economie Rurale Indigène au Congo Belge,* Vol. 43, 1952, pp. 159-92. *Numero Spécial du Bulletin Agricole du Congo Belge.*

(66) G. M. Howe: Climates of the Rhodesias and Nyasaland according to the Thornthwaite Classification, *Geographical Review,* Vol. 43, No. 4, 1953, pp. 525-39.

(67) R. W. Howe: Losses Caused by Insects and Mites in Stored Foods and Feeding Stuffs, *Nutrition Abstracts and Reviews,* Vol. 35, No. 2, 1965, pp. 285-303.

(68) N. Humphrey: The Relationship of Population to the Land in South Nyeri, Kenya, Miscellaneous Official Publications (Nairobi, 1945).

(69) N. Humphrey: Thoughts on the Foundations of Future Prosperity in the Kikuyu Lands, Kenya, Miscellaneous Official Publications (Nairobi, 1945).

(70) George Kay: Agricultural Change in the Luitikila Basin Development Area, *Rhodes-Livingstone Journal,* No. 31, 1962, pp. 21-50.

(71) George Kay: Changing Patterns of Settlement and Land Use in the Eastern Province of Northern Rhodesia, Occasional Papers in Geography No. 2 (Hull University Publications, 1965).

(72) Joan M. Kenworthy: Rainfall and the Water Resources of East Africa, in: Geographers and the Tropics—Liverpool Essays, (London, 1964).

(73) Joan M. Kenworthy and J. Glover: The Reliability of the Main

Rains in Kenya, *East African Agricultural Journal,* Vol. 23, No. 4, 1958, pp. 267-272.

(74) Kenya Central Land Board: Final Report (Nairobi, 1965).

(75) Land and Population in East Africa (London, 1952).

(76) I. Langdale-Brown: The Vegetation of Uganda (Excluding Karamoja), Memoirs of the Research Division, Series 2. Vegetation, No. 6. Department of Agriculture, Uganda Protectorate, 1960. There are five other volumes in this series covering in detail the vegetation of the several provinces of Uganda.

(77) I. Langdale-Brown, H. A. Osmaston and J. G. Wilson: The Vegetation of Uganda and Its Bearing on Land Use (Government of Uganda, 1964).

(78) H. Laudelout: Dynamics of Tropical Soils in Relation to Their Fallowing Techniques (FAO, 1960).

(79) H. P. Ledger: The Role of Wildlife in African Agriculture, *East African Agricultural and Forestry Journal,* Vol. 30, No. 2, 1964, pp. 137-41.

(80) The Locust Handbook (London, 1966).

(81) A. S. MacDonald: Some Aspects of Land Utilization in Uganda, *East African Agricultural and Forestry Journal,* Vol. 29, No. 2, 1963, pp. 147-56.

(82) J. S. G. McCulloch: Tables for the Rapid Computation of the Penman Estimate of Evaporation, *East African Agricultural and Forestry Journal,* Vol. 30, No. 3, 1965, pp. 286-95.

(83) Guy Malengreau: Les Lotissements Agricoles au Congo Belge, *Contribution à l'Étude du Problème de l'Économie Rurale Indigène au Congo Belge,* Vol. 43, 1952, pp. 193-218, Numero Spécial du *Bulletin-Agricole du Congo Belge.*

(84) H. L. Manning: The Statistical Assessment of Rainfall Probability and Its Application to Uganda Agriculture, *Research Memoirs,* No. 23, Empire Cotton Growing Corporation, 1956, pp. 460-80.

(85) Hugh Martin-Leake: Defects in the East African Groundnut Scheme? *Crown Colonist,* Vol. 17, 1947, p. 201.

(86) P. Meigs: World Distribution of Arid and Semi-Arid Homoclimates, UNESCO, *Arid Zone Research,* No. 1, 1953, pp. 203-9.

(87) Sir Philip Mitchell: The Agrarian Problem in Kenya (Nairobi, 1947).

(88) P. Mitchell: Agricultural Policy in African Areas in Kenya (Nairobi, 1951).

(89) J. Morrison: A Report of a Survey of Ranching in the Kenya Highlands (Nairobi, n.d.).

(90) A. C. Mossman: Wildlife Ranching in Southern Rhodesia, Conservation of Nature and Natural Resources in Modern African States (Morges, IUCN, 1963), pp. 247-49.

(91) C. P. R. Nottridge and J. R. Goldsack: The Million-Acre Settlement Scheme 1962-1966 (Nairobi, Department of Settlement, 1965).

(92) C. D. Ollier; The Soils of the Northern Province, Uganda (Excluding Karamoja District), Memoirs of the Research Division, Series 1: Soils, No. 3, 1959.

(93) C. D. Ollier and J. F. Harroy: The Soils of the Eastern Province of Uganda, Memoirs of the Research Division, Series 1: Soils, No. 2, 1959.

(94) ORSTOM: l'Office de la Recherche Scientifique et Technique d'Outre-Mer, whose work is summarized in a special issue of *Terres et Eaux,* No. 38, 1962, pp. 1-76.

(95) J. Papadakis: Climates of the World and Their Agricultural Potentialities. (Light and temperature relations of plants; water relations; fundamental characteristics of a climate from a crop ecologic point of view, terminology; diagrams as a means to comprehend weather and climate for crop ecologic purposes; climatic classification, types of climate and their agricultural potentialities; climatic requirements of crops; climates country by country; agroclimatic research. With a map of world climates and a table for computing potential evapotranspiration on the basis of maximum and minimum temperature) (Buenos Aires, 1966).

(96) D. J. Parsons: The Systems of Agriculture Practiced in Uganda. Memoirs of the Research Division, Series 3, No. 1. Introduction and Teso Systems, No. 2. The Plantain-Robusta Coffee Systems, No. 3. The Northern Systems, No. 4. Montane Systems, and No. 5. Pastoral Systems, 1960.

(97) H. L. Penman: Natural Evaporation from Open Water, Bare Soil and Grass, *Proceedings of the Royal Society of London (A),* Vol. 193, 1948, pp. 120-45.

(98) H. L. Penman: Vegetation and Hydrology (Harpenden, Commonwealth Bureau of Soils, 1963).

(99) H. C. Pereira: Practical Field Instruments for Estimation of Radiation and Evaporation, *Quarterly Journal of the Royal Meteorological Society,* Vol. 85, No. 365, 1959, pp. 253-61.

(100) H. C. Pereira, ed.: Hydrological Effects of Changes in Land Use in Some East African Catchment Areas, *East African Agricultural and Forestry Journal,* Vol. 27, Special Issue, 1962, pp. 1-131.

(101) H. C. Pereira and J. S. G. McCulloch: The Energy Balance of Tropical Land Surfaces, Tropical Meteorology in Africa (Nairobi, 1960).

(102) D. U. Peters: Land Usage in Serenje Districts, Rhodes-Livingstone Papers, No. 19, 1950.

(103) John Phillips: Agriculture and Ecology in Africa—A Study of Actual and Potential Development South of the Sahara (London, 1959).

(104) Philip W. Porter: Environmental Potentials and Economic Opportunities—A Background for Cultural Adaptation, *American Anthropologist,* Vol. 67, No. 2, 1965, pp. 409-20.

(105) Philip W. Porter: Environments and Economies in East Africa. (Berkeley, 1969).

(106) D. J. Pratt, P. J. Greenway and M. D. Gwynne: A Classification of East African Rangeland, with an Appendix on Terminology, *Journal of Applied Ecology*, Vol. 3, 1966, pp. 369-82.

(107) A. A. Prentice: Potential Evapotranspiration in Rhodesia, Notes on Agricultural Meteorology, No. 13, Rhodesian Meteorological Service, n.d.

(108) J. R. V. Prescott: Overpopulation and Overstocking in the Native Areas of Matabeleland, *Geographical Journal*, Vol. 127, No. 2, 1961, pp. 212-25.

(109) La Protection des Sols, Bulletin No. 9, 1955. Pertinent articles by C. Charreau, J. Faure, J. Dubois, and P. Gaudefroy-Demombynes.

(110) S. A. Radwanski: The Soils and Land Use of Buganda, Memoirs of the Research Division, Series 1: Soils, No. 4, 1960.

(111) A. Ringoet, A. L. Molle and C. O. Myttenaere: L'Evapotranspiration et la Croissance des Végétaux dans le Cadre du Bilan Enérgetique, *Série Scientifique*, No. 92, INÉAC, 1961, pp. 1-174.

(112) P. Robinson and J. Glover: The Reliability of Rainfall within the Growing Season, *East African Agricultural Journal*, Vol. 19, No. 3, 1954, pp. 1137-39.

(113) H. W. Sansom: The Climate of East Africa (Based on Thornthwaite's Classification), *Memoirs*, East African Meteorological Department, Vol. 3, No. 2, 1954, pp. 1-49.

(114) P. G. Schoch: Influence sur l'Évaporation Potentielle d'une Strate Arborée au Sénégal et Conséquences Agronomiques, *l'Agronomie Tropicale*, Série II, Vol. 21, No. 11, 1966, pp. 1283-90.

(115) G. G. M. Schulten: Protection from Insects of Stored Products in the Tropics, *Tropical Abstracts*, Vol. 20, No. 10, 1965, pp. 641-48.

(116) Thayer Scudder: The Ecology of the Gwembe Tonga, Kariba Studies Series (Manchester, 1962).

(117) A. T. P. Seabrook: The Groundnut Scheme in Retrospect, *Tanganyika Notes and Records*, Nos. 47 and 48, 1957, pp. 87-91.

(118) P. de Schlippe: Shifting Cultivation in Africa: The Zande System of Agriculture (London, 1956).

(119) V. Sheddick: Land Tenure in Basutoland, Colonial Research Studies, No. 13 (London, 1954).

(120) R. O. Slatyer and I. C. McIlroy: Practical Microclimatology (UNESCO, 1961).

(121) M. Sordoillet: Une Operation de Développement Rural en Pays Mossi (Haute Volta), *l'Agronomie Tropicale*, Série II, Vol. 19, No. 7, 1964, pp. 579-97.

(122) G. Stanhill: The Accuracy of Meteorological Estimates in Nigeria, *Journal of the Institute of Water Engineers*, Vol. 17, 1963, pp. 36-44.

(123) R. J. M. Swynnerton: A Plan to Intensify the Development of African Agriculture in Kenya (Nairobi, 1954).

(124) C. G. Trapnell: Ecological Methods in the Study of Native Agriculture in Northern Rhodesia. Reprinted from Kew Bulletin, No. 1 (London, 1937).

(125) C. G. Trapnell: The Soils, Vegetation and Agriculture of North-Eastern Rhodesia (Lusaka, 1943).

(126) C. G. Trapnell and J. N. Clothier: The Soils, Vegetation and Agricultural Systems of North-Western Rhodesia (Lusaka, 1937, 2nd edition, 1957).

(127) C. G. Trapnell and J. F. Griffiths: The Rainfall Altitude Relation and Its Ecological Significance in Kenya, *East African Agricultural Journal,* Vol. 25, No. 4, 1960, pp. 207-13.

(128) G. Tondeur: Surpopulation et Déplacement de Populations, *Bulletin Agricole du Congo Belge,* Vol. 40, No. 3/4, 1949, pp. 2325-52.

(129) B. Tourte, P. Vidal, L. Jacquinot, J. Fauché, and R. Nicou: Bilan d'une Rotation Quadriennale sur Sols de Régénération au Sénégal, *l'Agronomie Tropicale,* Série II, Vol. 19, No. 12, 1964, pp. 1033-72.

(130) UNESCO Conference on Principles and Methods of Integrating Aerial Survey Studies of Natural Resources for Potential Development, 1964.

(131) United Nations Development Progam: East African Livestock Survey, 3 vols. (Rome, 1967).

(132) C. V. Vincent and R. G. Thomas: An Agricultural Survey of Southern Rhodesia, Part I. Agro-Ecological Survey (Salisbury, 1960).

(133) H. O. Walker: Application of Penman's Method for the Estimation of Open Water Evaporation, Meteorological Notes, No. 3, Gold Coast Meteorological Services, n.d.

(134) A. J. Wakefield, D. L. Martin and J. Rosa: Report of a Mission to Investigate the Practicability of the Mass Production of Groundnuts in East and Central Africa, appendix to A Plan for the Mechanized Production of Groundnuts in East and Central Africa, Cmd. 7030 London, 1947).

(135) C. M. N. White: A Preliminary Survey of Luvale Rural Economy, Rhodes-Livingstone Papers, No. 29, 1959.

(136) J. G. Wilson: The Soils of Karamoja District, Northern Province of Uganda, Memoirs of the Research Division, Series 1: Soils, No. 5, 1959.

13. LANDSCAPE EVOLUTION: A TOOL FOR ANALYZING POPULATION-RESOURCE RELATIONSHIPS: NORTHEAST BRAZIL AS A TEST AREA

Kempton E. Webb

Northeast Brazil is an ideal laboratory for students of population-resource relationships and problems. It has the dubious distinction of being the largest underdeveloped area of the largest developing country of the entire Western Hemisphere.

The purpose of this study is not to relate the long history of droughts, crippling poverty, and famine which has been the unfortunate lot of the Northeast but, rather, to propose a way of examining the whole complex of man-land relations there which may illuminate its component parts and processes. In short, it is proposed that a valid approach to the study of population pressure on resources is the analysis of the processes of landscape change.

The main contribution of this study is a *concept of landscape evolution* which can be stated as follows. *The cultural and physical processes which shape any landscape interact continuously, in varying degrees of intensity, with each other, and also with the earth's surface; this surface becomes altered, thereby presenting a continuously changing base upon which subsequent interactions occur.*

One implication of this concept is that it embraces a comprehensive yet dynamic view of the earth's surface by considering orders of priority and dominance within the often bewildering complexity of area content and processes, rather than seeking simple explanations.

Because the stimulus of this idea came directly from field experience in Northeast Brazil, it may be useful to present it against the regional setting in which it was conceived. Northeast Brazil is portrayed,

then, not as a unique situation but rather as simply one "laboratory" of population pressure on resources in which the concept of landscape evolution may be applied.

Field work was carried on in Northeast Brazil from September 1963 to June 1964. An initial research objective was the formulation of physical and cultural definitions which distinguish the warm humid *Zona da Mata* (Forest Zone) from the low dry *Sertão* of the interior, and also the *Agreste* transitional zone. A second objective was to find out how each of these zones had shifted geographically in time.

The original proposal underwent several changes as a result of the first few months of reconnaissance and background work. The most drastic reorientation stemmed from the nature of the primary sources. A comparison of about 400 air photographs taken during World War II with 430 recent air photographs of the same areas afforded a trustworthy and indelible document of observable areal change in each of the above-mentioned zones. From over 150 detailed interviews with local residents in all zones, it was possible to become familiar with the functional processes which produced the images recorded on both sets of photos, and even to become conversant with the earlier geography. Old farmers recalled clearly what habitat and life were like back to the earliest years of this century.

Such excellent primary source materials impressed one more and more with the processes of landscape alteration *within* each zone, however defined, than with any supposed areal shifts *of* the zones. The theme, borne out by field study on a topographic scale, became a recurrent one: landscape characteristics differed from place to place in different periods for different reasons. These reasons were invariably founded in a unique mix of cultural and physical factors in any given place. Time and time again, the analytical mind of the rural Brazilian informant identified the interwoven threads of a complex fabric of areally expressed facts, processes, and institutions which made sense out of the old photos as well as the present landscape.

Strange and unfamiliar patterns began to emerge. For example, rainfall amounts and slope variations seemed to assume less importance as explainers of land use; on the other hand, land tenure systems, inheritance laws, and rural land tax structures appeared to have a very direct relevance to land use patterns.

The actual observable land use could be only partly explained by correlating it with cut-and-dried rational assessments of the physical resource base. Frequently, the fundamental decision-making with regard to land use had its origins more deeply rooted in traditional uses of land, in folk beliefs about certain qualities or attributes of areas, or in a rigid feudal system of sharecropping, just to name a few examples. In short, the experience of doing a field study dealing with man-land relations in a small area over a period of several decades proved to be profoundly rewarding. The experience was use-

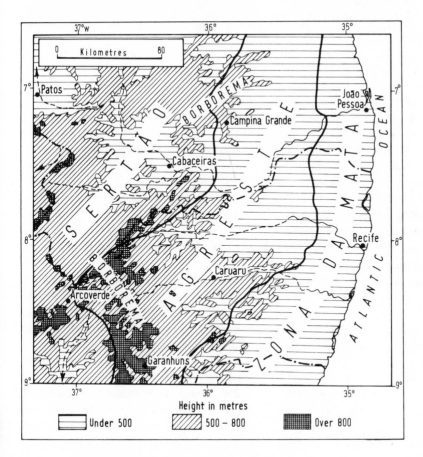

Fig. 13-1. NORTHEAST BRAZIL: NATURAL REGIME

TABLE 13-1 BRAZIL'S POPULATION, 1890-1960

Physiographic Regions (IBGE)	Population				
	1890	1920	1940	1950	1960
Norte	476,370	1,439,052	1,462,420	1,844,397	2,601,519
Nordeste	3,771,319	7,434,392	9,973,642	12,494,477	15,677,995
Leste	6,950,359	12,874,275	15,625,953	18,893,007	24,832,611
Sul	2,815,468	8,129,355	12,915,621	16,975,293	24,848,194
Centro-Oeste	320,399	758,531	1,258,679	1,736,965	3,006,866
	Percent of Brazil's Total Population				
	1890	1920	1940	1950	1960
Norte	3.32	4.70	3.55	3.55	3.65
Nordeste	26.31	24.27	24.19	24.05	22.09
Leste	48.49	42.01	37.89	36.38	34.99
Sul	19.64	26.54	31.32	32.68	35.01
Centro-Oeste	2.24	2.48	3.05	3.34	4.24

Source: População–SNR–Sinópse Preliminar do VII Censo Demográfico–Brazil–1962. Preliminary Results.

ful for the knowledge gained about the study area itself, but even more valuable were the insights which it provided into the more universal subject of man-land relations in general.

The Northeast is the third most populous region of Brazil, following the South and the East. According to the 1960 census, the Northeast (including Bahia) had 17,973,413 inhabitants. The following table, based upon physiographic regions only, shows the total population of all regions of Brazil with each census; but the Northeast's share of Brazil's total population has declined steadily from 26.3 per cent in 1890 to 22.1 in 1960. (See Table 13-1.)

The Northeast has crude birth rates which are as high as 45 to 48 in some areas, while the mortality is also high, with crude death rates between 18 and 25. The density of population within the Northeast is approximately double the average density of the nation.

The most notable characteristic of the population of the Northeast is, however, its great mobility. Both intraregional and interregional movements of people are great. A consequence of these movements is regional imbalance of age groups. In 1950, 44.1 per cent of the Northeasterners were less than 15 years old, while only 4.3 per cent were more than 60 years old.

The state capitals of the Northeast have been the destination of many migrants; and their rates of growth have increased from 1940 to 1950, and even more from 1950 to 1960. (See Table 13-2.)

The quality of the Northeast's population reflects gross undervalorization in that only 25 per cent of the persons 5 years of age or older are literate; only 4.97 of those 10 years of age or older have completed elementary school; only 0.14 have completed high school.

The two different worlds of Northeast Brazil are separated by a vast gap. The urban world has lower birth rates which are balanced off by massive rural-urban in-migra-

TABLE 13-2   URBAN GROWTH IN NORTHEAST BRAZIL

Selected State Capitals of Northeast Brazil	Absolute Population			Per cent Increase	
	1940	1950	1960	1940-50	1950-60
São Luis	58,735	79,731	124,606	35.7	55.2
Teresina	34,695	51,418	100,006	48.2	94.6
Fortaleza	152,134	205,052	354,942	34.8	79.7
João Pessoa	71,158	89,517	135,820	25.8	54.7
Macejó	80,045	99,088	153,305	23.8	51.3
Aracaju	50,306	67,539	112,516	34.3	66.4
Salvador	290,443	389,422	630,878	34.1	62.6

tion. The rural world has higher birth rates which are compensated for by out-migration to areas of greater economic opportunity and hope.

NORTHEAST BRAZIL AS A LABORATORY OF POPULATION PRESSURE ON RESOURCES AND OF CULTURAL AND PHYSICAL CHANGE

Geographers have their laboratories in the field where theories and techniques may be tested and applied. A judicious selection of categories of definition, of scale of analysis, and of the test area itself can do much to aid the geographer in his "laboratory" work. Northeast Brazil is such a laboratory, and particularly the eastern parts of Paraiba and Pernambuco where, in a small-scale view, sharp gradients of physical and cultural features are observed in space and through time.

Well-Defined Geographic Regions

A traverse of 180 km westward from the coasts of Paraiba and Pernambuco takes the traveler rapidly from the warm humid low-lands of the *Zona da Mata* into the *Agreste,* up onto the Borborema highlands, and then down into the warm, dry *Sertão*. Maps of a scale of 1:5,000,000 and smaller show the alignment of these three zones approximately parallel to the coast. The names *Zona da Mata, Agreste,* and *Sertão* have specific physical connotations as well as less specific cultural connotations as used by the local people.

ZONA DA MATA
The name Forest Zone refers to the contiguous area bordering the coast which was originally covered by a tall, dense, evergreen, semideciduous forest. The former forest and its present day remnants thrived on most soils derived from crystalline rocks less than 200 m in elevation, and receiving over 1200 mm of rainfall yearly. The width of this north-south zone varies from 30 to 70 km. Exceptions to these conditions are the broad, flat sedimentary interfluves, called *tabuleiros* (low tablelands), whose sandy soils are more conducive to savanna (*campo cerrado*) (literally, a closed field, meaning grassland with scattered trees and bushes) than to a thick forest growth. The cultural connotation of the *Zona da Mata* is "land fit

for sugar cane," which has been the traditional use of the richer vally soils.

AGRESTE

The word *Agreste* has the sense of "aggressive," "rustic," or "hard to farm." That is how the *Agreste* must have appeared to the early settlers approaching it from the more humid and verdant *Zona da Mata* to the east. The *Agreste* receives only 800 to 1200 mm of rainfall each year, has thinner, sandier soils, and originally had a natural vegetation of something between a *mata seca* (dry forest) and a dense *caatinga* (tropical thorn scrub forest). It is found at both higher elevations over 500 meters and at lower elevations in the rain shadows of low mountains and *tabuleiro* tablelands. A common cultural definition is that the *Agreste* is "land suited to the growing of manioc," the main food staple of the Northeast's interior. It is commonly called the transition zone between the *Zona da Mata* and the *Sertão*. Calling it simply a transition zone, however, does not illuminate the myriad of interesting aspects that give it its distinctive character.

SERTÃO

The *Sertão* is the famous hot, dry low backlands area characteristic of most of the Northeast's interior. *Sertão* has uncertain origins in the Portuguese language. One meaning is the geographic area of the dry interior of Northeast Brazil. A second is simply the backlands or "sticks" wherever they occur, areas largely unpenetrated or unoccupied by man.

Average rainfall of 270 to 800 mm with great irregularity from one year to the next, shallow sandy stony soils, and *caatinga* vegetation are its characteristic features. The cultural connotations of the *Sertão* are extensive cattle raising in all of the area, subsistence and cash crops grown only with the first autumn rains (if they come that year), and sporadic flood-plain (*vazante*) farming.

Well-Defined Physical Processes and Patterns

The range of physical processes which have produced the varied habitats in the Northeast, discounting the works of man, is best shown by the extremes exhibited by the *Zona da Mata* and the *Sertão*. In the *Zona da Mata* conditions of high temperature and high humidity and rainfall give chemical weathering the upper hand in shaping the particular character of landform and soil. The depth to sound bedrock in the crystalline areas of the *Zona da Mata* is often many meters, and is the result of dominantly chemical weathering of soils *in situ*. These soils are high in clay content and are given the local name of *barro* (clay). They are generally good for agriculture. Landforms in the crystalline areas of the *Zona da Mata* are rounded, which is partly the result of a thick soil-and-vegetation mantle which holds against the underlying bedrock and reduces it to a gently undulating terrain.

The *Sertão* experiences a completely different natural action of the elements. Mechanical processes of weathering and erosion dominate. Not only are the amounts of rainfall there much less than in the *Zona da Mata,* but there is the added factor of a long unmistakable dry season. The general regime of rainfall is one of autumn rains separated by seven or eight months of practically no rain. Accordingly, the natural vegetation has to be drought-resistant. The soils of the *Sertão* are shallow, due to the shortage of water and the sparseness of the vegetation cover which would otherwise hold moisture against bedrock and produce a more deeply weathered soil mantle. In the majority of areas, soil depth is less than half a meter, and in some places bedrock is actually exposed. The general aspect of landforms there reflects dry-cycle weathering and erosion processes, with their accompanying angular forms. Inselbergs, pediplains, and dry-cycle colluvial and alluvial surfaces abound.

Between the *Zona da Mata* and the *Sertão* is the *Agreste* (sub-humid or semi-arid Transition Zone) which is truly transitional in terms of physical processes, but which owes most of its distinguishing landscape character to cultural processes. Because of its higher elevation, the upper surfaces of the Borborema highlands are considerably cooler, thus decreasing the temperature component of the rate of chemical decomposition of soils. The *serras,* or small mountain ranges, comprising the eastern outliers of the Borborema and the actual eastern escarpment of the Borborema are truly classic orographic barriers to the constant humid easterly winds. A multiple effect of high elevation, exposure, and high moisture produces denser vegetation cover and deeper soil where they have not been greatly disturbed by man.

In short, if one looks at this part of Northeast Brazil on a small scale, the physical processes which have shaped the distinctive habitats are fairly well defined. Naturally, any detailed, large-scaled analysis reveals a much higher degree of area differentiation and the need for greater qualification in each of the zones and their variants.

Well-Defined Cultural Processes and Patterns

The laboratory aspect of Northeast Brazil, with its definable physical divisions and processes, is further enhanced by a comparable categorization of cultural patterns and processes in any over-all view. The sequence and patterns of occupance can be related partly to economic and historical factors and partly to the character of the habitat. One consideration to remember while viewing the evolution of settlement and land-use patterns is the changing ratio of available man-power to the definitions of economically or socially justifiable activities of land exploitation. In space and time, the cultural processes and features expressed by land use in the study area exhibit the following divisions.

The brazilwood cycle was the earliest yet the least permanent form of exploitation in its extent and intensity. The cutting down of randomly located trees of *pau•brasil* (literally, brazilwood) was carried on most energetically throughout the first fifty years or so of Brazil's history, principally in the *Zona da Mata.* This activity resulted in practically no permanent settlements and very few changes in the habitat.

The sugar cane cycle was the outstanding economic and social influence in the *Zona da Mata* from about 1550 to 1700. Even today, sugar cane still represents the chief source of income in the rural sectors although there is higher population density and greater economic diversification.

The vast *Sertão,* on the other hand, was, from the beginnings of Brazil's colonial period, very definitely regarded as land suited for open range cattle raising. The cattle were raised in the *Sertão* to supply the needs of the growing population in the *Zona da Mata,* for meat, hides, and draft animals. A classic symbiotic relationship evolved and still persists to a certain degree today.

The *Agreste* was left by default as not being ideally suited to either sugar cane, nor exclusively to grazing under the conditions of limited available manpower throughout the colonial period and well into the nineteenth century. The people who eventually settled the *Agreste* came from both the *Sertão* and the *Zona da Mata.* They fled toward the humid east from the periodic droughts which destroyed crops and decimated the herds pasturing in the *Sertão.* Upon reaching the *Agreste,* which was a more well-watered locale where subsistence crops could be grown with little fear of droughts, these refugees took root. People also migrated to the *Agreste* from the *Zona da Mata,* where most of the best land had already been titled to the landholding elite and therefore, offered few possibilities for anyone getting started in agriculture.

The year 1930 marked the beginnings of an industrial revolution and its uneven impact in Northeast Brazil. From then onward, the three zones began, in varying degrees, to become more integrated into the economically effective territory of the Northeast and of Brazil as a nation. The crucial transportation links with city and export markets tended to valorize areas hitherto untouched, and still subject to a feudal or subsistence way of life.

One cultural process which affected all areas in one way or another was the generally underrated activity of deforestation. In the *Zona da Mata* and the *Agreste,* men cut the forests to clear for crops. In the *Sertão* they cut to a lesser extent for the same reason, and to a greater extent for firewood, house construction materials, and more recently for locomotive fuel and charcoal making for the urban markets of today. The *caatinga* (tropical thorn scrub forest) underwent a gradual but relentless process of "desertification" in which only the worthless species were spared the woodsman's axe.

In summary, one can regard this part of Northeast Brazil as a test area, characterized by marked physical contrasts, cultural contrasts, and identifiable turning points in its historical development, where each zone is evolving within its own boundaries and at the same time stimulated by outside influences.

ANALYTICAL FACTORS

By way of introduction, several factors and assumptions underlying the concept of landscape evolution should be stated.

One valuable and interesting guide in the search for enlightenment on man-land relations is Robert Braidswood's and Gordon Willey's *Courses Toward Urban Life.* It is an historical-anthropological analysis of the kinds of conditions out of which cities emerged in different parts of the world in different epochs. In essence, the authors look at the "take-off" point for population clusters as they become cities in the generally accepted definition of what a city is. They cite, among others, basic requirements of water, food supply, a viable economic or other base, and a system of individual and group productivity which, through sound administration, enables a greater diversification of tasks and responsibilities. It is the diversification and specialization of occupations and roles which mainly distinguish urban from rural culture.[1]

Braidswood's and Willey's analysis suggests that the degree to which the natural habitat or man's works dominate an area depends upon the scale of elaboration of the culture occupying it. This line of reasoning further implies that the habitat[2] would influence indirectly the loci or limits of land use and the human activities in a place occupied by people with a low level of cultural evolution and technology. Preston E. James speaks to the same problem when he defines the significance of the habitat in terms of culture: "The significance of the land is determined by the attitudes, objectives, and technical abilities of the people who occupy it."

What is suggested here is that a carefully qualified extension of the cultural determinist point of view would lead us back to "environmental" influences, but *indirect* ones of a very different nature from those cited by the environmentalists themselves. The reasoning is as follows:

1. See also (23).
2. I am using "habitat" in the ecological sense, meaning the physical or natural environment; this is in contrast with the cultural or man-made environment. Landscape embodies elements of both.

1. It is man's culture which gives *meaning* to the habitat.

2. In any one culture area, the habitat will have a specified significance. To take one example, in the *Sertão* of Northeast Brazil the habitat has the following meaning to local inhabitants:

   (a) Forest lands are desirable for crops.

   (b) Dry areas as well as moist areas are to be planted with humid-land crops such as maize and beans.

   (c) Steeply sloping areas are to be planted wtih crops whose rows will run up and down the slope, not on the contour.

   (d) The end of the dry season is the signal to cut over and burn areas for crops.

3. The kind of environmental influence is therefore *indirect*, not direct, as in classic environmental determinism. In other words, by his cultural make-up and predispositions, man unconsciously endows his habitat with an imaginary influence or control over his activities.

4. As with so many things which are related to human nature, it is not necessarily the measurable fact or the scientifically defined reality which men take to be the baseline of their actions. Rather, it is man's personal, and often irrational, conception of what he sees and feels that forms his particular reality as well as the basis of his actions. In this sense, the habitat can be said to exercise an indirect influence on human activities insofar as man's culture imbues that habitat with a quasi-deterministic role.

It must be remembered, moreover, that neither the habitat nor the culture of a place is static. Both evolve at varying rates of speed in interaction with each other, with the local landscape, and with outside influences.

The distinction may appear to be fine, but merits emphasis. Instead of stating the significance of the land mainly in terms of man's culture, let us recognize indirect or "imag-ined" environmental influence as a part of the functional reality, especially in those situations where the level of cultural elaboration is low. In other words, the relative dominance, direct or indirect, of the natural habitat or of man's culture on the landscape varies with the state and quality of cultural elaboration existing there.

The Study of Processes on a Topographic Scale

One thesis of this study is that area study on a functional level in general, and landscape interpretation in particular, is most effectively pursued by the detailed study of processes on a topographic scale.[3] Naturally, there is no substitute for an overview of an area's gross features or of reconnaissance in order to provoke first impressions and to elicit meaningful questions which may be the focus of later detailed studies. However, a familiarity with the actual functioning reality is gained only by observing and mapping the individual features of the landscape and by probing, through extensive interviews with local inhabitants, the day-to-day and year-to-year details of their activities as they throw light upon man-land relationships. Time spent studying in detail an area representative of a larger zone is more efficiently invested than the same time spent trying to cover the whole area.

The topographic scale approach enables one to examine at close range physical processes, cultural processes, and even, by talking with elderly people, historical processes over as much as half a century. The scarcity of published documentary material on certain areas or on certain subjects need not hinder the field worker who, if he is an adept interviewer, can tap the riches of information of

3. A scale where the individual features of human occupance can be distinguished and analyzed.

an almost limitless number of local experts.

The optimum scale for any area analysis would appear to vary within the general category of topographic scale and with the nature of the area itself; the size of the discrete features of land use, the size of land use associations, the nature and location of land use decision-making, the degree of complexity of economic relationships (market versus subsistence economy), the rate and directions of areal change, the degree to which land use patterns are representative over a wider area, and the incidence of extraneous features.

Decision Making and Local Land Use

A basic block to sound area analysis is an incomplete awareness of the many stages that exist between the observable fact revealed to the field worker's eye or recorded on an air photo and the published map or statistics. There are also many stages of processes of a material and a nonmaterial nature of which the image on the air photo is simply the final product. Sometimes investigators try to infer or deduce the actions and motivations of the man on the land from an inspection of gross data in the form of inadequate maps and figures, and without a functional knowledge of the processes which are only dimly reflected by the maps and figures.

A more time-consuming, but sounder, approach is the reconstruction of the fabric of daily and seasonal activities and relationships observed in the context of land use patterns. One valid analysis in depth of functional relationships in a representative area may then be extrapolated and, with limitations, applied to a wider area. Thus, the time spent by anthropologists on community studies (21) and by geographers on regional studies which probe universal themes (23) and not narrowly local ones appears to be well invested. The approach is inductive, from the specific to the general.

The following chart is an attempt, based upon field experience, to approach the complexities underlying the rural landscape and how it assumes its particular aspect.

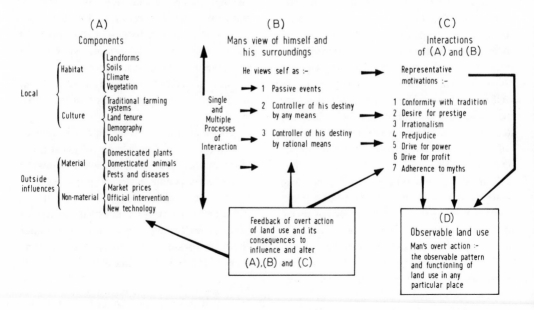

Fig. 13-2.   A FUNCTIONAL VIEW OF THE DETERMINANTS OF LAND USE

The components (A) of the locale, physical and cultural, material and nonmaterial, are the raw materials which undergo their own individual processes of transformation and which, in greater or lesser degree, interact with other components. Some examples would be over-cropping resulting in loss of top soil by erosion, the introduction of new domesticated plants or animals into an agricultural setting, or the impact on a traditional farming system by governmental expropriation of large properties.

The several processes of interaction are then filtered, and refracted through man's mind (B) and, depending upon his individual and collective view of himself and of the world about him (19), he takes overt action by engaging himself physically with the earth's surface. His overt action produces an observable pattern of land use (B), and may have been underlain by one or more different motivations (C). The sequence of stimuli continues with a certain amount of feedback from the actual land use and its consequences (for example, minifundio, sheet erosion from over-grazing, larger and more productive economic units, blights) to each of the original components. Over a period of time, this feedback may alter some aspects of the individual components and even change man's view of himself and of his place in the world.

The Balance Between Available Manpower, Exploitable Resources, Technology, and Market

An awareness of the above-mentioned factors and how they vary in space and time in a particular area is most helpful in regional analysis of population-resource problems. Preoccupation not only with the observable, mappable features but also with the reasons for their existence and how they are evolving illuminates the more general concern with processes in an area and gives substance to regional interpretation.

To cite an example, extensive cattle-raising occupies by far the greater area of the *Sertão*. Some students mistakenly conclude that cattle-raising is the chief source of income there. This is not true. Today, agriculture, carried out in a small fraction of the *Sertão*, accounts for more than half of the income generated in all parts of the *Sertão* studied. Others infer that the *Sertão* is well suited to cattle-raising. On the contrary, it is poor for cattle when compared with the rest of the world's grazing lands. The fact is that cattle ranching yields the highest return for the available manpower and the low rate of investment *locally considered reasonable* on lands that are not regarded as good for any other activity, and which, for that matter, are not very good for cattle.

It is difficult today to imagine the low densities of population which prevailed throughout the Northeast's interior until the twentieth century. Even now there are some *municipios* like Cabaceiras with an average population density of only five people per km². In the context of the colonial period this meant that the land *per se* had value only in proportion to the number of workers available to valorize it. Low productivity per worker and per unit area persists as a general condition. Only in the sugar cane *engenhos* (primitive sugar mills) of the *Zona da Mata* was productivity relatively high. But, then again, the sugar economy was based upon slaves who had only to be fed and clothed. The chief capital investment was in slaves and machinery rather than in land.

The policies of the Portuguese Crown and of the donotories who received immense tracts of land to develop, and who subsequently subdivided it to others in the form of *seismarias* (land grants), were expressly to valorize the empty areas, to put people on the land to make it productive, and thereby generate tax revenues. Today, the undervalorization of both the rural areas and their workers operates against a truly efficient agricultural sector of the economy. One economist, Stefan Robock, who has studied the Northeast thinks that possibly one of the best ways to develop Northeast Brazil is to provide opportunities for work outside of the Northeast. This would make labor scarcer in the Northeast and thus force the entrepreneurial classes in the Northeast to become more efficient in order to remain competitive. In such a process, the worker of the Northeast himself would possibly become more productive and thus be able to secure a higher income and a higher standard of living.

CONCEPT OF LANDSCAPE EVOLUTION USING NORTHEAST BRAZIL AS A TEST AREA

The idea presented here concerns the nature of the earth's surface as a medium of multiple processes of cultural and physical change, and as an organizing refractor of those processes in time and in space. The concept of landscape evolution holds that the cultural and physical processes which shape any landscape interact continuously, in varying degrees of intensity with each other *and also* with the earth's surface; this surface becomes altered, thereby presenting a continuously changing base upon which subsequent interactions occur.

Easternmost Paraíba and Pernambuco lend themselves well to a schematic, three-dimensional model illustrating the concept of landscape evolution. The functional relationships of the model will be first discussed in a universal context and then as they apply to Northeast Brazil.

In the model, three undulating surfaces represent, from top to bottom, three successive landscapes of the same area as they have evolved through time. The earliest landscape is at the top; the most recent at the bottom. Two vertical lines separate the area into three distinct regions: S, A, and M, thereby introducing the element of areal diversity into the model.

We start with landscape S^1 as the given situation. Two sets of processes interact with one another: H^{S1} referring to the total physi-

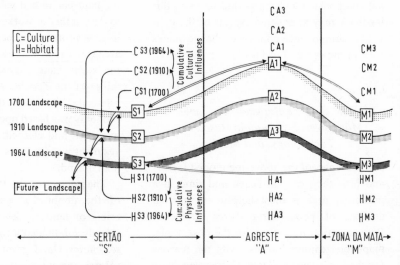

Fig. 13-3. THE PROCESS OF LANDSCAPE EVOLUTION IN THE THREE NATURAL REGIONS OF NORTHEAST BRAZIL

cal properties and processes as they are expressed in the habitat, H, for example in the year 1700. C^{S1} refers to the total cultural properties and processes as they are expressed in that same area at the same time. Habitat and culture (H and C) interact within the landscape context of S^1 thereby transforming S^1 into S^2, which is the observable landscape at a later date, say 1910.

The cultural state of 1910, C^{S2}, is the recipient of holdover cumulative influences from that of 1700 (C^{S1}), as indicated by the upward curving arrows. Similarly, the habitat of 1910, H^{S2}, bears many marks of the one existing in 1700 (H^{S1}). Nevertheless, the distinctive culture of 1910, C^{S2}, interacts with the transformed habitat of that same era, H^{S2}, in the context of the 1910 landscape, and eventually produces the new landscape of 1964, S^3.

It must be emphasized that there is a twofold interaction: (one) the processes operating within the natural setting or habitat (vegetation, soils, water regimes, landforms, and, to a lesser extent, climate) interact with the processes operating within the cultural complex (land use, population density, agricultural tenure systems, level of technology, attitudes toward the land, etc.); *and at the same time* (two) each of these sum processes of habitat and culture (H and C) interact with the existing landscape. The existing landscape is obviously the visible manifestation of both natural and cultural processes, in variable degrees of intensity, as they are frozen at a given moment in time in a particular place. The landscape at any given time represents the starting base from which contemporary habitat-culture interactions must begin their transformation of that landscape.

In similar fashion, the landscape in region A is transformed successively from A^1 to A^2 and finally to A^3, as is the landscape in region M. The mechanics of change mentioned thus far refer only to *intraregional* influences.

There must also be allowance for *interregional* influences. The two-way arrow linking landscape A^1 in region A with landscape M^1 in region M is meant to indicate the influence that, for example, a growing market for food supplies in region M in 1700 had upon land use in region A. Other combinations of interregional influences in either direction can be imagined, such as S^1 with A^1 or S^3 with M^3. Not all of the possible combinations of interregional influences are shown in the model, nor are the details of Culture-Habitat-Landscape interactions for regions A and M for the practical reason of not crowding the diagram.

The model and the following chart attempt to spell out in abbreviated form how the concept of landscape evolution may be applied to an actual area, in this case, those areas of Paraiba and Pernambuco east of 37°W Longitude. The letters S, A, and M refer respectively to the *Sertão, Agreste,* and *Zona da Mata.* I have selected the earliest time section of around 1700 in order to portray this part of the Northeast at the high point of characteristic colonial culture, when the sugar cane cycle was still in its heyday and the *Sertão* was already occupied, though very sparsely populated. The second period, taken around 1910, represents a sort of threshold year in terms of area diversification within the *Agreste,* and, to a lesser extent, in the other two zones. It is also a date for which exists extensive source material from interviews with local inhabitants in all three zones. The present-day situation is supported by air photographs going back over the last twenty years, interviews, and personal observation. The choice of exactly where the time cross-sections should be taken is meant to convey some sense of the tremendous rate of acceleration of many processes of landscape alteration since the beginning of this century, and particularly during the last thirty years.

A more satisfactory selection of time periods would be 1500, 1700, 1900, 1944, and 1964. The advantage of the 1500 date would be the presentation of the pre-colonial (pre-European) situation as the starting base, insofar as it could be reconstructed from colonial documents, the accounts of early travelers, and other means. The year 1944 would be another convenient time section simply because of the photo coverage taken then. These refinements will be presented in another study and, moreover, are not essential to simply demonstrating the method of approach as applied to Northeast Brazil.

CONCLUSIONS

How, finally, can one generalize about the impact of population pressure upon landscape and the evolution of landscapes? Field research in Northeast Brazil has revealed that it is man's technology and his individual attitudes and perceptions of the habitat which strongly determine the actual character of the landscape-shaping processes. Other things being equal, the vegetation and soil cover has suffered more drastically in more sparsely inhabited areas of the *Sertão* and *Agreste* where vegetation survives within the context of a variable and precarious soil-water regime. The soils in the drier areas cannot tolerate the abuses by even a few people and their grazing animals. The wetter *mata* zone has been more successful in accommodating more people with relatively less damage to the productive habitat base.

The valorization of an area (*Zona da Mata*) through the valorization of the crop (sugar cane) that grows best only there will tend to protect that limited habitat. The valorization of a commodity (cattle or firewood) by a distant market has a deleterious effect if the commodity can be gathered or produced over a vast area; hence no perceived need to conserve the habitat because "there is always more land over the hill."

Most people of Northeast Brazil do not yet perceive their problems in terms of "population pressure upon resources." In fact, they prefer large numbers of people and delight in the *movimento* (movement or social interaction) which large numbers of Brazilians generate. However, they do understand the primary fact of life—jobs. They understand labor supply as *bracos* (literally, arms, with the implication of unskilled manual labor). When there are too few jobs for the number of available *bracos,* the people migrate to other regions. The notion of valorization of all components: land, people, better ideas and skills by raising the productivity of the land, the people, and the technology is not yet fully realized in Northeast Brazil, or in any other developing part of the world.

This presentation has attempted to be relevant to several themes: population pressure on resources, man-land relations, a philosophy of geography, and a technique of landscape interpretation. It has tried to treat all of these topics by focusing on an actual landscape and watching how and why it has become what it is today. Direct observation and use of primary sources, such as air photos and interviews, help to reduce the incidence of factual errors and thereby of misinterpretations. The more one becomes removed from the basic data, the greater the chances that an ethnocentric bias may creep into the interpretation. Possibly one of the most valuable educational experiences for someone nutured in the cradle of our computerized, industrial society is to understand and *believe* that a rational view of one's life, activities, and habitat is not necessarily an integral part of the cultural baggage of all societies. Unless the investigator is sensitive to these "indeterminant" factors as well as to the more determinant factors, his interpretations and portrayal of the geographic facts of life may be wrong and even misleading.

REFERENCES

(1) Abastecimento de Generas Alimenticios da Cidade do Recife, Banco do Nordeste do Brasil, ETENE, (Fortaleza, 1962).

(2) Abastecimento de Generos Alimentieros da Cidade de São Luis, ETENE, Banco do Nordeste do Brasil; SUDENE, (Fortaleza, 1965).

(3) G. O. de Andrade and R. C. Lins: O 'Brejo' da Serra das Varas (Arcoverde), Ministério da Educação e Cultura, *Boletim do Instituto Joaquim Nabuco de Pesquisas Socials, Recife,* No. 12, 1963, pp. 5-22. A most perceptive analysis of rainfall regime and the distribution of upland "wet spots" (*brejos*) in relation to air mass movement and location. The best explanation of the Northeast's droughts to date. Authors relate effective moisture to the number of and degree of exposures to rain-bearing air masses, wind exposure and elevation, etc.

(4) Banco do Nordeste do Brasil S. A.: Efeitos da Sêca Sobre a Economia Apropecuária do Nordeste, 1958.

(5) C. Barreto: Considerações Sobre o Exodo Rural, *Boletim Geográfico,* Vol. 4, No. 45, pp. 1, 127-131, 135.

(6) S. Barros: Exodo e Fixação, *Serviço de Informação Agrícola, Série Estudos Brasileiros,* No. 5, 206 pp. (Rio de Janeiro, 1953).

(7) Souza Barros: O Nordeste, Ministério da Viação e Obras Públicas, Serviço Documentação, Coleção Mauá, (Rio de Janeiro, 1957).

(8) T. P. A. Borges: Expansão do Mercado Regional, Comissão B-2, Seminário para O Desenvolvimento do Nordeste (26 de Abril a 3 de Maio de 1959), Garanhuns, Pernambuco, Confederação Nacional da Indústria, Divisão de Estudos e Planejamentos, SESI, DN.

(9) C. C. Botelho: Aspectos Geograficos da Zona Cacueira da Bahia, *Revista Brasileira de Geografia,* Vol. 16, No. 2, pp. 161-208.

(10) M. E. T. de Castro: Ritmos de Crescimento Urban o do Nordeste, *Revista Brasileira de Geografia,* Vol. 27, No. 3, 1965, pp. 484-90. Revealing cartographic representation of evolving population change rates. Concludes that the larger centers grow at a faster rate than the smaller cities. Compares 1940-50 and 1950-60 data. Distinguishes progressive and repressive rates of change.

(11) J. F. de Carmargo: Exodo Rural no Brasil (Rio de Janeiro, 1960).

(12) M. F. T. C. Cardoso: Caruarú: A Cidade e Sua Area de Influencia, *Revista Brasileira de Geografia,* Vol. 37, No. 4, 1965, pp. 587-614. Caruarú occupies a comparable site and exercises a similar function as *Campina Grande* (*Paraiba*). Interesting determination of its various hinterlands along lines of *Campina Grande* study and *O Grand Regiaõ do Rio de Janeiro,* IBGE, CNG, 1964. Location is in the key transitional zone of the Pernambucan *Agreste.*

(13) M. F. T. C. Cardoso: Campina Grande e Sua Funcão como Capital Regional, *Revista Brasileira de Geografia,* Vol. 25, No. 4, 1963, pp. 415-51.

Solid study of the impact of *Campina Grande* upon a vast hinterland. The radius of influence of businesses, banks, schools, hospitals, newspapers, and transportation modes is shown on maps. City occupies a key position regarding road and railroad routes. It will be a key center in the future of the Northeast.

(14) R. L. A. Correa: A Colonia Pindorama: uma Modificação na Paisagem Agraria, *Revista Brasileira de Geografia,* Vol. 25, No. 4, 1963, pp. 479-84.

Thumbnail sketch of the famous and apparently successful Pindorama Colony in the municipio of Coruripe in Alagoas state. It is unique because a productive agriculture based upon maracujá and coconuts has been established on the *tabuleiros,* which have been traditionally avoided by farmers.

(15) Manuel Diégues Júnior: O Banguê nas Alagoas, (Instituto do Açúcar e do Alcool, Rio de Janeiro, 1949).

(16) E. G. Egler: Distribução da População no Estado do Maranhão, em 1940, *Revista Brasileira de Geografia,* Vol. 13, No. 1, 1951, pp. 71-81.

(17) Faculdade de Filosofia de Pernambuco: Aspectos da Geografia Agrária do Brejo Paraibano, Universidade de Recife, Secção E., Geografia e História, pp. 2-40. (Recife, 1953).

(18) E. Fischlowitz: Las Migraciones Internas en Brasil, *Revista Mexicana de Sociologia,* Vol. 24, No. 3, 1962, pp. 705-33.

(19) C. Glacken: Changing Ideas of the Habitable World, in: W. L. Thomas, Jr., ed.: Man's Role in Changing the Face of the Earth (Chicago, 1956), pp. 70-92.

(20) Grupo de Geografia da População da Divisao de Geografia: Potencial Humano do Nordeste e do Leste Setentrional, *Revista Brasileira de Geografia,* Vol. 27, No. 1, 1965, pp. 146-64.

Very interesting group project presents basic maps of population density, population distribution (dot map), occupational structure (farming, industry, services), and degree of rural or urban concentration. Map of illiteracy, schooling, and population growth rates. Map of population regions distinguishes areas of demographic expansion, stabilization and decline for urban and rural areas. Unfortunately, quality of map printing is poor.

(21) M. Harris: Town and Country in Brazil (New York, 1956).

(22) R. Maack: Devastação das Matas no Estado do Parana, Suas Consequencias e Problemas de Reflorestamento, *Boletim Geografico,* Vol. No. 178, 1964, pp. 40-48.

Excellent capsule of enlightenment on the effects of the deforestation of Parana's forests. Results: lowered water tables, destructive water erosion, more intense dry seasons. Author is a long-term student of Brazil and witnessed much of today's booming northern Parana when it was virgin forest in the 1930's.

(23) A. S. Mayor, S. T. Silva, and E. Gentile: Crescimento Médico Anual

da População do Nordeste Períodos de 1920 a 1950 e de 1950 a 1960, *Revista Brasileira de Geografia,* Vol. 27, No. 2, 1965, pp. 295-304.
Underlines the two different worlds of Northeast Brazil: the urban, where lower birth rates are compensated for by in-migration, and rural, where out-migration is compensated for by high birth rates. Map part of larger study, "Human Potential of the Northeast," done in 1961.

(24) M. L. de Melo: Nordeste Planejamento e Geografia, *Revista Brasileira de Geografia,* Vol. 25, No. 3, 1963, pp. 327-42.
Emphasizes the new conception of problems in the Northeast by SUDENE, with droughts as only one aspect. Compares Northeast with the Center-South and finds great disparities, stresses the contribution geography can make to solution of Northeast's problems, citing specific examples. Aurthor has since been made chief of GERAM, Group for the Rationalization of Sugar Production.

(25) L. de Melo and A. A. Coelho: Contribuição a Integração da Pecuaria un Agro-Industria Canavieira. *Boletim do Instituto Joaquim Nabuco de Pesquisas Sociais. Recife,* No. 11, (Recife, 1962) pp. 133-55.
Convincing economic and social and ecological argument for the integration of livestock raising and sugar cane production in the *Zona da Mata.* Provides statistics and cost comparisons. An added point favoring the economic diversification of that troubled area of the Northeast.

(26) J. M. da Rosa e Silva Neto: Contribuição ao Estudo da Zona da Mata em Pernambuco, (Aspectos Estruturais e Economicas da Area de Influencia das Usinas de Acucar) Instituto Joaquim Nabuco de Pesquisas Socialis, MEC. (Recife, 1966).
Useful information on the sugar cane zone of Pernambuco. Only 38 per cent of the areas is owned by *usinas.* Attempts to consider the range of choices available for more diversified economic base.

(27) Pesquisa sobre Condição de Lavoura Canaveira, *Revista Brasileira de Economia,* Vol. 19, No. 4, 1966, pp. 24-54.
Empirical study of production costs of sugar cane in Pernambuco, Alagoas, Minas Gerais, Rio de Janeiro, and Sao Paulo states. Some 496 producers studied. Another step to accurate appraisal of conditions of a traditional crop area. Does not mention whether sugar cane protection is recommended mainly as an economic or as a social measure.

(28) T. L. Smith: The Social Relationships of Man to the Land in Portugal, *Sociologia,* Vol. 25, No. 4, 1963, pp. 319-43. Comparative analysis of land use, attitudes, and tenure systems between Brazil and Portugal with emphasis on Portuguese antecedents. The outlook for the average Portuguese is not hopeful in view of Roman-age techniques still used.

(29) Ney Strauch: Contribuição ao Estudo das Feiras de Gado, *Revista Brasileira de Geografia,* Vol. 14, No. 1, 1952, pp. 101-10.

(30) Suprimento de Generos Alimenticios para a Cidade de Fortaleza,

Banco do Nordeste do Brasil, S. A., ETENE, SUDENE (Fortaleza, 1964).

A restudy of the geography of food supply of Fortaleza which was first done by Kempton E. Webb in 1957 and published by BNB. The techniques for the original study were extended and applied by BNB staff for all major cities in the Northeast. Basic information gathered by extensive field study, questionnaires, and interviews.

(31) Suprimento de Generos Alimenticios para a Cidade de Fortaleza, Banco do Nodeste do Brasil, ETENE, SUDENE (Fortaleza, 1964).

A restudy of the basic food supply of Fortaleza, which was originally done by this reviewer in eight weeks, May-July 1957, with a staff of three Brazilians. The Brazilians have continued to improve the techniques and to apply them to Recife, Salvador, Sao Luis, and Campina Grande.

(32) Suprimento de Generos Alimenticios da Cidade de Campina Grande, Banco do Nordeste do Brasil, SUDENE, ETENE (Fortaleza, 1962). The geography of food supply—how the Northeast's key interior city is fed. Interesting ecological setting between the forest *Mata* zone and the *Sertão*. One of a series.

(33) Suprimento de Generos Alimenticios da Cidade de Salvador, Banco do Nordeste do Brasil, SUDENE, ETENE (Fortaleza, 1965).

Another of the Northeast food supply studies designed to serve as a basis for economic and social planning by development agencies in Northeast Brazil. Based upon extensive field work and questionnaires.

(34) O. Valverde: O Sertão e as Serras—O Centro-Norte do Ceará, Estudos Geográficos para Localização de uma Missão Rural, *Boletim Carioca de Geografia,* Vol. 5, Nos. 3-4, 1952.

14. DEMOGRAPHIC PRESSURE AND MOUNTAIN LIFE, WITH SPECIAL REFERENCE TO THE ALPINE-HIMALAYAN BELT

Xavier de Planhol

Criteria for demographic pressure in a mountain environment can be detected either in the changing structure of mountain life itself or in the impact of the overload on the natural environment.

The Development of Mountain Life

The most basic characteristic of mountain life in the broadest sense is the vertical stratification of resources and a staggered schedule for their exploitation within an annual cycle. Seasonal migrations thus take place within what may be a very complicated schedule, combining to various degrees both human-animal and agricultural-pastoral migrations. In the subtropical Mediterranean zone where the seasonal temperature contrast between summer and winter is reinforced by a contrast in rainfall, migrations entail an organization of pastoral shifts of great magnitude in order to realize fully the alternating potentials of pastures in the moderately warm plains during the winter and those in the mountains which remain verdant and fresh in the summer. Historical and political conditions have further produced two distinct kinds of migration: Transhumance *sensu stricto,* the migrations of major herds of livestock accompanied by solitary shepherds, has become a characteristic form along the northwestern side of the Mediterranean, from Spain to Italy, including southern France. Early development of centralized royal government made it feasible, in accordance with very strict regulations, to arrange with complete security the passage of shepherds through generally hostile areas. On the other hand, mountain nomadism, in which the entire human group accompanies the herds, and its derivative

forms, ranging from seminomadism to complete sedentarization of community and herd, essentially characterize the Islamic Mediterranean areas and Eastern Asiatic sectors. Here only rarely were conditions favorable for the establishment of secure transhumance. In either form, the migratory rhythms generally remain simple, with large-scale movements occurring in single episodes in spring and fall.

Mountain life attains its greatest complexity in the northern Alpine area. In a climate with a better balanced pattern of seasonal precipitation, mountain areas cease to be attractive for summer pasturage. Pastoral migrations are of interest only to the inhabitants of the mountain valleys—narrow, confined spaces with restricted resources. Alpine meadows contribute a much appreciated supplementary subsistence—hay for the winter-feeding of flocks stable-bound by the rugged climate. Movements are thus limited to short distances, on the flanks of the valleys immediately above the main dwellings. But the very proximity of these migrations is responsible for their complexity. In contrast to seminomadism, a division of the family group becomes the rule. The short distances permit an incessant coming and going. At the same time the calendar is complicated by numerous supplementary stages which take advantage of the lesser gradations of levels and minor peculiarities of the environment. The end result is an extraordinarily complicated rhythm.[1]

1. The best summary for all of Europe is still that by Frodin (25). Arbos (2) provides a penetrating analysis for the French Alps. The general synthesis by Blache (8) sets the pastoral way of life within the larger context of categories of highland life. This type is found

Let us now try to determine the conditions whereby this sort of pastoral life might have been established. One possibility is that a nomadic pastoral people settled in mountain country, and gradually shortened their range of migration in order to adapt to the environment. Or a group of sedentary peasants, confined to a mountain valley, could gradually have become conscious of the possibilities offered by high Alpine meadows and by the seasonal supplementation of resources at various elevations. Thus the herd, as it increased in number, could have been sent to a nearby mountain in the summer, where hay was collected for winter feed. In actual fact, the first possibility seems rather remote. Reconstructions made in Scandinavia on the basis of this hypothesized fixation of large-scale nomadism imply special climatic circumstances (such as a boreal phase during the first centuries B.C.) which gradually promoted winter stabling, a concentration of dwelling places, and conversion of regular settlements into summer cottages for temporary occupation.[2] Further, contemporary stabilization of mountain nomads indicates that they continue to make long-distance migrations to other mountain masses or plains (depending on the elevation of the settlement).[3] Thus, a direct passage from nomadism to Alpine pastoral life is far from clear.

On the other hand, the progressive de-

velopment of this Alpine life in contemporary times, beginning with stationary villages, is well documented. Let us cite, for example, Lighwan, a high village in Sahend, Iranian Azerbaijan). Until about thirty years ago, the use of the mountains there was limited to a very short pastoral phase in the summer and restricted to levels immediately above the village. Since then, in combination with demographic pressures and increases in number of sheep, higher elevations have been utilized in the heart of the summer while on the other hand migrations toward the plain of Tabriz have taken place at the end of the spring, a time when food resources become exhausted (44; 46). One thus sees migratory rhythms becoming progressively more complicated. Only recently have the inhabitants of high-altitude settlements in the upper Sahend become less dependent on immediate resources, and more conscious of the advantages offered by seasonal phasing.

This multiple layering is an expression of growing demographic pressure. Peasants in these mountain valleys agree only grudgingly to separate themselves temporarily from a part of their grazing stock, doing so only when they are constrained by the growing scarcity of the local resources.

An entire continuum can thus be defined with the aid of examples taken from the Alpine pastoral life of Anatolia and Iran (44: 226-33; 51: 24-28; 44-50). The first animals sent to the mountain are ones that are not milked: working stock first, i.e. beasts of burden or draft animals. In many Anatolian villages only oxen, frequently accompanied by horses and asses, are sent to the mountains. Pastoral patterns are initiated next for cattle without milk—young or sterile animals. In northern Iran, and particularly in Elborz, this separation is routine. The migrations of these groups are often the only ones to be organized, and are always longer and farther than for dairy animals. Migrations of sheep and goats develop along parallel lines. Dairy

throughout the Alpine, Carpathian, and Hercynian mountains of Europe, and extends into Scandinavia, especially Norway. (In Sweden, a land of less marked relief, it gives way to transfers of the same type, but occurring horizontally within forests.) Similarly, nomadism extends into the east within the Alpine-Himalayan Belt, just as it does within the mountainous regions of North Africa and the Mediterranean; there it exists in mountain valleys with peasant communities sufficiently stable to maintain themselves amidst territories generally given over to pure nomadism.

2. Concerning the origins of pastoral life in Scandinavia, see Cabouret (10; 11).

3. See, for example, the evolutionary stages of nomadism and montane seminomadism set forth by Planhol (44: 202-222).

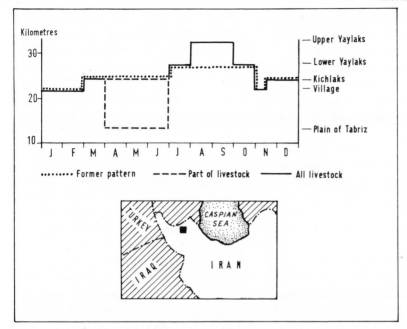

Fig. 14-1. MOVEMENTS OF SMALL LIVESTOCK AT LIGHWAN IN NORTH-EAST IRAN

cattle are always the last to be assigned to the mountain. They are frequently the only non-migrating stock; they are pastured close to the village, and returned to it each evening. To this multiplication of stages, there is added a growing differentiation of the flock, a steadily increasing complexity of movement, which may reach absurd lengths. Let me cite a remarkable example. In some instances some of the new higher elevations are so distant and difficult to reach that it becomes almost impossible to bring hay back to the village. In this case the flocks must be sent there during the winter to consume the hay on location. This ascending hibernation, where the migration takes place in reverse, characterizes a maximum expansion of pastoral migrations, where the search for remote pastures has been pushed to the ultimate.[4]

The development of pastoral migrations thus assures an increasingly complete utiliza-

tion of the mountain environment. But when the latter becomes too obviously confining for an ever-growing population, people decide to leave. Whether temporary or definitive, emigration as a reaction to demographic pressure is a frequent component of this type of mountain life. Transhumance *sensu stricto,* which draws livestock from the mountains during the winter, may be placed in the same category.

We must still carefully note certain nuances even in this rough outline. Types of mountain emigration vary, and their significance depends on the demographic situation they express. The earliest form of emigration in Sahend—an exodus at the end of spring—manifested itself no more than a quarter of a century ago (46:406-10). The decision to migrate is made when the previous year's grain harvest has been entirely exhausted and famine threatens. Possibly this *migration de soudure* is the most elementary type, motivated immediately and without pattern, by the threat of starvation. Emigrations gener-

4. Its significance has been worked out clearly by Isachsen (33). I have assembled a number of references in (49).

ated in a context of demographic congestion —those summertime out-movements expressing an imbalance between the supply and demand for labor at the very peak of the season might be placed in the same general category. On the other hand, wintertime emigrations, which utilize the period of almost total inactivity imposed by harsh climatic conditions for the acquisition of supplementary resources, reflect a land-occupance regime already highly rationalized, but one that does not necessarily presume an excessive human overload.[5]

The Impact upon the Natural Environment

To what extent is this demographic overload related to deteriorating natural conditions? The coincidence of periods of artificially induced erosion with periods of rural population growth is a well-documented fact in lowland tracts, even under climatic conditions as temperate as those of Central Europe.[6] There is even more reason for this to obtain in the infinitely more fragile and exposed environment of the mountains. But it is precisely the intrinsic harshness of the mountain environment that has placed the human contribution to these phenomena in some doubt. This question has been explored with some care in the southern French Alps (40: 735-37). Not long ago the sequence—demographic pressure $\longrightarrow$ deforestation $\longrightarrow$ torrential rains—seemed proven. Since the middle of the nineteenth century, research of engineers such as Surrell has continually established the connection between deforestation and rains (60).

5. For the respective significance of summer and winter migrations, consult Guichonnet (27: 504-506).
6. For example, Vogt (66), who posits a man-induced wave of erosion in eastern France and southern Germany related to demographic pressure in the eighteenth century.

Later historians and geographers correlated pastoral overload and peasant demographic pressure with the advance of deforestation (12: 1945-47; 57; 58). But a vigorous reaction began to take shape with the ideas of Lenoble (41), who credited the precarious situation of forests in the southern Alps much more to physical than to human conditions. This took the form of criticizing historical texts which exaggerated the complaints of mountain communities—confirmation that the devastation has been continuous and not connected with periods of demographic pressure; the observation that grazing, because it prevents the growth of underbrush, can be beneficial to the regrowth of forest trees; and, finally, the probability that the deforestation has no effect upon torrential rains, a morphological phenomenon completely independent of the vegetative cover. Although these positions may be exaggerated, they do serve to draw attention to the precariousness and modest profitability of reforestation in the southern Alps, and to illuminate the difference in scale between the action of man and the effect of natural phenomena in the mountain environment.

This is indeed the relatively moderate position of P. Veyret (65: 436-42), who, while admitting that deforestation *may* increase torrential rains, has shown clearly that the human effect, reflected most strongly on the flows at lower altitudes, can be responsible only for an insignificant portion of the destruction caused by floods. As for deforestation, the most recent investigations (9; 23; 40: 717-22) lead to similar conclusions. The historic fluctuations of the Alpine forests have been slight. On the whole, the forest frontiers seem to have been relatively stable; and the documents have certainly exaggerated shifts in forest location since the population may have been overly impressed by slight variations. The human effect cannot be denied, but it has undoubtedly been limited. Any essential cause-and-effect connection between deforestation and demographic overload has not been definitely established. Deforestation can progress rapidly even in a setting of relatively moderate human density. The log house, for example, is a great devourer of forests. In Saint Maximin de Beaufort (Savoie) there are 3500 log dwellings, averaging 150 years in age. It has been calculated that 4416 trees are needed annually to maintain the houses, in a commune where forests yield 500 trees at most, and where population density has been declining since the nineteenth century (14: 121).

From the above one can see that in mountain areas the effect of demographic pressure on the physiographic and biological environment is particularly difficult to estimate. That pressure exists is not at issue; what is difficult is the evaluation of its precise extent, and

great caution is indicated in this area. Taking everything into account, the criteria derived from the structure and movements of the human population appear more solid.

Demographic Pressure in the Alpine-Himalayan Belt

RETROSPECTIVE STUDY OF THE PHENOMENON In the western sectors of the Alpine-Himalayan belt, an extensive historical documentation has already been subjected to a number of investigations which permit retrospective analysis.[7] First, it is frequently possible to pinpoint the period when the pastoral mountain life originated. In the Bavarian Alps, it can be shown that around the middle

7. We shall not consider data drawn from the deforestation and the deterioration of the environment, which are sometimes questionable.

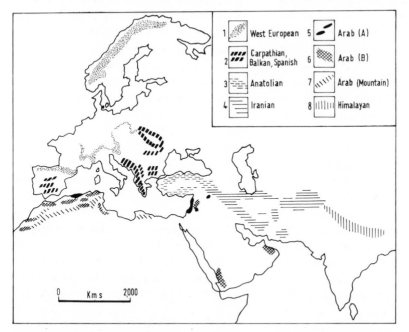

Fig. 14-2. TYPES OF POPULATION PRESSURE IN HIGHLAND REGIONS.
(1. Highland life in decline. 2. Transitional. 3. Low population pressure—in process of recolonization. 4. Overpopulated areas and regions of low population pressure being recolonized. 5. Mountain refuge regions with very high population pressure. 6. Appreciable population pressure. 7. Low population pressure. 8. Low population pressure.)

of the eleventh century, small stock farms and a pastoral life were established during a phase of demographic pressure contemporary with the major movement of clearing and settling the plains. This was followed by intense development during the twelfth and thirteenth centuries. Organization was at first individual; forms of communal agreements for the keeping of livestock did not appear until about the mid-thirteenth century (19: 437-42). Similarly, in the volcanic mountain masses of the Massif Central of France, the pastoral way of life started by monastic groups along the periphery did not become fully established until late in the Middle Ages (24). Biogeographic arguments trend in the same direction. In pastoral areas of the northern French Alps (Col des Glieres, near Annecy) as well as in the Central Pyrenees (Lac de l'Oule in the Neouvielle Massif), it has been possible to establish that grazing originated in the twelfth and thirteenth centuries by determining the age of forest stands in which younger specimens have been killed off by browsing (13). Human conquest of most of the upper Alpine meadows is indeed related to the major land colonization movement linked, in turn, with demographic pressures in the late Middle Ages.

The period of maximum complexity of Alpine pastoral life, in the eighteenth and nineteenth centuries, before the present-day rural exodus, can be seen with still greater clarity. Nowhere has it been analyzed in more detail than in the Norwegian mountains (54: 1955-1961). It is generally assumed that here multiple stages were established in the seventeenth and eighteenth centuries during a period of great expansion in pastoral life that corresponded to population growth in the interior of the mountain region.[8] After a severe

recession in pastoral life following the Black Plague during the epoch of low demographic pressure from the fourteenth to the sixteenth century, this expansion brought about the very complicated systems known in the nineteenth century and, in particular, the ascending hibernation. While it may seem legitimate to extend this rhythm, at least as a working hypothesis, to the entire Alpine chain of Western Europe, it is probable that evolution there was more continuous. Given a population well dispersed and thus much less susceptible to epidemics, regressive demographic fluctuations appear to have been much less appreciable. Much of the history of seasonal emigration from the Savoie and Valais Alps to the German-speaking areas is marked by a continuous increase in the number of emigrants, at least from the fifteenth to the eighteenth century (28). The abandonment of villages has been rare in these Alpine areas since the time of the medieval desertions (1).

In any case, the period of maximum population in the western Alps is placed in the nineteenth century, although it is rather widely spread out. In the French Alps, for example, the peak of the curve averages around the year 1848 for the region as a whole, but the decline starts as early as the beginning of the century (maximum in 1806 for some communes in Devoluy in the southern Pre-Alps) (31); or may be delayed until the beginning of the twentieth century (Maurienne in the inner high Alps of the north). But the present-day depopulation is very pronounced everywhere in this area; and it actively continues in the majority of the purely rural high valleys, although the development of the industrial and urban centers has been

---

8. Much less convincing is Reinton's hypothesis (54, I: 50): In Norway the splitting off of springtime from summer locations would have been the result of a worsening climate in the early Middle Ages, involving a shorter period

spent in huts at higher elevations. The springtime dwellings would thus have been more recent than summer ones. Undoubtedly the system did operate in a few cases, but its presence need not exclude a progressive evolution, certainly more widespread and generally recognized by other Norwegian authors.

some compensation for the region as a whole. In the central Alps, the exodus was later and less universal. In 1931, E. de Martonne indicated that depopulation seemed less pronounced in the east than in the west, i.e. less in Germanic and Slavic countries than in Latin countries (37: 129); and the map which he furnished for population change between 1880 and 1910 (37: 130-31) emphasized the contrast. The population is still actively growing today in the Austrian massif of the Oetztal (northern slope) (42), and now exceeds the nineteenth-century level by more than 30 per cent. Even superficial examination indicates overexploitation, particularly of the Alpine meadows, that has resulted in an accelerated deterioration of the environment. This has brought about a general reduction in the carrying capacity and a quantitative decline of the summertime occupation of the high pastures. Only a very small proportion of the population, from 1 to 3.6 per cent, depending on the sector, continues to pursue a pastoral life. Basic resources lie elsewhere—in tourism, or in labor migrations (occasionally on a daily basis) into other districts.

GEOGRAPHIC EXTENT OF THE PHENOMENON

The case of the Oetztal, exceptional as it is in Austria, nonetheless attests to a demographic development much less advanced than that of the western Alps. Thus a major geographic contrast takes form in the Alpine-Himalayan belt: the western sectors of the chain, those that are integrated into highly developed economies, with depopulation in full swing except for some industrial and urban centers, as opposed to the eastern sectors, where many people continue to mount assaults against mountains, only to find there ever more meager livelihoods. The problem is to delineate the two sectors, the one in which mountain life is on the decline and the other in which it is still advancing.

Actually, all the Asiatic sectors of the Alps as well as the North African chains may be included in the eastern sectors. There are extremely localized exceptions, the hinterland of the great Teheran agglomeration, for example, where accelerated growth in the last quarter-century has brought about a noticeable abandonment of the near mountain valleys of the Elborz and a pronounced retreat in the upper limit of cultivation, which dropped from 2700 meters to 2300 meters in Laridjan since 1930 (51: 33). But this involves a zone extending no more than 80 to 100 kilometers around the capital. In all of Anatolia, mountain life is even today at its maximum development and new *yayla* are constantly being occupied on the slopes of the mountains, while others are being transformed into permanent dwelling places. On the other hand, in Western Europe (including Austria), it is the *retreat* of Alpine pastoral life which is general, again with only local exceptions.[9] An indication of this in the Alps is the present swing northward of Mediterranean transhumance herds, replacing local flocks on the high pastures, a tendency currently reaching as far north as the Mont Blanc region. A transition zone probably occurs in the Balkans and the Carpathian Mountains, where the density of smaller livestock has greatly increased within the last thirty years (5: 527-29; 6), and the annual cut of lumber now exceeds natural forest growth (5: 532). An isolated case of ascending hibernation was pointed out as late as 1958 (18: 139). On the other hand, a decline is perceptible in the Slovakian Tatra Mountains, which are integrated into a country with a distinctly more industrialized economy (30). In Yugoslavia, contradictory features

9. See the contributions collected by Hartke and Ruppert (29), and for Norway, Sömme (59). Only Spain, with a quite different economic context, can be regarded as having a montane way of life still developing or classified as transitional.

seem to manifest themselves (35, 38). Decline and simplification of the pastoral regime
already appear in the urbanized regions in
the northwest, but on the whole mountain
cattle seem to be increasing considerably. Ascending hibernation is still being practised
here as well.[10] The Balkan Peninsula and
East-Central Europe, or in the wider sense,
from the Carpathians to the Adriatic, seem
indeed to form a transition zone, where the
two developmental tendencies occur in juxta-
position, in a detailed and complicated combination.

REGIONAL ASPECTS OF THE PHENOMENON

Remaining to be studied are those margins
that may be available for the expansion of
montane pastoral life in the Asiatic and
African sectors of the Alpine-Himalayan
belt, a region particularly subject to demographic pressure. The dominant factor in
most areas is the manner in which the population was initially implanted, as determined
by historical and cultural conditions.

1. In the Himalayas, the chief demographic accumulations are associated with
irrigated rice culture in valleys and interior
basins, an occupation that generally precludes and cannot be reconciled with pastoral
mountain life. In the central Himalayas, the
pressure of the sedentary civilizations of the
plain, blocked until very recently by the un-
healthy barrier of the Terai, has barely
reached the mountains. A painstaking mono-
graph devoted to the village of Sirkanda (7)
indicates that while pastoral life is developing
freely in the forested zone of Dehra Dun
(1600 m), constant settlement is taking place
as well. The high interior valleys of the chain
have most frequently been exploited by in-
filtrating populations of Tibetan origin, an

10. It has recently been noted in the Kremna
in the western portion of Herzogovina (34)
and on Mučanj Mountain in western Serbia
(55).

indication of the abundance of space. A recent analysis of Sherpa life in the Everest
region demonstrates that pastoral life there is
a reality only for a small minority; in Khum-
jung, only 17 households out of a total of 108
practised pastoral migrations. Most of these
owned large commercial herds of yaks. The
cattle-keeping families did not feel compelled
to migrate. The Sherpas are essentially farmers, occupying themselves only incidentally in
part-time commerce between Tibet and India. Only gradually are they developing herds
whose ownership induces them to organize a
pastoral life (38).

2. Farther to the west, where natural starting points exist at fairly high altitudes, rural
colonization has moved vigorously up the
mountain slopes. In Kashmir, settlers from
the overpopulated valley floor are installing
themselves in ever greater numbers in the
adjacent mountain valleys, there to lead a
life based at least partly on pastoral migrations of the Alpine type. But they share the
alpages (high summer pastures) with the
Bakerwal and Gujar, full-time nomads whose
presence expresses a still quite extensive land-
use pattern (61). The same is true in the
nearby Swat country (22).

In Iran and in Afghanistan, this sort of
relationship is even more prevalent where the
traditional sedentary Iranian mountain life,
based on intensive irrigated cultivation in
the valleys or on terraces, has been strong
enough to resist the upheavals of the Turkish-
Mongolian invasions, remaining at high elevations and maintaining the old population
nuclei, either by preserving its former ethnic
distinctiveness, or by absorbing the invaders
into its material culture. This is the general
case in Aberbaijan, which is linguistically
Turkish, but where ancient agricultural traditions persist at high elevations (46; 53). The
limits of expansion have already been frequently reached there. Typical, for example,
is the case of Nouristan, in eastern Afghanis-

tan, converted to Islam and open to the outside world only since the beginning of the century. There integration into the Afghan nation-state has initiated an active emigration of workers and itinerant merchants. We have seen how labor migration in Sahend during the course of the last generation appeared to indicate saturation. In Iran the last patches of timber in the interior mountains are rapidly disappearing with the settlement of hamlets at high altitudes. This colonization seems quite marginal and unstable; having profited ephemerally from the capital derived from these last vestiges of forest, it is bound to suffer a setback with their disappearance (21: 60-63, 105-6). It is estimated that the oak forest of Zagros is now reduced to only 10 per cent of its original extent, and the cedars of the interior slope of the Elborz and of Khorassan to less than 5 per cent; the pistachio-almond forests of the piedmonts of interior Iran have been almost entirely destroyed. This sort of situation extends as far as Kurdistan, where old high-altitude populations have survived medieval invasions. It was also characteristic of the Armenian uplands before the disappearance of the population during World War I produced a situation of the Anatolian kind.

3. The region affected by the nomadic Turkish-Mongolian invasions offers a quite different starting point for present-day demographic pressures. Nomads from the cold steppes, with their Bactrian camels, easily adaptable to the mountain environment, found a preferred habitat in the uplands; and they often sought out fresh pastures at high elevations, above the overheated high basins of the interior Near East. The "bedouinization" of the mountains, reduced to a transient summertime occupance, and an extremely sparse permanent population, was the fundamental anthropogeographic characteristic of this process. Already widely distributed over vast portions of Iran and Afghanistan, where

bedouinized mountains alternate with old permanent settlements, this transient occupance is represented in almost all of Anatolia. The upper limit of permanent habitation had fallen extremely low there by the beginning of the current demographic expansion, descending, for example, to a mere 500 meters in the southwestern Taurus (43). The Anatolian mountains as a whole still appear quite empty. This explains why the present recolonization of the mountains has not yet regained the upper limits of the permanent habitation of the Byzantine period (3). On the whole, the Turkish mountains still have a significant margin for altitudinal expansion of the permanent population, a process vigorously paralleling the rapid demographic growth of present-day Turkey. Another reserve territory, but in an equally marginal situation, is the central steppe, where temporary pastoral dwellings are also being converted into permanent dwellings (32), and where the total cultivated area practically doubled between 1937 and 1960. Although a period of relative forest recovery undoubtedly followed the invasion of the pastoralists (52), the current decline in mountain forests, the only remaining ones of any extent, is particularly noticeable and serves to indicate the present, final phase in the conquest of the soil. Nevertheless, the wooded areas are still more important in Turkey (13 per cent of which is at least theoretically wooded if areas of bush are included) than in other countries of the Near East. Emigration of a strictly montane character still remains insignificant. The major currents of internal migration flow from high basins that are already congested or from the East-Pontic slopes, where an exceptional demographic accumulation was established at an early time in hot, humid forest, impermeable to the nomads (39; 50).

4. The situation in the Arab world, from the Near East to North Africa, is notably different. Arab nomadism has, in effect, spared

the mountains. Dromedaries, which are animals of the hot desert, were unable to adapt to upland climates. Only mountains of modest dimensions, skeletal chains barely emerging from the desert (such as the Saharan Atlas of Algeria) were bedouinized (16). Even places of very low relief such as the Cuestas of South Tunisia and Tripolitania, from Djebel Matmata to Djebel Nefousa, had dense permanent human settlements clinging to them, resisting bedouinization (15). The high massifs were even more difficult for the pastoralists to penetrate—the Ancient Massif of the Moroccan Grand Atlas, or the highlands of Asir and Yemen in Arabia. The human density in these places was $22/km^2$ for the Ancient Massif in 1936; $25/km^2$ for eastern Djebel Nefousa in 1915 before the disturbances of World War I (15: 95; 20). But to such "intact" mountains must be added the much greater demographic accumulations in the mountain refuges: interior mountains that have sheltered populations, often religious minorities barred from the irrigable steppes; Djebel Druze, for example, where nearly 150,000 persons have settled, achieving a density of more than $100/km^2$ in a subdesert environment with an average of only six liters of water per day for each person; or Djebel Sindjar in the Levant; or the primarily coastal mountains along the Mediterranean rim which support extraordinary concentrations in a much more humid natural environment, such as Greater Kabylia in North Africa ($173/km^2$ in the district of Tizi-Ouzou in 1954 (17)), Lebanon $161/km^2$ without Beirut (64)), or the Alawi Mountains in northern Lebanon and adjacent Syria (88 per km^2).

Under these conditions, symptoms of demographic congestion have appeared early. Deforestation of the Levantine mountains has been pushed to the extreme, offering a contrast to the relatively good preservation of the Taurus. A particularly striking historic inver-

sion appears in Lebanon, formerly the great forest reserve for the whole Near East, where the forest has gradually disappeared since the settling of the Maronites in the Middle Ages (64: 268-85). Further eloquent testimony to the pronounced imbalance between population and resources which has existed in these mountains for some time past are the following: the extraordinary Lebanese transoceanic emigration, involving more than 400,000 persons (56); the emigration from Greater Kabylia, reported in the Algerian regency at the end of the eighteenth century, oriented toward France during the colonial period, and accounting in all for several hundred thousand persons; the more amorphous and shorter-range Alawi emigration toward El Ghab, the steppe of Mamoura, and the Cilician plain since 1850 (67: 370-72); and the recolonization of Salamiye (the area in which the Ishmaelite sect originated and where some 30,000 of its members now live, as against only 10,000 in the Alawi mountains (36)). Although there was a less appreciable initial concentration in the "intact" mountains, emigration from them is just as apparent, i.e. the commercial out-movements of the Nefousi toward Tripoli or Tunisia or the "military" emigration of the Chleuhs, who have always supplied the backbone of the Moroccan army, from the High Atlas.

The Algerian situation must be put into a separate category in this discussion. The settlement of large numbers of French colonists in the plains during the last century seriously increased congestion in the mountains, where the indigenous population was confined. An accelerated deforestation was the consequence (58). An entirely new equilibrium was established following the years of insurrection (1954-62), when the mountains were practically emptied of a large portion of their population who fled insecure zones and generally regrouped in new villages in the piedmont areas (47, 48). This displacement affected more than two million people, some 24 per cent of the Moslem population of the period. The first data gathered since Algerian independence reveal that the abandoned mountains have not been repopulated, and that the situation thus created appears indeed to be irreversible. Consequently, conditions for forest recovery and a new equilibrium in the mountain environment have been achieved, but without a solution to the larger problem of population pressure in Algeria as a whole, where the imbalance between population and resources seems in every sense particularly severe.

Thus one finds a variety of regional situations, products of historical processes working in opposite directions. The equilibrium of population and resources in a mountain environment has been achieved in the western portion of the Alpine belt as a result of a general economic development which has an effective impact, even after some delay, on mountain occupance. In the Middle East, where this phase has not yet been attained, the imbalance of population and resources is universally menacing; but it is still very unevenly distributed. Figure 14-2 summarizes these contrasts. Population pressure is generally present throughout the Arab world, more specifically in Iran, side by side with areas that still offer considerable amounts of space. It remains the exception in Turkey, which has paradoxically benefited from a predominance of nomads since the medieval invasions. Assuredly, it is remarkable that the countries in which the retreat of sedentary pattern was sharpest only a short time ago find themselves, in the present period of scarcity, in a better situation than those in which important sedentary settlements have remained intact.

REFERENCES

(1) W. Abel: Land- und Ernährungswirtschaft in Mitteleuropa seit dem hohen Mittelalter (Hamburg, 1965).

(2) P. Arbos: La Vie Pastorale dans les Alpes Françaises (Paris, 1922).

(3) G. Bartsch: Siedlungsgang und Siedlungsraum im südostlichen anatolischen Hochland, *Bericht der oberhessischen Gesellschaft für Natur- und Heilkunde zu Giessen, Neue Folge, Naturwissenschaftliche Abteilung,* Vol. 28, 1957, pp. 58-81.

(4) M. Benchetrit: Les Modalités de la Dégradation des Forêts dans le Tell Oranais, *Revue de Géographie de Lyon,* Vol. 41, 1966, pp. 303-38.

(5) St. Berezowski: Problèmes Economiques des Karpates Polonaises, *Revue de Géographie Alpine,* Vol. 51, 1963, pp. 515-44.

(6) St. Berezowski: Les Migrations Pastorales et l'Aménagement des Alpages dans les Carpathes Polonaises, *Geographica Polonica,* Vol. 2, pp. 115-22.

(7) G. D. Berreman: Hindus of the Himalayas (Berkeley, 1963).

(8) J. Blache: L'Homme et la Montagne (Paris, 1933).

(9) R. Blanchard: Déboisement et Reboisement dans les Préalpes Françaises du Sud, *Revue de Géographie Alpine,* 1944, pp. 335-88.

(10) M. Cabouret: Les Recherches sur la Vie Pastorale en Norvège, *Revue Géographique de l'Est,* Vol. 3, 1963, pp. 258-98.

(11) M. Cabouret: Etat des Recherches sur la Vie Pastorale en Suède, *Revue Géographique de l'Est,* Vol. 6, 1966, pp. 291-320.

(12) J. Chardonnet: Le Relief des Alpes du Sud, 2 vols., (Grenoble, 1947).

(13) P. Chouard: L'Origine de la Vie Pastorale en Haute Montagne d'après des Documents Botaniques, *Compte Rendu Sommaire des Séances de la Société de Biogéographie,* Vol. 20, 1933.

(14) P. Deffontaines: L'Homme et la Forêt (Paris, 1933).

(15) J. Despois: Le Djebel Nefousa (Tripolitaine), Etude Géographique (Paris, 1935).

(16) J. Despois: L'Atlas Saharien Occidental d'Algérie; Ksouriens et Pasteurs, in: Mélanges Géographiques Canadiens Offerts à Raoul Blanchard (Québec, 1959), pp. 403-16.

(17) J. Despois: La Répartition de la Population en Algérie, *Annales, Economies, Sociétés, Civilisations,* 1960, pp. 915-26.

(18) K. Dobrowolski: Die Hauptypen der Hirtenwanderungen in den Nordkarpaten vom 14. bis zum 20. Jahrhundert, in: Viehzucht und Hirtenleben in Ostmitteleuropa (Budapest, 1961), pp. 113-46.

(19) P. Dollinger: L'Evolution des Classes Rurales en Bavière depuis la Fin de l'Epoque Carolingienne jusqu'au Milieu du XIIIe Siècle (Paris, 1949).

(20) J. Dresch: Documents sur les Genres de Vie de Montagne dans le Massif Central du Grand Atlas (Tours, 1941).

(21) P. W. English: City and Village in Iran (Madison, Wisc., 1966).

(22) B. Fautz: Sozialstruktur und Bodennutzung in den Kulturlandschaft des Swat (Nordwest Himalaya), Giessener Geographische Schriften, 3 (Giessen, 1963).

(23) P. Fourchy: Remarques sur la Question du Déboisement dans les Alpes, *Revue de Géographie Alpine,* 1944, pp. 113-28.

(24) G. Fournier: La Vie Pastorale au Moyen-Age dans les Monts Dore, in: Mélanges Géographiques Offerts à Philippe Arbos, Vol. 1 (Paris, 1953), pp. 173-76.

(25) J. Frödin: Zentraleuropas Alpwirtschaft, 2 vols. (Oslo, 1940).

(26) C. von Fürer-Haimendorf: The Sherpas of Nepal (London, 1964).

(27) P. Guichonnet: L'Emigration Saisonnière en Faucigny pendant la Première Moitié du XIXe Siècle, *Revue de Géographie Alpine,* Vol. 33, 1945, pp. 465-544.

(28) P. Guichonnet: L'Emigration Alpine vers les Pays de Langue Allemande, *Revue de Géographie Alpine,* Vol. 36, 1948, pp. 544-76.

(29) W. Hartke and K. Ruppert, eds.: Kolloquium Rottach-Egern 1962, zusammengestellt von Almgeographie, Deutsche Forschungsgemeinschaft: Forschungsberichte 4 (Wiesbaden, 1962).

(30) V. Häufler: Zmiany w Pasterstwie w Tatrach Słowackich i w Niznich Tatrach za Okres Ostatnich 25 Lat., *Przeglad Geograficzny,* 1954, No. 1, pp. 89-96.

(31) E. Henriet: L'Evolution de la Population dans le Dévoluy depuis le Début du XIXe Siècle, *Bulletin de la Section de Géographie (Comité des Travaux Historiques et Scientifiques)*, Vol. 45, 1952, pp. 97-105.

(32) W. D. Hütteroth: Getriedekonjunktur und jüngerer Siedlungsausbau im südlichen Inneranatolien, *Erdkunde,* 1962, pp. 249-71.

(33) F. Isachsen: Vintersaetringen i Vågå, *Norsk Geografisk Tidsskrift,* Vol. 7, 1938, pp. 203-39.

(34) H. Isnard: Notes sur la Transhumance Pastorale en Herzégovine, *Méditerranée,* 1961, No. 2, pp. 37-47.

(35) V. Klemenčič: Probleme der Almwirtschaft in Jugoslawien, in: W. Hartke and K. Ruppert, eds.: Kolloquium Rottach-Egern 1962, zusammengestellt von Almeographie Deutsche Forschungs gemeinschaft: Forschungs bericht 4 (Weisbaden, 1962), pp. 43-55.

(36) N. N. Lewis: The Ismailis of Syria Today, *Journal of the Royal Central Asian Society,* 1952, pp. 59-77.

(37) E. de Martonne: Les Alpes, Géographie Générale (Paris, 1931).

(38) A. Melik: Planine v Julijskih Alpah, Dela Instituta za Geografijo, I (Ljubljana, 1950).

(39) S. Öngör: Türkiye'de Dahili Muhaceret Hakkinda [On Internal Migration in Turkey], *Turk Coğrafya Dergisi,* No. 18-19, 1958-59, pp. 101-17.

(40) Ch. P. Péguy: Haute Durance et Ubaye: le Climat, la Végétation, les Eaux, les Glaciers, *Revue de Géographie Alpine,* 1947, pp. 585-737.

(41) F. Lenoble: La Légende du Déboisement des Alpes, *Revue de Géographie Alpine,* 1923, pp. 5-116.

(42) Alice Picard: Les Vallées Septentrionales du Massif de l'Oetztal, 2 vols. (Paris, 1963).

(43) X. de Planhol: La Vie de Montagne dans le Sandras Dağ, *Revue de Géographie Alpine,* 1954, pp. 665-73.

(44) X. de Planhol: de la Plaine Pamphylienne aux Lacs Pisidiens, Nomadisme et Vie Paysanne (Paris, 1958).

(45) X. de Planhol: La Vie de Montagne dans le Sahend, *Bulletin de l'Association de Géographes Français,* No. 271-272, 1958, pp. 7-16.

(46) X. de Planhol: Un Village de Montagne de L'Azerbaïdjan Iranien, Lighwan (versant Nord du Sahend), *Revue de Géographie de Lyon,* 1960, pp. 395-418.

(47) X. de Planhol: Nouveaux Villages Algérois, Atlas Blidéen, Chénoua, Mitidja Occidentale, Publications de la Faculté des Lettres et Sciences Humaines d'Alger, XXXIX (Paris, 1961).

(48) X. de Planhol: Les Nouveaux Villages d'Algérie, *Geografiska Annaler,* 1961, pp. 243-51.

(49) X. de Planhol: L'Hivernage Ascendant et sa Signification dans la Vie Pastorale de Type Alpestre, *Revue Géographique de l'Est,* Vol. 2, 1962, pp. 310-11.

(50) X. de Planhol: A travers les Chaînes Pontiques: Plantations Côtières et Vie Montagnarde, *Bulletin de l'Association de Géographes Français*, No. 311-312, 1963, pp. 2-12.

(51) X. de Planhol: Recherches sur la Géographie Humaine de l'Iran Septentrional, Mémoires et Documents, IX, 4 (Paris, 1964).

(52) X. de Planhol: Les Nomades, la Steppe et la Forêt en Anatolie, *Geographische Zeitschrift*, 1965, pp. 101-16.

(53) X. de Planhol: Aspects of Mountain Life in Anatolia and Iran, in: S. R. Eyre and G. R. J. Jones, eds.: Geography as Human Ecology (London, 1966), pp. 291-308.

(54) L. Reinton: Saeterbruket i Norge, 3 vols. (Oslo, 1955-1961).

(55) R. Rušmovič: Stočarstvo no Mučanju, *Bulletin de la Société Serbe de Géographie*, Vol. 40, 1960, pp. 31-41.

(56) E. Safa: L'Emigration Libanaise (Beirut, 1960).

(57) Th. Sclafert: A propos du Déboisement des Alpes du Sud, *Annales de Géographie*, 1933, pp. 266-77, 350-60.

(58) Th. Sclafert: A propos du Déboisement des Alpes du Sud: le Rôle du Troupeaux, *Annales de Géographie*, 1934, pp. 126-45.

(59) A. Sömme: Recent Trends in Transhumance in Norway, in: Comptes Rendus du Congrès International de Géographie, Lisbonne, 1949, Vol. 3, pp. 83-93.

(60) A. Surell: Etudes sur les Torrents des Hautes Alpes (Paris, 1841).

(61) H. Uhlig: Typen der Bergbauern und Wanderhirten in Kaschmir und Jaunsar-Bawar, in: Deutscher Geographentag Köln, 1961 (Wiesbaden, 1961), pp. 211-25.

(62) E. de Vaumas: La Répartition de la Population au Liban, *Bulletin de la Société de Géographie d'Egypte*, Vol. 26, 1953, pp. 5-75.

(63) E. de Vaumas: Le Liban, Etude de Géographie Physique, 2 vols. (Paris, 1954).

(64) E. de Vaumas: Le Djebel Ansarieh, Etude de Géographie Humaine, *Revue de Géographie Alpine*, 1960, pp. 267-312.

(65) P. Veyret: Le Relief des Pays de la Moyenne Durance Alpestre, *Revue de Géographie Alpine*, 1945, pp. 121-213, 331-464.

(66) J. Vogt: Erosion des Sols et Techniques de Cultures en Climat Tempéré Maritime de Transition (France et Allemagne), *Revue de Géomorphologie Dynamique*, 1953, pp. 157-83.

(67) J. Weulersse: Le Pays des Alaouites, 2 vols. (Tours, 1940).

MIGRATION AND URBAN GROWTH: INTRODUCTION

The movements of large numbers of people in the countries of the developing world are clearly recognized, but for the most part they are evaluated and understood imperfectly. Mobility is one of the most neglected aspects of population study. The first paper in this section (*Kosiński and Prothero*) outlines some of the basic characteristics of mobility and explores some of the relationships with population pressure. It is not intended to be original but is designed to give perspective. Many of the points raised in it are illustrated by papers in this and other sections of the Symposium. This overview is complemented with the greater detail of Simkins's Philippine study, which underlines the complexities of the migration process, in respect to the pressures upon people to move, the alternative opportunities which are open to them, the decision to move, and subsequent developments. It shows that there is much variety as well as uniformity in migration behavior.

Apart from movement to metropolitan Manila, internal migration in the Philippines is directed to rural rather than to urban areas. In the majority of the developing countries, the towns are the major foci for migrants from rural areas, who usually are aiming to improve their economic (and subsequently their social) status. For many migrants these hopes are illusory, and *Mme Beaujeu-Garnier* reviews the major problems of the large overpopulated cities which exhibit characteristics of economic and social imbalance between increasing urban populations and the urban opportunities, facilities, and amenities available to meet their needs.

The cities of India are faced with these problems on a very large scale, though during the last two decades there has been evidence of a deceleration in the rate of urban growth (*Brush*). Between 1951 and 1961 while the urban growth rate was above that for the total population, it diminished relative to the percentage growth, which rose higher than ever before. This deceleration is associated with the restricted opportunities, facilities, and amenities which Indian cities have to offer rural migrants.

Urban problems are exemplified in detail in *C. G. Clarke's* study of Kingston, Jamaica, which employs a variety of parameters to measure the weight and distribution of population pressure. Causal relationships among socioeconomic status, unemployment, and inadequate accommodation are demonstrated. There are long-established, and frequently illegal, adaptations to perpetual poverty, and dissatisfaction with conditions is manifest in urban protest movements. Furthermore, *Clarke* shows that the problems of Kingston must be viewed in the context of the problems of Jamaica. The former might be solved with massive government action, but only at the expense of the country as a whole.

However, while the urban problems of developing countries are of seemingly overwhelming proportions, *Mme Beaujeu-Garnier* cautions that it would be wrong to deny the important role that towns must play in economic and social transformation. Through the very concentration, and therefore the accessibility, of population, urban areas provide a more efficient milieu than do the rural areas for promoting the processes of modernization.

15. MIGRATIONS AND POPULATION PRESSURES ON RESOURCES

L. A. Kosiński and R. M. Prothero

Migrations reflect, among other things, differences in the levels of economic and social development of people and the areas in which they live. They may be both the cause and consequence of spatial and temporal variations. They have been associated with the opening of new areas for settlement, and with the prosperity of areas which attract people from others less fortunate. These circumstances may be noted from the experience of past migrations in areas now developed, but in developing countries, the relationships between migration and economic processes are not always so clear and may not be so close.

Migration studies have tended to focus attention on the factors causing the movement of people (especially the so-called "push" and "pull" factors), and on the consequences of these movements. They have dealt for the most part with great intercontinental movements, such as the slave trade between Africa and the New World, the European colonization of the Americas, Australia, New Zealand, and parts of Africa. But the scope of research has been expanding and techniques have become more refined. Today, there is a considerable literature on migrations, and typologies based on various criteria have been developed. As interest and concern for migrations in developing countries have come into focus, the inadequacy of many existing concepts and methods of study has become evident. The present discussion is concerned with migration in developing countries, particularly those movements caused by or associated with population pressure.

Migration and Population Mobility

The United Nations defines migration as the geographical mobility of persons between areas, generally involving a change of residence over a specific period of time. It is a definition which is most applicable to relatively settled populations, and it presents problems when applied to movements of population in developing countries. In many countries of Africa, for example, there are several kinds of large mobile elements. Some are transhumants or nomadic pastoralists (*de Planhol*); some are involved in forms of shifting cultivation. The degree of mobility varies: Muslim pilgrims may travel, sometimes for many years, to visit Mecca and Medina. People may move seasonally from their home areas to work in others. These and other types of mobility are not normally included in the classical definition of migration.

It is essential in such circumstances either to extend the concept of migration to include all kinds of spatial movement—temporary as well as permanent—or to replace the term "migration" with "mobility." Among French geographers only permanent movement is defined as *migration,* temporary movements of varying duration are termed *turbulence* (Pierre George) or *oscillation* (*Beaujeu-Garnier*). In this discussion the term "migration" is used in the broadest sense to include all kinds of movements.

Sources of Data

Generally speaking, statistical data on migrations are much more difficult to obtain than those for other demographic phenomena. This is true for developed countries, but is even more so for developing ones, where there may be no data at all. Often these countries have no regular statistical service and if there is a census, it may yield only limited data. Migration studies based on census data,

even when these give information on place
of birth and duration of residence, are concerned only with the total amount of movement. A person who moves several times but
returns to his original residence during the
inter-censal period will not be recorded as a
migrant, and the migrant who dies before
the census is taken goes unrecorded. Depending on the time and nature of a census, seasonal migrants are most likely to be missed
completely. Thus, migration data based on
censuses are inevitably underestimated, and
information must be sought elsewhere. Only
from specifically designed studies will it be
possible, for example, to follow the stages in
the movements of individuals from rural to
urban areas, back to rural, and then perhaps
again to urban areas. The number and range
of such specific studies are obviously limited.

Types of Migrations

Migrations may be classified on the basis of
various criteria, such as *distance* (intercontinental, international, internal), *duration*
(permanent, seasonal, daily), *cause* (economic, political, religious), *nature of decision-
making* (compulsory, voluntary). A combination of these criteria is required to classify the situations which arise in developing
countries.

The time of great intercontinental migrations has passed, and international and internal ones are now the more important. The
most usual are movements from rural to urban areas, which are influenced mostly, but
not entirely, by economic factors. These occur not only in the largest of the developing
countries, such as China, India, and Indonesia, but also within and between small states,
as in West Africa. In the earlier decades of
this century, there were few restrictions on
movements among these smaller developing
countries, though some are now being introduced. Migrations of an economic character

are associated with disparities in labor demands and wages between rural and urban
areas, though migrants' expectations may frequently be excessive. If resources in rural
areas are developed to the maximum, then
growing pressure caused by continuing population increase is likely to lead to out-migration. Examples of such migration, both past
and present, may be found in every part of
the world. Most frequently the possibilities
open to migrants are to be found in cities.
Migrations between one rural area and another may occur where there are ecological
differences or marked disparities in levels of
economic development (*Gosal; Simkins*).

Migrations may often be seasonal or temporary. Daily commuting occurs not only
among permanent urban dwellers but also
among people from rural areas on peri-urban
fringes (*Kiuchi; Brush; Gosal*). The latter
results either from the absence of possibilities
for permanent migration to the cities or from
habits and customs peculiar to the local culture. Seasonal migrants do not move permanently, either because they cannot or because
they do not wish to. However, such short-
term movements, when the possibilities
offered by new environments are first explored, may be the first stages toward permanent migration. Only later when these possibilities have been tested, and/or when there
is further pressure in the home areas, may the
final decision be taken. Migrants may thus
oscillate between rural and urban areas, or
move in stages from rural to peri-urban and
suburban areas and finally to the urban core.
Or they may move through a number of
smaller urban centers to larger ones.

Pioneer migrations to develop new land,
which are often associated with an attachment to rural life, in fact may be a response
to a lack of alternative possibilities. Migrations of this type were much more frequent
and widespread in the past, though they are
still to be found in the Philippines (*Simkins*)

and in Costa Rica (*Sandner*). The reserves of land for first development are fast diminishing, and more intensive methods of farming are being introduced into areas already settled. At present, those who make a decision to move are much more likely to break away from agriculture and to settle in a city if the opportunity is open.

Emigration overseas, once an important safety valve for countries experiencing population pressure, is now of limited importance in developing countries since freedom of movement has become more restricted. In limited cases, for example in Jamaica (*C. G. Clarke*) or in Samoa (*Pirie*), emigration may play an important role; but in general the labor market for immigrants from developing countries is contracting. This trend is very unlikely to be reversed for social as well as economic reasons. Where countries in Western Europe have extended their zones of labor recruitment to include some developing countries, the numbers involved are relatively small and those employed are usually admitted only temporarily.

In many developing countries, the flight of refugees from political situations and civil wars has been an important form of migration. The largest movements in this category, which may often involve the crossing of international boundaries, have been in the Indian subcontinent, following partition (*Gosal; Robinson*), and in Africa (Congo, Nigeria, Rwanda, Sudan). Pilgrimage is another form of migration motivated by non-economic factors.

Obvious similarities can be detected between the migrational patterns in the developing countries and those observed in advanced nations; but it would be unwise to push them too far, given the kinds of data and analysis currently available. If we can recognize the familiar rural exodus to the city in both classes of countries, a surge to attractive agricultural frontiers in many individual cases,

and the pre-eminence of economic factors in a majority of migrational movement, there are still major differences in volume, intensity, timing, demographic composition—and probably motivation—of the streams of migrants. As of this date, no analyst has attempted the broad, critical comparison of migrational phenomena for both sets of countries that would permit us to use the experience of one to help understand that of the other with any degree of confidence.

Population pressure variously defined may be a factor in almost every type of migration outlined. Even political migration may be indirectly the result of tensions between different ethnic or political groups competing for scarce or limited resources.

Causes of Migration and Selection of Migrants

It has already been indicated that migration flows are influenced by two sets of factors, operating in areas of origin and destination, respectively. These operate with different strength spatially and temporally. Many of the regional papers in this volume emphasize that factors at the destination end of the migration continuum are tending to increase in importance, although frequently their strength is based upon a myth of opportunities which are restricted if not actually nonexistent (*Beaujeu-Garnier*). Along with potential attractions of destination points, several other factors must operate: these include the spread of information and the susceptibility of potential migrants to incentives. Low living standards, illiteracy, and limited communication media all restrict the spread of accurate information in developing countries. There is much dependence on personal experience and contact, and there is some evidence to suggest that spatial mobility of population increases more quickly than the level of formal education of those involved. There is probably a feedback element, with increasing mobility contributing to the spread of information, which in turn leads to increased mobility. High levels of unemployment and underemployment, and the existence and continued growth of shanty towns (*bidonvilles, favellas,* etc.), indicate that the absorptive capacity of towns is much smaller than migrants may expect (*Beaujeu-Garnier, Brush, C. G. Clarke*).

In so far as incentives to migrate are related to individual experience and attitudes (e.g., felt pressure, aspiration, expectation) migrants in developing countries do not differ markedly from those in developing countries. The first who risk a trip into the relatively unknown are the more adventurous and energetic, seeking an opportunity to test their abilities. West Indian (*C. G. Clarke*) and Punjabi (*Gosal*) migrants to Britain are examples of such people. Yet the quality of migrants is difficult to measure. While active people tend to dominate in the first stages of migration, the more passive ones who simply follow the call and example of the enterprising may become the more numerous. Migration often has a communal character in developing countries, which contrasts with the individually based system usually prevalent in more developed areas.

Community ties may hold people back from migration. These ties have their greatest influence in societies where traditional structures have survived with least change. Though clearly less strong, community ties may also be important when migration does occur. Where there is seasonal migration, links are maintained with areas of origin; where migrants are away for longer periods but send remittances to their families, they are reacting positively to the centripetal influence of community ties (*Pirie*). It is likely, however, that the importance of these ties will decrease with time as a result of inevitable erosion of traditional forms of social organization.

Simkins suggests that the rapid increase of migration in the Philippines in the 1930's was the consequence of the fact that "some critical threshold was reached so that the psychological bloc involved in cutting community ties was overcome." All migration factors are presumably evaluated consciously or otherwise by a prospective migrant, whose final decision will depend on the immediate situation in his home area as well as in the proposed destination. The balance between all the factors involved is probably very delicately adjusted.

Consequences of Migrations

Examination of the consequences of migration may be concerned with the analysis of areas especially affected by out- or in-migration or may deal systematically with different types of consequences—economic, demographic, social, political.

In areas of out-migration, excessive population pressure may be relieved. When migrations are temporary, and especially if they are seasonal, the departures of people in the economically active age-groups will probably not affect economic potential. Rather, these people may contribute to prosperity since they return with money and their labor at home is available when needed. And when they are absent, they do not draw upon resources in their home areas. Mobility of population will have an effect on existing social structures; new patterns of thought and attitudes of mind develop from experience gained in other places, and as a result social mobility is likely to increase (*Browning*). The demographic consequences of permanent migration or the long absences involved in temporary migration may be noted in population changes. Sex and age structures are upset and the normal patterns of family life are disturbed, with consequent decline in fertility. In populations where natural increase is very high, this decline is welcome. However, as a result of migration the most able members of communities may be lost completely, or may be away for long periods of time, thus hindering the process of social change and limiting economic potential.

In areas of in-migration, a major economic consequence is pressure on the labor market, which in turn affects the level of wages and may encourage the development of labor-absorbing industries. Where wages are low, it is difficult for the local market to expand, and as a result, quite a large proportion of employed persons are engaged in nonproductive occupations (*Brush*). The overgrowth of the tertiary sector in these situations is typical. In theory a migrant who joins a new and developing community can rapidly ascend in the economic and social hierarchy. But the rapid growth of urban slums indicates that actual material and social improvement can be difficult to achieve, that in many cases social degradation occurs, and that this may be a permanent condition (*C. G. Clarke*). In the case of in-migration to rural areas, migrants often insist on practicing traditional methods of farming even though they may be in environments that require totally different treatment. The result may be catastrophic.

The demographic consequences of in-migration are very apparent. Again, the age-sex structure is upset, and in Africa and Asia males tend to dominate among immigrants. Where whole families are involved, the influx of people in reproductive age-groups contributes to an increase in birth rates. Newcomers do not immediately adopt urban family patterns, and high fertility exists among them for some time. In this way migration promotes still further increases in population and produces pressure in the destination areas. There may also be significant demoralization among people coming from traditional closed societies to open urban ones where strict controls in social relationships

do not exist. The problems may be greater if men migrate without their families. In the areas of origin the moral consequences are more limited, but here long absences of a high proportion of the male population may also produce problems.

From these points of view, and also from those of town-planners who would like to check or at least to slow the influx to towns, the question of whether massive rural-urban migration is desirable is open. The latter viewpoint is reinforced by the fact that urban growth tends to be concentrated in major cities (*Beaujeu-Garnier*). If a more balanced growth of towns of various sizes could be achieved, urban living might be improved, though it would not necessarily have any effect on rural areas (*Rościszewski*). In the future governments of developing countries may be forced to check migrations to large urban areas. *Brush* notes a deceleration in growth rates of urban population in India during the last two decades, and that further growth will be hampered without greater economic opportunity and improved urban infrastructure.

Advantages and Disadvantages of Migration

In developing countries the majority of migrations are the result not of sustained socio-economic growth, but of pressure associated with population increase, limited economic development, and rising expectations. May they be considered as a solution to problems caused by population pressure, or do they simply bring about a redistribution of pressure rather than its reduction?

Two possible answers are to be found in the literature, and both are represented in papers in this Symposium. The majority of contributors are skeptical of migrations as a solution. They are rather inclined to think that spontaneous migrations, which are neither reflected in nor caused by economic growth, create additional economic and social stresses (*Gosal*). The opinion that migrations can be considered as a solution is very limited (*Sen Gupta*). They may help to solve problems if they lower excessive pressure in one place, then assist in the development of new resources in another. The transfer of population alone, without economic development, is not a solution. It can even be a menace to social and economic stability, and may force political leaders to adopt policies which are disadvantageous to the population at large.

Official restrictions are likely to affect the international movements of peoples in developing countries, with the possible exception of Latin America, where the efforts to create a common market could contribute to the exchange of labor between countries. On the other hand, this development may be limited by political instability.

What are the over-all perspectives on migrations in developing countries? Most likely they will grow with continuing increases in population and continuing pressures on resources, and will be supported by the hopes and aspirations of those who seek a better life. In some instances they will add to the gravity of population-resource problems; in others, migrations generated by rural population pressures may be a necessary but ultimately beneficial part of the modernization process.

REFERENCES

(1) K. M. Barbour and R. M. Prothero, eds.: Essays on African Population (London, 1961).

(2) A. Beltramone: La Mobilité Géographique d'Une Population (Paris, 1966).

(3) W. D. Borrie et al.: The Cultural Integration of Immigrants: a Survey Based upon the Papers and Proceedings of the UNESCO Conference Held in Havana, April 1956 (Paris, 1959).

(4) A. T. Bouscaren: International Migrations since 1945 (New York, 1963).

(5) J. C. Caldwell and C. Okonjo, eds.: The Populations of Tropical Africa (London, 1968).

(6) H. A. Citroen: Les Migrations Internationales; un Problème Economique et Social (Paris, 1949).

(7) J. Denis: Le Phénomène Urbain en Afrique Centrale (Brussels, 1958).

(8) J. C. Elizaga: Les Migrations Intérieures en Amérique Latine. Aspects et Résultats Méthodologiques, *Rev. Intern. des Sciences Sociales*, Vol. 17, 1965, pp. 229-48.

(9) P. M. Hauser, ed.: Le Phénomène de l'Urbanisation en Asie et en Extrême-Orient (Calcutta, 1959).

(10) International Labour Office: International Migrations 1945-57 (Geneva, 1959).

(11) International Union for the Scientific Study of Population: Cultural Assimilation of Immigrants (London, 1950).

(12) J. Isaac: Economics of Migration (London and New York, 1947).

(13) E. Kant: Classification and Problems of Migration, in: P. L. Wagner and M. W. Mikesell, eds.: Readings in Cultural Geography (Chicago, 1962), pp. 342-54.

(14) L. Kosiński: Migrations of Population in East-Central Europe from 1939-1955, *Geographia Polonica,* Vol. 2, 1964, pp. 123-31.

(15) H. Kuper, ed.: Urbanization and Migration in West Africa (Berkeley and Los Angeles, 1965).

(16) E. S. Lee: A Theory of Migration, *Demography,* Vol. 3, 1966, pp. 47-57.

(17) D. Lowenthal and L. Comitas: "Emigration and Depopulation; Neglected Aspects of Geography," *Geographical Review,* Vol. 52, 1962, pp. 195-209.

(18) J. J. Mangalam: Human Migration. A Bibliographic Guide (Lexington, 1968).

(19) Milbank Memorial Fund: Selected Studies of Migration since World War II (New York, 1958).

(20) H. B. M. Murphy et al.: Flight and Resettlement (Paris, 1955).

(21) H. Panofsky: Migratory Labour in Africa (Bibliographical article), *Journal of Modern African Studies,* Vol. 1, 1963, pp. 521-29.

(22) W. Petersen: A General Typology of Migration, *American Sociological Review,* Vol. 13, 1958, pp. 256-66.

(23) R. M. Prothero: Continuity and Change in African Population Mobility, in: R. W. Steel and R. M. Prothero, eds.: Geographers and the Tropics; Liverpool Essays (London, 1964), pp. 189-213.

(24) R. M. Prothero: Migrants and Malaria (London, 1965) *and* Migrants and Malaria in Africa (Pittsburgh, 1968).

(25) M. J. Proudfoot: European Refugees, 1939-52: A Study in Forced Population Movement (Evanston, 1956).

(26) A. I. Richards, ed.: Economic Development and Tribal Change (Cambridge, 1956).

(27) F. D. Scott, ed.: World Migration in Modern Times (Englewood Cliffs, N. J., 1968).

(28) M. Sorre: Les Migrations des Peuples (Paris, 1955).

(29) J. Sutter, ed.: Les Deplacements Humains. Aspects Méthodologiques de leur Mesure (Paris, 1963).

(30) D. R. Taft and R. Robbins: International Migrations: the Immigrant in the Modern World (New York, 1955).

(31) B. Thomas, ed.: Economics of International Migration (New York and London, 1958).

(32) B. Thomas: International Migration and Economic Development (Paris, 1961).

(33) United Nations. Department of Economic and Social Affairs: Analytical Bibliography of International Migrations Statistics, Selected Countries, 1925-1950, Population Studies, No. 24 (New York, 1955).

(34) United Nations. Department of Economic and Social Affairs: The

Determinants and Consequences of Population Trends: a Summary of the Findings of Studies on the Relationships between Population Changes and Economic and Social Conditions, Population Studies No. 17 (New York, 1953).

(35) United Nations. Department of Economic and Social Affairs: Economic Characteristics of International Migrants, Statistics for Selected Countries, 1918-1954, Population Studies No. 12 (New York, 1958).

(36) United Nations. Department of Economic and Social Affairs: Handbook of International Measures of Protection of Migrants and General Conditions to be Observed in their Settlement (New York, 1953).

(37) United Nations. Department of Economics and Social Affairs: Problems of Migration Statistics, Population Studies No. 5 (New York, 1950).

(38) United Nations. Department of Economic and Social Affairs: Sex and Age Structure of International Migrants; Statistics for 1918-1947, Population Studies No. 11 (New York, 1953).

(39) United Nations: World Population Conference 1965, Vol. IV, Migration, Urbanization, Economic Development (New York, 1967).

(40) P. Wigny: Migratory Movements in the Underdeveloped Countries in Course of Industrialization, *International Labour Review*, Vol. 68, 1953, pp. 1-13.

16. MIGRATION AS A RESPONSE TO POPULATION PRESSURE: THE CASE OF THE PHILIPPINES

Paul D. Simkins

Prior to colonization, the islands of the Philippines were sparsely occupied by diverse peoples practising a generally extensive, largely subsistent agriculture. The impact of colonization was to initiate a rather continuous population gain but, at the same time, a progressive inequality in population density among the island groups. Those areas under the most direct and continuous contact with the colonizing power, particularly where the organization and techniques of agriculture were strongly altered, gained greatly in population, whereas, more remote areas maintained their primitive agriculture and low population densities. Almost from the beginning of historical record, therefore, areas of heavy population concentrations existed alongside areas that were only sparsely settled, providing space that could absorb redundant population through internal colonization. However, the filling-in of empty areas was slow until recently. It is the intent of this paper to examine the nature of population pressure in the more crowded areas of the Philippines and to determine the nature of the migration response to the growing population congestion.

A lack of appropriate data precludes any detailed analysis of the progressive growth of the Philippine population or of its changing distribution much before the beginning of the twentieth century. However, partial records and estimates of population growth during the nineteenth century suggest that even during this period, when one can assume relatively high crude death rates, increases in population size were fairly rapid; rates of growth generally fluctuated between 1 and 2 per cent per year (9:2). It is interesting to note that if these estimates are correct, population growth in the Philippines was as rapid as that of northwestern Europe during the demographic revolution of the nineteenth century. By 1903, when the first census under American auspices was taken, the population of the Philippines was slightly more than 7.6 million. At this date the arithmetic density for the whole of the country was still fairly low—about $25.5/km^2$. However, in some areas densities had already reached rather high levels. About one-third of the total population lived in the bloc of provinces extending from Manila Bay northward through the Central Plain and along the Ilocos coast of northwestern Luzon on about 10 per cent of the national territory. Throughout this belt, provincial densities exceeded $38.6/km^2$ and were commonly more than double that figure. Similar high densities were characteristic of most of the provinces in the Visayan islands. On the other hand, settlement was quite thin in the areas peripheral to these concentrations. Mindoro, Palawan, and Mindanao, which included more than 40 per cent of the land area of the Philippines, had less than 10 per cent of the population, and the over-all density of Mindanao, about $5.8/km^2$, was only around one-tenth that of the central plain of Luzon.

Population pressure, locally burdensome by the opening of the twentieth century, intensified as birth rates continued high and death rates slipped downward. By 1939, the national population total, 16 million, was more than twice the size of the 1903 total. After World War II, growth rates, which had fluctuated around 2 per cent in the prewar period, accelerated to over 3 per cent per year. This latter rate of increase is conspicuously rapid even among underdeveloped countries, and, if maintained, is sufficient to double the population in less than 25 years. The present population of the Philippines is now about 35 million and is increasing by approximately one million persons per year. The problem of population pressure, which in 1903 was of local concern, has now become one of national scope.

Population Pressure in the Philippines

Admittedly, an operational definition of population pressure is difficult to devise, and a definition that would meet universal acceptance quite likely is impossible to construct. A large part of the social and economic deprivation of underveloped countries is only indirectly a product of population numbers, and would remain even if population size were to be sharply reduced. Nevertheless, the components most commonly included in measures of population pressure have reached such magnitude in the Philippines that few would deny the existence of severe pressures. For the whole of the island group, the population density is now about 386/km² of cultivated land, the latter term defined as the total area in crops, lying idle, or included in permanent pasture. Although physiological densities are considerably higher in some countries of Asia, such as South Korea and Taiwan, the density of the Philippines is somewhat above the average for the non-Communist countries of East Asia. This density, combined with the nature of the terrain and prevailing land practice, has produced a temporary, if not permanent, deterioration of the land base. Nearly 40 per cent of the land surface of the Philippines has been subjected to serious erosion (11:79). The increasing concentration of people on cultivated land, coupled with the reality or threat of declining land quality, is all the more troublesome in

the Philippines where two-thirds of the labor force is still dependent on agriculture for livelihood.

Several responses are possible to increasing numbers of people on the land—intensification of land use, which implies a greater capitalization of agriculture; reduction in levels of living, exemplified by increasing tenancy, farm fragmentation, and underemployment; and out-migration, either to cities or to frontier agricultural areas. All of these responses have occurred in the Philippines with considerable variation by type of response and by region. Although the various responses to pressure occurred simultaneously in the past, one could, as a first-order generalization, suggest that the build-up in densities in the Philippines was at first largely accommodated by gradual reduction in living levels, followed somewhat later by increasing colonization of empty areas. With the progressive exhaustion of pioneer lands, the Philippines must now emphasize intensification of land use in order to avoid further deterioration of living conditions.

The pressure of numbers on the land has seriously affected the economic viability of the agricultural sector in the Philippines. For the whole of the country, the average size of a farm in 1960 was 3.7 hectares (a bit over nine acres), a result of the progressive decline in size since the prewar period. Although average farm size exceeds that of most countries in East Asia, these restricted holdings provide little, if any, surplus for the average farmer, given present techniques and organization, and limits the options open to any farmer who desires to increase the productivity of his land. Moreover, there is an uncomfortably high proportion of micro-farms—slightly more than one-tenth of all farms in the Philippines contain less than one hectare of land.

The limited access to the land is also reflected in the high tenancy rates in the Philippines. Less than one-half of all farms (46 per cent) are operated by owners, whereas nearly 40 per cent are operated by tenants. The proportion of farms operated under various forms of tenancy has increased gradually during the postwar period, rising from 35 per cent in 1948 to about 40 per cent in 1960. The rate of growth of tenancy may have increased significantly since 1960. One estimate made for the 1962-63 agricultural year suggests that more than one-half of all Philippine farms may now be operated under various forms of tenancy (7: 197). Although laws exist which limit the share of the crop that a landlord may receive, the pressure for land has become so intense in some areas that prospective tenants have bid the right to the land well beyond the legal maximum.

Limited access to land has also caused serious problems of unemployment and underemployment. Data obtained from the continuing Philippine Statistical Survey of Households suggest that about 8 per cent of the labor force of the Philippines is unemployed, and an additional 20 per cent of employed workers are occupied less than 40 hours per week and desire additional employment. Even these figures do not reveal the full extent of underemployment, for almost 7 per cent of the labor force, working a full 40-hour week, wishes additional employment (5:176-80).

Although agricultural productivity climbed rather sharply after World War II, the agricultural worker receives considerably less real income than does his nonagricultural counterpart. One estimate suggests that the per capita income of the agriculturalist may be no more than one-quarter of the average income earned outside agriculture (6:266). Moreover, the increasing agricultural productivity during the 1950's was not sufficient to obviate the need for food imports. Between 1954 and 1959, 18 per cent of the value of all imports was comprised of food-stuffs. Although wheat, flour, dairy products, and the like could be expected among the imports, heavy importation of rice has also become necessary. Between 1963 and 1965, over one million tons of rice were imported to meet domestic needs (10:2-6).

The depressed state of agriculture together with the increasing difficulty in gaining access to the land has been responsible in part for sporadic outbreaks of social unrest which reached a peak with the Huk uprisings of the early 1950's. Although the agrarian dissatisfactions were blunted, they were not fully suppressed, and there has been a resurgence of discontent in recent years. It is impossible to determine how widespread the active unrest has become or to know the numbers directly or indirectly involved with the renewed Huk movement. Government releases suggest that the number of active Huks is few, but indications are that they have achieved a considerable measure of political influence in the provinces of the Central Plain.

Migration Response to Population Pressure

The migration response to intensified population pressure cannot be determined directly from Philippine census returns. Data are available from only the 1960 census on province of birth cross-classified by province of present residence. These data, although of considerable value, do not indicate the trends of migration volume through time, do not reveal intermediate moves, and apply only to the survivors of all those who have moved within the Philippines. In addition, special tabulations of data from a 0.5 per cent sample have been made by province of residence in 1948 cross-tabulated by province of residence in 1960 (8:315-353). Further, the more commonly employed indirect methods of estimating net migrations, such as vital statistics or census survival techniques, are inappropriate given the nature of Philippine data. Therefore, in this paper I have resorted to a crude index of migration. The Philippine population is assumed to be a closed system, i.e., there is no migration into or out of the country, so that the total national population change is solely a function of natural increase. Although the assumption is not realistic, it is doubtful if the magnitude of external migration relative to the size of the national population is sufficient to introduce much error into subsequent calculations.

A more critical assumption, and one much more difficult to defend, is that provincial birth and death rates are uniform throughout the country, or that the differences are self-canceling. Thus, the natural increase in each province is assumed to be equivalent to the national percentage gain in population. All inter-censal population change not accounted for when the population of each province is increased by the national percentage gain is credited to net migration. The degree of error introduced by this assumption may be considerable. The more urban provinces, where health facilities are more abundant, may have death rates well below the national norm. Provinces which have experienced heavy age-selective migration, either in or out, may differ from the national average in both birth and death rates. Yet there is no evidence for sharp urban-rural differentials in fertility, (1:74-76, 105-8) and child-woman ratios, marriage rates, etc. do not differ greatly between the frontier and the maturely settled provinces. Admitting the possibility of substantial error, the method of estimation is still helpful, for any provincial growth that departs greatly from the national average must depart because of the effect of net migration. To account for considerable differentials in growth rates by invoking natural increase alone would require unrealistic assumptions of birth and death rates.

The total mobility within the Philippines appears to be rather considerable. In 1960, about 16 per cent of the native-born population was living in a province other than that of their birth. This proportion is below that of the United States, where for the past 100 years about 20-25 per cent of the population has moved from the state of birth, but it is considerably more than corresponding proportions in such countries as India (3 per cent) or Sudan (4 per cent). The volume of internal redistribution of population within the Philippines has sharply increased, but it is not so certain that the rate of internal migration has also risen. Using the crude methods of estimation described, it would appear that the rate of internal redistribution was rather slow during the 1903-18 census interval and again during the war-interrupted 1939-48 period. Higher, but apparently comparable, rates of internal migration are characteristic of the 1918-39 and the 1948-60 census periods. If the crude index employed is at all reliable, the implication is that internal migration during the postwar era has not been commensurate with the increase in population pressure.

The degree to which the relocation of residence has been caused by agricultural pressures cannot be established. Even the migrants themselves are only vaguely aware of the aura of hopes and dissatisfactions which surrounded them at the time of migration. One surprise, however, given the nature of agricultural pressure in the Philippines, is the low rate of urbanization since World War II in comparison with that of other developing countries. The generalization is somewhat suspect since the census definition of "urban" does not properly distinguish between rural and urban residents, including among the latter significant numbers of agriculturalists, while omitting from the category many residents of places urban by function. Indeed, it is hard to obtain a reasonable estimate of the degree of urbanization in the Philippines. According to the 1960 census the number of urban dwellers in the Philippines was about 4 million, roughly 15 per cent of the total population; but estimates based on minimum population size and residential density place the proportion as high as 30 per cent (2:192). The primate concentration, the Manila Metropolitan Area, which in 1960 contained 2.1 million persons, included one-half of the total urban population of the country. Much of the urbanization which did occur between 1948 and 1960 took place in metropolitan Manila, which added 700,000 persons during the census interval. The percentage increase in the metropolitan population was 55.9 compared with 40.8 for the nation as a whole. This increase, rapid though it may have been (about 3 per cent per year) is not extraordinary when compared with growth of primate cities in other parts of the world during the same period.

Exclusive of metropolitan Manila, the census urban population (27 of the remaining 28 chartered cities for which comparable data exist) gained in population at a rate only slightly in excess of the nation, the increase being 44.5 and 40.8 per cent, respectively. During the 1948-60 period, one-half of the chartered cities grew at rates below the national average. Assuming even fair accuracy of the census counts, and assuming that rates of natural increase in cities did not depart greatly from the national average, one must conclude that about one-half of the larger cities of the Philippines outside the Manila Metropolitan Area may not have kept their natural increase and did experience out-migration. Thus, the rapid growth of the Manila Metropolitan Area not withstanding, the intensified population pressure of the Philippines has not produced any substantial increase in rural-urban migration. Other data support a similar conclusion. "Taking male workers alone, an estimate of 1.2 million

farm workers were added since 1939. It could be assumed that there was only a slight movement out of agriculture during the last two decades" (2:194). Unless the Philippine census data on urban growth are extremely faulty or misleading, the urbanization experience is unusual among the underdeveloped countries and stands in sharp contrast with Latin America, for example, where the rural population during the 1950 decade grew about 1.5 per cent per year and the urban sector by around 5 per cent (4:177-182). In the Philippines both sectors increased about 3 per cent per year.

Frontier Settlement in the Philippines

Although the push of agriculturalists to Philippine cities has lagged behind expectations, the movement to frontier lands, a long-established practice, has involved increasingly large numbers of persons. It is conceivable that the presence of free land on the pioneer fringe has drained off some of the surplus agricultural population which otherwise might have piled up in the cities and so reduced the rate of urbanization. If this has been the case, then the situation again differs considerably from other underdeveloped areas, such as Latin America, where the surge to the cities has been very strong despite the availability of frontier lands.

From the beginning of modern census records in 1903, the frontier provinces have grown at rates well above the national average. Mindanao particularly has gained large numbers through inter-island migation, increasing its share of the total population from less than 8 per cent in 1903 to almost 19 per cent in 1960. Between 1948 and 1960, had the population of Mindanao grown at the national rate of increase, it would have grown by 1.1 million persons. Instead the population increment was 2.3 million. It is assumed that most of the difference was contributed by net migration. Very little of the frontier expansion has been due to colonization schemes, although since 1913 the government has attempted to encourage and even to sponsor movement from the crowded areas of Luzon, and to a lesser degree from the Visayas, to the frontier provinces. But success was limited, and by 1936 only 30,000 to 35,000 persons remained in the several agricultural colonies established in Mindanao. Even by 1963, only about 69,000 individuals had been accommodated on six projects operated by the National Resettlement and Rehabilitation Administration (3:102).

The great bulk of the movement to the pioneer lands, therefore, has been voluntary, individual migration. Although the number of families actually resettled by the government has been small, it may have helped to increase information about the nature and availability of frontier land, indirectly stimulating further voluntary migration. A body of friends and relatives in the pioneer provinces would reduce the psychological barriers to migration felt by potential migrants; so that contacts between the two groups could have been instrumental in forming a migration stream.

On the other hand, population growth in the more densely settled provinces of the Ilocos coast, the central plain of Luzon, and

the Visayas has failed to keep pace with the national average. Between 1948 and 1960, the provinces in these areas would have added some four million persons had the population growth matched the national average. They failed to achieve this growth by 1.8 million persons—an index of the out-migration which occurred during the census interval. Within these longer-settled areas, only one of the 19 provinces included appears to have experienced a positive net migration between 1948 and 1960.

Regional Variations in Migration Response to Population Pressure

In a general way the internal relocation of people in the Philippines conforms to the expected—a movement down the pressure gradient from areas of high density and economic distress to the sparsely settled frontier lands. This observation tends to be confirmed by Spearman rank correlation analysis. There are strong positive correlations between net migration and density, farm size, and the proportion of farms under one hectare to all farms. On the other hand, there appears to be no association between net migration and tenancy rates. However, when the analysis is limited to out-migration provinces only, the

TABLE 16-1   PHILIPPINES. DIFFERENTIAL GROWTH OF HIGH-DENSITY AND LOW-DENSITY RURAL PROVINCES

	1903	1918	Increase %	1939	Increase %	1948	Increase %	1960	Increase %
High Density	517,473	822,045	58.9	1,727,141	101.1	2,269,174	31.4	4,738,091	108.8
Low Density	4,582,702	6,000,260	30.9	8,526,677	42.1	9,809,511	15.0	12,008;219	22.4
Total*	7,635,426	10,314,310	35.1	16,000,303	55.1	19,234,182	20.2	27,087,685	40.8

* The Metropolitan Manila and intermediate density provinces are not included. Provinces included represent 31 of the 55 provinces of the Philippines.
Source: Republic of the Philippines, Bureau of the Census and Statistics: Census of the Philippines, 1960, Vol. 2, Summary Report. (Manila, 1963).

strength of the correlation weakens substantially. The only relationship that remains significant at the 0.5 per cent level is net migration and the proportion of tiny farms among all farms. The implication is that migrants are moving into low pressure areas, thus raising the level of correlation between net migration and population pressure variables when all provinces are considered; but that migration from the more crowded areas is not simply a function of density or economic pressure. The provinces which have the greatest population pressure, to the degree that this pressure is reflected in the variables employed, are not the provinces having the highest out-migration rates.

The three dominant areas of out-migration in the Philippines are the Ilocos coast, the central plain of Luzon, and the Visayan Islands. Each of these areas has its own peculiar pattern of population pressure and migration response. The Ilocos coast region of northwestern Luzon is composed of a narrow, discontinuous strip of coastal lowlands backed by a sparsely occupied and severely eroded hilly and mountainous interior. Although the soils are of moderate fertility, agriculture is handicapped by marked seasonal rainfall, the drought period extending through almost half of the year. Population densities are well above the national average and the physiological density of the area approaches 772/km² of cultivated land. The average farm size in the four provinces that comprise the area is less than two hectares. In the province of Ilocos Norte, 44 per cent of all farms are less than one hectare. The region has long been a primary source of out-migration, not only within the Philippines but to Hawaii and the continental United States as well. Ilocanos are found in every province throughout the Philippines, although the majority of the migrants have gone to nearby thinly occupied areas in northeastern Luzon (29 per cent) or to metropolitan Manila (36 per cent). Only

about 15 per cent have moved outside of Luzon, and more than half of these long-distance migrants have gone to Catabato province in Mindanao. One wonders if the government-sponsored settlement of Ilocanos in Catabato earlier in the century may have influenced the much larger subsequent migration. During each of the four census periods since the beginning of the century, the rate of population growth in the Ilocano provinces was much less than the national average, indicating a heavy and persistent out-migration. In fact, in comparison with other provinces the Ilocos coast has experienced a much higher rate of exodus than could have been predicted from the common measures of population pressure, such as farm size and fragmentation, tenancy, and agricultural density.

The Visayan Islands—Leyte, Bohol, Cebu, Negros, and Panay—share many characteristics of the Ilocos region. Lowlands are few and generally small; agricultural restrictions are compounded by modest rainfalls and seasonal drought. Population densities per km² of cultivated land in each island are above the national average, reaching a maximum of 910.6 on Cebu, which has the highest density of any of the Philippine provinces. Farm size varies considerably, being below the national average on all islands except Negros, where the average farm is somewhat larger than the national norm. On Cebu, farm sizes average 3.17 hectares, the smallest of any province in the Philippines. The presence of many land seekers has resulted in large numbers of micro-farm units, especially on Cebu, where 46 per cent of all farms are less than one hectare. Moreover, the steep slopes and prevalent cultivation of corn have resulted in serious erosion problems. As was true for the Ilocano area, the Visayan region has also experienced persistent and heavy out-migration. Even during the Spanish period, there was a slow but persistent drift of Visayans, especially Cebuanos, southward to the Misamis coast of northern Mindanao. This southward drift, especially to Davao and Catabato provinces, has intensified in the twentieth century. Heavy out-migration rates occurred first in Cebu and western Panay where, since the beginning of record, growth rates well below the national average have been characteristic. The out-migration was particularly strong and widespread during the 1948-1960 census period, when the national population increased by 40.8 per cent, but the Visayas grew by only 19.3 per cent. Of the 222 Visayan municipalities with boundaries that remained constant between 1948 and 1960, 194 grew at rates less than the national average, and nearly one-fifth of them actually lost population. As is true for the Ilocos coast, although to a somewhat lesser degree, the provinces of the Visayas tend to rank higher among all Philippine provinces in out-migration rate than they do in other measures of economic distress.

The provinces of the central plain of Luzon, are in many respects as crowded as the Ilocos coast and Visayan Islands, yet have quite a different migration response. Agricultural densities in the central plain, well above the national average, are not so uniformly high as they are in the Ilocos region, nor is the average farm so small, ranging from 1.87 hectares in Pangasinan province in the north to 3.67 in Nueva Ecija on the eastern fringe of the plain. Moreover, a smaller proportion of farms are less than one hectare than in the Ilocano and Visayan regions. On the other hand, tenancy rates are higher in the central plain than in any other region of the Philippines. Throughout the areas, more than one-half of all farms are operated by tenants. The intensity of tenancy reaches its maximum in Pampanga province, just north of Manila Bay, where 85 per cent of all farms are so operated. The central plain provinces, moreover, have been the areas where agrarian un-

rest has reached maximum intensity. Although a greater share of persons born in the provinces of the central plain are living outside the province of their birth than is true for the national average, the out-migrants do not tend to diffuse so widely or to migrate with the same frequency as do movers from other out-migration provinces. Nearly as many lifetime migrants are found in provinces of the central plain as in all non-Luzon provinces combined, and more than two-fifths (45 per cent) of these migrants now reside in the Manila Metropolitan Area. Despite lesser intensities of population pressure in the Ilocos and Visayan regions, indices for the central plain are still well above national averages. Yet, out-migration is not so large as one would have expected from the nature of economic pressures present. The provinces included commonly rank considerably higher among the Philippine provinces in tenancy, agricultural density, and proportion of farms under one hectare than they do in out-migration.

Conclusions

The pattern of population redistribution relative to economic pressures within the Philippines has unique features, but it still prompts speculations which may have general applicability. It would seem that migration is not an automatic response to increasing population pressure—there are a number of other alternatives open that may be more acceptable to the persons involved. Even lower levels of living may be chosen, at least until pressures become severe, above leaving a home environment. Indeed, it is strongly suspected that migration is chosen reluctantly by most people in areas where family ties and community bonds are keenly felt. The lack of close correspondence between out-migration and agricultural density, tenancy, and farm size, together with the apparent failure of migration rates to accelerate commensurate with increasing population pressure since World

War II, lends credence to these suppositions.

Further, the regional variations in migration response to population pressure suggest that some areas evolve a tradition of migration in which outward movement becomes an accepted feature of the culture. Although the initial phase of voluntary migration in developing societies requires much more attention than it has received so far, one can venture some guesses. As economic pressures mount in an area in which a tradition of migration has not become established, those persons less attached to family and place—the more ambitous and daring—gradually move out in search of greater opportunity. The search pattern of these migrants is likely to be random and restricted to nearby areas, rather than remote but perhaps more attractive areas. In the Philippines, relative to experience in many other developing areas, there is a greater tendency to remain in agriculture and move to the frontier rather than to nearby cities. In some instances, knowledge of more distant places, such as may have been provided by government sponsorship of agricultural colonization in Mindanao, may fix a particular migration stream early.

Having reached various destinations, the pioneer migrants begin to create information links with the home area, gradually attracting more migrants. As the body of friends and relatives in the frontier areas widens, the psychological block involved in cutting community ties is progressively eroded. Not only does the potential migrant have greater knowledge of the frontier conditions, but he also has available persons with whom he can live until he can accommodate himself to his new surroundings. It seems likely that some threshold may be involved—a little bit of migration may not trigger off much subsequent movement, but once the build-up of friends and relatives reaches a critical level—the point at which concern for severance of ties diminishes. Once the threshold is reached, out-migration is sharply accelerated. In time, a tradition of migration becomes accepted. Where this occurs, the migration response is likely to be in excess of that expected, given the nature of economic pressures. Such a tradition seems characteristic of the Ilocos coast and the Visayans, but less so of the central plain of Luzon.

A final point remains. The direction any movement takes is largely a function of the preceding migration. As any destination has a fixed amount of land available, accelerated migration soon brings mounting pressures. When this occurs, negative information passes back to the source regions, and the migration stream is ultimately redirected. The progressive filling of given frontier areas and the delay in the redirection of migration flows may help explain the apparent lack of accelerated migration rates in the postwar period in the Philippines. Easily accessible frontier lands capable of being cultivated without a heavy input of capital are almost exhausted. Although continued migration to the remaining frontier and less densely occupied areas is expected to reduce regional differentials in density and agricultural pressure, the agriculturalist of the Philippines must increasingly turn to the city, must intensify his cultivation, or have forced on himself continued decline in an already precarious living level.

REFERENCES

(1) Mercedes Concepcion: Fertility Differences Among Married Women in the Philippines (Ph.D. dissertation, University of Chicago, 1963.)

(2) Mercedes Concepcion: The Population of the Philippines, in: First Conference on Population, 1965 (Quezon City, 1966), pp. 185-99.

(3) Maynard W. Dow: Nation Building in Southeast Asia (Boulder, Colorado, 1966).

(4) John D. Durand and Cesar A. Pelaez: Patterns of Urbanization in Latin America, *Milbank Memorial Fund Quarterly,* Vol. 3, Part 2, 1965, pp. 177-82.

(5) P. R. Franche: The Problem of Underemployment in the Philippines, *The Philippine Statistician,* Vol. 8, 1959, pp. 176-80.

(6) Frank Golay: The Philippines: Public Policy and National Economic Development (Ithaca, 1961).

(7) Robert Huke: Shadows on the Land (Manila, 1963).

(8) Elvira Pascual: First Conference on Population, 1965 (Quezon City, 1966), pp. 315-53.

(9) Republic of the Philippines, Bureau of the Census and Statistics: Census of the Philippines, 1960, Vol. 2, Summary Report (Manila, 1963).

(10) F. C. Rodriquez: The Rice Situation, *Philippine Geographical Journal,* Vol. 10, 1966, pp. 2-6.

(11) Frederick L. Wernstedt and J. E. Spencer: The Philippine Island World (Berkeley, 1967).

17. LARGE OVERPOPULATED CITIES IN THE UNDERDEVELOPED WORLD

Jacqueline Beaujeu-Garnier

Given the rate of development of large cities in the underdeveloped countries, their most characteristic phenomenon appears to be an imbalance between the number of inhabitants and, in its wider meaning, the urban assimilation capacity.

This essay will attempt first to state precisely the fundamental cause of this imbalance: the vigorous demographic growth of the cities. Second, it will endeavor to show how the imbalance expresses itself, and last, it will indicate that it is the future of the Third World which is emerging from this undoubtedly painful, but necessary, passage.

Demographic Growth

The majority of the countries in the Third World[1] are characterized by rapid growth in total population and by a still more pronounced growth in the number of persons living in cities. According to official statistics and some special studies in Brazil, the number of cities with more than 100,000 inhabitants increased from 6 to 31 between 1920 and 1960, and the proportion of the national population contained in these cities from 8.7 to 18.6 per cent (4; 5; 11); in Egypt, there were 1.9 million city dwellers in 1897 and more than 9 million today, and the urban population has grown twice as fast as the national population (Rościszewski, p. 334); in Cameroon the two largest cities, Yaounde and Douala, have seen an average annual growth of 6 per cent in the course of recent years (J. Clarke, p. 359).

This urban development is linked to two phenomena: the influx of population through

1. "The Third World"—a literal translation of the French term Le Tiers Monde referring to the underdeveloped countries as a group.

migration; and the volume of natural growth. In the eight largest agglomerations of Brazil, 29 per cent of the increase between 1940 and 1950 was attributable to natural increase and 71 per cent to migrations; for the smaller cities (with more than 5000 inhabitants), the percentages were 51 and 49, respectively (10). In Calcutta, natural growth supplied 49 per cent and migration 50.3 per cent of the total increase between 1911 and 1921; the values were 56.6 and 43.4 per cent, respectively, between 1951 and 1961 (8).

Statistics indicate the importance of these immense movements into the cities. In India in 1961, 53 per cent of the people of Calcutta were immigrants (Sen Gupta, p. 435), but the proportion was still greater in the nearby cities of the industrial region; in Bombay, the proportion reached 70.8 per cent (10). In São Paulo in 1959-60, only 27.1 per cent of the men and 29.3 per cent of the women had been born in the municipality; but the proportion coming from rural districts was small (3.9 per cent of the men, 6.6 per cent of the women) (Bonasewicz, p. 566). In Dakar, 41.6 per cent of the inhabitants are originally from areas beyond the Cape Verde districts (6; 7), and in Mexico, the proportion is the same: 42 per cent were born outside the district (2; 16).

The several preceding examples indicate that this cityward influx is general. Its causes are multiple, but they can all be categorized under the complementary forces of urban attraction and rural repulsion. In the less favored regions of the underdeveloped countries, it seems that the second factor is the more important one. This is the general conclusion given by G. Mortara (17) in studies of rural-urban migrations of Brazil; and it is

269

also the impression experienced during an inquiry I made in Bahia in 1961 in collaboration with Milton Santos (20). Large property
holdings offer little hope to the unfortunate
rural population and virtually force migration
to the city. This is also the conclusion drawn
from studies on India; but there it is the landless peasant who abandons overpopulated
tural tracts, as Miss P. Sen Gupta indicates.

Means of transportation play an important
role. In the Punjab, those cities experiencing
the greatest growth are found in the southwest, and are located, according to Gosal,
along branch lines connected to chief railway
lines. The example of Brasilia could also be
cited, a city which has attracted migrants
from everywhere in Brazil because of the
opening of roads linking it to all parts of the
national territory, or that of São Paulo, which
is recruiting more and more migrants from
the center of Bahia since a hard-surface road
tapped this region.

As far as the balance of the sexes is concerned, the make-up of the migratory stream
is quite diverse, varying from one continent
to another; but it is very uniform with respect
to age. The migrants are young: in Africa,
more than four-fifths are less than 30 years of
age, and in Brazil, more than two-thirds.
When women take part in the movement, they
migrate at still younger ages, beginning at 15.
Consequently, these are distinctly young
adults who arrive in the cities, frequently in
search of their first job.

Composition by sex differs sharply between
Latin America—where women migrate to the
cities as frequently, if not more often than
men—and Asia or Africa. In Mexico, among
the urban dwellers arriving from elsewhere,
there are 82.2 men for each 100 women. In
Brazil, there are generally only 91.4 men to
each 100 women in the urban population as
a whole; but in São Paulo the figure reaches a
level of 98, thus almost achieving equilibrium
between the sexes. In Africa and in Asia, on

the other hand, the men dominate, and the
larger the city the more decidedly is this the
case. In India in 1931, 120 men were counted
for each 100 women in cities with 50 to
100,000 inhabitants; in metropolises of more
than 500,000 the ratio was 161:100. This disparity has tended to narrow with further development, so that by 1961 the ratio was only
127:100 in the larger cities. In these two con-
tinents, men frequently move to the city
alone, either as unmarried individuals or as
husbands who leave wife and children behind
in the village, to which they return periodically. This custom has serious consequences
from the economic and social viewpoint.

The abundance of migrants not only has
the effect of swelling urban populations and
favoring their development by supplying
adults in the high-fertility age-groups, but it
also promotes the great territorial extension
of major population centers. In fact, many
recent migrants prefer a residence on the periphery of the city, which allows them to
keep certain semi-rural customs; thus in Libreville, as G. Lasserre (14) showed strikingly, the women continue to cultivate the
land, while the men solicit work in the city;
in Conakry, farming is done around the huts
in a seemingly endless belt of suburbs. This is
perhaps typical of societies in which the females cultivate the soil and also of cities of
relatively small size: Libreville has only 31,-
000 inhabitants, and Conakry 43,000.

But, in general, it is extreme poverty which
forces a good part of the recent migrants to
live far from the urban center, for there they
find available housing possibilities at far less
cost. At any rate, it is found that the recent
migrants are more numerous the further one
goes from the central portion of the large
population centers. Although in Calcutta
proper only 53 per cent were born outside the
city one may still count 54 per cent in Howrah, 61 per cent in Bhatpara, and 70 per cent
in Baly, according to Miss Sen Gupta. In

Mexico City, although the more central districts are stationary in population, or have even decreased since 1950, those on the periphery have increased 2.6-fold, and the furthest extremes of the metropolitan area 7.4-fold. The percentage of migrants in the latter case is one-quarter higher than in the center of the city.

Natural growth contributes on a comparable scale to the increase in the number of inhabitants, doing so by virtue of three factors: (1) the inflow of migrants furnishes the cities with a population of young adults; (2) these migrants bring with them traditions of high rural fertility, which they generally do not lose in the first generation; and (3) the mingling of groups, general promiscuity, and breaking of taboos and of customs all tend to bring the sexes together, further augmenting fertility.

The birth rate is therefore high, particularly in those cities with many recent rural migrants, and the more so the less developed the countryside of the region. In the region of Calcutta, more than 50 per cent of the new city-dwellers come directly from the countryside. Thus, in 1951 the number of children less than 5 years old per 1000 women between 15 and 39 years of age was 712 for all of India, 726 for the cities of between 100,000 and 500,000, but only 632 for cities with more than 500,000 inhabitants. This difference in behavior correlates, in effect, with degree of education and social status: the very large cities, which have a higher proportion of women who have been educated and belong to higher social categories, are able to report relatively significant reductions in birth rate. In Brazil, an inquiry regarding the prevalence of contraception has shown that 74.5 per cent of women from higher social categories practiced it, while the percentage was only 49.7 for members of humbler classes (13). In Puerto Rico, 40 per cent of the city dwellers acknowledge birth control practices and only 26 per cent of the rural population (22).

One may therefore conclude that birth rates in the large cities of the Third World still remain quite high in spite of certain tendencies toward reduction among certain groups of the population. This selectivity in birth control practices results in widening the disparity between the development of the various social classes.

Mortality in these cities follows an almost identical pattern. In an early stage, when the influx is rapid, the abject misery and inadequate sanitary facilities of the underdeveloped country—the promiscuity and the urban overcrowding—encourage the spread of epidemics, the incidence of certain diseases, and, above all, high infant mortality. Thus in India, it is thought that 20 to 35 per cent of the individuals in rural areas are afflicted with tuberculosis, but the proportion rises to 80 and even 90 per cent in the poorer neighborhoods of the cities. The infection may remain latent in the rural areas, but reaches the pathological level much more frequently in the urban environments (7 per cent of the people in the cities of Bengal are afflicted) than is true for the countryside (only 0.6 per cent).

But the situation has changed with the development of modern means of combating the disease, and the transition has taken place right before our eyes. In Libreville, a sanitation campaign was initiated in 1946, followed by the use of insecticides, the drainage of swamps, a program of vaccination, and the distribution of preventive medications in the schools; the malaria index declined from approximately 75 in 1945 to 24 in 1954 (14). The same transformation has taken place in the Brazilian cities: the rate of general mortality is estimated as 22 per thousand, while it amounts to only 16.7 per thousand for the eight largest cities. São Paulo, the richest and most developed of all, is located on a low plateau in a healthy climate, and has a rate of

11.5 per thousand; Rio de Janeiro, the second city in economic importance, but one located on a low coastal plain, with less favorable climatic features follows with 14.4 per thousand. In addition, a comparison of mortality levels for tuberculosis, for example, shows that they are two and a half times higher in Rio than in São Paulo. Inversely, in the tropical, impoverished large cities of the Northeast which continually receive waves of migrants the mortality rate is still 27 per thousand (5; 11). In India, improvement in mortality is about to occur; but the situation still varies considerably among the regions of the country.

It follows from these rather divergent trends in birth rate and mortality that natural growth is now important in many cities of the underdeveloped countries. Added to the intense migratory movements, the result is a quite rapid rate of growth, and an increase not at all related to the possibilities of urban assimilation.

Symptoms of Demographic Disequilibrium

Burdened thus with galloping population growth, the large cities of the Third World are incapable of properly fulfilling their functions, namely, as places of residence, social centers, and places of employment for men.

In order to form an approximate idea of the profound imbalance between rate of urban development and the possibilities of economic assimilation, one can roughly compare the index of development of the cities with more than 100,000 inhabitants and the trend in gross per capita national product. It appears that in Brazil, the population of the cities with more than 100,000 souls has doubled between the census enumerations of 1950 and 1960; during the same period, the GNP registered an increase of only 29 per cent. For India, the increments were 49.3 and 11.2 per cent, respectively, during the same period (25).

Demographic pressure expresses itself most immediately through housing difficulties. Providing habitations for a population growing at an annual rate of 5 per cent calls for a doubling of floor space every 18 years, and more than a doubling in supporting facilities. In countries where economic advance is difficult, and investment capacity is consequently limited, such a rate cannot be sustained. This is all the more true insofar as investments for housing are socially beneficial, but economically unproductive. Therefore as the urbanization rate in these countries rises, we witness a proportionately gigantic development of *bidonvilles* (shantytowns). According to a recent report of the United Nations, "the annual rate of housing construction in a large number of developing countries averages only 2 dwelling units per 1000 inhabitants, whils it is 7 per thousand in Western Europe. But this rate would have to reach 10 per thousand in order to cope

TABLE 17-1   MORTALITY PER 1000 INHABITANTS

| | *Madras* | | *Bombay* | | *India* | |
	Rural	*Urban*	*Rural*	*Urban*	*Rural*	*Urban*
1951	25.7	26	17.2	13.1	13.8	14.5
1955	13.9	14.9	16.7	12.1	11.6	12.3
1958	12.6	14.4	17.3	12.4	11.4	11.5

Source: N. V. Sovani: International Migration and the Future Trend of Population in India, *World Population Conference, 1965,* Vol. 2, New York, 1967, pp. 40-43.

with the growth in population in thirty years, satisfy the present needs, and replace the hovels. If one takes into consideration the massive migration of rural populations towards the city, the rate of construction would have to exceed 11 per thousand in order to be able to hope to satisfy the needs in a hundred years. . . !" (18)

In the course of the last ten years, 1800 new apartments were built each year in Belo Horizonte, for an influx of 13,000 migrants; in Santiago the figures were 2500 for 25,000 respectively; in Luanda, 200 for 9500; and one may even cite the less recent experience in Madras, where the population increased by 458,000 souls between 1941 and 1946, and only 1600 new houses were built (20).

Between 1946 and 1959, only 40,000 persons were housed in buildings constructed by the government for all of Jamaica. For those who do not work, there are no solutions other than the *bidonvilles;* in 1961 the Kingston police estimated the number living in such quarters at 20,000. "In certain respects, however, the "squatters" enjoyed better conditions than the inhabitants of the tenements; they rarely slept more than 3 persons to a room and paid no rent . . ." these bad living conditions bring all kinds of unfortunate consequences with them (theft, idleness, discouragement, self-abandon. . .) as shown very well by C. G. Clarke in his paper on Kingston.

"In general, these *bidonvilles* are the result of recent development. Their presence is above all related to a break-down of the equilibrium in relation to the rural world, helped along by the development of transportation," wrote Milton Santos in 1966 (20). Shanty-towns had been unknown in Rio before 1930, in Salvador before 1940, or in Lima before 1945. The problem becomes worse from one year to the next. In Casablanca, the number of inhabitants in shanty-towns was about 100,000 around 1950 and 180,000 in 1960. In Lima, the *barriadas* sheltered 9.6 per cent

of the population in 1958 and 27 per cent in 1963. The phenomenon is overwhelming in certain cities: in Rio de Janeiro almost 20 per cent of the population dwell in *favellas*. In Mexico City in 1952, housing conditions were deficient for 58.5 per cent of the population, but the record seems to belong to the Peruvian city of Chimbote, where 70.5 per cent of the population live in the *barriadas*.

And what can be said about the throngs in numerous countries who do not even have a roof over their heads? In Madras in 1954, 20,000 persons slept in the street; in every street in Calcutta or in Bombay, bundles of blankets are encountered in which human beings, and sometimes an entire family, sleep.

Generally, *bidonvilles* are located at the periphery of the cities in the most unfavorable areas: swampy valleys in Bahia, steep hillsides in Rio de Janeiro, the wrong side of hills far from the center of Algiers. In certain cases, such as on the lagoon of Bahia, actual pile-dwellings develop, for there at least one doesn't have to pay for the ground. But some unfortunates also live in dilapidated houses in the old urban centers.

This wretched housing is not only due to insufficiencies in public investments and in social policies, but also to inadequate incomes among the urban proletariat, who are neither capable of building decent housing nor paying the necessary rent out of their own means.

Many of the people living in *bidonvilles* are unemployed, especially the newcomers; and among those who claim a job, how many are underemployed or even in a state of partial unemployment?

In the area of Rosario in Caracas, an unemployment rate of 18 per cent is reported. In Porto Alegre, only 54.5 per cent of the heads of families indicated steady employment, 5.3 per cent are without work, and 40.4 per cent have only part-time occupations (20). In Kingston, where the population more than doubled between 1921 and 1943, a governmental inquiry made in 1936 showed that

5000 persons had no employment whatsoever (40 per cent of them came from rural districts); considering the potential labor force at that period, this indicates an unemployment rate of about 11 per cent. Earlier, in 1934, 2000 men and 187 women sought work, but only 10 women and 4 men found effective employment. In 1946, 15.5 per cent of the total population above 14 years of age were unemployed, and in the census of 1960, the proportion had risen to 18.4 per cent, with 30 per cent of the active persons working less than five days during the week preceding the census, according to C. Clarke.

"In Egypt, 37.3 per cent of the total urban population was without definite occupation"; and to this must be added the manual laborers without permanent jobs, who constitute 2.3 per cent according to the study by M. Rościszewski.

In Mexico City, although the active population of the district represents 36 per cent of the total population (a higher proportion than the national average of 32 per cent), the outlying parts of the metropolitan agglomeration seem less favored: the active population accounts for only 30 per cent of the population there, and only one woman out of six or seven available for employment actually works as compared with one out of three within the city.

It must be acknowledged here that official figures are being used. But inquiries made on the spot reveal that many of these unfortunate people do not dare admit their misery. In 1950, in Belo Horizonte, 30,509 persons pretended to have industrial jobs, while the employers' statements disclosed only 18,097 employed in this sector of the economy. Many who have lost their jobs do not dare admit it.

Conversely, certain categories seem particularly prone to unemployment or employment difficulties: young people who arrive at the working age and immigrants recently settled in the city are susceptible to such problems. Thus in Kingston, almost one-third of the total number of unemployed persons were in search of their first job, with about 70 per cent of this group less than 21 years old; the lack of jobs is chronic among those who leave school. In this same city, where the government built dwellings after 1950 in order to relocate the poorest elements coming from the "Yard" zone of West Kingston, the unemployment rate among those relocated remained extremely high (39.4 per cent), according to C. Clarke.

It seems indeed, as all the examples show, that the situation is currently worsening in the majority of the regions that have not acquired a certain economic potential, and, above all, a certain degree of industrialization. The figures cited above for Kingston shows this, as do those for Bahia, where the population increased by 238,000, and the number of industrial jobs by less than 6000 between 1950 and 1960 (1:591).

However, a ray of hope has appeared for the large cities of certain countries whose recent economic progress is indisputable. In Mexico, the per capita income has increased by 24 per cent and industry supplies 40 per cent of the gross national product. Thus, despite a near quadrupling of the capital's population since 1930, the number of active persons has been multiplied by 4.5 and that of active women by 7.8. This represents undeniable economic development, though far from satisfactory.

Yet these statistics may create illusions. A large proportion of the active population of many of these cities work in tertiary industries (normal for highly developed cities), and only a moderate or small proportion in secondary industries. The second item is realistic: it reflects the weakness, not to say the deficiency in certain cases, of the industrial economy. For Egypt, M. Rościszewski estimates that in 1965 no more than 20 per cent of the urban population was employed in industrial production (Rościszewski, p. 336).

Even when the industrial sector appears statistically significant, manpower is actually largely grouped within two or three rather disparate occupations. In Concepción, 60 per cent of the working population of the northern quarter of the city, as studied by H. Hernandez (9), were included in the secondary sector, but "the most important group consists of construction workers, an activity which in Chile includes a considerable number of unskilled laborers. This type undoubtedly includes a large number of self-employed persons in newly built residential quarters. The second group is that of metallurgical and mechanical industries, as exemplified by a foundry in Huachipato, an important magnet for labor migrants. The third group is that of unskilled laborers, who typify populations of rural origin in the process of adapting to the urban life.

As for the tertiary industries of these cities, they are primitive and based essentially on domestic service and minor handicrafts. In Bahia, the tertiary category includes under the heading of "trade" cigarette peddlers and people who sell baked goods on street curbs, in doorways, or on the beaches. In Concepción, it has been pointed out that "the attraction of the city is greater than its need for labor, and what is more, makes itself felt in those population groups which are poorly qualified or entirely unqualified for urban activity, bringing about an unemployment that is masked by the proliferation of small trades (the number of acknowledged unemployed is not great, but many workers work only two or three days a week)" (9). In Kingston, "personal service industry was important as an employer of domestic servants, gardeners, yard-boys and odd-job men, but at wages which barely exceeded subsistence rates." The almost equal number of people who are employed in industry (23.9 per cent) and in personal services (21.5 per cent), as brought out by the Jamaican census of 1960, is an indicator of excess "demographic pressure." In

Egypt, domestics represent 20.3 per cent of the urban population. In Latin America, Africa, and India, it is not uncommon for a city family to have several domestics at their disposal; sometimes even poor families have young girls from the country to help them, and they are often younger than the children in the house.

Finally, who is there among us that, traveling in the countries of the "Third World," has not been struck by the abundance of useless labor in the hotels, in the restaurants, in the stores? In India, there is a servant behind every door.

Correspondingly, wages are very low. The range of salaries is great, and there is a tremendous disparity between the highest and the lowest wage levels. But there is a great predominance of low salaries. Thus in Niamey, two-thirds of the families had annual incomes below the average, low as it is, of 7000 francs C.F.A.[2] ($30) in 1961-62. In Egypt, according to 1958 data, 70.2 per cent of the urban population, including unemployed and part-time workers, domestic and industrial workers, and those employed in handicrafts, reported incomes representing only 15.2 per cent of the total; at the opposite extreme, high-level officials, the bourgeoisie, and the aristocracy represented 3.8 per cent of the urban dwellers, but realized 34.6 per cent of the total income.

Uprooted, miserable, without employment, deprived of housing, a major segment of the urban population leads a wretched existence. It is prey to malnutrition and disease. In Kingston, in one neighborhood of shanties, pit latrines are used, although this is illegal; in 1961 some 1000 persons in a certain quarter had only one water pipe, while tuberculosis and typhoid fever were widespread.

The greatest part of the low income is ab-

2. C.F.A.—monetary units (Francs) in former French Africa, introduced after the Second World War, but still in circulation. The initials stand for *Communauté Française d'Afrique.*

sorbed by food purchases. In the poorest quarters of the city of Recife, 75 per cent of the budget is allotted to food. An inquiry made in 1953 in Brazil indicated that the proportion of expenditures for food tended to be inversely proportional to the degree of industrialization, going from 41.1 per cent in São Paulo to 58.3 per cent in Salvador. In Pointe Noire, food represents 63 per cent of the family budget; but the percentage varies with income level, ranging from 73.2 for budgets of only 5000 francs C.F.A. to 46.5 for those who make more than 30,000 francs.

Under these conditions, the urban populations are not always better fed than the rural populations, contrary to what one might believe. Dietary deficiencies are noted, and have long been pointed out by physicians. Africans who have just moved into the cities have a tendency to adopt the dietary regime of the whites; and since they do not have much money, they can only consume inexpensive products, and very frequently replace the natural products and savory sauces of the indigenous cuisine with bread and preserves. Dental caries quickly appear. An inquiry made in Bahia has shown that the new city-dwellers drink 30 per cent less milk, eat 50 per cent less fruit, and 64 per cent less vegetables than in the countryside where they lived previously.

In Mexico City, 8 per cent of the population eat no meat, fish, milk, or eggs and in the poorest suburbs the proportion goes up to 12 per cent. These people must have recourse to every expedient in order to obtain enough to live on: begging by children, prostitution by the women. In Africa, in particular, as soon as an individual has a paying job, he may find all the members of his family flocking to join him, and sometimes even those who merely belong to the same tribe or the same village. One sometimes finds 12 to 15 persons in an apartment intended for four or five in the housing constructed by the administration or by the mining communities. Thus an urban

proletariat is created. The countryside and the cities suffer equally from this.

"The drift towards the cities precedes the industrialization process, and this causes many difficulties. The considerable outflow of the population from the countryside and small towns resulted in a drop in the agricultural production because of the shortage of manpower and almost complete lack of mechanization in field work. In spite of this, the income of farm laborers is not increasing. The reduced supply of agricultural porduce on the anization in field work. In spite of this, the income of farm laborers is not increasing. The reduced supply of agricultural porduce on the turn, makes an increase in wages in the cities inevitable. This is the source of the inflationary spiral leading to a devaluation of money and to inflation. This process is particularly acute in Brazil and is largely due to the fact that the growth of the urban population precedes industrialization" (Bonasewicz, p. 566).

Future Prospects

As serious as it may be for the economic equilibrium of both the cities and the open country, this swelling of population centers, unrelated to immediate demand or capacity for absorption, plays an essential role in the development of the Third World.

Demographically, after a more or less prolonged period of initial adaptation—its duration depending on the initial conditions and type of urban environment—individual behavior is modified: fertility decreases, as does mortality. During the initial stage, as certain examples in India or Northeast Brazil indicate, natural growth is maintained and even increased, but with different components. In the second stage, the excess of births over deaths diminishes, and a transformation occurs analogous to Western Europe's demographic development in the nineteenth century—but much more rapidly. In São Paulo, Brazil, the rate of growth is only 10 per thousand, while it exceeds 22 per thousand for the country as a whole.

A second major factor is the development

of literacy. In India, illiterates still accounted for 82.5 per cent of the rural and 55.2 per cent of the urban population just ten years ago. The proportion of those who had finished primary school was only 0.36 per cent and 3.06 per cent, respectively. This transformation has a twofold significance. First, it allows progress in the diffusion of contraceptive methods, further favoring the speed of demographic development. The statistics are all formal: the greater the amount of schooling, particularly among women, the more likely is the desire for knowledge of the techniques for family limitation. Moreover, is not the press—above all women's magazines—one of the media of information most frequently cited in inquiries on this subject? Secondly, anyone who talks about "education" is also talking about "better possibilities for professional training," and therefore improved employment.

The cities, even though they cannot employ the entire influx of those flocking into them, do offer new and infinitely superior opportunities as compared with the rural world. Again in India, the income per active person is twice as high in industry as it is in occupations associated with agricultural life and almost three times higher in "tertiary" occupations of any category whatever. Higher, more regular incomes, concentration of purchasing power, and modifications of customs and tra-ditions are factors that influence consumption patterns, amplifying and diversifying them. Thus are born the nuclei of transformation which stimulate construction, usually the first industry with national impact in underdeveloped countries, acting as it does simultaneously on the rural economy and on local industries, as well as generating demand for imported foods. The mechanism of economic development is under way, even if it creaks a bit and even if it is almost crushed by its burden.

Finally, mental attitudes also change. The urban dweller is better informed as to what is happening in his country and elsewhere. He is liberated from the rural institutions that often held him under their thumb. Proximity to other liberated souls gives him more courage, more power. He feels himself ready to claim, occasionally through violence, whatever is needed for a fuller life. One wonders how long the social restraints that prevail in certain countries, especially in Latin America, can delay radical changes in those conditions that have until now "riveted the poor to their poverty"?

Thus in spite of their misery, their lack of adaptation, their economic and social difficulties, the cities—and especially the larger cities—of the Third World appear to be the unhappy stage on which the promises of a better future are taking shape.

REFERENCES

(1) J. Beaujeu-Garnier: Les Migrations vers Salvador, *Les Cahiers d'Outre-Mer,* No. 59, 1962, pp. 291-300.

(2) J. Beaujeu-Garnier: La Population de Mexico, *Bulletin, Association des Géographes Français,* Nos. 355-56, 1967, pp. 2-16.

(3) J. Beaujeu-Garnier and G. Chabot: Traité de Géographie Urbaine (Paris, 1963).

(4) Brazil, Serviço Nacional de Recenseamento: Censo Experimental de Brasilia: População, Habitação, 17 de Mais de 1959 (Rio de Janeiro, 1959).

(5) Brazil, Serviço Nacional de Recenseamento: Sinopse Preliminar do Censo Demográfico (Rio de Janeiro, 1962).

(6) O. Dia: The Urban Growth of Cap-Vert, Dakar, in: World Population Conference, 1965, Vol. 4 (New York, 1967), pp. 416-17.

(7) France, Haut Commissariat de la République en Afrique Occidentale: Recensement Démographique de Dakar (1955); Résultats Définitifs (Paris, 1958-1962).

(8) A. Ghosh: Immigration from Rural Areas into Calcutta Metropolitan Region: Analysis and Projection, in: World Population Conference, 1965, Vol. 4 (New York, 1967), p. 551.

(9) H. Hernandez: Le Secteur Nord de Concepción (Chili), *Bulletin, Association des Géographes Français,* Nos. 355-56, 1967, pp. 17-33.

(10) India, Office of the Registrar General: Census of India, Volume 1. India, for years 1931, 1941, 1951, and 1961.

(11) Instituto Brasileiro de Geografia e Estadistica: Contribucoes para o Estudo da Demografia do Brasil (Rio de Janeiro, 1961).

(12) International Labour Office: Yearbook of Labour Statistics (Geneva, annually).

(13) S. Iutaka: Inter-Generational Mobility and Family Planning in Urban Brazil, in: World Population Conference, 1965, Vol. 2 (New York, 1967), p. 316.

(14) G. Lasserre: Libreville, Cahiers Foundation, *Sciences Politiques,* No. 98, 1958.

(15) M. Macura: Les Conséquences Démographiques du Développement Economique Retardé: l'Exemple de l'Inde, in: International Population Congress (New York, 1961), p. 473.

(16) Mexico, Dirección General de Estadística: VIII Censo General de Población, 1960, 8 de Junio de 1960 (Mexico, 1962).

(17) G. Mortara: Factors Affecting Rural-Urban Migration in Latin America, in: World Population Conference, 1965, Vol. 4 (New York, 1967), pp. 509-12.

(18) J. Ridell: The Housing Needs of Developing Countries, *Civilisations,* Vol. 15, No. 1, 1965, pp. 38-54.

(19) W. C. Robinson: Urban-Rural Differences in Indian Fertility, *Population Studies,* Vol. 14, No. 3, pp. 218-34.

(20) M. Santos: Vues Actuelles sur le Problème des Bidonvilles, *Information Géographique,* No. 4, 1966, pp. 143-50.

(21) N. V. Sovani: Internal Migration and the Future Trend of Population in India, in: World Population Conference, 1965, Vol. 2 (New York, 1967), pp. 40-43.

(22) J. M. Stycos: Education and Fertility in Puerto Rico, in: World Population Conference, 1965, Vol. 4 (New York, 1967), pp. 177-80.

(23) United Nations, Food and Agriculture Organization: Production Yearbook (Rome, annually).

(24) United Nations, Statistical Office: Demographic Yearbook (New York, annually).

(25) United Nations, Statistical Office: Statistical Yearbook (New York, annually).

18. SOME DIMENSIONS OF URBAN POPULATION PRESSURE IN INDIA

John E. Brush

The process of urbanization is world-wide today. Some thirty-five years ago, when Mark Jefferson wrote his seminal article "The Distribution of the World's City Folks" (11), the concentrations of urban populations, especially those in large cities, were mainly in northwestern Europe, North America, and certain outlying areas of European colonization in the southern hemisphere. Subsequently, the urbanization trend not only continued in these areas, but spread throughout the rest of Europe and America as well. Japan has become as highly urbanized as much of Europe, while on the mainland of Asia the urbanizing process is under way in China, India, and other countries. Those nations most developed economically find that half to three-quarters or more of their citizens now live in urban settlements. There appears to be a positive correlation between economic progress and urban population concentration, although significant variations exist in the degree of urbanization in particular countries and regions due to historical lag and spatial differences in social and political structure. One may concur with Zelinsky (16) that the transfer of rapidly growing rural populations to urban areas will not solve any of the fundamental problems of population pressure. Yet it may be anticipated that most of the population increase in the next generation or two will be absorbed in urban settlements—until in the mid-twenty-first century, mankind will inhabit a world-encompassing system which Doxiadis has called the "Ecumenopolis" (8).

At the time of the 1961 census, about 79 million people lived in India's cities and towns. In absolute numbers the country's urban population exceeded that of Japan, and it was outranked only by the United States, the Soviet Union, and most probably the People's Republic of China (Table 18-1). Despite varying definitions of "urban" and reservations regarding the validity of international comparisons, these figures are roughly indicative of magnitude and degree of concentration of urban population in the five countries.

In 1961, India's urban population represented only 18 per cent of the total and during the preceding decade the rate of urban growth was less than expected on the basis of trends determined from earlier censuses. At the conference on "Urbanization in India" held in 1960 at Berkeley, California, it was anticipated there would be 90 million urban residents in India by 1961, comprising 21 per cent of the projected total population of 430 million (14: 185, 188). But the total population in 1961 exceeded by some nine million the projections of the Planning Commission of the Government of India and every other specialist who had studied the matter. Thus, there was an "excess" rural population of about 20 million and an urban "deficit" of 12 million. The proportions of urban population in the total increased only one-half of one per cent—from 17.3 in 1951 to 17.8 in 1961. Evidently, the rate of natural increase had been accelerating, while the rate of rural-urban migration had been slackening in the 1950's.

In this paper I propose to show more precisely the deceleration of India's urban growth and to point out some of the factors which may account for this trend. With the generous aid of many Indian officials involved in urban development and planning, I was recently able to assemble comparative measurements of population density in some

TABLE 18-1   THE WORLD'S FIVE LEADING URBAN COUNTRIES

Date	Country	Total Population 1,000's	Urban Population 1,000's	% of total
1957	Chinese People's Republic	538,650	89,150	14.2
1961	Republic of India	439,325	78,937	17.8
1959	Union of Soviet Socialist Republics	208,823	99,978	47.9
1960	United States of America	179,323	125,284	69.9
1960	Japan	93,347	59,347	63.5

Sources: *Demographic Yearbook: 1963, Population Statistics II*, New York: United Nations, 1964; for China, Leo Orleans, The Recent Growth of China's Urban Population, *Geogr. Rev.* Vol. 49, No. 1 (Jan. 1959), pp. 43-57; for India, *Census of India 1961*, Vol. I, Part II-A (i), *General Population Tables*, 1964.

twenty urban settlements of varying sizes and economic types.[1] Other data include sample surveys conducted by economists and demographers under the auspices of the Planning Commission of the Government of India during the 1950's.

1. I had the benefit of a study tour in India during 1966 under the auspices of the American Institute of Indian Studies, Philadelphia and Poona, whose aid I acknowledge with thanks.

The Rate of Urbanization in India

Looking at the changes occurring during the period from 1901 to 1961, it is clear that urbanization has been an important feature of the current demographic growth cycle in India. At the beginning of the century urban population comprised only 10 to 11 per cent of the total. Since then, the urban faction has

TABLE 18-2   POPULATION IN INDIA: 1901-1961

Year	Total Population 1000's	% Change in Decade	Urban Population 1000s	% Change in Decade	Class I Cities* 1000's	% Change in Decade
1901	238,391	—	25,852	—	6,225	—
1911	252,093	3.75	25,942	0.25	6,472	3.98
1921	251,321	−0.31	28,086	8.27	7,593	17.32
1931	278,977	11.00	33,456	19.12	9,498	25.09
1941	318,660	14.22	44,153	31.97	16,004	68.49
1951	361,088	12.31	62,444	41.43	26,426	65.12
			60,413**	36.80**		
1961	439,235	21.64	83,674†	30.70†	38,177	44.47
			78,937**	26.41**		

Source: *Census of India 1961*, Vol. I, *India*, Part II-A (i), *General Population Tables*, Delhi, 1964.
* Class I Cities had population of 100,000 or more in 1961.
** According to the new urban definition, 1951 and 1961. (see text)
† According to old urban definition, 1961. (see text)

multiplied threefold, while the total growth has been less than twofold. The collective growth rate of urban settlements, especially in the largest cities, has exceeded that of the whole population in each successive decade since 1911.

However, further study of trends since 1901, excluding the present area of Pakistan, shows that growth rates decreasing during the period 1941-61 in contrast to the previous 40 years when there was a tendency toward acceleration. (See Table 18-2, Figs. 18-1 and 18-2) The relative growth rate in Class 1 cities (i.e. all municipalities and town groups with more than 100,000 inhabitants in 1961) dropped from 68 per cent (1931-41) to 65 per cent (1941-51); and during the 1950's, the rate of increase was only 44 per cent. From 1951 to 1961 there was also a drop in the general rate of urban growth for the first time since 1901. This pronounced change in

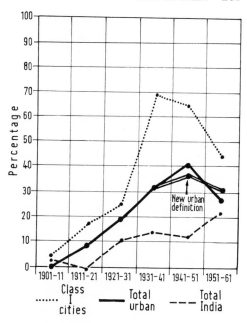

Fig. 18-2. RATE OF POPULATION GROWTH IN INDIA, 1901-61

urbanization, especially at a time of unprecedented increase of total population, calls for explanation.

Because of changes of the definition of "urban" in the most recent census, data from previous surveys are not strictly comparable. Ashok Mitra, the 1961 Census Commissioner, explains that in 1961 more precise distinctions were made between rural and urban residence (42: Vol. I, Part II-A (i), 262-63). All persons living within the jursidiction of municipal corporations or other types of municipal or quasi-municipal bodies, including town committees and cantonment boards, were to be classified as urban residents, as in previous censuses. Additional areas were considered urban if (1) the density exceeded 1000 persons per square mile (386/km²), (2) the population total was at least 5000, and (3) three-fourths of the working population was employed in nonagricultural production. In previous censuses every collection of houses inhabited by not less than 5000 people was classified urban without reference

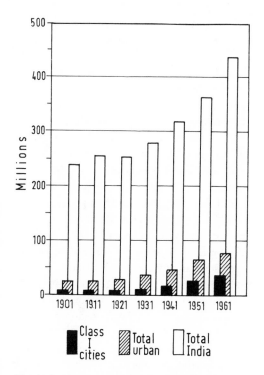

Fig. 18-1. POPULATION GROWTH IN INDIA, 1901-61

to density or the relative concentration of agricultural employment. But local census superintendents were able to exercise discretion regarding settlements smaller than 5000, some of which were classified urban, such as mining camps, industrial communities, and military bases (cantonments). Exceptions to the above rule were closely restricted in 1961, being permitted only with approval of the Census Commissioner in Delhi.

The result of the 1961 policy was to remove 803 settlements (4,737,000 persons) classified as urban in 1951 from the list of urban places. However, 497 additional settlements qualified for the list in 1961. Thus, the total number of urban places decreased from 3060 in 1951 to 2700 in 1961. But the majority of places affected by reclassification had less than 10,000 inhabitants and, if the population of the 803 places mentioned above were added to that of the 2700 qualified in 1961, the total of urban residents would be some 83,674,000. This addition would have raised the percentage of urban population to 19.0. A hypothetical 60,413,000 urban residents can be calculated for 1951, reducing the percentage of urban population to 16.7, simply by including only those places considered urban in 1961, and excluding those that lost urban status in 1961. Such manipulation suggests that the 1951 data on urbanization were inflated. Application of the new urban definition to those figures reduces the gain during the 1940's to 16,260,000 or 36.8 per cent, but increases the gain in the 1950's to 18,524,000 or 30.7 per cent (Fig. 18-2).

These amendments do not alter the fundamental features of the trends described above. The basic fact remains that the rate of urban growth in India diminished during the period 1951-61. It is also clear that if the growth rate of Class I cities had been higher during the two decades previous to 1951, the aggregate urban population in India would have approached the projected 90 million in 1961.

Studies of Representative Cities

A series of representative urban areas, including 24 of the 113 cities and town groups in Class I reported in the 1961 census exemplifies growth trends and resultant levels of population concentration.

Statistics for the period 1901-61 measure population change in broadly defined urbanized areas, with the exception of Calcutta and Howrah, the two principal urban centers in the Calcutta Metropolitan District. The latter is a continuous metropolitan agglomeration of 1170 km^2 and contained about 6.5 million people in 1961 (49). In Madras, Sholapur, Tiruchirapalli, and Gaya (Table 18-3), where growth is reported for municipalities rather than town groups, the municipalities were extended in 1961 to include either adjacent urban areas, or relatively undeveloped outlying areas. Similarly, Greater Bombay which was constituted in 1951 and enlarged in 1961, is a single municipal corporation, which includes areas of growth on Salsette Island. The Bombay Municipal Corporation is listed in the census as India's largest city (Table 18-3). In contrast, Calcutta and Howrah are listed separately, along with the 33 other municipalities and 37 nonmunicipal urban areas that are also part of "Greater Calcutta" and are located in belts along both sides of the Hooghly River in West Bengal.

Official recognition of town groups for the first time in 1961 reflects the fact that metropolitan sprawl is occurring in India and that demographic data for these agglomerations are useful in governmental planning and development programs. Town groups are made up of two or more closely related urban settlement units linked by road and rail (42: Vol. I, Part II-A, p. 53). Ordinarily, they also include nonmunicipal areas, such as railway or industrial housing tracts, former British civil stations, unplanned slum settlements,

TABLE 18-3   INDIA. POPULATION GROWTH IN SELECTED URBAN AREAS:
1901 TO 1961

Municipality or Town Group	Population 1901 1000's	Population 1961 1000's	Density, 1961 Persons per Sq.Mi./Sq.Km.	Per Cent Variation		
				1901-31	1931-51	1951-61
Greater Bombay M.C.	813	4,152	169.00/411.8	56.0	133.9	40.0
Calcutta M.C.	934	2,927	39.75/193.0	30.8	120.9	8.5
Delhi T.G.	214	2,359	126.08/326.5	109.0	221.2	64.2
Madras M.C.	541	1,729	48.93/126.7	31.8	98.5	22.1
Hyderabad T.G.	448	1,251	85.08/220.4	4.1	141.9	10.9
Bangalore T.G.	161	1,207	193.52/501.2	91.8	153.8	53.5
Ahmedabad T.G.	186	1,206	47.83/123.9	68.8	179.6	37.5
Kanpur T.G.	203	971	114.50/296.6	20.2	189.4	37.7
Poona T.G.	164	737	65.65/170.0	52.4	140.0	22.8
Lucknow T.G.	256	656	52.29/135.4	7.2	80.9	32.0
Howrah M.C.	158	513	11.13/28.8	42.7	92.8	18.2
Agra T.G.	188	509	34.29/88.8	22.2	63.5	35.4
Varanasi T.G.	215	490	32.66/110.5	−3.5	71.3	37.7
Allahabad T.G.	172	431	31.45/81.5	6.9	80.7	29.6
Patna T.G.	135	364	22.33/57.8	18.5	77.5	28.6
Sholapur M.	75	338	8.63/22.4	92.1	91.6	21.8
Jamshedpur T.G.	N.U.	328	30.50/79.0	—	76.0	50.4
Coimbatore M.	53	286	8.86/22.9	79.3	107.7	44.8
Meerut T.G.	119	284	21.58/55.9	15.3	70.6	21.8
Bareilly T.G.	133	273	15.41/39.9	8.0	44.4	31.1
Tiruchirapalli M.	105	250	8.98/23.3	36.4	53.3	14.1
Hubli-Dharwar T.G.	81	248	15.90/41.2	53.3	57.7	26.7
Dhanbad-Jharia-Sindri T.G.	N.U.	200	45.37/117.5	—	351.3	172.6
Gaya M.	71	151	11.78/30.5	23.4	51.9	13.0

Source: *Census of India 1961*, Vol. I, *India*, Part II-A (i), *General Population Tables*. Delhi, 1964, pp. 363-691.
M.C. = Municipal Corporation
M   = Municipality
T.G. = Town Group
N.U. = Non-Urban 1901

and erstwhile rural villages. Occasionally, military cantonments are included in the groups, but they are always governed as separate municipal units under the jurisdiction of the Defence Department in Delhi. Cantonments, which India inherited from the days of British imperialism (5: 60-62), not only house military personnel but may also contain ordnance and military supply factories, airports, shopping areas, and often large civilian populations. Where there is geographic sep-

aration among urban settlement units the Census Commissioner has stipulated that any place falling within a radius of two to four miles and sometimes five miles from the main and most populous municipality is to be considered eligible for inclusion. Field observation reveals that this limitation has been interpreted loosely; for example, in Hubli-Dharwar town group the cities are nine miles apart, and in Dhanbad-Jharia-Sindri group the maximum intertown distance is about

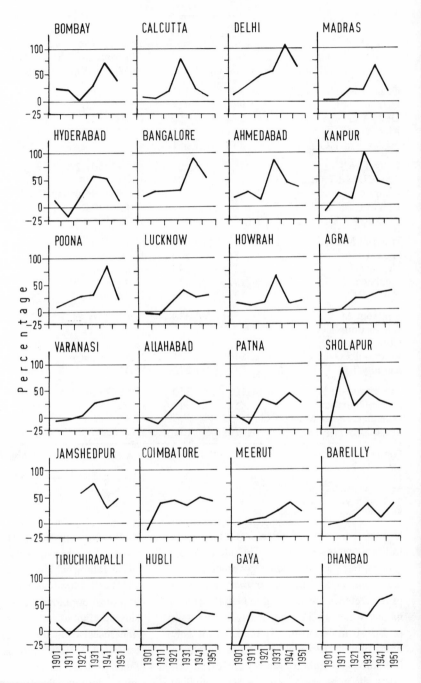

Fig. 18-3.   PERCENTAGE VARIATION OF POPULATION IN SELECTED
URBAN AREAS OF INDIA, 1901-61

eight miles. In addition, prior to the 1961 census the municipal boundaries of certain major cities were extended as much as two or three miles beyond the urbanized zone to include nearby villages and extensive tracts of cultivated land or waste. While such extensions are a commendable means of gaining jurisdiction over roadside ribbon development, preventing encroachments on potential housing tracts or industrial sites, and providing for maintenance of green belts and circumferential highways, they tend to create statistical anomalies in the census series and cause exaggerations of recent population growth. Nevertheless, we may now use census data more confidently because consistent criteria have been applied retroactively to the records from six censuses preceeding 1961.

The three stages of general urban growth alluded to in the previous section are exemplified in the percentage variations of population in the 24 cities and town groups (Table 18-3). A period of slow growth and even absolute decline is recorded in most of these places before 1931, followed by abrupt increases in the two following decades. Finally, there is a general slackening of growth during the period 1951-61. Consecutive percentage variations for each urban area are shown graphically by decades (Fig. 18-3) and cumulatively by the three periods, 1903-31, 1931-51, and 1951-61 (Table 18-3).

Urban areas may be divided into two groups: those with growth rates exceeding 50 per cent in one or more decades since 1901, and those in which the rate was rapid, but did not exceed 50 per cent in any decade. Cities and town groups belonging to the first category include all nine of the largest metropolitan centers—Bombay, Calcutta, Delhi, Madras, Hyderabad, Bangalore, Ahmedabad, Kanpur, and Poona. Each had a population in excess of 700,000 in 1961, with the exception of industrial Kanpur, and highly diversified economic bases. Also included in this

group are five smaller urban areas—Howrah, Sholapur, Jamshedpur, Coimbatore, and Dhanbad-Jharia-Sindri—all centers of the manufacturing or mining industries. The ten cities or town groups in the second category —Lucknow, Agra, Varanasi, Allahabad, Patna, Meerut, Bareilly, Tiruchirapalli, Hubli-Dharwar, and Gaya—tend to be less industrialized. Most of them have important political, religious, or educational functions but evidently these are less potent factors in attracting growth.

As a rule, urban areas of the first category grew a total of 100 per cent or more during the period 1931-51. Only Howrah, Jamshedpur, and Sholapur fell significantly below the other centers. India was then feeling the stimulating effects of World War II on urban employment, but toward the end of the period the country was to undergo the throes of independence and partition of Pakistan with the consequent refugee movements. The fact that more growth occurred in nonindustrial centers than in some heavily industrialized ones and that this growth was almost as concentrated in the southern parts of the country as in the north where refugees from Pakistan were likely to arrive, suggests that these decades were a time of general migration towards the large cities, wherever their location and whatever the economic base.

Delhi has the most outstanding growth record among the urban areas of the first category. In each of the last three decades the city experienced population increases of more than 50 per cent, with a maximum percentage growth of 107 during the 1940's, an absolute gain of some 741,000. From 1951 to 1961, a total of 922,000 was added, although the percentage gain dropped to 64. The largest absolute increments occurred, however, in Calcutta, where the gain was 946,000 (77 per cent) in 1931-41, and in Bombay, where it was 1,280,000 in 1931-41 (76 per cent) and 1,185,000 (40 per cent) in 1951-61. Madras is the only other metropolitan city where the absolute increment exceeded half a million, 531,000 in 1941-51, although relatively it had the lowest growth rate among the large Indian cities at that time. Hyderabad, Bangalore, Ahmedabad, Kanpur, and Poona exhibit growth rates exceeding 14 per cent from 1931 to 1951, which means there were absolute gains ranging from 100,000 to 400,000 per decade in most of these cities. Sholapur experienced its most rapid relative growth before 1931, 92 per cent in 1911-21. Jamshedpur had immense percentage growth between 1901 and 1931 simply because the great iron and steel town was then undergoing the initial stages of establishment, but in no decade before 1951 did the absolute increment there exceed 100,000. The urbanization of the Jharia coalfield during the 1930's, '40's, and '50's accounts for the accelerating rise of Dhanbad in an area which did not qualify as urban at the turn of the century. Jamshedpur and Dhanbad-Jharia-Sindri were the only cities among the urban areas of the first category in which percentage gains in 1951-61 were higher than in the preceding decade.

A look at the ten cities that grew less rapidly during the six decades under consideration reveals that after an initial period of decline lasting for as long as 20 years in Lucknow, Varanasi, Allahabad, and Bareilly, growth began to accelerate slowly, without massive population influxes during the 1930's and 1940's. Yet there was a tendency toward deceleration after 1951 in Patna, Meerut, Tiruchirapalli, and Hubli. Only the old pilgrim town of Gaya in southern Bihar showed a decelerating tendency over a 40-year time span, following a sharp influx in the decade 1911-21. Population increments in the ten cities of this category were less than 100,000 persons per decade and generally much less, except in Lucknow, Agra, and Varanasi in the period 1951-6, when the gains ranged between 130,000 and 160,000.

Intra-Urban Population Pressure

Extreme urban congestion is a well-known phenomenon in India. In view of the developing metropolitan sprawl and the decelerating rate of urban population growth, it might be supposed that the central parts of Indian cities would become less crowded as peripheral expansion occurred, following the geographic pattern of residential redistribution common in the United States and other Western countries. However, two features of distribution noted in a previous analysis (5: 64-66) were apparently still present in 1961: (1) maximum concentration in the central bazaars and old compact settlement areas and (2) sharp density gradients between the central areas and the peripheral or suburban areas.

The high concentration of urban population is not revealed by densities of areas now included in town groups or in recently enlarged municipal corporations. Gross densities in the 24 selected urban areas (Table 18-3) do not exceed 173 persons per hectare except in Calcutta and Howrah, both central cities hemmed in by satellite and suburban towns of the Calcutta Metropolitan District. Densities in Madras and Sholapur run between 136 and 148/hectare. Otherwise, typical densities of the Class I cities in India range between 74 and 124/hectare, with a lower limit of about 25/hectare in the Bangalore Town Group. Gross and net densities are somewhat higher when calculations are based on the less extensive areas of the major municipalities, which contain the vast majority of people living in town groups (Table 18-4). The true degree of concentration within urban areas is seen only when internal distribution data for municipal wards or other census statistical units are examined.

The three national metropolises—Bombay, Calcutta, and Delhi—have the highest densi-

TABLE 18-4   INDIA. POPULATION CONCENTRATION IN SELECTED URBAN AREAS, 1951 OR 1961

Municipality or Urban Area	Population** 1951 or 1961	Area (ha)	Statistical Tracts*	Persons per ha		
				Whole Area	Upper Decile	Lower Decile
Greater Bombay M.C.	4,152,056	43,771	88	94	1500-3756	4-10
Bombay Island only	2,771,933	6,706	38	413	1930-3756	91-133
Calcutta M.C.	2,927,289	9,562	80	306	1082-1875	32-151
Delhi Planning Area	1,383,577	18,542	40	74	1231-1972	7-20
Madras M.C.	1,729,141	12,875	100	133	697-1132	17-96
Hyderabad-Secunderabad M.C.	1,129,345	16,365	35	69	398-675	10-22
Bangalore M.C.	864,203	7,112	50	121	714-1243	20-54
Ahmedabad M.C.	1,155,344	9,293	45	138	1161-1250	5-10
Kanpur M.C.	807,356	7,662	133	106	1275-2098	5-35
Greater Poona M.C.	597,419	11,003	37	54	1102-1208	0-2
Greater Poona M.C.[1]	597,419	11,003	37	N.A.	1512-2842	0-91
Lucknow M.C.	595,440	7,547	32	74	524-959	17-27
Howrah M.	512,598	2,478	10	170	613	52
Varanasi T.G.	489,864	8,061	30	62	647-890	5-20
Allahabad T. G.	411,966	6,238	27	67	509-556	17-22
Patna M. (1951)	297,436	4,543	37	64	301-502	10-35
Sholapur M.	337,583	2,484	16	136	1025-1043	30-89
Jamshedpur N.A.	303,516	7,770	42	40	158-195	0-12
Coimbatore M.	286,305	2,112	30	136	623-872	40-57
Tiruchirapalli M.[2]	249,862	1,342	8	376	798	156
Hubli Division[3]	170,109	688	4	247	638-744	47-94
Dharwar Division	77,235	1,531	10	49	398	47
Dhanbad M.	57,352	2,709	27	22	427-672	7-15
Gaya M.	151,105	1,843	10	86	521	22

Source: Census reports and town planning agencies. See bibliography. Population as of 1961, unless otherwise noted.

M.C. = Municipal Corporation; M. = Municipality; T.G. = Town Group; N.A. = Notified Area (quasi-municipal status)

* Statistical tracts are the municipal subdivisions or other territorial units variously termed wards, sections, sectors, divisions, census blocks, census circles, and urban or planning areas.

** Population data refer to the municipal or other areas as noted, and not to the whole area of the Town Group unless so indicated.

Density is gross density only, unless noted as follows:

[1] Greater Poona, residential density.

[2] Tiruchirapalli, net residential acreage and density.

[3] Hubli, developed acreage only and residential density of developed area.

ties, with maxima ranging from 1,875/hectare to 3,756/hectare. The latter density was found in Bhuleshwar, a Bombay census division where 65,681 persons lived in 1961 on 19.5 hectares (42: Vol. X, Part X (I-B), p. 33). Bombay Island is unquestionably the apex of Indian population concentration, exceeding Calcutta's general density by 35 per cent. Ward C (179 hectares) in the old "native city" just outside the Bombay "Fort" has a density of 1900/hectare; and the general density on the island exceeds more than fourfold that of the Greater Bombay corporation. In 1961 doubtless a higher concentration of population existed in the central wards of Old Delhi than that revealed in 1951 (50: Vol. II, pp. 1-2), but details of the distribution of people in the Indian capital unfortunately are not amenable to geographic analysis because of the lack of the necessary cartographic base and area measurements. Three wards situated in the heart of Calcutta north of Dalhousie Square and east of the Howrah Bridge reported densities in excess of 1236/hectare in 1961; and two adjacent census circles, comprising 4.55 hectares, within one of these wards (Bara Bazar), had over 2470/hectare. Kanpur is the only other Indian city among those analyzed in which maximum density in 1961 was equal to the upper decile levels in the three national metropolises.

Since the foregoing statistics are expressed in terms of gross land area, we may translate into terms of ground space per capita, which amounts to about 2.8 m² at the peak densities of Bombay and Calcutta and less than 9.3 m² where densities are more than 1236/hectare. Buildings are commonly two, three, or four stories high. But nonresidential structures, streets, and other publicly used land may reduce private living space by 50 per cent, causing the most extreme kind of pressure on physical and social resources.

The most pronounced population gradient in India exists in Greater Bombay, where the density difference between the medians of the upper and lower deciles is about 300:1. In the Delhi Planning Area it was 130:1 in 1951, in the Calcutta Metropolitan District, 66:1 as of 1961, comparing the central part of Calcutta with nonmunicipal towns on the urban fringe, where mean densities vary between 16 and 32/hectare (49). In Kanpur municipality the density difference is 85:1. Thus, residential congestion is markedly reduced on the peripheries of these four crowded cities with 465 to 1858 m² per capita available.

Such a gross density, with less than 25 persons per hectare, is more than three times that of urban fringes in the United States. There, gross densities in the large central cities seldom exceed 247/hectare, while 7.4 is typical on the metropolitan fringes.

The intra-urban population pattern is essentially similar in the other Class I cities for which data are available (Table 18-4), with some variations relating to size, regional location, and age of the cities. Generally speaking, large Class I cities experienced the most rapid growth since 1931—Madras, Bangalore, Ahmedabad, and Poona had central densities ranging from 699 to 1230/hectare in 1961. In Poona, the residential density for the occupied area, excluding streets, large public sites, and open land was 2842/hectare in the central bazaar area. Some smaller, rapidly growing cities—Howrah, Sholapur, Coimbatore, and Dhanbad—also had fairly high gross densities. But in Jamshedpur, the twentieth-century city created by the Tata Iron and Steel Company, densities remained less than 198/hectare because of developmental planning and closely controlled employee housing. Certain North Indian cities with less rapid growth—Lucknow, Varanasi, Allahabad, Patna, and Gaya—show central densities of 494 to 988/hectare. Data for net residential density in Tiruchirapalli and density of the developed land in Hubli show that population congestion is found even in relatively small and slow-growing cities. Here the ratios between upper and lower deciles vary from about 100:1 to 20:1, demonstrating again that population concentration is a pronounced feature of India's urban development.

Theories of Intra-Urban Density Variation

Interpretation of the geographic pattern of population in India's cities must take account of theories and mathematical modes of urban structure. Colin Clark (6) and Brian J. L. Berry, together with R. J. Tennant and J. W. Simmons (2), found the negative exponential formula,[2] first proposed by Bleicher (3), to be a satisfactory description of the progressive decline of density outward from the center of any urban area and further found it to be applicable to some 100 cities. While this model of the population density gradient provides a statistically significant fit for most cities now under examination, a better model is needed to describe relationships between density and distance, in which maximum concentrations occur in a semicircle or ring near but not in the commercial center of an urban area. Such a configuration, which exists only in Bombay, Calcutta, and a few other large Indian cities, is a well-known feature in the Western world.[3]

A second aspect of intra-urban population concerns differential changes in distribution. Newling (13) has offered evidence of an inverse relationship between density and growth rate, using American examples. In both Pittsburgh, Pennsylvania, and Kingston, Jamaica, he observed that population tends to decrease in municipal wards where the density exceeds 124/hectare, while increases occur in wards where it is below this level, which he has called the "critical density." In other words, general population growth in an urban area is accompanied by lessening of concentration in the central wards and diminution of the density gradient. Berry *et al.* (2), on the contrary, observed continuous increases of density in the central wards of Indian cities, e.g. in Calcutta from 1881 to 1951, in contrast to Western cities, e.g. Chicago, where there was an increase between 1860 and 1910, but a decrease as metropolitan sprawl accelerated. Berry then proceeded to theorize that non-Western (particularly Indian) cities follow a pattern of concentrated growth and increasing residential congestion in contrast to the Western patterns of growth, which are accompanied by residential dispersion. As previously suggested, recent data lend support to Berry's theory. Let me be specific.

At the beginning of the twentieth century, population density in the largest Western cities was higher than in contemporary Bombay and Calcutta, but since then the relationship has been reversed. According to the best knowledge of Mark Jefferson (10), the world peak of urban density was once in New York's Lower East Side, where in 1900 the Eighth Assembly District (40 hectares) had an average of 1821/hectare, and the Tenth Ward (44.5 hectares) had 1614/hectare. In 1901, Bombay stood in second rank with a maximum density of 1478/hectare in Kumbharwada. At about the same time, higher densities were found in London's Spitalfields (788/hectare) and Paris's 3rd Arrondissement (766/hectare) than in Calcutta, where the density of Coloootola (Kalutola) was 692/hectare. In New York, as well as in many other United States cities, intra-urban densities were highest in 1910, but in India they continued to rise. In 1961 Bombay's Kumbharwada (part of Ward C), recorded 2627/hectare—second only to the adjacent Bhuleshwar (Ward C), the highest present-day concentration in India. Calcutta's Ward 40, comprising in part the Kalutola area, had 1213/hectare in 1961, nearly double the density of the previous 60 years. Clearly, there has been

2. Population density is a negative exponential function of distance in the equation: $D_d = D_o e^{-bd}$, where D_d is the population density at distance d; D_o is the population density at the center of the city; e is the base of the natural logarithms; and b (the density gradient) is an exponent expressing rate of change in density with distance from the center of the city.
3. The problem of density-distance relationships is further analyzed by the author in an article entitled "Spatial Patterns of Population in Indian Cities," *The Geographical Review*, Vol. 58, No. 3 (July, 1968), pp. 362-91.

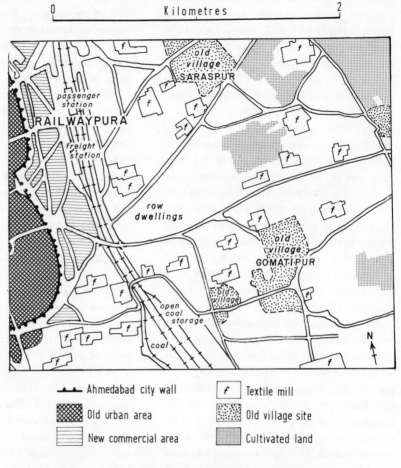

Fig. 18-8. CENTRAL PORTION OF AHMEDABAD, GUJARAT STATE.

Ahmedabad was founded by a Muslim ruler, Ahmad Shah, in A.D. 1411 and enjoyed some four centuries of intermittent growth, based on handicraft industries and its role as a leading seat of government and center for trade in the Gujarat region of western India. During the early seventeenth century, in Thomas Roe's time, "Ahmedabad was a goodly city as large as London." The city came under British rule in 1818 and entered a period of renewed growth, when its economic base was revolutionized by railway construction, linking it to Bombay some 480 km south, and by establishment of the cotton textile industry. By 1950 Ahmedabad had about sixty weaving and spinning mills and it was second in India only to Bombay in aggregate productive capacity. Population growth accelerated in the first half of the twentieth century, culminating during the twenty years from 1941 to 1961, when metropolitan Ahmedabad increased from about 595,000 to 1,206,000, placing it seventh in rank among the cities of India.

The nucleus of Ahmedabad is the old city within the wall, part of which appears in the western margin of the photograph, while significant elements of new urban growth appear outside the wall, where an intensely industrial landscape has been superimposed on the previous landscape of fields and villages. The area seen here within the wall (partially demolished subsequent to the date of the photograph, 1939) had residential population densities between

1000 and 1235 persons per hectare (400 and 500 per acre) in 1961. Few open spaces are visible among the small two- or three-story structures, built wall-to-wall and back-to-back along the narrow streets and dead-end alleys. Population concentration within the wall resulted initially in the pre-British days from the need for protection against brigands and invaders and from competition among officials and merchants for locations of prestige near the ruler's palace in the heart of the city. Today congestion in the old city is intensified by natural increase and in-migration from smaller towns and villages.

However, the old city is ringed by industrial and residential suburbs. In 1961 population densities ranged from 86 to 285 persons per hectare (35 to 115 per acre) in the extra-mural area seen in this photograph, which includes the main railway passenger and freight terminals, numerous cotton textile mills (identified by their tall chimneys and ridged parallel roof lines), the barrack-like tenements for factory laborers, and various unplanned housing clusters. Thus, the process of centrifugal movement of economic activities and residential shift away from the old city is already under way and may be expected to increase as resources for urban decentralization become available.

The area covered by this photograph is shown on Fig. 18-6.

divergence of density trends in America and India.

The compact urban growth pattern of India can be more fully documented by two case studies: Gaya illustrates changes in a relatively small, slowly increasing Class I city and Poona, one of India's ten largest metropolitan cities, illustrates conditions of rapid population increase. Data for the wards have been converted to mean density gradients for each census year simply by striking compass arcs and grouping the wards according to median airline distances from the centers of the cities (Figure 18-4, Tables 18-5 and 18-6). It is possible to trace changes in density because in Gaya, the municipality and ward boundaries have remained unchanged for more than 30 years; and in

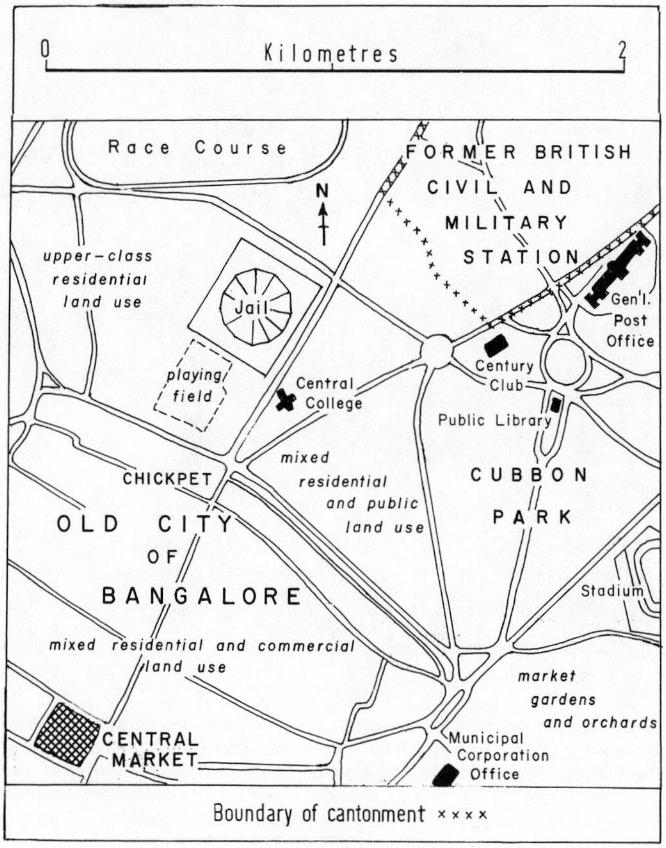

Fig. 18-9. CENTRAL PORTION OF BANGALORE, MYSORE STATE.

The landscape of Bangalore, as seen in a 1948 aerial photograph, represents two historical patterns of urban development in India: (1) the compact indigenous city; and (2) the sprawling British cantonment. In the southwestern portion of this photograph lies Bangalore City which, according to tradition, was founded by Magadi Kempe Gowda in 1537. It was defended by a fort, called *Bengaluru,* beyond the photo margin, located close to the site of the present Central Market. After the conquest of Mysore by the British East India Company in 1799, the British cantonment was created in the nineteenth century, with its center some two miles northwest of the main city. Bangalore Civil and Military Station, administered as a separate municipality from 1882 to 1949, had its own business center, its own services and public facilities catering to the European and Indian elite, many of whom lived in spacious houses in the midst of gardens. Meanwhile, the subrectangular grid of the old native city (south of Chickpet) became progressively more and more congested with stores, small shops for hand industries, and living quarters of the tradesmen and laborers. Between the two urban centers was a green belt of cultivated land, institutional grounds, and parks, substantial traces of which are identifiable in the central portion of the photo-

graph. By 1951, density of population in the Old City was about 740 to 1,240 hectare (300 to 500/acre), while in adjacent areas outside, density was only 37 to 74/hectare (15 to 30/acre).

Formation of the Bangalore City Improvement Trust in 1945 and the amalgamation of the former Civil and Military Station with the City in 1949, provided unified administrative control over an urban area of 79.5 km² (17,500 acres) with total population of 779,000 in 1951, which grew to 906,000 in 1961. Jurisdiction of the Trust Board has been extended to the villages outside the Corporation area in which industrial estates and residential tracts are being developed. In 1961 the population of metropolitan Bangalore was about 1,207,000 in an area of 309 km² (193 sq. mi.). Population density in the Old City was stabilized or reduced between 1951 and 1961, and a pattern of decentralization and development became evident due to the above-mentioned extensions and encroachments on the open land in or adjacent to the old Civil and Military Station. The boundary of former British territory appears in the northeastern portion of the photograph. The new Vidhana Soudha, which houses the Mysore Legislature and Secretariat, stands on a site within the photo area, opposite the General Post Office. The area of cultivated land has diminished rapidly, as Bangalore's population has grown. But it remains a garden city and is probably the least congested and slum-ridden of India's eight largest metropolitan cities.

The area covered by this photograph is shown in Fig. 18-7.

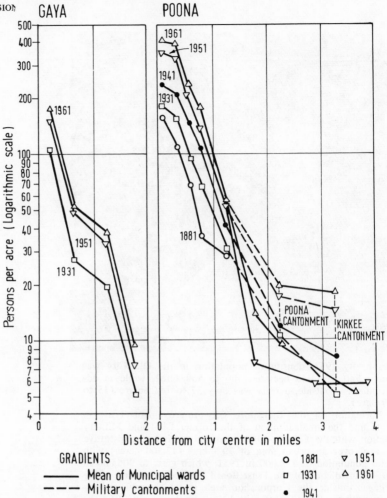

Fig. 18-4. CHANGES IN GROSS POPULATION DENSITY, GAYA AND POONA, 1881-1961

TABLE 18-5   POPULATION DENSITIES IN GAYA MUNICIPALITY, 1931-1961

Median Distance from Center (miles/km)	Gross Density (persons per acre/per ha)		
	1931	1951	1961
0.20/0.32	104.9/259	155.7/385	171.6/424
0.65/1.05	27.0/67	47.8/118	51.8/128
1.25/2.01	19.8/49	33.3/82	37.9/94
1.75/2.82	5.3/13	7.4/18	9.3/23

Source: Based on wardwise area and population data for census dates, as reported by R. L. Bawa, Chief Town Planner, Local Self-Government Department (Town Planning), State of Bihar, Patna, 1966. Data for 1941 not available.

TABLE 18-6   POPULATION DENSITIES IN POONA MUNICIPALITY,
POONA CANTONMENT, AND KIRKEE CANTONMENT, 1881-1961

Median Distance from Center (miles/km)	*Gross Density (Persons per acre/per ha)*				
	1881	*1931*	*1941*	*1951*	*1961*
Poona City[1, 2]					
0.10/0.16	159/393	184/455	233/576	354/875	410/1013
0.35/0.56	109/269	159/393	208/514	332/820	393/971
0.60/0.97	68/168	95/235	147/363	208/514	236/583
0.80/1.29	36/89	68/168	108/267	137/339	178/440
1.25/2.01	27/67	33/82	41/101	52/128	56/138
Suburban Wards of Greater Poona[2]					
1.70/2.74	N.A.	N.A.	N.A.	8/20	14/35
2.25/3.62	N.A.	N.A.	N.A.	–	9/22
2.85/4.59	N.A.	N.A.	N.A.	6/15	–
3.60/5.79	N.A.	N.A.	N.A.	–	5/12
3.80/6.12	N.A.	N.A.	N.A.	6/15	–
Poona Cantonment[3]					
2.20/3.5[3]	N.A.	10/25	12/30	17/42	19/47
Kirkee Cantonment[3]					
3.25/5.23	N.A.	5/12	8/20	15/37	18/44

Sources: Based on wardwise area and population data for census dates as reported by:
[1] D. R. Gadgil, *Poona: A Socio-Economic Survey, Part II, Poona:* Gokhale Institute of Politics and Economics, Pub. No. 25, 1953.
[2] *Master Plan for Greater Poona.* Poona Municipal Corporation, 1952. B. D. Talim, Director of Town Planning, State of Maharashtra, Poona, 1966.
[3] *Census of India 1961,* Vol. I, Part II-A (i), 1964.
N.A. = Not available.

Poona City the ward boundaries have been relatively fixed for more than 80 years—although in the last two census decades the municipality has been greatly enlarged. These two cities exemplify the basic dimensions of India's urban population pressure.

The Growth of Gaya

Gaya is an ancient town in the southern Bihar uplands, located 85 miles south of Patna on the Phalgu River, where the main railway crosses between Calcutta and the Damodar industrial region on the east and Varanasi and the Gangetic plain on the west. During the 30-year period, 1931-61, population growth was recorded as follows: 88,005 (1931); 105,223 (1941); 133,700 (1951); and 151,105 (1961). Before 1931, the population of the city had fluctuated between 80,383 (1891) and a low of 49,921 (1911). The city's role as administrative headquarters of Gaya District and its importance as a commercial and transportation center account largely for its modern growth. Although large numbers of devout Hindus—reputed to be as many as 200,000 to 300,000—visit the celebrated Vishnu temple in Gaya each year, and Budh Gaya nearby is an international Buddhist shrine, the resident population of the old pilgrim quarter has recently declined. Instead, growth has been concentrated in the relatively new part of Gaya, situated between the Phalgu highway bridge and the railway station. Here in the central bazaar, maximum density in one ward exceeded 494/hectare in 1961. The innermost arc, with a radius of 0.3 km, comprising two wards, shows a progressive increase of combined density from about 260 to 424/hectare in the 30-year period (Table 18-5). In the three adjacent wards (median radius of 1 km) growth around the railway and the offices of the district court and tax collectorate counterbalanced the stagnation and decline in Old Gaya. Increase of density in the five outer wards was commensurate, rising from about 49 to 94/hectare in the arc of 2 km and from 12 to 22/hectare in the outermost arc of 2.8 km. Thus Gaya's density gradient, graphically expressed in logarithmic terms (Fig. 18-4), has remained almost constant. The ratio between central and peripheral density remained about 19:1 during the three decades considered.

Ward areas on which the above density-distance relationships are calculated exclude steep uninhabited hill areas and the river bed, which is subject to seasonal inundation, amounting in all to 1188 hectares. The total municipal area of 3051 hectares is therefore reduced to a net of 1863 hectares. Only 1047 hectares or 57 per cent of the net area is actually developed (50); and it is evident that a great deal more urban development could take place. Indeed, Gaya's peripheral density is very little above the levels of neighboring rural villages. Further, it can be assumed that with a sudden economic surge, the majority of in-migrants would be absorbed in developed areas unless development were controlled and directed elsewhere. The pattern of

growth in Poona since 1881 provides an example of the trend which might follow in Gaya.

The Growth of Poona

Poona is located in Maharashtra State, 193 km inland by rail from Bombay on the Deccan lava plateau near the confluence of the rivers Mula and Mutha. Its elevation is 564 m. The old city was formed during the seventeenth and eighteenth centuries around the Maratha castle on the Mutha River. It prospered under British rule from 1822 to 1947, becoming a major railway center and serving as the rainy season capital of Bombay Presidency and seat of Poona District administration. During the British era, Poona Cantonment, known as the "Camp," situated adjacent to the old city and Kirkee, the original British military establishment some three miles up the Mula River, had an important role as military headquarters for western and southern India—a role maintained and enlarged by independent India. Today Poona's economy is largely commercial and industrial; it also serves as an upper-class residential satellite for Bombay and the prime educational center in the northern Deccan. Until 1881, the population of Poona city remained below 100,000, fluctuating between 73,299 in 1851 and 99,421 in 1881. Greater Poona, including the cantonments and the British civil administrative area along the railway outside of the old city, reached 144,340 in 1881. By 1931, it had increased to 250,187 and the City Municipality to 162,901. After this date, municipal boundary changes created new geographical areas for Poona Municipal Corporation as of 1941 and the Greater Poona Municipal Corporation as of 1951. Census records show the following population for Poona, including suburbs: 198,078 (1931); 257,554 (1941); 480,982 (1951); and 597,562 (1961). Cantonment population, not included above, in Poona

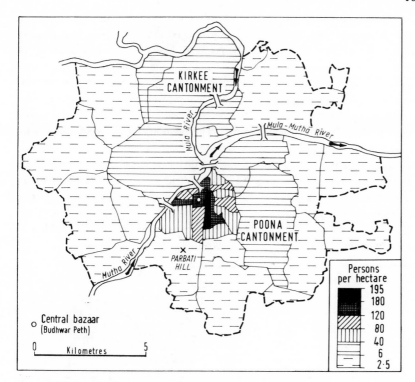

Fig. 18-5. POPULATION DENSITY OF GREATER POONA, 1961.
(The small circle that marks the central point of the city is Budhwar Peth. Reprinted from the Geographical Review (Vol. 58, 1968), by permission of the American Geographical Society of New York.)

was: 35,807 (1931); 40,447 (1941); 59,011 (1951); and 65,838 (1961); and in Kirkee: 16,302 (1931); 26,285 (1941); 48,552 (1951); and 59,496 (1961).

The series of population gradients for Poona from 1881 to 1961 (Fig. 18-4 and Table 18-6) shows a consistent pattern of change in distance-density relationships. By 1881 the Poona gradient was at about the same level (within 2 km) as obtained in Gaya in 1961. It is worth noting that Poona, including suburbs and cantonments, had about the same population in 1881 as Gaya in 1961. Thereafter, successive increases of density occurred in each arc of distance up to 2 km without much over-all change in slope. But the gradients also show two features not apparent in Gaya. First, the gradient representing the first 0.8 km from the city center flattens progressively, beginning in 1931 and becoming pronounced in 1951 and 1961 after a sudden rise during the 1940's when the greater Poona population gain was 85 per cent. At present, a gross density of about 1000/hectare is evidently the "ceiling" in the central area of the city. Second, the profiles show that while growth in the cantonments decreased after 1951, it got well under way in the innermost portions of the newly annexed suburbs and erstwhile villages. Civilian residential and commercial enclaves exist in the cantonments, but land use is largely dictated by military requirements which restrict population growth in these areas.

A shift in locus of growth from the old city to the periphery has not been as rapid as might have been anticipated, although the development of commerce and transportation in the congested central wards has resulted in the displacement of residential land. In Budhwar Peth (the central business area) the net residential density in 1961 was 2842/hectare, compared with a gross density of 1013/hectare, indicating that almost two-thirds of the ward area was taken up in streets, market areas, and other uses. Adjacent wards showed equally high rates of residential displacement. Yet the gross density on the periphery was as little as one-fiftieth or one-sixtieth of that in the center of the city. Most of Poona's inhabitants are unable

to afford new housing or public costs of extending transportation, utilities, and schools. The result of these deterrents, plus restrictive governmental policies on conversion of agricultural land and prevention of land speculation in the peripheral wards, has been to contain Poona's incipient metropolitan "explosion." The phenomenon of commuters who bicycle daily to new factories in Dapodi and Chinchwad (located respectively some 10 and 13 km away along the Poona-Bombay road) indicates that residential areas of the old city may be preferred to outlying wards of Greater Poona or the above-mentioned industrial localities.

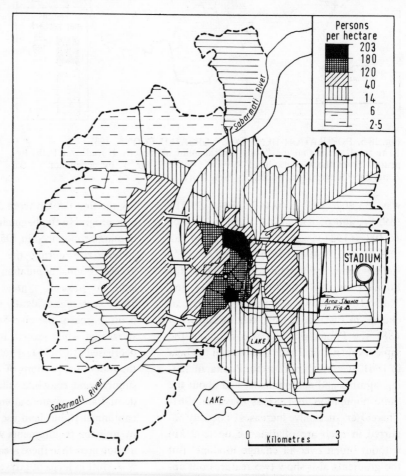

Fig. 18-6.   AHMEDABAD, GUJARAT STATE, WESTERN INDIA

Problems of Urbanization

This paper has offered evidence for (1) the marked decline of India's urban growth rate, particularly during the census decade ending in 1961 (2) the extreme concentrations within built-up areas of selected metropolitan cities. Studies of population growth and progressive rise of densities in Gaya and Poona suggest that India's cities are now in a stage of development which might be described as urban "implosion." Urban dwellers tend to stay as close as possible to work and marketplace. But housing and other amenities in the city centers are inadequate to meet current needs. The demand for private living space is minimized by economic, technological, and institutional barriers. The result is retardation of urban development and suppression of the potential urban "explosion" which must occur as India's people begin to enjoy the fruits of economic development. Foreign observers are frequently appalled by the many problems of urbanization in India today, and the general consensus among Indian social scientists and governmental officials is that the need for prompt action is desperate. An abundance of factual data necessary for understanding problems and establishing policies is now at hand. (See Bibliography, especially Bulsara's summary and interpretation of findings in socio-economic surveys in nine cities, 20). In conclusion, I wish to touch briefly on a few of the demographic and economic facts that will influence any program of urban development.

First, India's urban people are better educated and receive higher earnings than do rural people; and on the whole, migrants to cities and towns are more literate, talented, and enterpising than those who remain in rural areas. Somewhat more than half the urban growth appears to be due to natural increase of the resident population, which is estimated at about 15 per mille annually (births 25-30 per thousand; deaths, 9-14 per

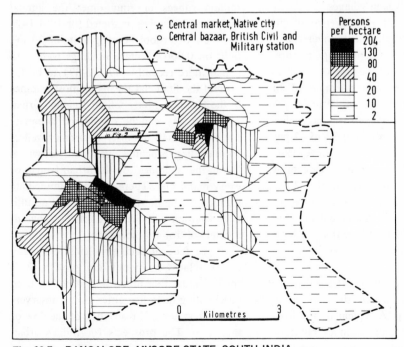

Fig. 18-7. BANGALORE, MYSORE STATE, SOUTH INDIA

thousand), on the basis of households sampled during the late 1950's (20: 183, 184). The rate of in-migration to a city may be approximately equal to the rate of natural increase, but one-quarter to one-half of the former consists of movement from other cities and towns. Contacts with friends and relatives and transfers in service are strong factors in migration. There was a preponderance of families with four to six members in the sample surveys; but some 8 to 12 per cent of urban households were uni-member (mainly adult males, separated from their wives and children), and a slightly higher percentage were young married couples. Thus, there was an imbalance in urban age distribution, as compared with village populations, and a disparity of sex ratios, particularly in the largest metropolitan centers and cities based on mining or manufacturing. Urban migrants frequently maintain joint-families under conditions of extreme crowding, or during separation provide regular remittances to their relatives in villages.

Despite the apparent attractiveness of cities, problems of unemployment, poverty, and destitution present a depressing picture. About 4 to 8 per cent of the employable persons questioned were found unemployed. In the late 1950's, the income of 10 to 20 per cent of the families surveyed was no higher than 40 rupees per month, and 33 to 42 per cent received only from 41 to 75 rupees (20: 141). It is estimated that 36 to 85 per cent of the families lived in poverty, and that 20 to 39 per cent lived in destitution. More recent findings yield essentially the same distressing conclusions. It is difficult to see that the level of living for urban dwellers has improved much.

No aspect of urbanization portrays the economic crisis facing urban dwellers more sharply than housing. A typical family lives in one room in a tenement or in a temporary shelter in squalor and perpetual discomfort.

About one-third of the households in the sample surveys had less than 3.72 m² (40 sq. ft.) of living space per person (20: 155). In 1957 it was estimated that 77 per cent of all families in Calcutta had less than 4.1 m² (44 sq. ft.) of living space available per person, and in 1961 the census revealed ratios of three persons per room and 1.55 rooms per dwelling unit. Simple amenities such as access to water supply or private cooking and sanitation facilities are in short supply, and vast numbers of people continue to live like villagers in urban environments, depending on distant sources of water, cooking with cow dung fuel, and getting along without even rudimentary means of waste disposal. Of the families surveyed, a substantial share were unable to pay rents of more than 10 rupees per month nor were they willing to move to better quarters even when subsidized (20: 180). Construction of new urban dwellings was so far below needs that a deficit of some 6 million housing units, at a cost of 42,000 million rupees or four times the annual budget of India was predicted for 1961 (42: 3). New two-room housing units of 20 m², built on 0.0067 hectare holdings were estimated more recently (49: 76-87) to be far beyond the financial means of most families in the Calcutta Metropolitan Region. Urban housing today can be considered adequate for only a small minority of urban dwellers from the upper income levels, many of whom live in the "colonies" on the urban fringes of every major city. There seems no immediate solution of the housing problem and no ultimate solution without some form of governmental control and financing.

In the face of such problems and many others related to population growth, it is small wonder that urban migration has been decelerating in Indian cities. Some observers advocate systematic restriction of the flow of migration. The prospects for India's urban future will remain clouded until employment opportunities increase, production in nonagricultural sectors of the economy is accelerated, and a substantial rise of income makes available the savings and investment necessary for urban expansion. Of course, relief for India's population pressures is being sought in fields and villages as well as in mines and factories. Urban development is merely a piece of the whole fabric of economic development in any nation.

REFERENCES

I. General

(1) Kazi Ahmad: Indian Cities: Characteristics and Correlates. (Chicago, Ill., University of Chicago, Dept of Geography, Research Paper No. 102, 1965).

(2) Brian J. L. Berry, R. J. Tennant, and J. W. Simmons: Urban Population Densities: Structure and Change. *The Geographical Review,* Vol. 53, 1963, pp. 389-405.

(3) Heinrich Bleicher: Statistische Beschreibung der Stadt Frankfurt am Main und ihrer Bevölkerung (Frankfurt am Main, 1892).

(4) Gerald Breese: Urban Development Problems in India. *Annals, Association of American Geographers,* Vol. 53, 1963, pp. 253-65.

(5) John E. Brush: The Morphology of Indian Cities, in: Roy Turner, ed.: India's Urban Future (Berkeley and Los Angeles, 1962), pp. 57-80.

(6) Colin Clark: Urban Population Densities. *Journal, Royal Statistical Society,* Ser. A, Vol. 114, Part 4, 1951, pp. 490-496. See also under same title, *Bull. Inst. Internationale de Statistique.* Vol. 36, Part 4, 1958, pp. 60-68.

(7) Kingsley Davis: Urbanization in India: Past and Future, in: Roy Turner, ed.: India's Urban Future (Berkeley and Los Angeles, 1962), pp. 3-26.

(8) C. A. Doxiadis: Ecumenopolis: Toward the Universal City (Athens, 1961).

(9) G. S. Ghurye: Cities and Civilization (Bombay, 1962).

(10) Mark Jefferson: The Anthropography of Some Great Cities. *Bull., American Geographical Society,* Vol. 41, 1909, pp. 537-566.

(11) Mark Jefferson: The Distribution of the World's City Folks. *The Geographical Review.* Vol. 21, 1931, pp. 446-465.

(12) Bert F. Hoselitz: The Role of Urbanization in Economic Development: Some International Comparisons, in: Roy Turner, ed.: India's Urban Future (Berkeley and Los Angeles, 1962), pp. 157-81.

(13) Bruce E. Newling: Urban Growth and Spatial Structure: Mathematical Models and Empirical Evidence. *The Geographical Review,* Vol. 56, 1966, pp. 212-25.

(14) Pitambar Pant: Urbanization and the Long-Range Strategy, in: Roy Turner, ed.: India's Urban Future (Berkeley and Los Angeles, 1962), pp. 182-91.

(15) N. V. Sovani: Urbanization and Urban India (New York, 1966).

(16) Wilbur Zelinsky: The Geographer and His Crowding World, *Revista Geográfica,* No. 65, 1966, pp. 7-28.

II. Economic, Geographic, or Social Studies of Indian Cities.

(17) S. Manzoor Alam: Hyderabad-Secunderabad (Twin Cities). A Study in Urban Geography (Bombay, 1965).

(18) A. Bopegamage: Delhi. A Study in Urban Sociology, University of Bombay Publications, Social Series, No. 7, 1957.

(19) Nirmal Kumar Bose: Calcutta: A Premature Metropolis, *Scientific American.* Vol. 213, No. 3, September, 1965, pp. 91-102.

(20) Jal F. Bulsara: Problems of Rapid Urbanisation in India (Bombay, 1964). (Collation and summary of finding from socio-economic surveys in nine Indian cities.)

(21) B. R. Dhekney: Hubli City, A Study in Urban Economic Life. (Dharwar, 1959).

(22) Norma Evenson: Chandigarh (Berkeley, 1966).

(23) D. R. Gadgil: Poona. A Socio-Economic Survey. I—Economic (Poona: Gokhale Institute of Politics and Economics, Publication No. 12, 1945).

(24) D. R. Gadgil: Poona. A Socio-Economic Survey, Part II (Poona: Gokhale Institute of Politics and Economics, Publication No. 25, 1952).

(25) D. R. Gadgil: Sholapur City: Socio-Economic Studies (Poona: Gokhale Institute of Politics and Economics, 1965).

(26) S. Kesava Iyengar: A Socio-Economic Survey of Hyderabad-Secunderabad City Area (Hyderabad: 1957).

(27) V. A. Janaki and Z. A. Sayed: The Geography of Padra Town (Baroda: M. S., University of Baroda, 1962).

(28) D. T. Lakdawala, J. C. Sandesara, V. N. Kothari, and P. A. Nair: Work, Wages and Well-Being in an Indian Metropolis. Economic Survey of Bombay City University of Bombay, Series in Economics, No. 11, 1963.

(29) D. N. Majumdar: Social Contours of an Industrial City. Social Survey of Kanpur (Bombay, 1960).

(30) P. C. Malhotra: Socio-Economic Survey of Bhopal City and Bairagarh (New York, 1964).

(31) H. C. Malkani: A Socio-Economic Survey of Baroda City (Baroda: M. S., University of Baroda, 1957).

(32) B. R. Misra: Report on Socio-Economic Survey of Jamshedpur City (Patna, Bihar: Patna University, Dept. of Applied Economics and Commerce, 1959).

(33) Mohammad Mohsin: Chittaranjan. A Study in Urban Sociology (Bombay, 1964).

(34) Radhakamal Mukerjee and Baljit Singh: Social Profiles of a Metrop-

olis. Social and Economic Structure of Lucknow, Capital of Uttar Pradesh (New York, 1961).

(35) C. Rajagopalan: The Greater Bombay. A Study in Suburban Ecology (Bombay, 1962).

(36) V. K. R. V. Rao and P. B. Desai: Greater Delhi. A Study in Urbanisation 1940-57 (New York, 1965).

(37) S. N. Sen: The City of Calcutta: A Socio-Economic Survey. 1954-55 to 1957-58 (Calcutta, 1961).

(38) N. V. Sovani, D. P. Apte, and G. R. Pendse: Poona: A Re-Survey. The Changing Pattern of Employment and Earnings (Poona: Gokhale Institute of Politics and Economics, Public. No. 34, 1956).

(39) R. L. Singh: Banaras: A Study in Urban Geography (Banaras, 1955).

(40) R. L. Singh: Bangalore. An Urban Survey (Varanasi, 1964).

(41) Ujagir Singh: Allahabad. A Study in Urban Geography (Varanasi, 1961).

III. Official Documents

(42) Census of India 1961

Vol. 1, Part II-A (i), General Population Tables (Delhi, 1964).

Vol. IX, Madras, Part XI-C. Slums of Madras City (Delhi, 1965).

Vol. X, Maharashtra, Part X (1-B), Greater Bombay Census Tables (Delhi, 1964).

Vol. XV, Uttar Pradesh, Part X. Special Report on Kanpur City (Delhi, 1965).

(43) Ministry of Works, Housing and Supply, Government of India: The Problem of Housing in India (Delhi, 1957).

(44) Ahmedabad Municipal Corporation: Development Plan (c. 1962).

(45) Asansol Planning Organisation. Government of West Bengal, Development and Planning (T & CP) Dept.: Interim Development Plan. Asansol-Durgapur (1966).

(46) Bangalore Town Planning Office, Government of Mysore: The Outline Development Plan for the Bangalore Metropolitan Region (1963).

(47) Bombay Municipal Corporation: Report on the Development Plan for Greater Bombay 1964.

(48) Calcutta, Development and Planning (Town and Country Planning) Department, Government of West Bengal: Memorandum on Development Plan. Calcutta Metropolitan District 1966-1971 (1965).

(49) Calcutta Metropolitan Planning Organisation, Government of West Bengal: Basic Development Plan for the Calcutta Metropolitan District 1966-1986 (1966).

(50) Delhi Development Authority, Town Planning Organisation: Master Plan for Delhi (1962). Work Studies Relating to the Master Plan for Delhi, Vols. 1 and 11 (1964).

(51) Gaya Improvement Trust: Draft Master Plan. Prepared under Di-

rection of J. C. P. Sinha, Assistant Town Planner, Government of Bihar (Patna, c. 1965).

(52) Patna Improvement Trust: Master Plan Patna. Vols. 1 and 2 (c. 1962).

(53) Siliguri Planning Organisation, Town and Country Planning, Government of West Bengal: Interim Development Plan for Siliguri (1965).

19. AN OVERCROWDED METROPOLIS: KINGSTON, JAMAICA

C. G. Clarke

> . . . if you are like Abraham, and want your offspring to be numberless as the sands of the sea-shore, you don't choose an island to start breeding on. Too soon there would be over-population, overcrowding, and slum conditions.
>
> D. H. Lawrence: The Man Who Loved Islands

The terms "overcrowded" and "population pressure" are widely used by social scientists. Both, however, are relative in their meaning and lack diagnostic value unless they are applied to special spatial and historical contexts. Furthermore, both terms are generalizations which require careful definition. The words "population pressure" form a shorthand for the phrase "the pressure of population upon physical and human resources." Overcrowding, whether it applies to housing, school places, hospitals, or employment, is a product of population pressure. Pressure is caused by the imbalance between human numbers and *needs* and the physical and human resources of the area in question. Imbalance in varying degrees and at different levels of living is a ubiquitous condition; but while pressure at present occurs within restricted areas and social groupings in economically advanced nations, it is more elementary in nature and more widespread in the developing countries, and contributes to, and helps to perpetuate, their underdevelopment. For among the latter, the ever increasing population is almost invariably a more important contributor to population pressure than the destruction of a resource base upon which the population was once stabilized.

Most studies of population pressure on resources (PPR) have been concerned with rural areas, and the contents of this volume are no exception. Indeed, Browning has described himself as ". . . uneasy in trying to think of PPR in terms of urban areas without knowing quite why." (Browning: p. 74). Having asserted that ". . . we can determine

within broad error limits the carrying capacity of the land under various combinations of labor, capital, and other inputs," he concludes that "there are no comparable ways of estimating the limits to the growth of urban areas . . ." (Browning: p. 74). But, as this volume illustrates, it is impossible to determine the "carrying capacity" of land in other than a relative sense, that is, relative to certain specified criteria. Furthermore, "carrying capacity," or what Beaujeu-Garnier, in the context of the city, has called "the possibilities of urban assimilation" (Beaujeu-Garnier: p. 272), is profoundly influenced by the level of living which the inhabitants are prepared to tolerate; and their toleration is conditioned by their expectations and by the nature and structure of their social system.

Measurement presupposes the existence or creation of valid yardsticks. Despite the complexity of the problem, it is clear that in the large towns, and above all in the capital cities, of many developing countries, conditions of overcrowding are evinced by continuously high rates of unemployment and by a dire shortage of adequate housing (Beaujeu-Garnier: pp. 272-74). Kingston, the capital of Jamaica, is no exception. By examining rates of unemployment and the overcrowding of accommodation in Kingston, it is possible to arrive at a quantitative assessment of the qualitative phrase "population pressure." Moreover, it is also possible to examine the historical development of overcrowding and to measure its present-day incidence and implications.

How valid are these criteria of overcrowding? It may be argued that the index used to define overcrowding of accommodation, namely, a density of more than two persons per room or more than eight persons to each hygienic water closet, is setting too high a standard of living for the inhabitants of Kingston. Nevertheless, these are the criteria used by government agencies in Jamaica; in a practical sense they provide the basis on which political decisions affecting urban renewal have been taken. In all probability they fall below the level of expectations of indigent Kingstonians.

The second index of overcrowding—unemployment—is difficult to handle. Although the statistics have been drawn from official sources and enable increases in unemployment (and overcrowding in the broadest sense) to be measured through time, there is every reason to be cautious of them. Unemployment frequently masks illegal self-employment. But whichever way these statistics are interpreted, they lead to the inescapable conclusion that Kingston cannot absorb the rapidly growing population and provide jobs which the inhabitants consider desirable. By West Indian standards, the pressures on housing and employment in parts of Kinsgton are applied at a very low level of living, but at one involving malnutrition rather than starvation.

Kingston

Kingston is the capital and main port of Jamaica, and, with a population of 376,000 in 1960, the largest city in the former British West Indies. Located on the south coast of the island, Kingston has expanded across the Liguanea Plain, a coastal embayment which rises gradually from the sea to a height of 245 m at 13 km inland, and covers an area of slightly more than 130 km². On the landward side, a crescent of mountains, whose height rises above 600 m, almost encloses the city and the plain. The central business district

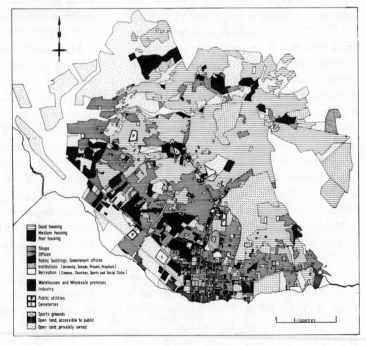

Good housing
Medium housing
Poor housing

Shops
Offices
Public buildings, Government offices
Institutions (University, Schools, Prisons, Hospitals)
Recreation (Cinemas, Churches, Sports and Social Clubs)

Warehouses and Wholesale premises
Industry

Public utilities
Cemeteries

Sports grounds
Open land, accessible to public
Open land, privately owned

0   Kilometres   3

Fig. 19-1. KINGSTON 1960: LAND USE

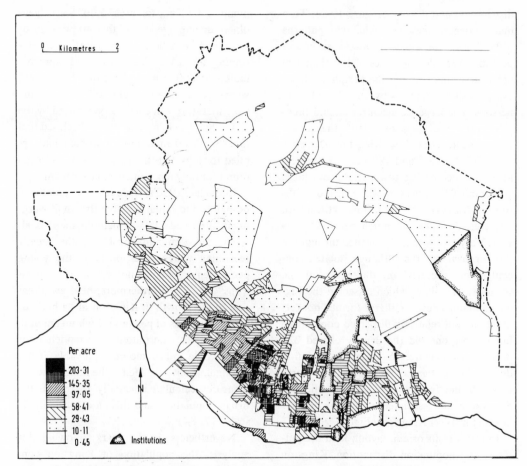

Fig. 19-2. KINGSTON 1960: DISTRIBUTION AND DENSITY OF POPULATION.
(This figure and Figures 19-3, 4, 5, 6, 9, and 10 from *Transaction and Papers of the Institute of British Geographers, Publication* No. 38, 1966.)

occupies the grid which was laid out during the seventeenth and eighteenth centuries (Figure 19-1). On its periphery concentric zones of poor, medium and good housing succeed one another in a northerly direction, there being a marked tendency, however, for poor housing to be confined to a wedge following the Spanish Town Road in West Kingston.

1. The census data used in Figs. 19-2, 3, 4, 5, 7, 9, 10, and 11 have been mapped by enumeration districts. The tabulation from which Fig. 19-2 was produced is on sale to the public; but Figs. 19-3, 4, 7, 9, 10, and 11 were constructed from tabulations of a 10 per cent sample of

By mapping data[1] for the 830 enumeration districts into which Kingston[2] was divided for the Census of 1960, it has been possible to distinguish areas of distinctive population

census cards drawn from all the enumeration districts in Kingston. This sample was made available by the Jamaican Department of Statistics, whose co-operation is gratefully acknowledged.
2. In 1960 the old parish of Kingston lying adjacent to the harbor and the suburban and rural sections of St. Andrew to the north were administered by a single corporation. The census distinguished between suburban and rural St. Andrew, and the division between the two has been used as the outer limit of the city.

distribution and density (Figure 19-2). To a marked degree, these coincided with patterns of land use. The central business district and port area recorded densities of less than 100 persons per hectare. On the periphery, however, densities rose to between 250 and 1000 persons. The largest concentration and highest density was associated with the single-story tenements of West Kingston. Densities ranging between 5 and 790 persons per hectare, and decreasing towards the outskirts, characterized the eastern, western, and southwestern fringes of this area. Only in the north, however, did they fall much below 25 persons. Very low densities prevailed throughout the northern suburbs, although isolated concentrations occurred on the banks of the storm-water gulleys which dissected the Liguanea Plain. These "outliers" formed pockets in the area of relatively dispersed population, but in only one did the density exceed 220 persons per hectare. In general, population density in the capital increased from north to south and from east to west, the highest densities being associated with areas of poor housing in West Kingston (Figure 19-1).

In terms of its origin, layout, land use patterns, and population distribution, Kingston is a transplanted European city. By contrast, its demographic problems are indigenous.

THE GROWTH OF UNEMPLOYMENT

Although unemployment was endemic in Kingston during the third quarter of the nineteenth century, the situation was created more by the decline in the sugar trade of the port than by an increase in the population of the city. During the economic depression of the 1930's, however, unemployment problems were aggravated and perpetuated by the rapid growth of the city's population, which more than doubled from about 89,000 in 1921 to 202,000 in 1943. In 1936 a government commission was set up to investigate unemployment. It reported that of the 90,000 people

living in the Kingston area[3] 5,000 were "genuinely unemployed," and that 40 per cent of these had been born in the rural areas. Assuming an urban labor force of approximately 45,000, it is probable that 11 per cent were "genuinely unemployed" at this date. Corroboratory evidence was submitted by the Times Store in Kingston, which disclosed that in 1934, 2000 men and 18 women had applied for jobs, but that employment had been found for only ten women and four men.

In the late 1930's, Orde Browne, an official despatched to Jamaica by the British Government, observed that: "Unemployment is already the dominant problem; the steady recruiting which takes place as the young people leave school is nothing short of disastrous" (7: 42). Furthermore, he drew attention to the growth in Kingston of "a body of some thousands of persons for whom employment is at best intermittent. The tendency for such people to become unemployable, if not criminal, is obvious. Hence the importance of measures calculated actually to reduce the urban population, and this on a considerable scale" (7: 84).

Nevertheless, in the years following this analysis, the population of Kingston continued to grow, and the problem of unemployment intensified rather than declined. During the week ending 28 September 1946, some 23,500 persons in Greater Kingston[4] were unemployed, representing 15.5 per cent of the total population aged over fourteen. Unemployment which had been originally cyclical, or associated with trade cycles, had been transformed into a permanent feature of the socio-economic structure of the city.

UNEMPLOYMENT IN 1960

Despite economic development in Jamaica,

3. The "Kingston Area" probably implied the parish of Kingston and the immediately adjoining sections of St. Andrew.
4. Greater Kingston probably comprised the entire urban and suburban area.

which was reflected in a threefold increase in the Gross Domestic Product from £70 million in 1950 to £215 million in 1960, a continuously high rate of unemployment was maintained in Kingston.[5] This was due to the high rate of natural increase in the city and to in-migration from the rural areas. Between 1943 and 1960, the number of inhabitants in the capital increased by 86 per cent to 376,-000, while the population of Jamaica as a whole expanded by 30 per cent to 1,606,500. Nearly a quarter of the country's population lived in Kingston, and the increase in its inhabitants in 1960 alone almost equalled the population of Montego Bay (24,000), the second largest town in the island. Approximately half the annual growth of 20,000 was attributable to natural increase and the remainder to migration from the rural areas. In 1960, therefore, the economy of the capital was encountering the problem of providing employment for an annual increment to the labor force in excess of 10,000 persons. This task was made almost impossible by the large numbers already out of work.

According to the 1960 census, 18.4 per cent of the potential labor force of 179,000 was either voluntarily or involuntarily unemployed. Part-time employment was also widespread in Kingston, and 30 per cent of the classified labor force of 169,000 received employment for less than five days during the week preceding the census. More than 10,-000 people were looking for their first job, and they accounted for almost one-third of the total number of unemployed. Approximately 70 per cent of this group were under 21 years of age, and unemployment was chronic among school-leavers. These conditions were primarily the result of secular and not seasonal, frictional, technological, or cyclical unemployment; they had existed in

5. Value of Jamaican pounds has been identical with British pounds—both before and after the 1967 devaluation.

Kingston for almost 30 years, and were associated with "an economy in equilibrium so that there is always a reservoir of involuntarily unemployed" (6: 8).

Unemployment in Kingston affected 15.5 per cent of the potential labor force in 1946, and 18.4 per cent in 1960; in the latter year the figure for the island as a whole was 12.6 per cent. The population of Jamaica was slowly concentrating in the capital, and so was unemployment, and opportunities for work in Kingston failed completely to meet the expectations of rural migrants. It is significant that 36 per cent of the males and 50 per cent of the females looking for their first job in 1960 were born in the rural parishes of the island. The manufacturing industry could not absorb the rapid growth of population, and no social security existed to cushion the effects of unemployment. Under these circumstances the personal service industry was important as an employer of domestic servants, gardeners, yard-boys, and odd-job men, but at wages which barely exceeded subsistence rates. The close approximation between the proportions employed in manufacturing (23.9 per cent) and personal service (21.5 per cent), as revealed by the 1960 census, was in itself an indicator of population pressure.

Using full-time unemployment as the first criterion, it can be seen that overcrowding and population pressure did exist in Kingston in 1960, and that 33,000 members of the potential labor force were affected. Since the latter comprised almost 50 per cent of the population of the city, the total number of workers and dependents directly affected by unemployment may be estimated as at least 60,000.

Figure 19-3 shows involuntary full-time unemployment; Fig. 19-4, part-time unemployment among the population aged over fourteen. The former (Fig. 19-3) defines areas experiencing "hard core" unemploy-

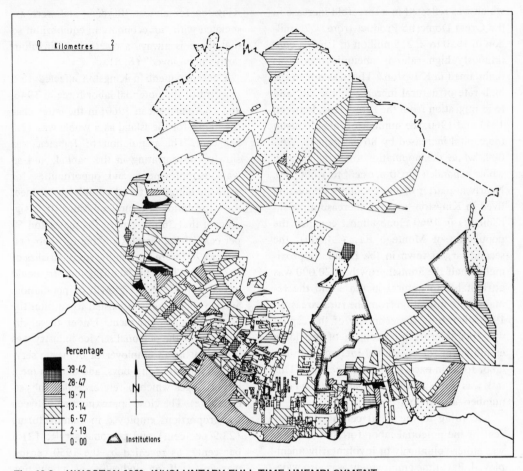

Fig. 19-3. KINGSTON 1960: INVOLUNTARY FULL-TIME UNEMPLOYMENT

ment and corresponds to the general pattern of population density. However, the correlation is only partial, for although the tenements of East and West Kingston recorded high densities of population, they did not suffer conspicuously from full-time unemployment. Rates in these areas rarely exceeded 13.1 per cent and the highest incidence, which surpassed 39.4 per cent, occurred at Tower Hill on the western extremity of the city, where the density of population was decidedly lower. The highest rates of unemployment in West Kingston ranged between 19.2 and 28.5 per cent. These were confined to areas peripheral to the tenements,

and, in particular, to some of the "yards" which lay adjacent to the Spanish Town Road. Rates were generally low throughout the suburbs, but some increase was recorded in pockets of denser population. An interesting feature is the relationship between high unemployment rates in parts of the "yard" area and in government housing schemes at Tower Hill. The latter were established after 1950[6], largely to resettle inhabitants from the depressed "yards." People were selected from the poorest elements and much of the hard-

6. The rehousing schemes at Tower Hill were initially designed for victims of the 1951 hurricane.

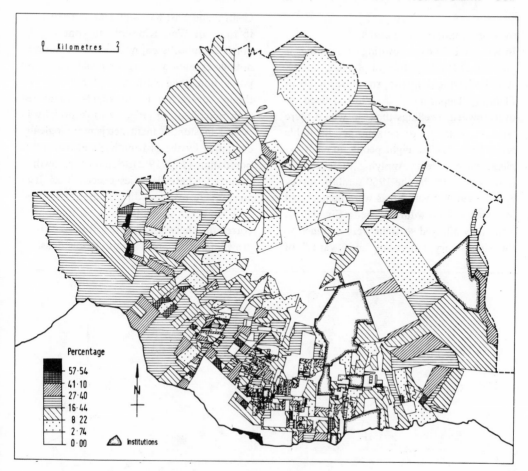

Fig. 19-4. KINGSTON 1960: PART-TIME UNEMPLOYMENT

core unemployment was transfered to, and reconcentrated in this area of low-density housing.

A closer correlation with high densities of population is shown in the map of part-time unemployment (Fig. 19-4). Although the highest rate of more than 57.5 per cent was once more recorded in the resettlement schemes at Tower Hill, and two other zones of unemployment were in evidence in the central and northern sections of the suburbs, "yards" and tenements suffered quite noticeably from part-time unemployment. In these areas the rates rose from 16 to 41 per cent.

While the incidence of unemployment formed a fairly regular geographical pattern increasing from north to south and east to west, and was generally related to increases in the density of the population, population density varied systematically, there being a tendency for part-time unemployment to be associated with the densely populated tenements and "yards," and for full-time unemployment to be linked to areas experiencing low densities. It was extremely difficult for persons suffering from long-term unemployment to pay a rent of approximately £4.10.0 per month for a room in one of the tenements; the solution to their housing problem lay elsewhere.

OVERCROWDING OF DWELLINGS

In Kingston the overcrowding of dwellings is one of the clearest indices of population pressure. Following standard procedure the Town Planning Department in 1960 defined as overcrowded dwellings those in which there were more than two persons per habitable room or more than eight people to each hygienic water closet. Applying these criteria to data provided by the 1960 sanitary survey and the 1960 census, areas were demarcated in which overcrowding existed (Fig. 19-5). The badly affected sections were confined to the single-story tenements and "yards" of Central and East Kingston and, in particular, to those of West Kingston. In contrast, the northern suburbs enjoyed better conditions, notable exceptions being the pockets of dense population along the storm-water gulleys. Although overcrowding is widely associated with poor housing (Fig. 19-1), especially in West Kingston, its incidence is more logically explained by the distribution and density of population (Fig. 19-2). Some overcrowding occurred where densities exceeded 25 hectare, severe overcrowding where it exceeded 250. However, while there is a cartographical correlation between high densities and overcrowding, some areas recording low densities

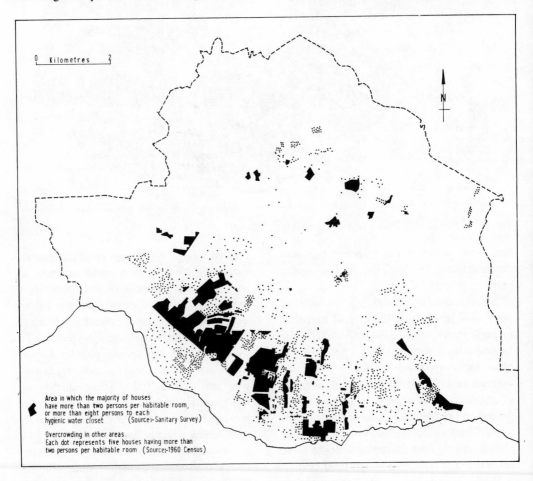

Area in which the majority of houses have more than two persons per habitable room, or more than eight persons to each hygienic water closet   (Source:-Sanitary Survey)

Overcrowding in other areas. Each dot represents five houses having more than two persons per habitable room (Source:-1960 Census)

Fig. 19-5.   KINGSTON 1960: OVERCROWDING

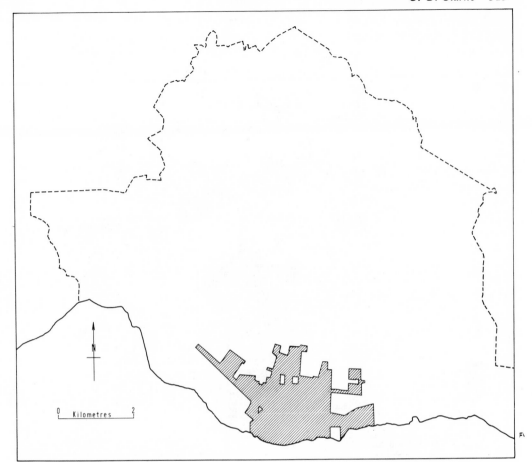

Fig. 19-6. KINGSTON 1960: SEWERED AREAS

also suffer from this condition. This "blanket effect" occurs because most high and low density areas in West Kingston are not served by the public sewage system (Fig. 19-6). The inadequacy or absence of social facilities, such as cess pits, in the sparsely populated parts is simultaneously a product and an index of population pressure.

In 1960 the Central Planning Unit of the Government of Jamaica estimated that 80,-000 people were living in overcrowded conditions in Kingston. Most of them were living in West Kingston or inner East Kingston, many were confined to areas which suffered from unemployment. The number of persons directly affected by both unemployment and

overcrowding is remarkably similar, and suggests that these two phenomena were probably closely connected. Overcrowding, in a socio-economic sense, affected between one-fifth and one-sixth of the inhabitants in 1960, and, further, had involved a similar proportion of the capital's population since the early 1940's.

MATERIAL ADAPTATIONS TO THE
PROBLEM OF OVERCROWDING

An index of socio-economic status for each census enumeration district is presented in Fig. 19-7. Occupational groupings are placed in three major socio-economic categories—(1) professional and supervisory; (2) cler-

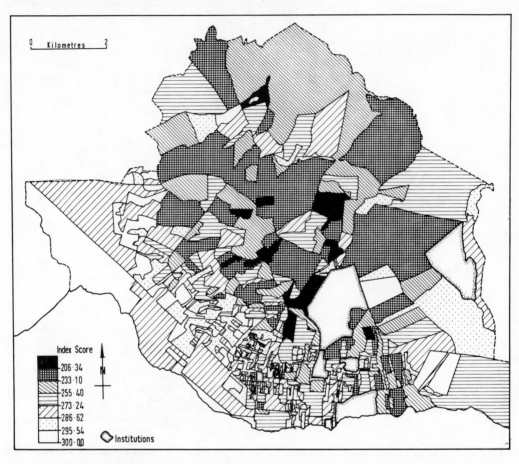

Fig. 19-7.   KINGSTON 1960: SOCIOECONOMIC STATUS

ical, sales, nonprofessional with special training, craft and technical; and (3) manual and service—and the percentage of the working population in each group was calculated for the enumeration districts. The percentages in groups one, two, and three were multiplied, respectively, by the constants 1, 2, and 3, and the result for each enumeration district summed to give an index with limits set theoretically at 100 and 300. Status scores actually ranged between 175 and 300. The greater the proportion of professional and supervisory occupations in an area, the higher its status and the lower its index score. Where manual and service occupations predomi-

nated, the reverse obtained. Areas of low status (index scores 273.24 to 300.00) were confined to West Kingston and to parts of East Kingston, while areas of high status (index scores < 233.10) extended throughout the northern suburbs. Those of median status lay between these two highly polarized social zones. The inverse cartographic correlation between areas of high, medium, and low socio-economic status and similar intensities of unemployment, overcrowding, and population pressure indicated a relationship between low status, unemployment, and inadequate housing which was causal rather than coincidental. Overcrowding was an integral part of the syndrome of poverty circumscribing the lives of most persons of low socio-economic status, especially those living in West Kingston.

It is clear that levels of living in West Kingston were much lower than elsewhere in the city. Population pressure affected even the most elementary human requirements, especially housing, work, and food. The solution to these basic needs was worked out within a subculture developed among persons of the lowest status. This subculture is suitably described by the Jamaican words "cotching" and "scuffling."

Between 1946 and 1959 only 40,000 people were housed in government schemes in the whole of Jamaica (8). Private, speculative building for rental at low rates was virtually nonexistent in Kingston, and high rents were charged even for overcrowded accommodation. Permanently unemployed persons were therefore forced either to "cotch" (to put up for the night as best they could) or, *in extremis,* to adapt to conditions of enduring poverty by becoming squatters. In 1961 the police estimated the squatters at 20,000. They were concentrated on government-owned land in West Kingston, and were located in two main zones, on the fringe of the tenements and on the outskirts of the built-up area of the city (Fig. 19-8). Ironically, even in the former, which dated back to the early

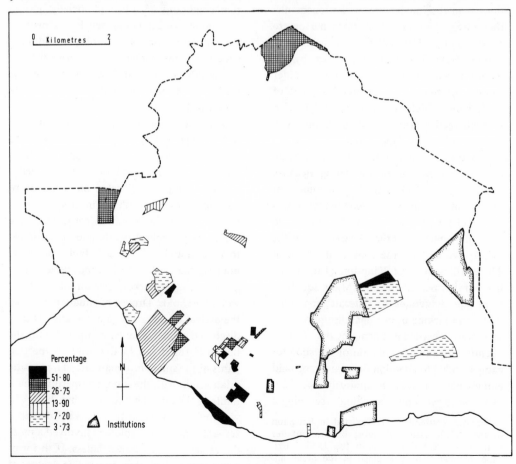

Fig. 19-8. KINGSTON 1960: DISTRIBUTION OF SQUATTERS

1950's[7], densities were lower (125 to 370/ hectare) than in the tenements. However, concentrations of population within squatter camps was out of all proportion to available housing. Dwellings consisted of one-room huts constructed from packing cases and fish barrels, cardboard, and polythene. In an attempt to deter squatters, the government had refused to supply public amenities, and pit latrines, though illegal, had to be dug and water collected from standpipes or stolen from fire hydrants. At the beginning of 1961, approximately 1000 people shared one standpipe in the Boys' Town squatter camp near the Spanish Town Road. In certain respects, however, the squatters enjoyed better conditions than the inhabitants of the tenements; they rarely slept more than three persons to a room and paid no rent for their accommodation. Nevertheless, tenancy was by no means absent from some of the squatter camps, for squatters "captured" a piece of land, built a high stockade around it, and then charged a ground rent to anyone who wanted to build on "their" land.

Squatting was a way of life as well as an expression of extreme overcrowding. Because of the stigma attached to the inhabitants of shanty towns and poorer tenements, it was very difficult for people from these areas to find employment; less than 10 per cent of the factory workers on the Industrial Estate at Three Miles in West Kingston (Fig. 19-1) lived in that part of the city. Many squatters were lapsed literates or illiterate, malnourished, and lacking in personal discipline; and most were regarded as unemployable. Consequently, the adult population of the squatter camps tended to abandon the search for paid employment, at least temporarily (4: 129-36), and to rely upon "scuffling" (scraping a

7. Squatter settlements had existed in Kingston in the 1930's. Although most of the squatter settlements were destroyed in the 1951 hurricane, regeneration took place in the areas adjoining the tenements.

living from pimping and prostitution, begging, stealing, and selling scrap salvaged from the city's dump or "dungle" which was located on the foreshore in West Kingston). The people involved in these activities were, technically speaking, self-employed; but most regarded themselves as unemployed, as did society at large. It is highly probable, therefore, that most who "scuffled" for a living were classified in the census as unemployed. "Scuffling" was an important alternative to paid employment, especially in the areas in which the incidence of full-time or secular unemployment was high. The availability of this alternative, and possibly illegal, system prevented wages from being depressed, so that conditions of full, and socially acceptable, employment could develop. However, while the incidence of unemployment did not necessarily imply idleness, the very existence of "scuffling" provided a socio-economic index of extreme population pressure and overcrowding.

The essence of "cotching" and "scuffling" was summarized by the phrase "living on the dungle." During the 1930's people had literally done so, and even in 1960 one major squatter camp was situated on the seaward edge of the dump in West Kingston. Furthermore, as all the squatter settlements lay within easy reach of the dungle, it continued to act as a major source of salable goods and building materials, and of food discarded by groceries, supermarkets, restaurants, and private households. Droves of squatters awaited the arrival of the garbage carts, and, as they disgorged their contents, competed with the buzzards for them. In this way the participants of the subculture maintained a parasitic relationship with the more prosperous inhabitants of the city. This relationship, however, was indirect, whereas that between domestic servants and their employers involved a more direct dependency. Nevertheless, both forms represented adaptations to varying degrees of

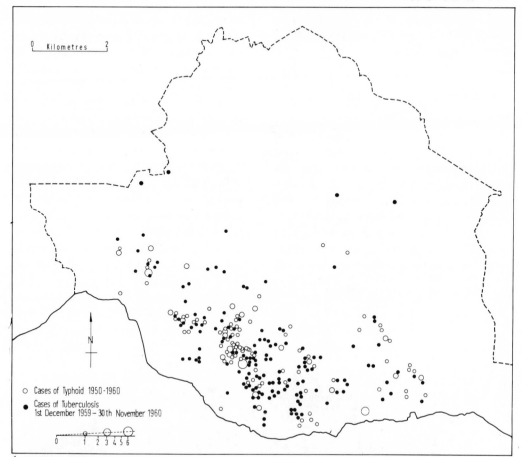

Fig. 19-9. KINGSTON: DISTRIBUTION OF NOTIFIED CASES OF TYPHOID (1950-60) AND TUBERCULOSIS OF THE RESPIRATORY SYSTEM (1959-60)

population pressure. Direct dependency occurred widely and within the norms of society: indirect dependency was localized and operated outside those norms.

The adaptations involving "living on the dungle" were achieved at a very low level of living: indeed, at a level so low that it automatically introduced the problem of disease. However, in one form or another social diseases affected most of the overcrowded sections of the city. Consequently, the squatter camps suffered no more conspicuously in this respect than the tenements and "yards." The two most prevalent social diseases were pulmonary tuberculosis and typhoid, the former

being associated with the overcrowding of rooms, and the latter with inadequate sewage disposal and the contamination of food and drinking water. Figure 19-9 shows the distribution of notified cases of tuberculosis occurring between 1 December 1959 and 30 November 1960, and reported cases of typhoid between 1950 and 1960. Both diseases were closely associated with the overcowded sections of Kingston, and their incidence was particularly high in the west of the city. Moreover, there was a tendency for tuberculosis to be associated with the tenements, for typhoid to be linked to the squatter settlements. This map is an expression of population pressure in Kingston and an indication of the failure of individuals and the community alike to solve this basic problem.

Nonmaterial Adaptations to the Problem of Overcrowding

The conditions of overcrowding and unemployment which occurred so widely in West Kingston are an integral part of Oscar Lewis's "culture of poverty" (5: XXIV). Poverty provides an obvious and natural breeding ground for discontent, particularly when social and geographical distinctions between the "haves" and the "have nots" are as marked as they are in Kingston. The "have nots," on whom the pressure of population really falls, may in some quarters seem ripe for revolutionary activity, either of a Marxist or an indigenous variety. However, the extent to which these protest movements develop, assuming they emerge at all, will depend upon changes in the traditional values which formerly inured the poor to a life circumscribed by poverty. While the growth of the culture of poverty in Kingston is largely due to population pressure and represents a potential powder keg, the powder trail is defined by cultural traditions and values and by competing innovations.

Until the mid-1950's, numerous revivalist cults thrived in West Kingston. They derived

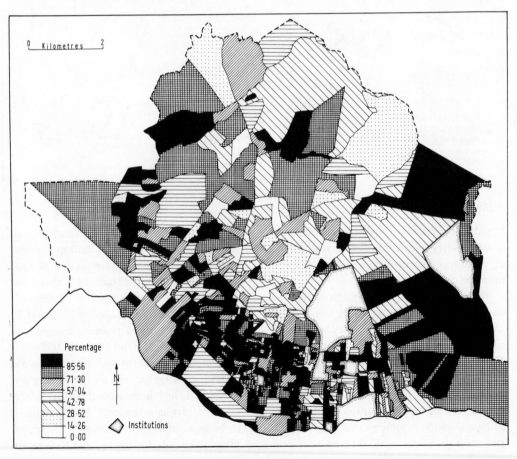

Fig. 19-10. KINGSTON 1960: DISTRIBUTION OF AFRICANS

their theology as much from African traditions surviving from the Negro slave trade as from Protestant Christianity (10: 416-33). Possession by spirits was an essential feature of the religious experience of the cultists; and there is little doubt that this religious movement offered an opportunity for emotional escapism which rendered the daily round of its participants more bearable. During the late 1950's, however, support for the cults waned, and they were partly replaced by the Ras Tafari movement (11: 17-18). This change was highly important, since the revivalists had stressed sublimation, whereas the Ras Tafarians rejected the social system of Jamaica and demanded radical change.

The strength of the Ras Tafari movement lay in the squatter areas, whose economy and material culture already set them aside from society. Nevertheless, the movement possessed a considerable following drawn from all the overcrowded sections of the city. Promulgating a revolutionary social and racial philosophy which argued that Ras Tafari, or Haile Selassie the Emperor of Ethiopia, was the living God, that Ethiopia was the black man's home, and that "repatriation" was the way of redemption for black men, its final premise that the ways of the white men were evil, especially for the black, found immediate support in the overcrowded sections of West Kingston, where the population was overwhelmingly Negro[8] (Fig. 19-10). Squatting and "scuffling" were therefore increasingly viewed in West Kingston as temporary adaptations to population pressure. While the white and colored members of the higher strata of society tended to attribute unemployment, overcrowding, and poverty to the idleness of the Negro, the solution advocated by the Ras Tafari emphasized migration to Africa, and, in the case of the Marxist ele-

ment within the movement, revolution in Jamaica. At the time of writing neither objective has been achieved.

THE ROLE OF MIGRATION

Since 1930 migration from the rural areas has made an important contibution to population growth and unemployment in Kingston. It is by no means clear, however, whether migrants contributed directly or indirectly to the housing problem; nor is it clear why so many people in recent years should have left the rural areas for the overcrowded capital.

In 1960, migrants who had been living in Kingston for less than one year were scattered throughout the suburbs or concentrated in the tenements and "yards," especially in West Kingston[9] (Fig. 19-11). The majority of the newcomers to the high status suburbs were probably domestic servants who lived with the family for whom they worked. Most of those who stayed behind were forced into the overcrowded sections of the city where they augumented population pressure. The relationship between in-migration and squatting, however, was indirect. Few of the squatter camps were even minor reception areas, and some of the largest ones were virtually devoid of newcomers from the rural areas.

There was a marked difference noted between the squatter areas and the tenements when rates of mobility were analyzed, and these helped to explain the role played by different types of migration in the two areas. Comparison of the electoral rolls for July 1960 and July 1961 indicated that the minimum annual rate of turnover for adults in a selected tenment area in West Kingston was 41 per cent, but only 5 per cent at Moonlight City, a new squatter camp on the foreshore. Yet, during the same period the adult

8. In view of the activities of the Ras Tafari, it is ironical that the census has called Negroes "Africans."

9. The migrants were persons born outside Kingston–St. Andrew. No movements between these two parishes have been included, although most of the migration from St. Andrew to Kingston parish came from the rural section.

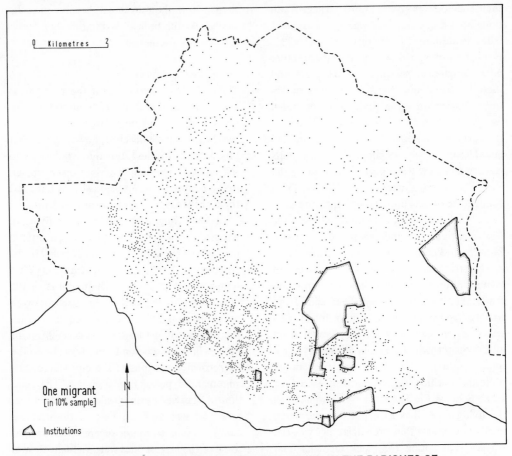

Fig. 19-11. KINGSTON: DISTRIBUTION OF MIGRANTS LIVING IN THE PARISHES OF KINGSTON AND ST. ANDREW FOR LESS THAN ONE YEAR

population of Moonlight City doubled from 54 to 106. The tenements and "yards" acted as the major reception areas for new migrants to the capital; and the population moved from area to area within this overcrowded tract, either because of the breakdown of family structure (14: 163-80), or to escape debts incurred during a period of unemployment. Unsuccessful migrants, however, eventually sank to the squatter slums, where they were joined by persons born in Kingston. In 1960, approximately half the population of the squatter areas was Kingston-born, but its plight was undoubtedly due, in large part, to the dilution of available jobs caused by the arrival of rural migrants. The squatter camps were settling basins for persons descending the social scale, and formed "slums of despair" rather than "slums of hope" from which newcomers might have ascended. Government policy of not supplying basic amenities in the squatter settlements, thereby inducing population pressure, clearly provided no deterrent to the migrants. However, these conditions did give added impetus to the Ras Tafari movement.

Migration to Kingston was the result of very real "push" factors and largely illusory "pull" factors. The most important "push" factor was population pressure, the rural symptoms of which were unemployment, shortage of land, and declining soil fertility. These conditions were well exemplified around Christiana in the center of Jamaica, where the dissected ridges of shale and conglomerate rise above 600 m, and densities of population reach 250 persons/km²—almost double the national average. However, shortage of land was related to the pattern of land ownership as well as to population distribution and growth, for more than 45 per cent of the island was owned by 900 individual proprietors or companies. Hoarding of land and shortage of land existed side by side, as they had done since the emancipation of the slaves, the former ensuring the latter. As a result of this induced population pressure few small farmers could purchase or rent sufficient land for themselves and their dependents without seeking additional employment for wages. In many instances this problem was compounded by seasonal unemployment in the sugar industry. Moreover, wages paid to casual agricultural labor were frequently pitched so low as to be virtually unacceptable. In 1955, 62 per cent of the males and 32 per cent of the females in rural Jamaica were looking for work (12: 55). These figures provide an index of population pressure and a measure of the potential reservoir of migrants.

A further stimulus to migration was provided by the values and aspirations of boys and girls in rural Jamaica. They rejected the socially stigmatized agricultural pursuits of their parents, usually with their encouragement, and aspired to predominantly urban professional, white collar, or technical jobs (13: 338). While the social amenities of the capital city clearly operated as "pull" factors, Kingston proved particularly attractive to migrants because it was believed that opportunities for these types of employment were greater there than elsewhere in the island. Since the failures rarely returned home, the myth of the "city of opportunity" was maintained. Migration to the capital therefore became the geographical expression of a conscious attempt on the part of the Negro to escape from the poverty and isolation of rural Jamaica: there was no aimless "drift to the towns." The rapid growth of Kingston's population was partly the product of population pressure in rural areas, and was, by 1962, one of the major problems facing the country as it achieved its independence.

PERCEPTION OF THE PROBLEM AND ACTION TAKEN

More than a quarter of a century has passed since the West India Royal Commission observed that: "Behind the various social and economic defects . . . the rapid increase in the population is to be found sometimes as a cause and almost always as an aggravating factor" (17: 242). However, very little has been done subsequently to publicize family planning in Jamaica. This failure was due to a combination of factors; the alleged difficulty of dealing with persons of low status among whom illegitimacy is the norm; pressure from the Roman Catholic minority (3: 107); fear that birth control would be regarded as an infringement of personal liberty, and that the political opposition would use this argument against a government advocating the use of contraception; and knowledge that even discussion of family limitation would be greeted by a spate of wall slogans in West Kingston stating that "birth control is aimed at wiping out the black man." In view of these difficulties, the government turned its attention to the other side of the population-resource ratio and embarked upon schemes for economic development in which industrialization was to play an important role (1: 173-175).

In 1952, an Industrial Development Corporation was established in Kingston to "stimulate, facilitate and undertake the development of industry." An attempt was made to offset the deficiency in industrial raw materials and power resources by a variety of tax incentives designed to attract both local and overseas investors. The real object of this scheme was revealed in the first annual report of the Corporation which disclosed that "Its origins lay in the growing awareness of the very serious problem presented by the pressure of population on existing resources." Industrialization was therefore to provide employment for the growing population, and not specifically to produce more wealth; the emphasis was placed upon social efficiency and not upon economic considerations.

The I.D.C. was responsible for the establishment of 58 firms, mostly in Kingston, between 1952 and 1960; all received tax concessions. These firms employed 3450 people in 1960, and approximately 450 jobs were created every year. Assuming, as the I.D.C. does, a multiplier effect of two, the total number of jobs created in all sectors of the economy cannot have exceeded 900 per annum. Over a period of ten years less than 10,000 jobs were created in this way, although this was the minimum number required each year. Since firms associated with the I.D.C. provided 3400 new jobs out of the 9000 added in all factories in Kingston between 1949 and 1960, or more than half the factory employment since 1952, the conclusion reached by W. D. Voelker in 1961 is particularly significant: "Assuming Jamaican I.D.C. plant employment grows as rapidly as in Puerto Rico, there will be about 40,000 people employed in Jamaica in ten years—but in Jamaica, about 400,000 more people will have been born" (16: 28). There is therefore no sign that manufacturing industry will be able to create sufficient new jobs in Kingston in the near future, eradicating unemployment and creating a stable basis for the development of the higher standard of living to which the poorest elements in the population increasingly aspire.

As long as it proved impossible to reduce the rate of natural increase, it was likewise impossible to limit Kingston's population growth, or to reduce it as Orde Browne had envisaged. In 1960, ideas about the growth of the capital tended to be divided along urban-rural lines. Agricultural experts insisted that the towns, and especially the capital, would have to absorb the surplus population, while urban planners hoped that rural migration could be slowed down. Despite extensive schemes for soil conservation and agricultural development, including the establishment in 1964 of a commission with powers of compulsory acquisition over land deemed underused, there seems little likelihood that the rural population of Jamaica can be stabilized in the near future.

Undoubtedly the main safety valve for population pressure has been provided by emigration to Britain. This, however, has been a personal and not a government-inspired solution. Between 1953 and 1961 the number of emigrants increased from 2000 to 39,000 per annum. Probably 70 to 80 per cent were inhabitants of the rural areas, and many of the migrants from Kingston were drawn from the ranks of privileged, unionized labor. The slum dwellers of Kingston were excluded from this movement which involved artisans, sugar factory workers, tractor drivers, members of the landowning peasantry, and their dependents. Two patterns of mobility emerged. The "landless peasantry" migrated to the capital, where most of them were confined to the slums of West Kingston, and dreamed of returning to Africa; the more prosperous folk, who had greater ability if less necessity to move, emigrated to Britain. Both patterns involve a transfer of population pressure and its accompanying problems, but through emigration Jamaica has lost some of its most highly qualified personnel.

Conclusion

The pressure of population in Kingston is increasing because population growth is self-generating whereas the economy is not; migration to Kingston is completely unrelated to the opportunities for employment. Unemployment was extensive in 1960, in spite of the efforts of the government, through the I.D.C., to create factory jobs. Consequently, the economy of the city had to support at least 60,000 too many people, most of whom lived in poor and overcrowded accommodation. Because of the failure to keep the rural-born population in the country, migration has carried many of the worst symptoms and problems of population pressure to Kingston. The disillusionment and frustration experienced by young migrants who fail to find employment is a major social problem only aggravated by the fact that many of them are forced to "cotch" in West Kingston, where they encounter worse conditions than in the rural areas. These migrants are potential recruits to the cult of Ras Tafari and other protest movements.

In theoretical terms the symptoms of overcrowding were not the inevitable result of population growth. Unemployment might have been reduced by a program of public works, while squatting and overcrowding might have been eased by public rehousing schemes. However, the short-term solution to these problems would have depended upon government action, and upon the diversion of considerable development funds into the least productive sectors. Consequently, even if these symptoms had been removed, overcrowding, or the effect of population increase, would still have been detectable on the country's financial balance sheet. In the long term, the fundamental problems are those of integrating the racial groups, and of balancing social and economic priorities, urban and rural population, internal and external migration, and people's aspirations and the educational and economic opportunities for achieving them. However, it seems that balance between these factors will rarely be attained. It will certainly prove extremely difficult to lower the expectations of all social groups to levels consistent with the resources of the island, and to instill in the minds of the people the idea that there is dignity in manual labor, both agricultural and other—that without it very little can be achieved for their society. Although such manipulation of expectations and values runs counter to the ideas of the government, it may be necessary because of population increase to reallocate resources, especially land, and to harmonize the various levels of living which typify Jamaican society. But, given the cultural complexity of the population, it will be extremely difficult to reallocate resources through consensus, though in theory there is considerable scope for doing so.

The question of future population growth in Kingston is critical. A recent projection made by the Central Planning Unit indicates that the city's population will increase by 184,500 between 1960 and 1970[10]. With emigration to Britain now reduced to less than 10,000 persons per annum, most of them dependents of previous migrants, the figure will probably be higher. The cost of housing this increase and rehousing the 80,000 already living in slum conditions was estimated in 1961 as £50 million, a sum almost equal to the national budget in that year. For political reasons it is unlikely that the government will be able to avoid investing in massive schemes for social improvement and urban renewal (2: 416), although it has the discomforting knowledge that such a development will attract more migrants.

10. A similar estimate has been published (9: 441).

Moreover, schemes for rehousing will probably be opposed by the upper strata of the society.

Under these circumstances it is hardly surprising that since 1964 the government has at last shown signs of aiming at the root of the problem and has embarked upon a family planning program. It is hoped to cut the birth rate from 39.9 per mille to a figure nearer the North American average of 21.2 per mille. According to the Minister of Health, the aim of the program is

> . . . to ensure that the people of Jamaica will be able to bring up their families so that their own and their children's future will not be blighted because of the sheer impossibility of finding the money to provide food and the means of taking care of their health, education and social needs.

Unfortunately, the receptivity of the people for whom this scheme is intended is still in doubt (15: 290-1). Furthermore, even if the program is successful,[11] full benefits cannot be expected for another generation, by which time the human-resource relationship may be no better than it is now, if not worse. It is highly probable, therefore, that population pressure will continue to aggravate the other social, economic, racial, and cultural problems which remain unresolved. Indeed, a solution to the population problem is unlikely without improvements in these other spheres too.

11. The independent members of the Standing Advisory Committee on Family Planning in Jamaica have recently suggested that the £3,-000 budget allocated to the scheme is inadequate "to handle the serious problem of population explosion."

REFERENCES

(1) C. G. Clarke: Population Pressure in Kingston, Jamaica: A Study of Unemployment and Overcrowding, *Transactions of the Institute of British Geographers,* Vol. 38, 1966, pp. 165-82.

(2) C. G. Clarke: Problemas de Planeación Urbana en Kingston, Jamaica, in: Union Geográfica Internacional Conferencia Regional Latino Americana, Vol. 1 (Mexico, 1966), pp. 411-31.

(3) E. Gordon Ericksen: The West Indies Population Problem (Lawrence, University of Kansas Publications, 1962).

(4) E. E. Hoyt: Voluntary Unemployment and Unemployability in Jamaica, *British Journal of Sociology,* Vol. 11, 1960, pp. 120-36.

(5) Oscar Lewis: The Children of Sanchez (London, 1961).

(6) W. F. Maunder: Employment in an Underdeveloped Area, A Sample Survey of Kingston, Jamaica (New Haven, 1960).

(7) G. St. J. Orde Browne: Labour Conditions in the West Indies (H.M.S.O. London, 1939).

(8) Report of the Department of Housing (unpublished, Kingston, 1961).

(9) G. W. Roberts: Provisional Assessment of Growth of the Kingston–St. Andrew Area, 1960-1970, *Social and Economic Studies,* Vol. 12, 1963, pp. 432-41.

(10) G. E. Simpson: Jamaican Revivalist Cults, *Social and Economic Studies,* Vol. 5, 1956, pp. 321-442.

(11) M. G. Smith, Roy Augier, and Rex Nettleford: The Ras Tafari Movement in Kingston, Jamaica (Institute of Social and Economic Research, University College of the West Indies, 1960).

(12) M. G. Smith: A Report on Labour Supply in Rural Jamaica (Kingston, 1956).

(13) M. G. Smith: Education and Occupational Choice in Rural Jamaica, *Social and Economic Studies,* Vol. 9, 1960, pp. 332-54.

(14) M. G. Smith: West Indian Family Structure (Washington, 1962).

(15) J. Mayone Stycos and Kurt W. Back: The Control of Human Fertility in Jamaica (Cornell, 1964).

(16) W. D. Voelker, Survey of Industry in the West Indies (Institute of Social and Economic Research, University College of the West Indies, 1961).

(17) West India Royal Commission Report (H.M.S.O. London, 1945).

PART TWO

REGIONAL PROBLEMS

AFRICA: INTRODUCTION

Until very recent times, the continent of Africa has figured little in discussions of population pressures upon resources. Compared with South Asia, and parts of East Asia and Latin America, it has produced no problems that might be judged on a subcontinental scale. Populations in Africa have experienced some of the demographic changes that have occurred elsewhere in the developing world, but they have tended to be less intense. Mortality rates have been reduced, but as compared with almost any other part of the contemporary world they still remain relatively high in many parts of the continent. Malaria is endemic throughout most of tropical Africa, and there are still high rates of incidence in some of the subtropical areas. Measures to eradicate the disease, or at least to reduce its incidence, have so far achieved only limited success and it continues to be a major factor affecting mortality rates. Yet these circumstances are not accepted complacently, and national and international agencies are working actively throughout the continent to change them. The impact of public health measures on population growth, is now being felt in many areas.

Projections of growth made by the U.N. suggest that by the end of the century Africa will have the highest rates of population increase in the world. If this is correct, then there is the distinct likelihood that population-resource problems will expand and increase in intensity. The papers in this section, and those in other parts of the volume which relate to Africa (*Mabogunje, Porter*), indicate that such magnification of problems already exists in some areas. There is no justification for complacency about population-resource relationships in the short term for particular parts of Africa, and in the longer term for larger areas throughout the continent. Pressures developing from population growth may be intensified through rising levels of expectation, related to levels of education and experience (*Mabogunje*).

Porter draws attention to relatively rapid changes initiated in the colonial era during the first half of the twentieth century, which have interfered with the slow and sustained evolution of agricultural systems. The results have been seen in "erratic and volatile responses in land use." These circumstances, together with increasing rates of population growth, have made difficult the kind of population-resource developments as postulated in the model suggested by *Mrs. Boserup*. That such development can occur is evidenced by the Kano close-settled zone in northern Nigeria (*Mortimore*), which expanded in an environment of little apparent potential but one in which there has been stability under a relatively well-organized socio-political system, and the stimuli of long-established trade and culture contacts and close rural-urban relationships. The agricultural system around Kano, which *Mortimore* shows to have a number of variants, has not only been able to meet many of the needs of the rural population, which has densities among the highest in tropical Africa, but has been able during the last fifty years to accommodate the large scale production of an export crop. *Mortimore* cautions that the Kano model should not be applied indiscriminately elsewhere; but it undoubtedly has features which are suggestive for development in other parts of Africa and the developing world.

Population-resource relationships in Egypt are in many respects specific (*Rościszewski*). A highly circumscribed physical environment favorable for human occupation has given rise over millennia to concentrations of rural population which produce the highest densities in Africa and among the highest in the world. Resources are being severely strained by the very high rates of population increase that have developed only during this century, and which are probably higher than any other country on the continent. Egypt has made much more than limited efforts in the face of these increases; changes in the system of government in the last two decades has been reflected in economic and social developments of a revolutionary nature. But it is still too early to judge fully their effect and barriers to the solution of many problems still exist. *Rościszewski* points out that these barriers may be environmental, demographic, or institutional. Though they may be separately identified, and individually studied, they are likely to be surmounted only by a full appreciation of their interrelatedness.

While the pressures upon resources are manifested in Egypt in terms of high densities of population, we need not emphasize that pressures may occur where densities over-all are low. This is the case in Zambia, where pressures may be identified in both rural and urban areas (*Kay*). This country has been the scene of many attempts to assess those critical densities that can be supported in different environments by different agricultural systems, with neither the environment nor the system suffering deterioration. *Kay* argues the need for greater totality in approach to population-resource relationships, stressing that a "population" makes a much wider range of demands on the environment than does agriculture alone (see Section 2, Introduction). He also draws attention to the possible conflicts that may arise from the good intentions of government to promote social progress in the short term by bringing resources to the people, and the long-term need to adjust rationally the distribution of population to significant physical and social resources. That such conflict may arise further emphasizes the need for comprehensive and integrated approaches in planning.

To plan in this way, with the prospect of successful results, requires a knowledge and understanding of the basic situations. All too frequently, planning is undertaken without sufficient of this knowledge. *J. I. Clarke* presents an important over-all view of the facts of the population-resource relationships of Cameroon, a large and diverse country. Clarke's study disposes effectively of any false ideas that may be entertained about uniform conditions existing over large areas, and further, it illustrates the physical and human diversity which may occur within one national unit. It is an excellent example of a national inventory, in which a wide range of related facts is presented in order to highlight basic problems. Similar inventories should exist for other countries in Africa and the developing world.

The Cameroon study is based upon data *readily available in the country,* and analyzed effectively on the basis of sound field experience. Because of inadequate records and a lack of interdisciplinary communication, it is frequently assumed that each new study of population-resource relationships, or of any other development problem, must start from the grass roots with a collection of data *ab initio.* It is a fact that African countries (and presumably others) are deluged with so-called "experts" asking questions that have been answered many times before. The multiplication of effort is wasteful for the inquirer and may be infuriating for those questioned. Very little effort has been put into *getting to know what is already known,* and making this information readily available. If more time and money were devoted to interpreting the store of existing knowledge, there would be fewer complaints about the paucity of data and information about the developing world. The Cameroon study indicates what can be accomplished unofficially with very limited resources. Given only modest support, and access to modern methods of data and information storage, future studies might well achieve much more.

20. POPULATION GROWTH AND ECONOMIC DEVELOPMENT IN EGYPT

Marcin Rościszewski

Egypt, like many other countries of the Third World, is now experiencing "population pressure." But there is no other country in the world where the whole population has to live on such a limited area of utilized land. The "environmental barrier" determines the ceiling for the technical possibilities of expanding arable land. A doubling of the present small amount of arable land (unattainable in any case at present) would not bring about any essential improvement and would not solve problems of overpopulation. The economic development of Egypt is also limited by the "population barrier," which is expressed by the high rate of natural increase, about 3 per cent per annum in the mid-1960's. This means that each year there are more than 800,000 additional persons who must be fed and clothed. Resources are modest: the country is not rich in raw materials, although great hopes are now being placed on the recent discovery of natural oil in the Libyan Desert; and in spite of considerable progress made in industry and agriculture, it is insufficient to solve the problem of full employment. Thus, Egypt is making particular efforts to take maximum advantage of its limited resources and to look for new solutions in the field of social and economic organization.

Population Growth and Rate of Natural Increase

During the 160 years fom 1800 to 1960, the population of Egypt increased from some 2.5 million to 26.1 million (20). In the period between the last two population censuses (1947-1960), the average annual rate of

TABLE 20-1   EGYPT. POPULATION, 1960-1965

Year	Population (thousands)	Population Growth (thousands)	Annual Increase %
1960	25,832	–	–
1961	26,557	725	2.807
1962	27,244	687	2.587
1963	27,968	724	2.657
1964	28,758	790	2.825
1965	29,620	862	2.997

Source: *Statistical Handbook, U.A.R.*, (Cairo 1966).

natural increase was 2.4 per cent. Table 20-1 shows population growth 1960-65. The rapid rate of natural increase (which in Egypt is at the same time actual increase since emigration and immigration are of marginal importance) may be explained first by the existing age structure of the population. The 1960 census showed that 45.8 per cent were under 16 years; 49.9 were in the group 16-65, and 4.3 were over 65 (3). A decided drop has occurred in the rate of infant mortality, with the development of mother and child care, popularization of hygiene, campaigns to build wells in each village to provide pure drinking water, and the increase in caloric intake per capita from 2360 daily in 1950 to 2930 in 1965, has been significant (14).

Migration within the Country

Two basic trends can be distinguished in internal migrations: movement from the Nile valley toward the Delta, and from the countryside to towns.

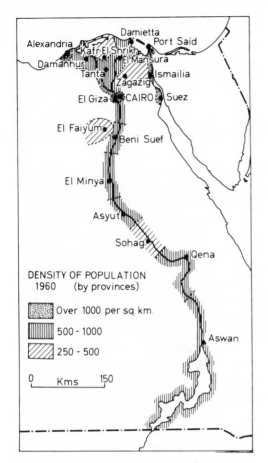

Fig. 20-1. EGYPT: DENSITY OF POPULATION IN 1960 (BY PROVINCES)

MIGRATION TO THE DELTA

Overcrowding in Upper Egypt has been responsible for both seasonal and permanent migration northward to the Nile Delta (21). While there are still possibilities of expanding irrigated areas in the Delta, the extension of arable land in the Delta would be impossible without expensive and power-consuming installations to pump water to higher levels. As a result the amount of arable land per capita in the Valley is only 0.176 hectares, compared with 0.248 in the Delta (excluding the population of Cairo and Alexandria). Apart from this, all the larger cities and the majority of industrial

development are concentrated in the Delta and in its vicinity. In the Valley, the gross per capita income derived from agriculture around 1960 amounted to $145 as compared with $210 in the Delta (29).

MIGRATION TO TOWNS

Urbanization is increasing in Egypt as a result of not only economic factors but social and political ones as well. Differences in living standards between town and countryside, the overpopulation in rural areas, the burden of agricultural work, the potential or actual possibility of urban employment, and the chances for social advance are all factors of great importance in stimulating the drive to towns.

Unfortunately, there is no definite criterion for determining urban population in Egypt (21). The automatic classification as "urban" of every center of local administration is obviously a quite inadequate method. Because of this, urban and rural population figures should be evaluated with caution, all the more so as administrative boundaries of towns often change. But it must be emphasized that the process of urbanization is gaining strength. From 1947 to 1963 the percentage of rural population dropped from about 75 to 62. In 1960 the number of rural dwellers was about 16 million; about 10 million lived in cities and towns. The urban growth rate amounted to 3.8 per cent compared with the national figure of 2.4 (3).

One reason for urban growth is undoubtedly the difference between incomes in town and countryside. For example, while the average per capita income was $200 in urban areas in 1958, it was only $48 in rural areas (42), and it does not seem that there have been any radical changes in rural living standards since then, despite economic and social developments. Assuming the average per capita income increased by 18.8 per cent (from $140 to $168 in the period 1960-65), the major part of this growth was in towns and in nonagricultural trades (8). Significant differences also exist within the rural society. Landless people and peasants owning farms smaller than one *feddan* (about 0.4 hectare) comprise nearly 80 per cent of the rural population, but receive less than 20 per cent of the total income of rural areas (32). The surplus population, estimated at about 10 million persons (20), is finding an outlet in urban areas. This has serious economic implications. Rural unemployment may be eased, but most of those who migrate are young people—meaning that the most active group of population is leaving agriculture. In addition, the mass movement to towns is the cause of considerable economic and social tension. The growth in the number of jobless people, those without a definite occupation, and part-time workers, exerts pressure on the labor market, lowering the incomes of those already employed.

Urban Population and Urbanization Processes

Intensity of urbanization is not the monopoly of Egypt. It is occurring in most of the countries of the Third World, and in highly developed nations as well. In the latter it results from and is motivated by the development of the economy as a whole. Indeed, sometimes urbanization is deliberately encouraged. But in the developing countries growth of urban population is not justified by the demand for manpower and is not in proportion to the rate of industrialization. "People attract people," and this is the reason for the "demonstration effect" exerted by a town, particularly a big city. People who cannot find employment in production look for jobs of a more or less parasitic character, thus creating the so-called overpopulation in services. The larger the city the greater the possibility of finding occupations of this kind.

The growth of Egypt's urban population is shown by the following data: In 1897 there were not quite 1,900,000 urban inhabitants—about 19 per cent of the total population. In 1960 there were 8,400,000, or 32 per cent of the total; by 1963 this percentage had risen to 38. The intensity of urbanization is shown in Table 20-2.

In the period 1897-1960, urban population increased almost 2.5 times more quickly than the total population. The growth was greatest in the region of the Suez Canal and in Cairo, which was above the national average. At present 40 per cent of Egypt's urban population lives in Cairo, and 56 per cent in Cairo and Alexandria taken together. In 1897 these two towns accounted for only 9.5 per cent of the total population, in 1960 the figure was 20.1 per cent. The share of all towns, with the exception of Cairo and Alexandria, in total urban population has

TABLE 20-2   EGYPT. URBAN POPULATION, 1897 AND 1960

Population (thousands)	1897 No.	1897 %	1960 No.	1960 %	% Growth 1897-1960
Population of Egypt—total	9,729	—	26,060	—	167.8
Urban population—total	1,861	100.0	9,373	100.0	403.6
Population of Cairo	612	32.9	3,723	39.8	509.8
Population of Alexandria	316	16.9	1,513	16.2	378.8
Other towns with a population above 200,000	66	3.5	723	7.7	993.6
Remaining towns	867	46.7	3,405	36.3	395.6

(Sources: 4; 42; 43)

dropped, indicating that the term "over-urbanization" cannot be applied to Egypt, but that the problem of "overconcentration" in a few cities is becoming more and more acute.

UTILIZATION OF MANPOWER IN TOWNS

The lack of detailed data concerning the urban population has made it necessary to base a calculation on approximate estimates, which give only a general idea of the basic range of values. Assuming that in 1965 about 40 per cent of the population lived in towns (12 million persons) and that about 50 per cent belonged to the working age group (49.9 per cent in 1960), it can be estimated that the total work force numbers about six million. This figure is probably too low, since migration to towns mostly involves young people, and since children work too.

An analysis of the growth in employment during the five-year plan (1960-65) supplies some interesting information concerning relative shifts of labor as between agriculture and manufacturing. Labor distribution by commodity sectors is shown in Table 20-3.

TABLE 20-3   EGYPT. DISTRIBUTION OF LABOR FORCE BY ECONOMIC SECTOR

Productive Sectors of the Economy	Labour in 1965 (%)	Increase (1959/60-1964/65) (%)
Total labour	100.0	22.1
All commodity sectors	67.7	22.8
Commodity sectors (excluding agriculture)	16.2	48.7
Industry only	11.2	37.1

supposed that no more than 20 per cent of the urban population is employed in production. But it should be emphasized that the rate of growth of employment was rela-

Assuming that these activities are in the main limited to urban centers, it may be tively high in these sectors.

In the service sectors the degree of urban concentration is rather lower, even though the towns claim a major share of the national total (Table 20-4). Total employment

TABLE 20-4.   EGYPT. DISTRIBUTION OF LABOR FORCE BY SERVICE SECTOR OF THE ECONOMY

Service Sectors of the Economy	Labour in 1965 (%)	Increase 1959/60-1964/65 (%)
Total labour	100.0	22.1
All service sectors	32.3	20.5
Transport and communications	3.8	27.0
Finance and trade	10.0	14.8
Housing	0.3	31.3
Public utilities	0.4	20.2
Other services	17.8	22.5

was 2,365,200 persons in 1965, with about 60 per cent, or 1,400,000, living in towns. Thus, about 2,500,000 urban dwellers were employed in the service and production sectors together—only 4 per cent of the urban population and about 17 per cent of the country's active population. This shows that there is great unemployment in towns, which is only intensified by the so-called overpopulation in services.

URBAN POPULATION AND ITS
SOCIAL STRATIFICATION

In the study of cities of the Third World, an analysis of social structure is very important. The pattern of urban employment, with large groups of nonworking and unproductively employed people, is especially significant, because in this respect Third World cities differ basically from those of developed countries.

TABLE 20-5   EGYPT. OCCUPATIONAL STRUCTURE OF THE
URBAN POPULATION

Occupational Groups in Urban Population	Urban Population Total (thousands)	%	Employed Population (thousands)	%	Income Total (million U.S. $)	%
1. Without definite occupation	2,983	37.3	—	—	—	—
2. Domestic servants	934	11.7	400	20.3	56	3.4
3. Manual workers without permanent job	186	2.3	80	4.1	14*	0.9
4. Workers employed in handicrafts	400	5.0	170	8.6	45	2.7
5. Workers employed in modern industry and transport	790	9.9	341	17.3	130	8.2
6. Junior office workers, trade and services	1,117	13.9	480	24.5	330	20.1
7. Owners of handicraft workshops	736	9.2	230	11.7	263	16.0
8. Middle class (office workers, professions with lower earnings)	614	7.7	192	9.7	232	14.1
9. Higher officials, upper middle class, aristocracy	240	3.3	75	3.8	568	34.6
	8,000	100.0	1968	100.0	1638	100.0

(Source : 42)

Table 20-5 presents a detailed social and occupational stratification of the urban population in Egypt in 1958.

People without a definite trade accounted for 37 per cent of the urban dwellers (49 per cent if domestic servants are included). The table does not show the percentage in this group of new arrivals from the countryside, but a survey conducted in 1961 in Cairo demonstrated that only 53 per cent of the population was born in the city, that 98 per cent of the newcomers came from the countryside, and that 94 per cent were under 45 years of age. The majority of the migrants had no definite skill or they were domestic servants. These people constitute the base of the parasitic occupations mentioned earlier. Those in effective employment included only 24 per cent of city dwellers, of whom 60 per cent were men (1.5 million out of a total of 2.5 million) over 15 years, and 7 per cent (200,000) children of both sexes under 15

years. The high index of unemployment among women is explained by the traditions of Muslim society. Worthy of note is the high percentage of domestic servants and lower administrative staff in trade and services. Contrary to this, workers employed in the modern sections of industry and transport account for only 17.6 per cent of the effectively employed (4.3 per cent of urban population and 1.3 of the total population).

The table also reflects clearly the concentration of incomes. Less than 4 per cent of the effectively employed accumulated about 35 per cent of the total income, while the first four groups, which constitute 50.3 per cent of the total earned only 15.2 per cent of all income. The degree of concentration has probably decreased somewhat since the inquiry was conducted (9), a result of social legislation and profit-sharing in industry introduced after the 1952 revolution. Nevertheless, it cannot be expected that these changes had much bearing on the incomes of the masses (9).

DEVELOPMENT OF INDUSTRY AND SERVICES
It is clear that the problem of nonutilized redundant manpower is particularly acute in Egyptian towns. So far the problem has not

TABLE 20-6   EGYPT. NATIONAL INCOME BY COMMODITY SECTOR

Commodity Sectors	National Income in 1965 (%)	Increase in National Income 1959/60- 1964/65 (%)
Total National Income	100.0	46.6
All sectors	56.7	48.6
Sectors without agriculture	28.6	68.9
Industry	22.4	65.2

(Source : 43)

been solved, despite the development of commodity sectors (excluding agriculture), above all industry. The development of these sectors in the last five-year plan, based on the synthetic index of shares in the creation of the national income, is shown in Tables 20-6 and 20-7.

TABLE 20-7   EGYPT. NATIONAL INCOME BY SERVICE SECTOR

Service Sectors	National Income in 1965 (%)	(%) Increase in National Income 1959/60- 1964/65
Total National Income	100.0	46.6
All service sectors	43.3	44.0
Transport and communications	9.2	86.7
Finance and trade	9.0	30.0
Housing	4.2	8.3
Public utilities	0.4	25.0
Other services	20.5	46.1

(Source : 43)

It should also be noted that there have been essential changes in the spatial development of industry throughout the country. They are evidence of the transformations taking place in the economy, particularly of the tendency toward a more even development of production potential, which will certainly influence the social structure of the country. The changes taking place in the distribution of industry are shown in Table 20-8.

The appearance of rapid development in

TABLE 20.8   EGYPT. LABOR DISTRIBUTION AND INCOME, BY REGION, 1952-1964

	Labour (%) 1952	Labour (%) 1964	Net Income (%) 1952	Net Income (%) 1964	Increase in Labour 1952-1964 (%)	Increase in Industry's Net Income 1952-1964 (%)
Egypt	100.0	100.0	100.0	100.0	63.0	328.2
Urban Governorates	54.5	51.6	55.1	49.7	54.4	286.8
Lower Egypt	33.4	33.2	26.8	21.8	61.9	248.5
Upper Egypt	12.1	15.2	18.1	28.5	104.4	571.9

Upper Egypt may be partly explained by the low level from which it started; nevertheless the influence of projects such as the Aswan High Dam and newly established industries in the valley of the Nile can already be seen. The figures in Table 20-8 show, however, that there is a strong (if not excessive) concentration of industry in the urban "governorates" (mainly Cairo and Alexandria, the region of the Suez Canal, and the Nile Delta). But it can be expected that there will be a relative decrease in the share of industry accounted for by these regions to the advantage of the Nile Valley, and that migration to the north will be checked to a certain degree because of the attraction of local urban centers.

Yet it does not seem probable that even the most intense development of industry will be able to solve the problem of existing unemployment in Egypt. In the years up to 1960 the growth of labor forces alone exceeded half a million annually (9), while the growth in all employment (including agriculture) during the five-year-plan period was no more than 1,500,000. Thus, although the need for industrialization should be stressed, even greater emphasis should be placed on the development of agriculture.

Transformations in Agriculture

THE PLACE OF AGRICULTURE IN THE ECONOMY
The following basic data depict the part played by agriculture in the economy of Egypt:

—rural population constitutes the majority of the population; about 60 per cent live in the countryside, and about 52 per cent earn their living in agriculture, according to 1965 estimates;

—agriculture provides a major part of the national income (43); in the year 1964-65 the share of agriculture was 28.0 per cent, and that of industry was 22.4 per cent

(note should be taken of the rapid growth of industry's share, which only amounted to 16.9 per cent in the year 1954-55);

—agriculture is predominant in the export structure (43); agricultural products accounted for about 86 per cent of the total export value in 1965, of which about 50 per cent was contributed by cotton.

THE "ENVIRONMENTAL BARRIER"
Most of Egypt lies within the desert, where annual rainfall is much below 200 mm. The life of the country is primarily concentrated in the Nile Valley and Delta, the zone of the Suez Canal, the oases of the Western Desert, and along the narrow strip of the Mediterranean coastal zone, where rainfall is more abundant.

Population/km² (1965)		
In relation to the total area of the country	In relation to the cultivated area	In relation to the area under crops
30	1,200	700

The main inhabited areas are the Nile Valley and Delta which, together with the Suez Canal zone and the Western oases account for 35,000 km²: only 3.5 per cent of the total area of the country. The semi-arid Mediterranean coast and parts of the Sinai Peninsula account for 1.5 per cent; the rest is uninhabited desert. The inhabited area of the Valley and Delta covers about 34,000 km², and contains some 25,000 km² of agricultural land.

Further expansion of the agricultural area will require major financial outlays for expansion of the irrigation system, because all the land that could be reclaimed through relatively inexpensive methods has already been utilized. The Aswan High Dam (33: 38), an example of the biggest investment of this kind, will make possible an increase of

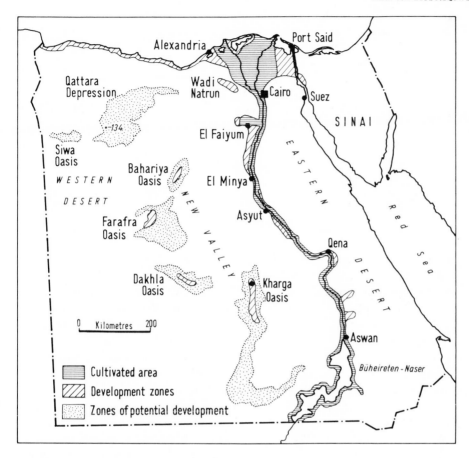

Fig. 20-2.   EGYPT: CULTIVATED AREAS AND DEVELOPMENT ZONES

the agricultural area by about 40 per cent. Still, it is not enough to solve the essential problems arising from limited land resources. What is more, advantages gained will be neutralized by the current population increase. These problems are best depicted by patterns of population distribution.

In 1965, the overall density was 30/km². But densities in inhabited and cultivated areas were about 400 times greater (Table 20-9). Apart from this, it should be borne in mind that favorable climatic conditions allow several harvests each year. The present coefficient of the utilization of arable land is 1.75, which means that the area of every

harvest amounts to about 10 million *feddans*.

What, then, are the prospects for development of Egyptian agriculture and the pos-

TABLE 20-9   EGYPT. PROJECTED RATIO OF
POPULATION TO CULTIVATED LAND,
1965-2000

	1956	*1980*	*1990*	*2000*
Population density/km² of cultivated land	1,200	1,324	1,696	2,143
Hectares per capita	0,083	0,076	0,059	0,047

TABLE 20-10   EGYPT. NUMBER AND AREA OF FARMS BY FARM SIZE, 1952-1965

| | 1952 | | | | 1965 | | | |
| | Farms | | Area | | Farms | | Area | |
	No. (thousands)	%	(thousands of feddans)	%	No. (thousands)	%	(thousands of feddans)	%
Below 5 feddans	2,642	94.3	2,122	35.5	3,033	94.5	3,693	57.1
5 — 10	79	2.8	256	8.8	78	2.4	614	9.5
10 — 50	69	2.5	1,291	21.5	67	2.1	919	14.3
50 —100	6	0.2	429	7.2	29	0.9	815	12.6
100—200	3	0.1	437	7.3	4[x]	0.1	421[x]	6.5
over 200	2	0.1	1,177	19.7	—	—	—	—
Total	2,801	100.0	5,982	100.0	3,211	100.0	6,462	100.0

[x] These figures presumably apply to estates of exactly 100 feddans and the state farms.
(Source : 43)

sibilities for absorbing the rapid natural increase of population? To answer these questions a short analysis of recent transformations in agriculture is needed.

INCREASE OF ARABLE LAND AND
ITS UTILIZATION

The main increase in arable land in Egypt took place during the nineteenth century. About 1800, the total cultivated area was 2,000,000 feddans. One hundred years later it had increased to 5,500,000, and by 1965, to 6,000,000. This means that within 165 years there was a threefold increase of arable land, while population during the same period increased more than ten times.

Since the introduction of perennial irrigation, the increased number of harvests has resulted in a relative growth of the area under crops. In 1965, 10,351,000 feddans were cultivated of which 45.8 per cent were in winter crops, 37.0 in spring crops, and 15.5 the "Nili" season crops. The remaining 1.7 per cent were in orchards (29). The changeover has also had some adverse effects; the level of ground water has been raised in many places; the salt content of the soil has increased, and parasites and plant pests have appeared (36). Artificial manuring has become necessary, because under the present system of irrigation natural manuring (silt carried by the Nile) has proved insufficient. For instance, in the year 1950-1964, the use of nitrogen fertilizers increased by more than 130 per cent, phosphorous fertilizers by about 250 per cent. The use of insecticides also increased greatly —some 225 per cent in the years 1962-64 alone (14).

Thrifty utilization of land is expressed, among other ways, by prohibiting public buildings in arable areas, by replacing drainage and irrigation canals with closed systems (it is expected that about 700,000 feddans of land will thus be rehabilitated). The use of sprinklers has aided considerably in conserving water, through controlling the amount used according to actual need, in intensifying agricultural production (24).

In the existing situation of land hunger, the maximum increase of cultivated area has top priority. The role of the High Dam has already been mentioned. This project will allow (1) an increase in the area of arable land by 1.3 million feddans and replacement of basin irrigation by perennial irrigation over an area of about 0.7 million feddans; (2) the creation of a "permanent water reserve" for year-long use through retention of the flood water of the Nile; (3) the regulation of irrigation in the Nile valley and Delta; (4) the gain of considerable quantities of electric power, not only to satisfy the needs of industry and towns, but also to drive the large pumps needed for irrigation. Rehabilitation of new areas is now taking place in the north, in the Delta region, along the Mediterranean coast, on the Sinai Peninsula, and in the so-called New Valley (31). By 1965, as much as 626,000 *feddans* had been rehabilitated, the greater part (547,000 *feddans*) during the 1960-1965 five-year-plan period (43).

The increase of irrigated area does not, however, solve problems of increased agricultural output and allocation of land to farmers. Transformation of the land utilization structure and reform of the agrarian system are required (26).

The maximum possible utilization of agricultural land is a problem of paramount importance in Egypt. Present plans provide for reorganization and the intensification of production in answer to the population's growing demands for food. Great efforts have already been made to increase yields: rice increased from 37.9 q/hectare in 1954 to about 5 in 1965; other crops increased as follows in the same period: wheat from 18.4 to 27.6, barley from 19.2 to 26.8, maize from 20.9 to 27.7. The average yields of the five cereals (wheat, barley, maize, sorgo, and rice) increased from 23.1 to 33.3 q/hectare in the period 1954-65, a 44.1 per cent increase (14). Similar trends are observed in the production of vegetables, sugar cane, and cotton.

Even so, it is doubtful if the country will be able to attain full self-sufficiency in food supplies. Despite the still latent reserves in the yields of various crops, there is a certain ceiling of yields that cannot be exceeded; and even attaining this ceiling involves an excessive growth of production costs. Already

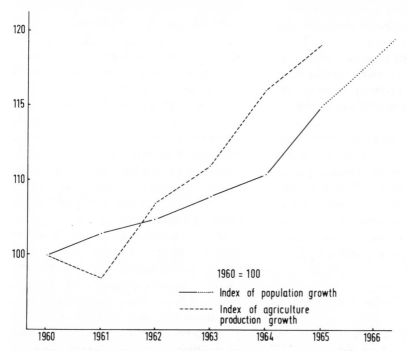

Fig. 20-3. EGYPT: INDICES OF THE GROWTH OF POPULATION AND OF AGRICULTURAL PRODUCTION, 1960-66

there is a trend toward reducing the area of certain crops (wheat, barley, cotton) in order to increase that of others (rice, sugar cane, maize, vegetables), which bring higher yields and are more profitable (28). So it may be expected that Egypt will continue importing great quantities of grain (at present about two million tons yearly) (5; 43). In this connection, the changes in the production structure have become an objective necessity in supplying food to the population and to the export market as well. In addition to shifting priorities in grain crops, much attention is being given to the expansion of vegetable and friut cultivation and to stock breeding (36). This emphasis is aimed at changing the present consumption pattern (from 1950 to 1964 the annual amount of grain consumption per capita increased by 23.6 per cent and that of vegetables by 98.4), and at limiting the monoculture of cotton by providing more varied exports. It would also allow for increased employment in agricultural production and processing (30). An initial outlay for equipment is required, but it would undoubtedly be much lower than in other industrial areas. The expansion of agricultural export also demands efficient organization and good quality production, not only to the standards of world markets, but also to win foreign markets, which are often characterized by limited elasticity of demand. There are possibilities both in the Middle Eastern markets (particularly in animal products) and in Europe: the climatic conditions of Egypt can help a lot by providing crops duing seasons when they are most attractive for Europeans (33; 34).

TRANSFORMATION IN SOCIAL RELATIONS
IN THE COUNTRYSIDE

Efforts aimed at modernizing irrigation systems and changes in land utilization have been and continue to be slowed down by the present structure of land ownership and social relations in the countryside (1; 33). The 1952 land reform fixed the upper limit of land ownership at 100 *feddans;* there have been improvements in the leasing of land, and incentives have been created to make tenants interested in the results of their work. But these reforms have not thoroughly changed the essence of the previous agrarian system. Although the political importance of the feudal landlords has in principle been eliminated, the economic position of the big landowner has been weakened only insignificantly (40). In 1965, estates of over 10 *feddans* accounted for 3.1 per cent of all farms and covered 33.4 per cent of the agricultural land of the country. The changes are shown in Table 20-10.

An interesting process took place in the years 1961-65. The average area of farms in the group up to 5 *feddans* showed an increase, while the average area of farms in the 5 to 10 *feddan* category grew from 6-7 to 7-8 *feddans*. But simultaneously a considerable drop took place in the average area of other farms. This testifies to progressive farm fragmentation and to a trend towards consolidating medium-size farms in the group of 5-10 *feddans*. Unfortunately, no data for 1965 are available to follow the changes in the group of farms up to 5 *feddans* (in this group land fragmentation is the greatest; farms of less than 1 *feddan* accounted for 71 per cent of all farms in 1957 and covered 14 per cent of the agricultural land of the country).

The land reform encompassed an area of over one million *feddans,* out of which 838,-000 were allocated by the end of 1964. Landless peasants (tenants and laborers) and small farm owners who benefited from the reform have been involved in a system of co-operative farms (33; 43). The same co-operative system is also obligatory in newly rehabilitated land. Within these cooperatives, it is possible to make more rational use of the land, improve planning of field work, and to take advantage of supply and purchase organizations.

Despite the above reforms, the existing property structure, with nearly 60 per cent of the land in farms of less than 5 *feddans,* and progressive land fragmentation, creates particularly unfavorable conditions for the increase of agricultural production. Hence the need has arisen to look for new solutions. The aim is to consolidate small lots within village areas into large fields covering from 20 to 50 *feddans* and to cultivate them in a rational way (2). By the end of 1964, this new type of co-operative encompassed 4,000 villages. The campaign is aimed at bringing about a quantitative growth of agricultural production on the basis of mechanization, rational water economy, modernization of the network of canals, etc. It is difficult to foresee the full results of these changes, but it has been noticed that the yield per land units has already increased.

In recent years, reform in agrarian relations have successfully limited Egypt's land lease system. In 1952 about 75 per cent of the cultivated land was farmed by tenants, against about 50 at present (19; 44). Although some former tenants obtained land as a result of the reform, unemployment has become more acute because direct farming (owner-managed with the help of hired labor) is being applied ever more widely in medium-size and large farms. The system of family farming applied thus far has made possible a considerable surplus of manpower (33; 41).

It is very improbable that the changes made in the agricultural sector will solve the problem of population pressure in the countryside. In the year 1965-66, the share of agriculture in the national income was 28 per cent, while 51.5 per cent of the total number of employed were agricultural workers (43). Because of the high rate of natural increase, the movement from countryside to town is expected to continue, and to counteract this process, employment in non-agricultural trades is being organized in rural areas. Within the framework of the so-called "combined centers" (*uakhdat mugammaa*) of which there were about 350 by the end of 1966 (800 are planned), jobs are provided in small-scale processing of food and other agricultural products, in handicrafts, etc. The centers are also entrusted with spreading general and agricultural knowledge, and health improvements. The first goal to be attained should be a maximum increase of employment, but this calls for more extensive structural transformations in the rural economy.

Conclusion

Since the 1952 revolution, profound economic and social changes have taken place in Egypt. The former has found expression in the ever more widely applied system of economic direction and the increasing share of the state sector in industry, home and foreign trade, transportation and agriculture. Social changes are not less important. The former feudal class and the upper middle class have been deprived of their former political influence, and their economic influence is being limited to an ever greater degree (e.g., the high progression scale in income tax calculated from the fixed ceiling of incomes, and further restrictions on extensive land ownership, etc.). Last, there is the interesting process of activating and mobilizing the population toward overcoming important economic difficulties and tensions in social relations. It is obvious that one could not expect essential changes in only 15 years, since these people had been previously denied the right to decide their own fate; neither could it be expected that the so-called economic pattern would be changed, so that growth in productive capacity would gain top priority at the expense of the traditional pattern of personal consumption (22; 25; 27). There are numerous individuals remaining in the present power elite who are evidently slowing down the development of the economy. For example, the present system of internal and external initiatives brings about a substantial waste. The character and mechanism of "intermediary systems" and their positive and negative elements could make an interesting study, from the point of view of social and economic geography (25).

Despite many negative facts, the analysis of the post-revolutionary period in Egypt shows that immense progress has been achieved in many fields. But one may ask whether the present utilization of resources and economic growth are able to keep pace with the rate of natural population increase. The results of the last five-year plan (1960-65) have shown that the annual rate of national income growth was 6.5 per cent and the average growth of per capita income was 3.5 per cent (the average annual rate of natural increase was 2.7 per cent in this period). The question of how long will it be possible to maintain the ratio of investment to the national income at the present level of 19.6 per cent (8) remains open—all the more so as the food balance becomes more unfavorable. Also, thus far economic development has depended to a considerable extent on foreign assistance.

The dilemma of present-day Egypt is first of all of a demographic nature. The scope of the dilemma is best shown by the following estimate. Assuming that up to the year 2000 the average rate of annual growth is maintained at a level of 2.5 per cent (it is 3 per cent at present), the relation of population density to the area of agricultural land (taking into account the 40 per cent increase

of cultivated area) will seriously deteriorate (33).

Because the Egyptian population is young, the rate of natural increase will be further accelerated at least for several years. The campaign for family planning can only bring results over a long period; especially in view of Muslim customs and traditions, which create problems that are difficult to solve.

In a situation of growing population pressure, a maximum increase in production and employment assume top priority. It may seem that these trends contradict each other, above all in industry. But while it would be difficult for any country to give up economically justified development of modern industry, neither can it follow the road traversed by the leading developed countries. A maximum effort towards industrialization is required, to produce both for the home market and for export, if only to make good the deficit of food. It is also necessary to develop those branches of industry in which considerable employment is needed. This is most important in towns, where only 40 per cent of the people able to work actually have a job.

Egypt, as well as many other countries of the Third World, is concentrating efforts on the problems of major urban areas. Yet it is the economic development of small urban centers that deserves particular attention, so that at least part of the rural population might be induced to settle there rather than in large cities. It can be assumed that the ruling circles are beginning to realize the importance of "intermediate urbanization" for a better balance of the economic and social development of the country.

But, at present, attention should be focused on rural problems and the development of agriculture. Only intervention in this sector will be able to check the mass drive of the population to the cities. This requires a long-term and deliberately planned economic and social policy. Much has already been done but, with the extreme shortage of agricultural land, efforts to insure more rational utilization of arable areas and intensification of crop production and stock breeding have been less than could be desired. No less important is the development of all kinds of nonagricultural occupations in the countryside. All this calls for social and economic reforms to change the traditional structure of rural population. Population pressure will finally determine the direction of these reforms.

The changes now taking place in Egypt reflect specific natural conditions and the economic, social, and political relations of the population. Hence, when discussing problems of the development of the Third World countries, one must be very cautious when speaking of the "Egyptian pattern." The avoidance of generalizations and the establishment of development patterns, by which various countries may be classified, does not mean, however, that typological studies of transformations in social and economic life lack value; rather such studies are of practical importance, and can often prove. useful in other countries or areas.

Studies of the geographic and economic problems of Egypt, like those of many other economically developing countries, prove how much attention should be given to social problems. In Egypt, breaking through the vicious circle of poverty, which is expressed by population pressure upon resources, or the greater rate of natural increase than that of resources, depends on the removal of the institutional barrier, or at least the maximum reduction of its influence. That is why, in studying the problems of the Third World countries, one cannot avoid studying the principles of distribution of national income. They are reflected in the degree of the present utilization of a given region, and also in the changes taking place in its regional organization (34).

There is no single answer to the dilemma of population pressure in Egypt. It depends on many factors, both internal and external. The present situation is no doubt particularly serious and calls for firm governmental intervention, for it seems that further development trends and the scope of social and economic changes in both town and country will be finally determined by population pressure.

REFERENCES

(1) A. Abdel-Malek: La Question Agraire en Egypte et la Reforme de 1952, *Tiers-Monde*, Vols. 9-10, 1962.

(2) A. Abdel-Malek: La Reforme Agraire en Egypte, *Développement et Civilisation,* Vol. 22, 1965.

(3) I. Abdel-Rahman: Manpower Planning in the UAR, *Et. Mens. sur l'Economie et les Finance de la Syrie,* Vol. 66, 1963.

(4) J. I. Abu-Lughod: Urbanisation in Egypt, *Economic Development and Cultural Change,* Vol. 3, 1965.

(5) The Africa and West Asia Agriculture Situation: Sup. 5 to the World Agr. Situation (Washington, 1963).

(6) P. Birot and J. Dresch: La Méditèrranée et le Môyen-Orient (Paris, 1952).

(7) K. Butzer: Environment and Human Ecology in Egypt during

Predynastic and Dynastic Times, *Bulletin, Société de Géographie d'Egypte,* Vol. 32, 1959.

(8) *Central Bank of Egypt, Economic Bulletin,* Vol. 2, 1961; Vol. 4, 1965.

(9) Le Développement Industriel et le Problème de l'Emploi en Egypte de 1945 à 1965, *Problèmes Economiques,* March, 1965.

(10) M. Dowidar: Le Développement Economique de l'Egypte depuis 1952, *Tiers-Monde,* Vol. 18, 1964.

(11) Economic Development in the Middle-East, 1959-1961 (New York, 1962).

(12) Egypt: *The Quarterly Economic Review,* Vol. 50, 1965.

(13) Egypt: Statistical Pocket Yearbook (Cairo, 1965).

(14) Food and Agriculture Organization: Production Yearbook (Rome, 1960 and 1965).

(15) I. Gordonow: Egipet (Moscow, 1953). [In Russian]

(16) *Federation of Industries in the UAR* (Yearbook 1964).

(17) G. Hamdan: Evolution d'agriculture irriquée en Egypte, in: Histoire de l'utilisation des terres des regions arides. UNESCO, 1961).

(18) H. Hurst: The Nile (London, 1962).

(19) Ch. Issawi: Egypt in Mid-Century (London, 1954).

(20) Ch. Issawi: Egypt in Revolution (London, 1963).

(21) A. Jagielski: Zaludnienie Afryki Pólnocnej w XX w.—Zarys Geograficzny (North African Population in the 20th Century—a Geographical Study) (Wroclaw, 1966).

(22) B. Jasinski: Struktura Rolna a Wzrost Gospodarczy (Agricultural Structure and Economic Growth) (Warsaw, 1965).

(23) M. Kalecki: Uwagi o Spoleczno-Gospodarczych Aspektach Ustrójow Posrednich (Socio-Economic Aspects of the Transitional Political Systems), *Ekonomista,* No. 3, 1965.

(24) J. Kratzman: L'Eau dans l'economie israelienne, *Tiers-Monde,* Vols. 9-10, 1952.

(25) O. Lange: Introduction, in: Agriculture Land Reforms and Economic Development (Warsaw, 1964).

(26) Y. Lacoste: *La Géographie du sous-développement* (Paris, 1965).

(27) W. Lipski: Rolnictwo Krajow Rozwijajacych Sie. (Agriculture of the Under-Developed Countries) (Warsaw, 1965).

(28) *Monthly Bulletin of Agricultural Economics and Statistics,* Rome, Vols. 1, 2, 3, 4, 5, 1965.

(29) *National Bank of Egypt, Economic Bulletin,* Vol. 3, 1955, Vol. 4, 1961, Vol. 3, 1965, Vol. 3, 1966.

(30) R. Nurkse: *Problems of Capital Formation in Under-Developed Countries* (Oxford, 1953).

(31) *Projets de l'Organisation Publique de Colonisation des Deserts* (Cairo, 1960).

(32) H. Rijad: L'Egypte Nasserienne (Paris, 1964).

(33) M. Rościszewski: Agricultural Geography of Egypt: Problems and Perspectives, *Africana Bulletin,* Vol. 5, 1966.

(34) M. Rościszewski: Badania Geograficzne a Kraje Slabo Roswiniete (Geographical Studies and the Under-Developed Countries) *Przeglad Geograficzny,* Vol. 1, 1967.

(35) M. Rościszewski: Egipt, in: Z. Dobrska, S. Golabek, M. Rościszewski, and M. Skotnicki: *Geografia Gospodarcza Afryki* (Economic Geography of Africa) (Warsaw, 1964).

(36) M. Rościszewski: Kierunki Przemian w Gospodarce Nawadnianej i Uzytkowaniu Ziemi w Egipcie (Changes in the Irrigation Economy and Land Utilisation in Egypt), *Prace i Materialy,* Vol. 1, 1966.

(37) M. Rościszewski: Niektore Problemy Bliskiego Wschodu (Some Problems of the Middle East), *Wies Wspólczesna,* Vol. 8, 1963.

(38) M. Rościszewski: Wielka Tama Asuańska (The High Aswan Dam), *Geografia w Szkole,* Vol. 3, 1959.

(39) M. Rościszewski: Z. Problemow Geografii Rolnictwa Bliskiego Wschodu (Problems of Agricultural Geography in the Middle East), *Geografia w Szkole,* Vol. 5, 1963.

(40) I. Sachs: W. Sprawie Istoty Ustroju Spoleczno-Gospodarczego Wspólczesnego Egiptu (On the Essence of Egypt's Socio-Economic System) *Ekonomista,* Vol. 3, 1965.

(41) Marei Sayed: UAR Agriculture Enters a New Age (Cairo, 1960).

(42) La Société Urbaine Egyptienne, *Tiers-Monde,* Vol. 6, 1961.

(43) *Statistical Handbook UAR* (Cairo, 1966).

(44) D. Warriner: Land Reform and Development in the Middle East (London, 1962).

21. POPULATION DISTRIBUTION AND DYNAMICS IN CAMEROON

John I. Clarke

In the politically fragmented African continent, the Federal Republic of Cameroon may be classed as a middle-size state. With 5,080,000 inhabitants (estimate of 31 December 1964) and 460,300 km², it has half the area and less than one-tenth of the population of neighboring Nigeria, but nearly twice the area and more than ten times as many people as another neighbor, Gabon. Its population density of 11/km² is only a little above the African average (10/km²) and comparable with several other African states: Tanzania, Malagasy Republic, and Guinea. Economically, Cameroon ranks among those African countries which are almost exclusively agricultural. About 85 per cent of its active population are engaged in agriculture, which accounts for half of the gross national product and three-quarters of the exports; and therefore Cameroon exemplifies some of the difficulties of those developing countries enjoying few benefits from mining.

Internal Diversity

Its internal diversity is sufficiently marked for Cameroon to claim that it synthesizes much of the variety of tropical Africa. Its peculiar shape, its hinge location between West and Central Africa (Fig. 21-1), its latitudinal extent from 2°N to nearly 13°N, its altitudinal range from sea level to 4,070 m (Mount Cameroon), and its deep penetration into the continent—from moist mangrove coast to remote semi-arid interior—have encouraged unusually contrasting physical environments. In particular, Cameroon demonstrates an ecological zonation from dense forests in the Equatorial south, through gradations of woodland savanna in

Fig. 21-1. CAMEROON: LOCATION

the Guinea Savanna and Sudan zones, to wooded steppes in the far north.

Cameroon also exhibits remarkable human diversity. Ethnically, it lies astride the "Bantu line," so that while Bantu and semi-Bantu peoples prevail in the southern half of the country (apart from some Pygmies in the sparsely peopled southeast), in the north there are Sudanese Negroes, Hamitic Fulani (Foulbe), and Arab Choa (Fig. 21-2). It also lies astride an important religious and social divide, the peoples of the south being mostly Christian and considerably Westernized, while those of the north are either Moslem or animist and are much less in contact with modern modes of life. This human diversity partly accounts for considerable re-

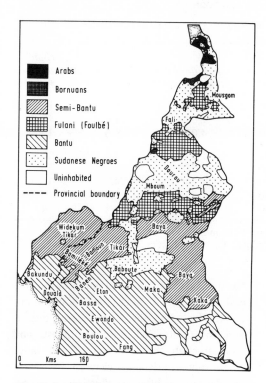

Fig. 21-2. CAMEROON: ETHNIC GROUPS

main stimuli for internal migrations, and intensify regional variations in the distribution and natural increase of population.

To this complexity must also be added Cameroon's unusual political framework. The Federal Republic, created in 1961, is an amalgam of the southern part of the for-Kuczynski (7). While West Cameroon was the whole of the former French trusteeship, both of which were parts of German Cameroons during the period 1884-1916. Today, Cameroon is a bilingual state with two official languages, French and English. The political, social, and economic contrasts between the small, anglophone province of West Cameroon, with only 9 per cent of the country's area but 20 per cent of its population, and the wealthier, Francophone province of East Cameroon are striking enough to post serious problems of integration.

Awareness of internal diversity induced

gional variations in demographic conditions, but the diversity of economies is also responsible. Although nearly all these numerous peoples gain their livelihood from agriculture, production varies from cattle to cocoa, and from manioc to millets. Agriculture also ranges from pastoral nomadism through bush fallowing and peasant polyculture to plantation agriculture, with great contrasts between tradition and modernity. Urban growth further emphasizes this distinction, because towns contain a high proportion of the 138,000 persons employed in the modern sector of the economy (including most of the 4600 employed expatriates), and because town growth in Cameroon is particularly polarized in Douala and Yaoundé. These vivid contrasts between (a) the "islandic" modern sector, partly urban and partly rural, and (b) the widespread traditional and semi-traditional sectors are the

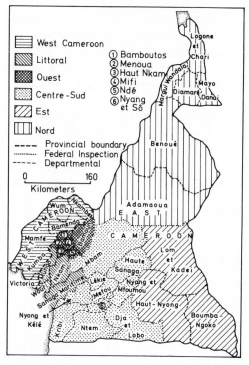

Fig. 21-3. CAMEROON: ADMINISTRATIVE AREAS

TABLE 21-1 CAMEROON: POPULATION ESTIMATES, DECEMBER 1964

	Area (km²)	Population (thousands)	Density (/km²)	Urban Population* %
REPUBLIC	460,300	5,080	11.0	16
WEST	41,800	1,030	24.6	12
EAST	418,500	4,050	9.6	17
Centre-Sud	117,600	1,000	8.4	18
Littoral	20,100	550	27.3	55
Ouest	13,700	740	54.0	16
Est	108,500	255	2.3	5
Nord	158,600	1,505	9.4	4

* Localities with 5,000 inhabitants or more
Source: Service de la Statistique, Centre d'Etudes du Plan, Yaoundé, June 1965.

the Cameroonian government to divide the Federal Republic into six economic regions corresponding to the "federal inspections of administration" (Fig. 21-3). Although of unequal size, each of these regions possesses a certain uniformity of physical, social, and economic conditions and have contrasting population distributions (Table 21-1). In more general terms, it is customary in Cameroon to distinguish between three broad regions: the province of West Cameroon, North Cameroon (corresponding to the federal inspection of Nord), and South Cameroon (including the four federal inspections of Centre-Sud, Littoral, Ouest, and Est, although the inclusion of the latter seems inappropriate in view of its sparse population). Table 21-2 illustrates the economic advance of the south, the backwardness of the north, and the intermediate condition in the west; and the gaps are growing. These regional contrasts arise partly from the fragmented diversity of indigenous cultures but mostly from the introduction of European activities, services, and amenities. They are symptomatic of a regional disequilibrium, common to developing countries.

TABLE 21-2 CAMEROON: REGIONAL IMPORTANCE (1963-64)

	North	South	West
Area	35%	56%	9%
Population	30	50	20
Internal production	13	74	13
Value of exports	8	79	13
Value of imports	5	80	15
Revenue	8	81	11
Investments	15	73	12
Salaries	6	85	9
Current expenses of administrations	9	79	12
Total household consumption	13	73	14
Private cars	5	83	12

Source: 9: 115-6

Population Data

Unfortunately, the Federal Republic has never had a national census. Moreover, because of its divided colonial past, it has experienced contrasting systems of population enumeration, examined in remarkable detail for the pre-World War II period by Kuczynski (7). While West Cameroon was under British administration, there were censuses, the last of which was carried out quite thoroughly in 1953. In the former French Cameroon, now East Cameroon, the main system of enumeration was the administrative compilation, which was last effected in 1956, although there were also urban censuses of Douala (1955-56) and Yaoundé (1957), and special inquiries in the towns of Edéa (1956) and Ebolowa (1958), as well as a complete census of the subdivision of Mbalmayo (1956).

Since 1960, a series of sample enumeration surveys has been organized to cover the whole of Cameroon—Nord-Bénoué in 1960, Sud-Bénoué in 1961, Est and Centre-Sud (with the exception of the departments of Kribi and Nyong-et-Kélé) in 1962, West Cameroon and Kribi and Nyong-et-Kélé in 1964, and Ouest and Littoral in 1965. In areas not visited by enumerators, these sample surveys have been supplemented by administrative estimates. Exhaustive censuses have been recently carried out only in the two largest towns, Yaoundé (1962) and Douala (1965-66), and in a few small localities.

The phasing of the surveys and the delays in processing data have provoked some confusion over the size of total population. In 1964, official publications in Cameroon stated that the population was "over 4 million," but a year later the estimate of the Statistical Service for 31 December 1964 was 5,080,000. One reason for the rising estimates of the total population is that the recent surveys have indicated that previous administrative compilations in East Cameroon resulted in underestimates. Some difficulties also occur over the comparative sizes of regional populations. The extremely useful *Tableau de la Population du Cameroun* (1965) (6) published by the Institut de Recherches Scientifiques du Cameroun contains population numbers of federal inspections, departments, arrondissements, cantons, native authorities, and towns, but

they date from various years between 1953 and 1964. No more official set of population data is yet available. In short, whereas the sample survey technique of population enumeration has several notable advantages, including the reduction of enumeration costs and of the dangers of falsification through political intrigue, as in neighboring Nigeria, it may be of less value to the administrator than to the demographer, unless sample surveys are synchronized or their results made more comparable. Certainly the new Federal Republic of Cameroon would have profited from the availability of more uniform population data.

Vital registration exists in Cameroon, but needless to say it is neither universal nor enforced. As in many other African countries, it is extremely difficult to enforce, because of such obstacles as the prevalence of illiteracy, the diversity of African languages, and the existence of nomadism.

Population Growth

In these conditions there can be no accurate assessment of population growth, especially as there is as yet no entirely satisfactory age-data. The figures in Table 21-3 are merely rough estimates. The official estimate of natural increase is 2.1 per cent per annum, assuming a birth rate of 40 per mille and a death rate of 19, all of which are below the African average. The key factor has been the decline of mortality, which has been greatly assisted by prophylactic successes against sleeping sickness, yellow fever, and smallpox, and to a lesser degree against malaria and leprosy, so that by Tropical African standards morbidity conditions are better than average. Apart from malaria, the major killers are pulmonary and parasitic diseases. Umbilical tetanus and measles also contribute to high infant mortality. It should also be mentioned that many people suffer

TABLE 21-3   CAMEROON: AGE GROUPS
(ESTIMATES, FEB. 1965)

Age-group	Numbers (thousands)			%		
	Males	Females	Total	Males	Females	Total
Under 5	392	396	788	7.6	7.7	15.3
5-14	566	520	1,086	11.0	10.1	21.1
15-39	876	1,117	1,993	17.0	21.7	38.7
40-59	485	494	979	9.4	9.6	19.0
60 and over	160	144	304	3.1	2.8	5.9
	2,479	2,671	5,150	48.1	51.9	100.0

Source : 9:15

from malnutrition, especially from a lack of protein and, during the dry season, of vitamins A and C. In theory there are more hospital facilities than on average in Africa; by 1966 there were about 11,500 public hospital beds, 1:490 inhabitants in East Cameroon and 1:710 in West Cameroon, apart from those in Christian mission, company, and private hospitals. On the other hand, in 1964-65 there were only 196 doctors—1:24,700 inhabitants in East Cameroon and 1:32,200 in West Cameroon—so there is considerable room for improvement.

Birth rates in Cameroon are not as high as they might be, because there are various checks upon fertility. Widespread polygamy, common among the wealthier, generally has a lowering effect upon fertility, as does the practice of prohibiting sexual relations during the period when a mother is feeding a child. More drastic is the influence of venereal diseases upon sterility. They are propagated by the migrations of population which adversely affect sex-ratios and encourage prostitution in towns; at present there are only three V.D. clinics, in Yaoundé, Douala, and Maroua. Abortions are also known to be numerous, especially in the larger towns. Modern methods of family planning have little effect upon fertility and are largely unknown, because, as in most Francophone territories of Tropical Africa, their import

and sale are illegal. Indeed, Cameroon has inherited from France a system of family allowances for *fonctionnaires* which is even extended in full to polygamists. There are cases of men drawing allowances for 50 children. Local traditions and the strong influence of Islam and Catholicism must prejudice the chances of any family planning program.

Like many other independent African countries, Cameroon has no population policy. The annual increase of about 100,000 persons is considered gratifying by some local statisticians because any higher figure would make it difficult to raise average per capita income, which in 1963-64 was U.S. $113, and any lower figure would not encourage urbanization, which many see as an essential stimulus to the economic development of the country. Nevertheless, this growth rate will strain Cameroon's productive capacity, because in order to double per capita incomes over a period of 20 years, production will have to triple through an annual increase of about 5.7 per cent—no mean task for a country which is primarily agricultural.

In view of the inadequacies of population data, population projections obviously cannot claim reliability. Mazure's calculations are only provisional, but envisage a total population of 5,799,000 by 1970 (1,209,000 in West Cameroon and 4,590,000 in East Cameroon) and 7,211,00 by 1980 (1,548,-000 in West Cameroon and 5,663,000 in East Cameroon). This means that in a period of 15 years there may be over 2,100,000 more people, an extra million jobs to be found (more than 65,000 a year), and a total school-age population of 1,500,000 or more than twice as many as attended school in 1964-65. The required growths in employment and in school places are severe development problems.

Population Distribution

Population distribution in Cameroon confirms its intermediate situation between West and Central Africa, for there are great contrasts between local concentrations of population with densities exceeding 100/km² and

vast virtually uninhabited areas (Fig. 21-4). No simple explanations offer themselves for these marked variations in population density. Direct correlations between environmental conditions and population distribution cannot be made for large areas, although in particular localities the combination of high soil fertility (especially of volcanic soils) and suitable rainfall may exercise a powerful influence. Often more satisfactory explanations can be found in the analysis of the history of human occupance, in past migrations of peoples, their modes of life, the effects of slavery and tribal warfare, the impact of European rule, economy, and culture, and in modifications in means and routes of transportation. The population distribution map is ever-changing.

As 84 per cent of the population of Cameroon live in rural areas, rural populations

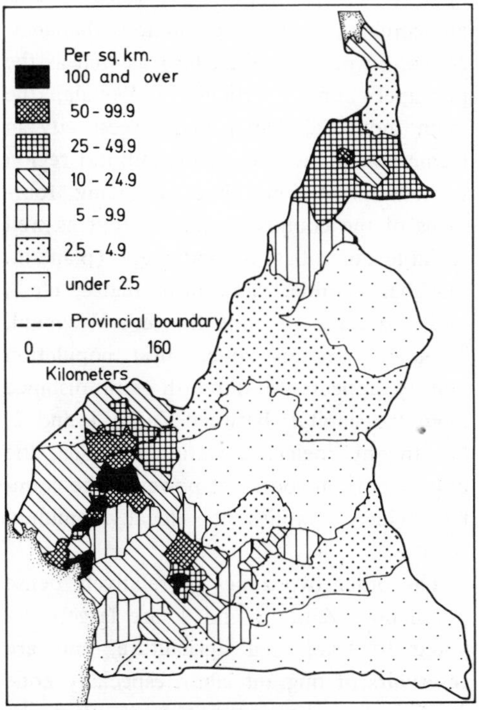

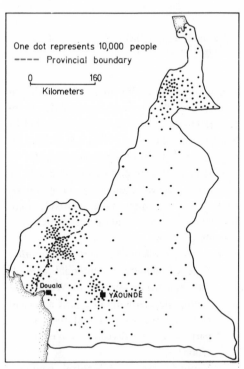

Fig 21-4. CAMEROON: DENSITY OF POPULATION (BY ARRONDISSEMENT)

Per sq. km.
100 and over
50 - 99.9
25 - 49.9
10 - 24.9
5 - 9.9
2.5 - 4.9
under 2.5
---- Provincial boundary
0   160
Kilometers

Fig. 21-5. CAMEROON: DISTRIBUTION OF RURAL POPULATION

One dot represents 10,000 people
---- Provincial boundary
0   160
Kilometers

Douala
YAOUNDÉ

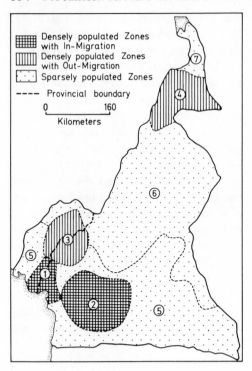

Densely populated Zones with In-Migration
Densely populated Zones with Out-Migration
Sparsely populated Zones

---- Provincial boundary

0   160
Kilometers

Fig. 21-6. CAMEROON: ZONES OF POPULA-
TION DISTRIBUTION

largely determine the map of population density (Fig. 21-5). With the notable exception of Douala, and less significantly that of Ngaoundéré, the main towns are all located in areas of high rural population density.

Schematically, the population map may be divided into seven main zones (Fig. 21-6), including four which have relatively high population density and three which are sparsely peopled:

A. *Densely peopled zones with in-migration*

1. Zone of modern commercial agriculture and urban growth in Wouri and Mungo departments in East Cameroon and Victoria division and the eastern part of Kumba division in West Cameroon.

2. Yaoundé region in central southern Cameroon.

B. *Densely peopled zones with out-migration*

3. Western high plateaus in East and West Cameroon.

4. Mountains and adjacent plains of the Sudan and Sahel zones.

C. *Zones of sparse populations*

5. Equatorial forests in the south and southeast of East Cameroon, as well as in the southwestern part of West Cameroon.

6. Guinea Savanna of East Cameroon.

7. Seasonally flooded lands south of Lake Chad.

The economies of Zones 1 and 2 developed largely under the impetus of European colonization, assisted by the construction of railways. Today they are the main zones of in-migration, migrants being mostly attracted by the opportunities of employment in the plantations and the main towns. Much of Zone 1 benefits from fertile volcanic soils and contains the major plantations (bananas, coffee, oil palm, rubber, tea) as well as the principal ports, particularly Douala, the main industrial center and largest city in Cameroon. Zone 2 is an agricultural region without plantations, but producing four-fifths of the country's cocoa output as well as large quantities of food crops (plantain, macaba, manioc, yam, taro, maize, etc.), and it is centered upon the federal capital, Yaoundé. In this zone, rural population density appears to diminish with distance from the capital.' Between Zones 1 and 2, lies the hydroelectric station at Edéa, the only important source of power in the country, which supplies the local aluminum works.

The other two zones of relatively dense population, Zones 3 and 4, are largely devoted to traditional agriculture, and are reservoirs of migrant labor, especially Zone 3. This zone is centered upon Bamiléké country, where volcanic soils have permitted the abandonment of the bush fallowing system, the intensive cultivation of food crops, and the commercial production of coffee and cocoa. Consequently, the forests have nearly disappeared although the area was initially occupied by the remarkable Bamiléké people only in the eighteenth and nineteenth centuries. Outward migration is vital as population pressure is very high, rural densities exceeding 100/km². Rather lower densities occur in Bamoun country to the northeast and in the adjacent Bamenda division of West Cameroon, where livestock are numerous and food crops are grown in quantity on the derived savanna grasslands. Although there is outward migration from both regions, the number of migrants is much less than from Bamiléké country. Zone 4 in the northern triangular area, known as the "duck's beak," beyond Garoua and the Bénoué Basin, contains densely peopled mountain massifs where pagan Negro peasants, known as Kirdi, farm at densities of 100-200/km², despite mediocre conditions for agriculture. On the surrounding northern plains, densities of 30-50/km² prevail among the more varied peoples, including Fulani and Arab pastoralists as well as pagan and Islamized cultivators, of whom the Tupuri (4) and Mandara are respective examples. Outward migration from Zone 4 is not important, but there is a downward movement from the massifs of Margui-Wandala to the plains of Diamaré.

The rest of Cameroon is only very sparsely peopled. Zone 5 is in the forested southern part of the country, and includes the major areas of primary forest in Cameroon, found especially in the southeast, which is mostly uninhabited except for small groups of Pygmies. The average population density of the department of Boumba-Ngoko in the extreme southeast is about 1/km².

Population is also sparsely distributed in the vast expanses of the Guinea Savanna (Zone 6) south of the Bénoué River. This zone is an extension of the Nigerian "Middle Belt" and has many similar characteristics: southern savanna climate, poor soils, tsetse infestation, history of slaving, no large tribes, and few towns. The conquering Fulani certainly drastically diminished the population, and have adapted themselves with difficulty to the supression of slavery. Most of the zone, especially the extensive Adamaoua plateaus, is utilized mainly for cattle farming. In contrast, the seasonally flooded lands of Zone 7 in the remote north are scantily peopled by Moslem Negro fishermen and Arab Choa stock-raisers.

Regional Variations in Natural Increase

Like many parts of Africa, Cameroon is experiencing a growing unevenness in population distribution, arising from regional variations in rates of natural increase as well as migration, although these two phenomena are closely interrelated in their demographic effects. Table 21-4 demonstrates these regional variations in general terms. High natural increase rates are common in the densely peopled and urbanized areas of the south and west, which enjoy more medical facilities (Table 21-5) and a more modern way of life than other parts of the country. Nearly half of the doctors and the two main regional hospitals (using 30 per cent of the total expenses for curative medicine) are in Douala and Yaoundé, which contain only 6 per cent of the total population (11: (c), 19-35). Table 21-5 demonstrates the great regional differences in medical facilities, and particularly their shortage in the north. The latter region is similarly deprived of nurses and midwives. Indeed, in 1964-65 only eight of the thirty-five departments had a qualified midwife. The Second Five-Year Plan (1966-70) attempts to even out some of these regional disparities in medical facilities by

TABLE 21-4   CAMEROON: REGIONAL POPULATION GROWTH

	Population (1962)	Population (1965)	Estimated Natural Increase (%)	Estimated Balance of Migration 1962-80 (thousands)	Projected Population 1980 (thousands)
	(thousands)				
REPUBLIC					
WEST	4,902	5,220	2.1		7,211
EAST	992	1,069	2.5		1,548
Centre-Sud	1,027	1,091			1,516
Yaoundé	87	96	3.5	+87	265
Remainder	940	995	1.9	−68	1,251
Littoral	514	557			1,092
Wouri (Douala)	178	196	3.3	+114	453
Mungo	188	202	2.4		
Sanaga Maritime	116	125	2.4	+127	639
Nkam	32	34	2.0		
Ouest	700	755	2.5	−284	867
Est	231	248	2.0	−7	327
Nord	1,438	1,494		−5	1,861
Nord-Bénoué	1,188	1,231	1.2/1.5		
Sud-Bénoué	250	263	1.7/2.0		

Source: 8: 65-66

creating two more regional hospitals (at Garoua and Bafoussam), seven more divisional hospitals (four in Nord, two in Ouest, and one in Centre-Sud), as well as many more health posts and health centers, especially in the north.

Natural increase also varies greatly between ethnic groups (Table 21-6), especially in northern Cameroon, where it ranges from near stationary to very rapid. Podlewski has demonstrated how some dense populations of mountain dwellers (e.g. Kapsikis) ex-

TABLE 21-5   CAMEROON: MEDICAL FACILITIES BY REGION, 1964-65

	Number of Medical Establishments	Number of Hospital Beds/1,000 Inhabs.	Number of Doctors	Number of Inhabitants per Doctor
REPUBLIC	837	27.8	196	25,900
WEST	109	16.7	32	32,200
EAST	728		164	24,700
Centre-Sud	326	43.5	64	15,600
Littoral	101	44.5	49	11,200
Ouest	100	39.4	21	35,200
Est	80	36.3	6	42,500
Nord	121	10.1	24	62,700

Source: 15: various tables

TABLE 21-6   APPROXIMATE NATURAL INCREASE RATES FOR 23 RURAL
STRATA IN CAMEROON

Geographical and Ethnic Description of Stratum	Estimated Population (thousands)	Approximate Birth Rate (‰)	Approximate Death Rate (‰)	Approximate Nat. Inc. Rate (‰)
North				
Fishing, rice	48	44.9	20.9	24.0
Cattle. Moslems	29	35.0	14.2	21.8
Mountains, terraces	168	62.2	40.0	22.2
Mountains, no terracing	75	40.1	37.0	3.1
Plains. Cotton. Pagans	232	42.6	24.9	17.7
Plains. No Cotton. Pagans	104	43.9	27.8	16.1
Cotton. Moslems.	153	27.6	20.1	7.5
No Cotton, Moslems.	105	29.3	26.1	3.2
Mountains. Kapsikis.	22	67.0	52.2	14.8
Centre & East				
Savanna. Bafia. Yambassa.	58	38.7	20.9	17.8
Savanna. Baya.	42	44.9	24.7	20.2
Cocoa. Kozime I.	32	35.0	20.4	14.6
Coffee. Maka.	48	29.9	21.6	8.3
Coffee. Kaka, Pol, Badoum, Kozine II.	73	48.6	20.8	27.8
Cocoa. Betis.	162	27.5	22.1	5.4
Cocoa. Eton.	137	42.4	18.5	23.9
Cocoa. Bane, Ewondo.	140	32.7	14.4	18.3
Cocoa. Boulous.	166	36.2	14.1	22.1
Coast				
Bassa tribe	86	42.1	18.7	23.4
Others	75	32.3	29.5	2.8
West				
North. Savanna	527	51.2	29.5	21.7
Centre. Forest	258	53.0	34.6	18.4
South. Plantations	49	48.0	22.2	25.8

Source: 13: 164-165

perience high fertility, high mortality, and low natural increase, while others (e.g. Mafa) have higher fertility, lower mortality, and greater natural increase. There are also great differences between Moslem peoples in the north, but the widespread Foulbe generally have moderate to low fertility, low mortality, and low natural increase. The main causes of low fertility of these Moslem women are incredibly high rates of divorce and remarriage as well as venereal diseases; childlessness of about 30 per cent has been reported among Moslem women aged 25-45. One result of ethnic differences in fertility and mortality is that the average expectation of life of a Kapsiki is as low as 17 years, while that of a Foulbe is 42 years (12: 35).

In rural areas of Cameroon it is rare to find low mortality coinciding with high fertility, except in the Bamiléké departments of Ouest, where natural increase is 30 per mille, or about 20,000 persons per annum. On the other hand, high natural increase rates are usual in the larger towns, especially Yaoundé and Douala, where there is low mortality, low infant mortality which raises fertility, and high proportions in the age-groups 15-39. In Yaoundé, where these age-groups comprise 50 per cent of the total population (10:(a) 35), the birth rate in 1962 was estimated at 45 per cent and the death rate just below 10, giving a natural increase of 3.5 per cent a year. Douala's natural increase rate in 1964 was estimated at 3.3 per cent. At the same time, these two cities are the main centers of attraction for migrants.

Urbanization

Town growth in Cameroon exhibits many of the characteristics common to urbanization in Tropical Africa; it is recent, rapid, and localized, and provokes major social and economic problems in both town and country.

If the lower limit of 5000 inhabitants is accepted as an arbitrary definition of urban status, then in 1963 there were forty-two towns and the urban population amounted to about 781,000 or 15.6 per cent of the total population. Table 21-1 illustrates that the proportion is higher in East Cameroon than in West Cameroon, and that there are wide regional variations. In general, the pattern of town distribution conforms fairly closely with the pattern of population distribution, the greatest concentration of towns being along the boundary zone between the two provinces (Fig. 21-7). However, if we examine the frequency distribution of towns according to size (Table 21-7), we find that

TABLE 21-7   CAMEROON: FREQUENCY OF TOWN SIZES, 1963

Size Category	Number of Towns	Population of Towns	Percentage of Total Population
90,000+	2	284,000	5.7
20-40,000	7	186,000	3.7
10-20,000	12	169,000	3.4
5-10,000	21	142,000	2.8
	42	781,000	15.6

Source: 6: 55-6

two towns, Douala and Yaoundé, contain about 36 per cent of the total urban population of the Republic and 43 per cent of that of East Cameroon. These are the major growth points of Cameroon, particularly Douala, which contains one-third of the country's wage-earners. In some respects Cameroon is fortunate in having a dichotomy of capital and main port, as the interior situation of Yaoundé has stimulated agricultural development and has restrained to some extent the drift to the coast, so typical of Tropical Africa. Consequently, the urban primacy so evident in many other African states is lacking in Cameroon.

Yaoundé and Douala were both European

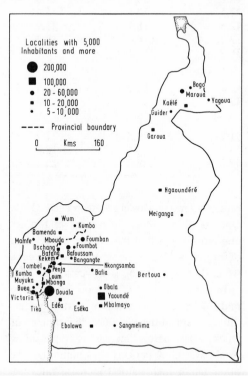

Fig. 21-7. CAMEROON: SIZE OF TOWNS

creations, and their growth has been stimulated not merely by European influence but also by continued European presence. Yaoundé has about 3000 Europeans and Douala about 8000, and together they contain four-fifths of all the Europeans in Cameroon, whose numbers have not changed greatly since independence. The Second Five-Year Plan notes that the 4600 employed expatriates still form high percentages in occupations demanding higher qualifications: 36 per cent of the supervisory staff, 27 per cent of the technicians, and 56 per cent of the trained personnel.

In view of the lack of accurate population data, it is hazardous to calculate an annual rate of urban growth, but it is generally estimated to be about 5 per cent (Fig. 21-8). Estimates of the annual growth of Yaoundé vary from 5 to 7.5 per cent, and of Douala from 5.1 to 6 per cent. In 1933, Yaoundé and Douala had 6500 and 27,000 respectively; by the mid-fifties, they had 58,000 and 119,000; by 1965, about 100,000 and 200,000. Mazure has estimated that the rates of increase of these two towns will diminish by 1980 to 2.5 and 4.5 per cent respectively; but then they may well comprise 265,000 and 453,000 inhabitants, or one in ten of all Cameroonians, instead of one in seventeen as now. Unfortunately, few towns have comparable data, although it seems that the only other towns experiencing rapid growth are in the west, especially Nkongsamba, Bafoussam, Bafang, and Foumban. Towns in the north and east are much more stable. The Second Five-Year Plan foresees that by 1970 about 19 per cent of the total population will be living in towns, and by 1980 about 26 per cent (Table 21-8).

TABLE 21-8   CAMEROON: PROJECTED URBAN POPULATION GROWTH, 1963-70

	Urban Population (*thousands*)		*Percentage* Annual Growth
	1963	*1970*	*1963-70*
REPUBLIC	785	1,100	5.0
WEST	135	170	3.6
EAST	650	930	5.3
Centre-Sud	150	230	6.3
Littoral	300	420	4.7
Ouest	90	140	8.4
Est	10	10	3.5
Nord	100	130	4.0

Source : 11 : (b) 38

Internal Migrations

Although natural increase is high in Cameroonian towns, a considerable proportion of the urban growth results fom rural-urban migration, which is gaining momentum annually and causing grave concern to the government: "the majority of the 25,000 rural inhabitants who emigrate every year to the towns is composed of young persons who have received an elementary and sometimes a

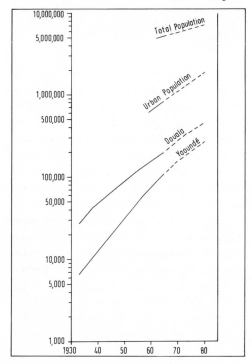

Fig. 21-8. CAMEROON: URBAN GROWTH

secondary education, and are thus lost for the progress of the rural world of which they should constitute the most activating element" (11: (b) 40). The government is anxious to check the "rural exodus" and to find ways of adjusting "the flow of rural emigrants to the possibilities of employment in the secondary and tertiary sectors," in order to limit the growing numbers of unemployed in the towns. One way chosen by the government is to restrain the uncontrolled growth in the number of educational establishments, which has not been accompanied by a similar increase in the number of teachers. It is increasingly perturbed by the orientation of the present system of education, entirely of European origin, toward the selection of white-collar workers in urban activities, and wants to put greater emphasis upon agricultural education.

Recent surveys of Yaoundé and Douala indicate that only 16-17 per cent of their populations were born within these cities; the remainder are in-migrants. The majority of migrants to Yaoundé are from the surrounding region of Centre-Sud (Fig. 21-9); but between one-quarter and one-third are Bamiléké from Ouest, many of whom are traders or are engaged in transport activities. In Douala there were 73,800 Bamiléké in 1964 (Fig. 21-10), mostly localized in the quarter of New Bell (2) compared with only 1432 in 1933; today nearly half of all the in-migrants are Bamiléké, although there is an important contingent of Bassa (8: 15-39). Neither city attracts many migrants from either West Cameroon or from the north. In making his projections for the future populations of Yaoundé and Douala, Mazure has assumed that the origins of migrants will largely remain the same (8: 25, 39).

The great reservoir of migrants in Cameroon is Bamiléké country (14), from which

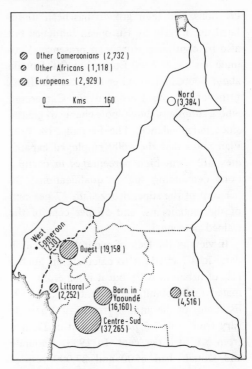

Fig. 21-9.   CAMEROON: ORIGINS OF THE POPULATION OF YAOUNDE 1962 (BY REGION)

about 7000 to 8000 persons leave annually. A variety of "push factors" have been cited (5: 11, 24) for this migration, first recorded in 1925: high population pressure; unpopularity of authoritative chiefs; social and family constraints; family structure involving one head who is often polygamous; spirit of adventure; indivisibility of property; forced labor; lack of land leading to excessive reduction in fallow and low yields; and rapid population increase. Migration is not only toward Yaoundé and Douala, but also to (a) the smaller towns in Bamiléké and Bamoun country, (b) the arrondissement of Foumbot, (c) the western part of the department of Mbam, (d) West Cameroon, and especially (e) the departments of Mungo and

Sanaga Maritime. The plantations of West Cameroon, Mungo, and Sanaga Maritime have long experienced an influx of migrants, not merely from the western high plateaus (1), but also from the densely peopled Ibo country of Eastern Nigeria, and areas such as the department of Nkam in East Cameroon, which has suffered from a veritable rural exodus owing to its broken relief, lack of communications, political insecurity, and the proximity of more favored regions.

As the great majority of migrants are males, migrations produce considerable abnormalities in sex-ratios, in regions of departure as well as arrival. Data for West Cameroon illustrate this point well (Table 21-9), for not only is there a marked contrast between north and south, but there is also a great concentration of men in the plantations and towns. It is necessary to stress the social significance of such migrations, studied in detail by Ardener, Ardener, and Warmington (1), but it may be noted that sex-ratios of Yaoundé (111 males per 100 females) and Douala are less unbalanced, owing to a growing migration of females.

TABLE 21-9   WEST CAMEROON:
SEX-RATIOS, 1964
(number of males per 100 females)

	All ages	15 years and over
West Cameroon	98	93
North	90	80
South	109	111
Rural zone	94	86
Bourgs	97	94
Plantations	125	145
Towns	124	132

Source: 11 : (a) 77

Conclusion

The population distribution and dynamics of Cameroon are not particularly unusual for Africa. They merely illustrate well the diversity of traditional distributions and of the impact of modern economy, combining to produce great variety of natural increase and migrations of population. While it is likely that the marked discrepancies in natural increase will be reduced by improved medical facilities and growing social evolution, it is unlikely that migrations will diminish, despite government attempts to create a more even distribution of economic development. The "islandic" character of population distribution will probably intensify. The main danger is that excessive concentration of population will increase rates of unemployment and underemployment, which are already high.

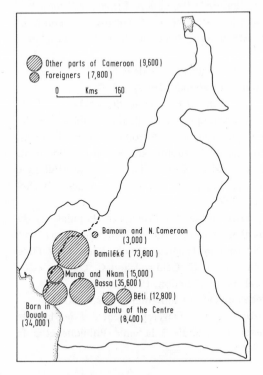

Fig. 21-10. CAMEROON: ETHNIC ORIGINS OF THE POPULATION OF DOUALA 1964

Other parts of Cameroon (9,600)
Foreigners (7,800)

0   Kms   160

Bamoun and N. Cameroon (3,000)
Bamiléké (73,800)
Mungo and Nkam (15,000)
Bassa (35,600)
Béti (12,800)
Born in Douala (34,000)
Bantu of the Centre (8,400)

REFERENCES

(1) E. Ardener, S. Ardener, and W. A. Warmington: Plantation and Village in the Cameroons (London, 1960).

(2) R. Diziain and A. Cambon: Etude sur la Population du Quartier New-Bell à Douala (Yaoundé, 1956).

(3) J. C. Froelich: Cameroun—Togo (Paris, 1956).

(4) J. Guillard: Golompoui (Paris, 1965).

(5) Inspection Fédérale de l'Ouest, Pays Bamiléké et Pays Bamoun, République Fédérale du Cameroun: Le Relance de l'Economie et les Perspectives de Développement (Yaoundé, 1963).

(6) Institut de Recherches Scientifiques du Cameroun: Tableau de la Population du Cameroun (Yaoundé, 1965).

(7) R. R. Kuczynski: The Cameroons and Togoland, a Demographic Study (London, 1939).

(8) C. Mazure: Perspectives Démographiques Provisoires de la République Fédérale du Cameroun (Secrétariat d'Etat aux Affaires Etrangères Chargé de la Coopération de la République Française, 1966).

(9) Ministère de la Coopération, République Française: Economie et Plan de Développement, République Fédérale du Cameroun (Paris, 1965).

(10) Ministère de l'Economie Nationale, Service de la Statistique:
a) La Population de Yaoundé (Yaoundé, 1963)
b) Enquête Démographique Centre et Est (Yaoundé, 1963).

(11) Ministère des Affaires Economiques et du Plan, République Fédérale du Cameroun: La Population du Cameroun Occidental (Paris, 1965). Second Five Year Plan of Economic and Social Development, July 1966-June 1971 (Yaoundé, 1966). Plan de Santé Publique (Yaoundé, 1966). La Population du Pays Bamiléké et des Départements Limitrophes (Paris, 1966).

(12) A. M. Podlewski: La Dynamisme des Principales Populations du Nord du Cameroun, entre Bénoué et Lac Tchad (Yaoundé, 1965).

(13) C. Scott: Vital Rate Surveys in Tropical Africa: Some New Data Relevant to Sample Design, in: J. C. Caldwell and C. Okonia, eds.: The Population of Tropical Africa (London, 1968), 163-71.

(14) C. Tardits: Les Bamiléké de l'Ouest Cameroun (Paris, 1960).

(15) M. E. Torfs: Planification pour le Développement des Services de Santé de Base (Commissariat Générale à la Santé Publique et a la Population (Yaoundé, 1966).

22. POPULATION PRESSURE ON PHYSICAL AND SOCIAL RESOURCES IN ZAMBIA

George Kay

Widely accepted precise definitions of the terms "overpopulation" and "population pressures" do not exist. Each has been used differently in the context of different circumstances, and each has thus acquired numerous shades of meaning. In most if not all cases, however, use of these terms is prompted by maladjustment between population numbers and either resources or production; and problems of population pressure consist of adverse consequences of such maladjustment upon resources or human beings or both. Several such problems are a direct function of the ratio between population and resources. Where the problems are associated with excessive population, if the numbers are reduced, immediate or early amelioration should be obtained. Similarly, problems associated with underpopulation would be alleviated or eliminated by an increase in numbers. Such problems are prevalent in Tropical Africa, where the populations of most countries are small, population densities generally are low, and primitive land-use systems are widespread. It therefore is not surprising that in geographical studies of Tropical Africa the term "overpopulation" has been used most frequently with reference to such problems and in particular to detrimental effects of excessive population pressure upon physical resources. Such circumstances led W. A. Hance to estimate that almost one-third of Africa is overpopulated (4).

The basic cause of other problems associated with maladjustment between population and resources or production lies not so much in the ratio between the two as with inadequacies of human or social resources, i.e. of the means whereby production is achieved and distributed. Changes in population numbers affect the scale of these problems and may thereby provide a palliative, but they cannot cure the basic ailments. If the term population pressure were used rationally, it would be restricted to the former type of problem; but, in fact, it is more commonly used with reference to the latter, in particular to problems of extreme poverty, land hunger, food shortages, and famine. This usage has the backing of history. For example, William Thomas Thornton, writing in 1846, gave the following definition of overpopulation:

> By Over-population is to be understood . . . that condition of a country in which part of the inhabitants . . . are permanently unable to earn a sufficiency of the necessaries of life [18].

This usage of the term refers to problems which are a product of acute economic malaise. They are infinitely varied and extraordinarily complex. They fall within the compass of no one discipline, and each specialist, although aware of the problem as a whole, ought to direct his attention to those aspects which he is particularly equipped to deal with. The geographer thus may profitably examine the significance of spatial differences and changes within the context of population problems as a whole. This essay reviews population pressure in Zambia. After providing a summary of the human background, it directs attention first to problems associated with direct pressure upon physical resources; and, secondly, it examines some of the geographical aspects of the inadequacies of Zambia's social resources, production, and distribution of wealth.

Zambia is a large country (720,000 km²) with a relatively small population which, in December 1965, consisted of 3,700,000 Africans and 80,000 non-Africans. The rate of population growth is not known with certainty, but estimates indicate that it was approximately 3.0 per cent in 1963 (when the first census of the country was taken) and that it is likely to rise to 3.5 per cent by 1975. If these rates are reasonably reliable, the population will increase to about 5,000,000 by 1975. Clearly, in general terms Zambia is not crowded and is not likely to become crowded in the near future.

The distribution of population, however, is extremely uneven (Figures 22-1 and 22-2). Nearly one-fifth of the total African population is to be found in the ten main towns, seven of which constitute the Copperbelt. The population of these towns has grown rapidly since 1945 and is still growing more rapidly than that of the country as a whole; between 1963 and 1965 it increased at a rate of 6.1 per cent per annum. Without doubt the urban areas are the most crowded parts of Zambia, and by some criteria they are among the more overcrowded parts too. In the rural areas the over-all density of population is only 3.8/km², but rural Zambia may be divided according to

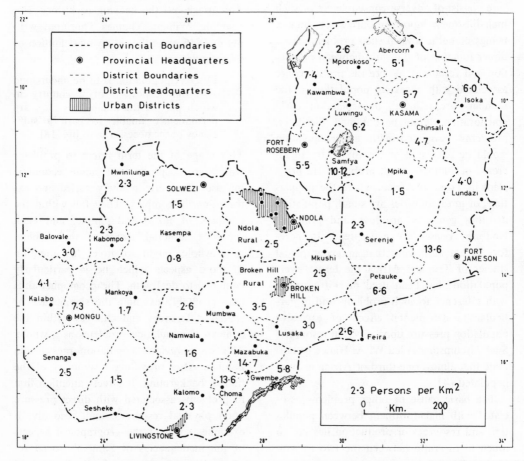

Fig. 22-1. ZAMBIA: ADMINISTRATIVE AREAS AND POPULATION DENSITY BY DISTRICTS.
(*Source: Institute for Social Research Communication No. 2,* Lusaka, 1967.)

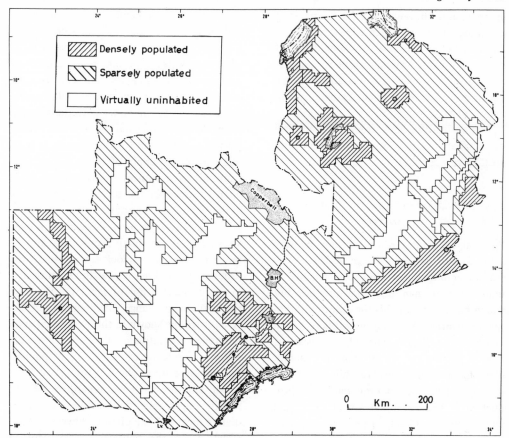

Fig. 22-2. ZAMBIA: POPULATION REGIONS.
(*Source: Institute for Social Research Communication No. 2,* Lusaka, 1967.)

differences in density into three categories which summarize the main inequalities of distribution (Fig. 22-2). Virtually uninhabited regions with an over-all density of 0.07/km² encompass 15.9 per cent of the rural area but accommodate only 0.3 per cent of the rural population. On the other hand, twelve densely populated regions, six large and six small ones, constitute only 12.4 per cent of the area, but accommodate 47.3 per cent of the population (Table 22-1.) The over-all density of population in these regions is 14.5/km², which is not a high figure by world standards but nevertheless is almost four times that for rural Zambia as a whole. Locally within these regions, densities in excess of 100/km² have been noted; but nowhere do such conditions occur over wide areas. Virtually uninhabited and densely populated areas together comprise 28.3 per cent of the rural area and accommodate 47.6 per cent of the rural population. The remainder of rural Zambia (71.7 per cent) is more in keeping with the image projected by national averages. The over-all density for this vast area is 2.8/km². There are, of course, differences in density conditions and in types of distribution within this area; but, taken as a whole, more than two-thirds of Zambia can be described fairly as sparsely populated without either vast empty spaces or significant concentrations of population. Because of their extent, such conditions may be regarded as typical of Zambia; but if this is so, it should be remembered that nearly half of the rural population live in atypical regions and that one out of every five Africans in Zambia lives in a town (12).

It is against this background of numerical data that any analysis of population pressure must be viewed.

Population Pressure on Physical Resources

Physical or natural resources may be usefully divided into two categories. One consists of commodities (animal, vegetable, or mineral) that man does not produce but which he extracts for his use from the lithosphere, hydrosphere, and atmosphere which make up the "land". The other consists of natural phenomena which man may manipulate to produce things for himself. Foremost amongst these natural means of production is the soil upon which plant and animal life are largely dependent, but also of major significance are sources of energy such as insolation, moving water, and wind. In any society, the relative importance of the two categories and of individual resources within each is determined by a wide range of interacting factors including the scientific knowledge, technological and organizational abilities, and cultural values of the people, and, of course, the range of resources available to them. These factors shape the land-use system of the society. Generalization on such matters is hazardous, but it seems clear that primitive economies are heavily and directly dependent upon items which occur naturally within the physical environment and that advanced or highly developed countries rely largely upon adaptation of natural forces to produce required commodities. Thus in developing countries such as Zambia, where primitive and advanced economies occur side by side, there are markedly different attitudes as to what constitutes important resources. These differences affect policies and behavior. For example, they have been and still are reflected in conflicting views as to the solution to problems associated with overcrowded land. The tribesman is inclined to look for a more plentiful supply of things he requires from his environment and demands more land, i.e. he sees the solution in a change in the population : resource ratio. The European and the Westernized African, with their knowledge of productive processes and of modern aids thereto, look toward increased productivity and argue that the solution lies in more efficient use of land, i.e. they see the solution in changes of organization, etc. Also, it will be shown in this paper that such differences in attitude affect the choice of criteria in defining critical levels of population pressure upon physical resources.

All land-use systems, regardless of the relative importance of extractive and manipulative means of exploitation, have profound effects upon the physical environment in which they occur. These effects may eliminate particular resources and may impair means of production. Destructive effects of African land-use systems in Zambia soon attracted the attention of European immigrants, and a sequence of degenerative processes associated with such systems has been observed. Land deterioration begins slowly, but gathers momentum as it progresses and as it increasingly affects soils. Usually the wildlife suffers first from direct and indirect effects of man upon its members and their ecosystems. Simultaneously, the vegetation cover is affected by clearing, burning, and, in some cases, grazing. Reduction of the vegetation cover and cultivation lead to soil deterioration; organic matter, plant nutrients, and soil structure are lost.

Subsequently, regeneration of vegetation becomes more difficult, and increased exposure to the elements leads to sheet erosion of topsoils. Sheet erosion is followed by gullying, and gullies spread into ever more intricate patterns as they eat into the earth. Run-off is increased, local water tables are lowered, water courses are silted up, and surface water supplies are threatened. Eventually the land becomes virtually useless as the soil is destroyed, and it must be returned to nature in the hope that she may heal herself.

Environmental change is a corollary of land use, but it is generally recognized by well-informed individuals that change which threatens the continued existence of soils is inimical to life itself. It is for this reason that "conservation measures" in general terms refers to measures to protect soils and water supplies—the basic means of production. Tribal societies with limited knowledge of productive processes and of modern conservation techniques may constitute a serious threat to soils. However, their heavy dependence on items occurring naturally in the biosphere provides a built-in protective device for soils, because shortages of such items occur early in the sequence of degenerative processes. In other words, population pressures often reach a critical stage for the traditional economy of such peoples before soils are endangered. At this critical stage there arises a demand for more land, and while this demand can be met by colonization, no serious consequences arise. Where, for any reason, a simple redistribution of population in relation to resources is not possible, then pressure on resources must increase as population density increases. For any given system of land use, for each individual resource, there is a critical population density above which that resource will become scarce (i.e. demand will exceed supply); increasingly pressure above this level leads to increasing scarcity, and the resource may be eliminated altogether. Clearly excessive population pressure not only has destructive effects on the physical environment, but it also has adverse effects on standards of living. The latter can be checked by compensating changes in man-land relationships—by changes in the system of land use or by changes in the dependence on local resources or by combinations of both.

From an independent objective viewpoint, the most significant critical density is that in relation to soils, and this density has been and still is greatly exceeded in parts of Zambia. In the 1930's the most serious situations were in the Native Reserves, where the rate of population growth had been greatly increased by in-migration from areas scheduled for non-African settlement. Furthermore, on the Tonga Plateau of the Southern Province, production of maize for sale was becoming increasingly common and was achieved not by raising productivity per unit area but by extending the cultivated area and thus adding to pressure on the land. For many years Africans throughout the country had been ineffectually harangued about their "wasteful methods of cultivation," but little had been done by the Africans themselves or by external agencies to improve matters. Eventually, in the mid-thirties, the government realized the dangers of overcrowded land and was alarmed at the situation it found in the worst problem areas. The Department of Agriculture recognized that ideally in such areas the balance between population and resources should be restored by more efficient use of land, i.e. by implementing compensating changes in the system of man-land relationships. However, it also recognized that alternative systems of land use had not been devised and tested; secondly, that any such innovations could be effected only over a relatively long period;

and, thirdly, that many localities were so crowded as to deny agricultural improvement any chance of success. Therefore resettlement was advocated wherever possible in order to reduce population pressure in the threatened areas, and massive resettlement schemes were undertaken in the Eastern, Central, and Western Provinces before and during the Second World War (1; 3). At the same time conservation measures and rehabilitation schemes were undertaken in the stricken areas. The contrasting landscapes of the resettlement or "new" areas and of the partially devastated areas in the Native Reserves continue to bear witness to the impact of excessive population pressure on physical resources (9).

In order to safeguard the future of the resettlement areas, it was necessary to calculate how much land per capita in a given area is required by a society pursuing a known system of land usage if that society is to maintain itself in perpetuity without constituting a threat to soils and water resources. A means of calculating this critical density or carrying capacity with a tolerable degree of accuracy was devised, and thus there emerged a specific fomula whereby one aspect of overcrowding may be assessed (1; 2). Because of the very primitive nature of many African land-use systems and because of the mediocre potential of large parts of Zambia, the carrying capacity or critical population density with reference to soil conservation is very low in many cases. For example, *chitemene* systems of agriculture commonly practised on the plateaus of northern and central parts of the country can safely support between 1.6 and 4 persons/km^2. On the Eastern Province plateau, a region of relatively fertile soils, the comparatively intensive land-use systems of the Chewa, Nsenga, and Ngoni can carry no more than 10/km^2 without endangering the soils. Such low carrying capacities mean that conditions of overpopulation are easily obtained while absolute population densities remain very low.

In recent years more emphasis has been placed on improvement of agricultural land use as a means of raising carrying capacities; but Zambia is not yet free of problem areas where excessive population pressure is such that it hinders or prevents progress. The *Annual Report of the Natural Resources Board for 1965* recorded that: "soil erosion has advanced to a critical degree in large areas of the Southern, Eastern and Central Provinces. It is not too much to say that the stage has been reached when conventional methods of conservation are unable to control this erosion let alone begin to rehabilitate the land . . . In some northern parts of the country a similar, if less spectacular, situation has developed . . . To remedy this state of affairs is an urgent and challenging task."

Nowadays resettlement must be looked upon as a last resort, particularly in view of the fact that long-distance movements now are unavoidable. Nevertheless, resettlement schemes designed primarily to afford relief to overcrowded areas are still being undertaken. They are very expensive and achieve relatively little. Such schemes demonstrate that, although Zambia as a whole is not crowded, locally very severe shortages of land do exist, temporarily at least (10).

Discussion so far of population pressure upon physical resources has been largely concerned with critical pressures in relation to soils. It is this aspect that receives most emphasis in literature on problems of overpopulation, so much so that in many cases "resources" and "soils" almost become interchangeable. This emphasis reflects the knowledge and viewpoint of Westernized society. African tribal societies, however, are heavily dependent upon resources of the local biosphere; and therefore effects of population pressure upon these resources are of more immediate significance to such societies than effects upon soils which have apparently remote consequences only.

Assessment of significant changes in the total physical environment has been vitiated by scant treatment afforded by many geographers and others to the full range of economic activities of African villagers. The polyfunctional behavior of the tribesman has been neglected, and too often studies of land use in Africa are little more than studies of *agricultural* land-use. It is noteworthy that when an African writes about the economy of his people (the Yoruba of Nigeria), even though that economy is relatively advanced, he devotes nearly 60 per cent of the account to nonagricultural activities (14). Two recent studies of rural economies in Zambia fully recognize the importance of a wide range of activities and the dependence of the people on a wide variety of natural phenomena. Significantly one of these is by an ecologist (16), and an appendix to his work lists 132 wild plants which the Tonga of Gwembe District make use of; equally impressive lists of animal and mineral products could have been compiled. In a Foreword to this book, H. A. Fosbrooke observed that "this work emphasizes the point that a sizeable proportion of village subsistence production in Africa comes not from agriculture or pastoralism but from a full utilization of the surrounding bush and forest." My study of Ushi village life (7) similarly directs attention to the dependence of the people on resources of the biosphere. For example, it shows that "a considerable proportion of the villagers' time—rather more than one-quarter of that spent in agriculture—is devoted to procuring wild foodstuffs" and that such foodstuffs contributed significantly to nearly 60 per cent of all meals consumed during a year. In addition to foodstuffs, a wide range of raw materials for the construction of buildings of all types and for the manufacture of a wide variety of tools, utensils, furniture, ornaments, and other items are collected from the land.

As noted above, excessive population pressure on particular resources will lead to and be indicated by scarcity of these resources. Adverse effects of such scarcities upon standards of living can be averted either by the use of alternative commodities which are readily available or by "importing" supplies of the scarce items and/or of substitutes for them. Changes in man-land relationships of the former type are restricted by the potential of the local physical environment and by cultural conservatism. Changes of the latter type depend upon the production of surpluses whereby the imported goods may be purchased. Such changes involve increasing areal and personal specialization in economic matters and, in most cases, an increase in productivity per capita. It is, however, frustrating to see fruits of such development vitiated by gaps in a deteriorating subsistence economy.

Some case material will illustrate consequences of excessive population pressure upon physical resources which are subject to extractive methods of exploitation. Game meat and fish everywhere are welcome additions to the diet, but except in highly localized areas they are no longer plentiful. Trapping of small animals and the collection of insects, fungi, roots, leaves, fruits, and honey also have become less rewarding occupations. There is, in fact, ample evidence that the subsistence diet has deteriorated as nonagricultural sources of foodstuffs have become less plentiful in either relative or absolute terms or both. So-called subsistence economies are no longer self-sufficient in even bare essentials, and in many rural areas of Zambia much hard-won money is spent on basic foodstuffs (8; 15).

TABLE 22-1   DENSELY POPULATED REGIONS OF RURAL ZAMBIA

Major Regions	Area (km²)	Population 1963	Density/km²
Luapula-Mweru valley	6,187	118,000	19
Eastern Province plateau	20,187	381,500	19
Tonga (Southern Province plateau)	12,750	211,000	17
Bangweulu basin	11,135	148,500	13
Upper Zambezi valley	15,187	165,500	11
Lusaka-Mumbwa	11,250	118,000	10
Minor Regions			
Fort Rosebery	1,812	24,000	13
Chirundu	875	11,500	13
Abercorn	2,625	33,500	13
Kawambwa	2,062	26,500	13
Kasama	2,837	36,000	12
Lake Kariba	2,500	25,000	10

(Source: 12)

In densely populated areas (Table 22-1 and Figure 22-2), basic commodities such as timber suitable for rafters, thatching grass, bark-fiber for ropes (all essential building materials), and even domestic fuel are now scarce. Trade has developed in such items, and those who can afford to do so pay others to fetch such things from relatively distant areas where population pressure is less severe. Those unable to offer cash or other acceptable goods in exchange must "pay" for these items with time and energy that must be expended in collecting them from far afield. The introduction of alternative materials generally is more costly than the import of customary commodities. Unfortunately, in most parts of Zambia rural land-use systems do not provide a large salable surplus. Furthermore in areas where opportunities to obtain cash do exist (as in the Luapula-Mweru valley and the Bangweulu Basin, where fishing is now a commercial activity, on the plateaus of the Eastern and Southern Provinces where cash-crop farming has developed, and in the various peri-urban areas), such opportunities are not equally available to all households. A simple socio-economic survey will reveal that prosperous households command sufficient wealth to make good the deficiencies of the local environment and to obtain a higher standard of living than most rural families. On the other hand it will reveal also that many households have very small cash incomes and their standard of living, depressed by population pressure on local resources, appears to be worse than that of most families in less well-developed areas where population pressure is low. In viewing the general prosperity of the developing parts of the country, it is too easy to overlook the plight of the numerous households who depend not so much upon new economic opportunities as upon customary land-use systems (5; 6).

The self-sufficiency of the rural African has been further reduced during the present century because he has been increasingly drawn into a wider sphere than that of his tribal group, and remote forces have extended his horizons and created new needs and wants. International trade has penetrated village life, and changing systems of values have led to a very real "crisis of expectations." In some cases this has led to abandonment of local resources as alternative trade goods have been universally accepted. For example, leather and bark clothing are rarely seen nowadays; iron-smelting has ceased to be a village industry; only the destitute manufacture salt from reeds and grasses; and mining of clay and the making of pottery are fast-disappearing activities. If rural society could achieve the levels of consumption it desires to have, then the lists of abandoned resources and of recently adopted goods would be very long. The wish to change and raise material standards of living is thwarted by the low productivity of the rural economy; but it is against this background of hopes and wishes that deterioration of the subsistence or customary economy must be viewed. Where population pressure is excessive, progress must be made in order to stand still.

Population Pressure on Social Resources

The foregoing discussion will have made it clear that definition of what constitutes a physical or natural resource is largely a function of man's abilities and viewpoint, which are conditioned by factors too numerous and complex to analyze here. Man's land-use system is a product of these same factors, and it conveniently circumscribes those parts of the total physical environment which a particular group at a particular time regards as resources. The definition of physical resources therefore can be achieved by analysis of land-use systems, and for a given society, time, and place, a finite list of tangible items can be compiled. The actual use of each physical resource and its contribution to the total production achieved by a society are largely determined by human attributes which might be defined as social resources. Analysis of land-use systems there-

fore also illuminates the field of social resources, but it is exceedingly difficult to enumerate such resources and to isolate the contribution of each, because none of them is tangible and few are susceptible to measurement. The labor force perhaps is the most obvious social or human resource, but to measure it simply in terms of numbers of persons is inadequate. How can qualities such as strength, intelligence, skill, aptitude, experience, industrial honesty, or enthusiasm be measured? What, in fact, is it that makes a good workman? How far can the labor force be measured in numbers of persons? What importance must be allocated to the organization of individuals? What is it that determines productivity?

Difficulties of definition should not lead to neglect of the survey and analysis of social resources because it is through development of these resources that organizations and institutions capable of solving Zambia's major problems may be obtained. Indeed, problems directly associated with excessive population pressure upon physical resources may be viewed either as local problems or as symptoms of a national imbalance between physical and social resources which results in low levels of productivity and poverty. This imbalance can be corrected by improvements of the national store of human resources, and the existence within Zambia of a dual economy illuminates the possibilities of such improvements. Hitherto the highly developed and very productive sections of the economy have been associated almost exclusively with non-African immigrants whose resources (knowledge, technology, skills, experience, organizing abilities, capital assets, etc.) coupled with local physical resources have produced great wealth and provided those concerned with large incomes and high material standards of living. The indigenous people with access to the same or similar physical resources have achieved no comparable level of production. The difference lies in contrasting social resources, technology, and organization.

The basis of progress in Zambia therefore, in the long run, must be through education in all its varied aspects; but perhaps of greater interest to geographers are problems associated with the maladjustment of population to resources which are of more immediate importance. One of these is to determine what part of this maladjustment may be corrected by redistribution of population in relation to physical resources or to realistically assessed development potential. The significance of current maldistribution of population is illustrated by recent and continuing spontaneous movements of population. The largest product of such movements is the Copperbelt—a prosperous urban region with more than half a million inhabitants, where only 40 years ago a handful of Africans scraped a poor living from the forest and its soils. Rural-urban migration, in fact, is a phenomenon of major importance in Zambia which reflects areal differences in economic opportunities. Relatively small-scale movements within the rural areas are not well documented, and many go almost unnoticed. Only those characterized by some notable feature receive wide attention. The recent rapid influx of "stranger" fishermen to exploit resources of the Kafue Flats and the settlement of large numbers of Rhodesian Africans in Mumbwa District (where they have become successful commercial farmers) are two such movements which have gained considerable attention because of actual and potential social strife in the receiving areas. But these are not isolated cases; they are symptomatic of more general movements of population at local, regional, national, and even international scales into areas which appear to offer the migrants better economic opportunities than those they had prior to moving (11). Several such

areas of in-migration, notably the major fisheries and peri-urban areas, already are densely populated and are overcrowded in respect of customary systems of land usage. Therefore, as noted above, these areas present a paradoxical mixture of problems and promise; uncontrolled in-migration and inadequate land-use planning in these areas aggravate the problems.

The challenge presented by the national situation, however, is not so much to identify existing movements engendered by maldistribution of population in relation to economic opportunities but rather to determine where the opportunities for the future should be created. This calls for a national stock-taking of resources and assessment of growth potential and, subsequently, a rational allocation of priorities for development. Full consideration must be given to bottlenecks likely to hinder progress, and this focuses attention upon *critical* human resources. In Zambia, shortages of suitably qualified and experienced personnel to man key positions in the motivation of economic growth constitute the most limiting factor. Recruitment of highly trained and skilled workers from abroad has helped to make good such shortages, and must continue to do so for many years in spite of unfortunate socio-economic, racial, and political problems created by this manifest dependence on expensive alien manpower. In view of the critical importance of such scarce human resources, the distribution and character of development will be greatly affected by their allocation to various industrial sectors of the economy and to various parts of the country. This allocation, as noted above, should be made with reference to growth potential and with special reference to the creation of employment opportunities rather than simply to the production of wealth. Such a national economic development plan must incorporate schemes for the necessary controlled movements of people, which should reflect a lasting revision of population distribution—a rational areal adjustment of population in relation to significant physical and social resources.

Two main groups of problems make such economic planning hazardous. First, too little is known about the physical resources of the country; the stock-taking is far from complete. Nevertheless, sufficient is known to make fairly realistic short-term plans and to justify exploration of several known possibilities. The scale of some development possibilities may be illustrated by reference to the estimated agricultural potential of the Kafue Flats which lie southwest of Lusaka. Pilot trials indicate that an intensively farmed, irrigated polder of 11,200 hectares could provide a population of 14,000 with acceptable income levels. Such a polder would encompass less than 5 per cent of the area capable of similar development. Therefore, successful development of the entire Kafue Flats could offer favorable economic opportunities for a total population of about 250,000. Such development would call for massive readjustment of population distribution and could provide a new life for many of those now living in areas with very limited potential. However, there may be more promising prospects elsewhere, and Zambia stands in need of extensive and intensive prospecting, experimentation, and assessment before projects such as the Kafue Flats development scheme can be viewed in true perspective.

The second group of problems is associated with forces which run counter to the strict application of economic criteria in allocating scarce manpower and capital assets. Social, humanitarian, and, more particularly, political factors have generated a strong feeling that economic opportunities should be taken to the people rather than the reverse. To what extent and in what manner should account be taken of these

factors? Their current stength is reflected in the *First National Development Plan 1966–1970* which seeks "to provide a radical improvement in the living standards of the whole population." In particular, it seeks to take development into the "forgotten areas":

> . . . the allocation of investment funds has been orientated firstly to divert resources to the rural areas rather than to the "line-of-rail," and secondly to allocate these by Provinces in such a way as to favour the development of such neglected regions as the Northern, Luapula, Barotse and North-Western Provinces.

The economically advanced areas of proven potential are not neglected, but emphasis undoubtedly has been placed upon pioneering development in areas hitherto regarded as having limited potential. This policy may be regarded as a somewhat expensive but politically necessary form of prospecting, and perhaps some of the problem areas of today will become growth areas of tomorrow. Eventually, however, when the hurlyburly which inevitably follows political independence is over, it seems likely that a relatively few, highly localized areas will emerge as the growth regions; and perhaps then controlled redistribution of population in relation to resources and economic opportunities will be accepted as a matter of policy.

Economic development in Zambia thus is seen to be restricted by a dearth of critical human resources which can be eliminated only by education in its widest sense. This is a slow process, and meanwhile production, productivity, and living standards may best be increased by equipping the more promising areas of natural potential with highly developed human resources and other prerequisites for economic growth insofar as they are available, and by controlled redistribution of the general populace in relation to the economic opportunities thus created. Inevitably, large parts of the country and, temporarily at least, large sections of the population will not be directly involved in and will not directly benefit from such economic development. However, the government is able to redistribute part of the wealth produced in the country in the form of social services, and it is duty-bound to provide basic services equally to all members of the nation. Furthermore, many social services are concerned with the betterment of the nation—with the development of human resources. As such they have an important role in the long-term economic development of the country.

Areal differences in the potential and needs of individuals and groups in Zambia are not marked; and, on political and moral grounds, the allocation of basic services should be made with reference to the spatial occurrence of population. The colonial government and the present government have, each in turn declared it their intention to extend social services equally to all persons; but in practice, because essential staff and capital goods have been in short supply, it has not been possible to apply this principle. Under such circumstances, in order to make the most efficient use of available resources, the provision of social services ought perhaps to be made with reference to cost-benefit ratios, those areas with the more favorable ratios being equipped first. In practice, political and historical factors and the *ad hoc* manner in which services have been provided have combined to prevent the distribution of services in accordance with economic criteria. However, because the level of services has been far beneath the optimum, few services, if any, have been seriously under-used. Nowadays high priority is given to universal or optimal provision of basic services to the nation as a whole; and

as the level of services increasingly approaches the optimum, the need for careful planning becomes more urgent in order to avoid wasteful use of scarce resources.

It is in the sparsely populated regions (Fig. 22-2) that the provision of services and infrastructure (including administration) is particularly difficult and costly, prohibitively so in some areas. More than half of the rural population lives in such regions, and they are conscious that they have been relatively neglected for many years. Therefore the problems posed by population patterns in these areas for the economical provision of services are viewed with the utmost urgency; and the government is exploring the possibilities of regrouping rural peoples in order to facilitate social progress.

Regrouping involves bringing together at (or in reasonable proximity to) a place where services exist or will be provided sufficient persons to justify the services involved. Three groups of important problems are inimical to such an exercise and must be tackled at an early stage. First, regrouping inevitably increases local population densities, and population pressure in the resettlement areas may well exceed the critical level in respect of many physical resources, including the soil. Where such overpopulation does occur, unless there are compensating changes in man-land relationships, the resource base and the standard of living will deteriorate. Some ecological or economic change in land use therefore is likely to be a prerequisite in many cases for successful regrouping. Secondly, the present distribution of population and the present form of settlements reflect deep-seated social and cultural preferences, and social obstacles to regrouping are extremely formidable. Rural-urban migration demonstrates that such obstacles are not insuperable, but it is unlikely that the provision of basic social services alone will constitute sufficient inducement to persuade rural people to change their place of residence (particularly if long distances are involved) or to adopt new forms of settlement. Regrouping, therefore, is likely to be more successful where opportunities for both economic and social advancement are available.

Thirdly, successful regrouping depends upon the existence or provision of a spatial and hierarchical network of service centers constituted in accordance with the philosophy which underlies Central Place Theory. At present no such framework exists. On the contrary, service functions in rural Zambia are dispersed in an extraordinarily haphazard manner. The situation in Mpika District is illustrative of prevailing conditions. Urban functions of the same order are distributed between five places along the line of the Great North Road. Traveling from the south, the first "urban" place encountered is at Chilonga Mission, where there is the only hospital in the district, an upper primary school, a church, and social activities associated with a major mission station. Chilonga has its own water and electricity supplies; it has its own peri-urban satellite villages. About 19.5 km further north lies Chibansa, which is the site of Mpika landing ground, of the transport and bus stations, and associated rest houses for Central African Road Services and other haulage companies using the Great North Road, of the district police station, of the only hotel in the district, and of several commercial premises. Three kilometers further north a large Public Works Department road camp and the residence of the district engineer is passed enroute to Mpika Boma, which is a further three kilometers away. The *boma* is the government's district headquarters, and is served by its own commercial and social institutions with several notable omissions as noted. It is, however, the largest and most developed of the various "urban centers." About 10.5

km north of the *boma* lies Chikwanda Rural Township, which was the former Native Authority Headquarters and now accommodates the staff of the Rural (District) Council. It is the site of the local court, a market, several shops, a church, and a school; and it is the home of Chief Chikwanda, the senior Bemba chief in Mpika District. Finally, rather more than 1.5 km north of Chikwanda is the new and very large Luitikila Secondary School for Girls. Such dispersion precludes the emergence of a sizable urban center in Mpika District and prevents "economies of scale." Also it deprives the rural population of a single focal point. No doubt there are historical reasons for this type of pattern, but its existence presents problems which must be tackled. It is contradictory to propose regrouping of rural peoples while at the same time permitting and even fostering widespread dispersion of services of the same order. Regrouping of service functions and careful siting of future installations are therefore urgently required, and this exercise also may be viewed as a prerequisite for regrouping of people.

Finally, the problem of providing services economically in sparsely populated areas appears to call for a combination of several measures of which regrouping people is only one. Attention might profitably be given to adapting services to the needs of the situation, and in particular the mobility of both services and people might well be increased (13).

Population Pressure in Urban Areas

Rural-urban migration in Zambia has reached such proportions that it is generally recognized as a source of serious problems in both the rural areas (which are depleted by selective effects of migration) and in the towns which are overcrowded. Most of these problems are intractable, and, in spite of hopes to the contrary, rural development can provide little relief in the near future. In the short term, many of the problems must be tackled individually, and a general solution must be sought in long-term economic development in both rural and industrial sectors.

Excessive population pressure in urban areas is manifest in two phenomena which may be used as indices; each has widespread ramifications which link one with the other. The first is the level of unemployment, which may be defined as the number of persons actively seeking work as a percentage of those in paid employment. The 1963 census showed that there were 27,500 men and youths seeking work in urban areas, and this figure represented 18.0 per cent of the actual labor force. It is generally believed that since 1963, and particularly since independence, the level of unemployment has increased markedly in spite of rapid expansion of the labor force. Where a migratory

system of labor exists and the stability of many workers is low, it is inevitable and probably necessary that there should be a considerable body of prospective employees in search of work. Even so, few would dispute the claim that a ratio of one unemployed person to every five employees constitutes an excessive level and is a symptom of gross overurbanization. Furthermore, those seeking work are only the vanguard of a much larger body of potential migrants who would flock to the towns if there were reasonable chances of obtaining paid employment. In fact, in 1962 there were approximately 90,000 Zambians at work in other countries, and it would require an increase of about 30 per cent of the present labor force to absorb these emigrants should they turn to their own country for work.

Extreme chronic pressure on limited employment opportunities has affected income levels. For example, numerous jobs have been created in response to a willingness to work for low wages; and, secondly, central

TABLE 22-2   THE NUMBER AND AVERAGE ANNUAL EARNINGS OF AFRICAN EMPLOYEES BY INDUSTRIAL SECTORS IN ZAMBIA

Industrial Sector	Employees	Earnings (U.S. $)[1]			
	1964	1954	1963	1965	1966[2]
Agriculture	34,500	114	184	230	235
Mining	42,500	370	836	1158	1240
Manufacturing	18,000	212	484	686	637
Construction	29,100	208	388	450	516
Commerce	14,500	205	438	648	680
Transport and communications	8,700	230	598	686	876
Services (including administration)	54,200	215	468	640	626
Domestic service	35,400	156	262	304	452
ALL EMPLOYEES	237,000	216	448	604	712

[1] Earnings include cash wages and the cash value of all income in kind (e.g. free rations, housing, uniforms) and employer's contributions to social benefits (e.g. pension funds).
[2] Estimates based on data relating to the first quarter only.
(Source: Monthly Digest of Statistics, Vol. III, No. 9, November 1967, Central Statistical Office, Lusaka.)

and local governments and many private employers have fostered labor-intensive projects and methods as a matter of policy. For these, and many other reasons, African earnings have been very low. The country now faces a serious dilemma. The demand for many more jobs is accompanied by a forceful demand for much higher remuneration. Higher labor costs are likely to foster capital-intensive rather than labor-intensive measures and to reduce employment within the existing industrial structure and to affect adversely the rate of economic growth and the creation of new jobs. Nevertheless, in recent years earnings have increased rapidly, but a large majority of urban workers still have very low incomes (Table 22-2.)

The low incomes and low productivity of the urban labor force give rise to the second index of population pressure in urban areas, i.e. the extent to which minimum standards of services and amenities are available to the urban population (which might be defined conservatively as the employed persons and their dependents rather than the total population found in the urban areas). Limitations of space prevent detailed discussion of this facet of Zambia's problems, but a few actual statements will illustrate its severity. In 1963 more than 10 per cent of Lusaka's population lived in unauthorized squatter encampments, and a further 10 per cent lived in miscellaneous settlements in the peri-urban areas. Probably more than one-quarter of the capital's population lived in temporary or semi-permanent buildings of types which have been recognized as unsatisfactory for more than twenty years. Furthermore, most African houses are very small, and a survey of houses within the city in 1960 showed that 23.8 per cent had one room only, 31.3 per cent had two rooms, and 40.5 per cent had three rooms, including kitchens (or cooking spaces) in all cases. The provision of other urban services and amenities also is at very low levels; and such conditions are widespread in both large and small towns. For example, in 1960 at Fort Roseberry, housing of any type was available within the township for less than half of those employed in the town; the remainder lived in peri-urban villages. The Copperbelt, the most prosperous and most rigorously administered region of Zambia, probably has the best record for the provision of urban facilities to its African population; but even there standards are poor and are recognized to be so. Some aspects of overcrowding in the urban areas call for early attention, but the ultimate solution lies in increased productivity—in more efficient use of Zambia's resources, both physical and social.

Conclusion

This essay has shown that Zambia, with an over-all population density of only 5/km², faces a formidable range of problems associated with population pressure on physical and social resources. Some of these problems can be and are being alleviated by redistribution of the population, i.e. by altering the ratio between population and resources or production. Foremost among such remedial measures are resettlement schemes to relieve pressure on devastated, overcrowded land; the regrouping or clustering of population to reduce pressure on scarce services and amenities and to make the provision of such facilities more economical; and the various efforts to persuade the unemployed in towns to go back to the land. In these problems and remedies the direct relationship between population and resources or production can be readily discerned as a major factor. Many other problems commonly associated with the phrase "population pressure," however, are related to and arise from deficiencies in technology, skill, organizing ability, and similar human assets. They are, in fact, *problems of development* which are aggravated and intensified by the rapid growth of population, by the dire poverty of the majority of the nation, by maldistribution of population in relation to resources or development opportunities, and by excessive direct pressure of population on physical resources in many localities. Such problems, however, are acute in many sparsely populated areas, where there is no shortage of land but where a large majority of the population is "permanently unable to earn a sufficiency of the necessaries of life." These conditions and the situation in Zambia as a whole demonstrate how inappropriate it is to label problems of poverty as problems of population pressure. In parts of the world where population densities are great, population numbers are large and rates of increase are high, and where poverty is so acute that it includes chronic food shortages, the term may appear to be more appropriate. But the problems are fundamentally the same as those of Zambia; they differ only in degree. The need is to raise production and levels of consumption and the designation of such problems as a function of population pressure seems to have little scientific foundation.

REFERENCES

(1) W. Allan: Studies in African Land Usage in Northern Rhodesia, Rhodes-Livingstone Paper 15 (Lusaka, 1949).

(2) W. Allan: The African Husbandman (Edinburgh, 1965).

(3) R. H. Fraser: Land Settlement in the Eastern Province of Northern Rhodesia, *Rhodes-Livingstone Journal,* Vol. 3, 1945, pp. 45-49.

(4) W. A. Hance: The Geography of Modern Africa (New York and London, 1964).

(5) G. Kay: A Social and Economic Study of Fort Rosebery Township and Peri-Urban Area, Rhodes-Livingstone Communication 21 (Lusaka, 1960).

(6) G. Kay: Population Surveys as Prerequisites for Community Development, in: R. J. Apthorpe, ed.: Social Research and Community Development, 15th Rhodes-Livingstone Conference Proceedings (Lusaka, 1961).

(7) G. Kay: Chief Kalaba's Village, Rhodes-Livingstone Paper 35 (Manchester, 1964).

(8) G. Kay: Sources and Uses of Cash in some Ushi Villages, Fort Rosebery District, Northern Rhodesia, *Rhodes-Livingstone Journal,* Vol. 35, 1964, pp. 14-28.

(9) G. Kay: Changing Patterns of Settlement and Land Use in the Eastern Province of Northern Rhodesia, Occasional Papers in Geography, No. 2 (Hull University Publications, 1965).

(10) G. Kay: Resettlement and Land Use Planning in Zambia: The Chipangali Scheme, *Scottish Geographical Magazine,* Vol. 81, 1965, pp. 163-77.

(11) G. Kay: A Social Geography of Zambia (London, 1967).

(12) G. Kay: Maps of the Distribution and Density of African Population in Zambia. Institute for Social Research Communication 2 (Lusaka, 1967).

(13) G. Kay: Social Aspects of Village Regrouping in Zambia. Miscellaneous Series No. 7 (Department of Geography, Hull University, 1967).

(14) G. J. Ojo: Yoruba Culture (London, 1966).

(15) D. U. Peters: Land Usage in Barotseland. Rhodes-Livingstone Communication 19 (Lusaka, 1960).

(16) T. Scudder: The Ecology of the Gwembe Tonga (Manchester, 1962).

(17) R. W. Steel: An Inventory of Land and People, *Journal of African Administration,* Vol. 12, 1960.

(18) H. R. Thornton: Overpopulation and its Remedy (London, 1846).

(19) H. R. Wilkinson: Man and the Natural Environment, Occasional Papers in Geography No. 1 (Hull University Publications, 1963).

23. POPULATION DENSITIES AND RURAL ECONOMIES IN THE KANO CLOSE-SETTLED ZONE, NIGERIA

M. J. Mortimore

The Kano Close-Settled Zone is the name applied to a large area of high population density and intensive land-use surrounding Kano in the Sudan savanna zone of Nigeria. It occupies the greater part of Kano State, which has an area of 26,608 km² and a population of 4.3 million (1962). The density of population diminishes outward from more than 240/km² in the immediate vicinity of Kano (249,281 inhabitants in 1962) to about 140/km² at distances of 20 to 25 km. These figures should be contrasted with average densities in Northern Nigeria (24/km² in 1952) and Tropical Africa (about 10/km²). Such high densities, and the intensive systems of land use associated with them, are especially rare in the savanna zones of marked seasonal rainfall. Yet the Kano Close-Settled Zone, which contains about 2.4 million inhabitants, is not generally regarded as overpopulated and may have considerable relevance to other parts of Africa and the tropics.

Soils and Agriculture

Pending a thorough examination of the limits of the Close-Settled Zone, it may be defined conveniently as an area in which the density of population exceeds 140/km², since the density gradient, if followed outward from Kano, steepens at this point (Fig. 23-1). The shape of the zone is elliptical, oriented from northwest to southeast. This boundary falls almost entirely within the limit of distribution of soils classified as brown or reddish-brown soils of arid or semi-arid regions (4; 9). These light, freely-draining sandy loams are found on gently undulating terrain about 500 m above sea level, and were developed on wind-transported dune sands during a relatively arid period of the Pleistocene. To the northeast, on the sedimentary rocks of the Chad series, the dune sands gave rise to inferior sandy soils, and to the south, heavier ferruginous tropical soils, developed under conditions of higher rainfall, predominate.

The wind-borne soils are well adapted to the system of intensive hoe farming which has developed over many centuries in the Close-Settled Zone. Their drainage characteristics render them easier to work than the better-watered ferruginous tropical soils further south, and because of higher organic content, larger clay-silt fraction, and greater mineral reserves they are also superior to the soil groups further north and east, where the rainfall diminishes progressively to about 500 mm. Their fertility is increased through large inputs of manure derived from household refuse and animals. Guinea corn, millet, groundnuts, and cowpeas are the basic crops. Guinea corn loses first place to millet on the sandier soils, while millet declines in importance on the ferruginous tropical soils of the better-watered south.

The Close-Settled Zone

Kano, which was once closely associated with the Kano Emirate, has been a center of power in Hausaland for a thousand years, a factor which has enabled a large sedentary population to grow in relative security. The distribution of population in Northern Nigeria reflects the political realities of pre-colonial times, and areas of chronic instability still have very low densities. In central Kano the degree of security was such that

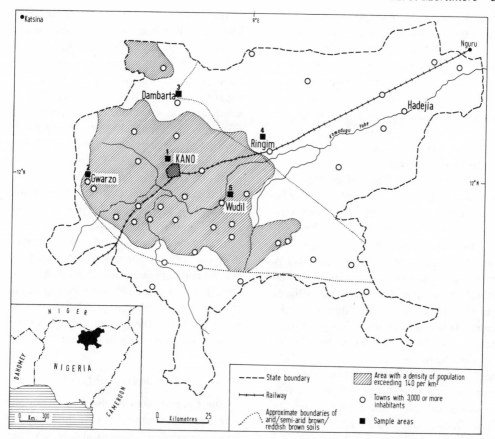

Fig. 23-1. THE KANO CLOSE-SETTLED ZONE AND THE LOCATION OF SAMPLE STUDIES.
INSET: THE LOCATION OF KANO STATE

the dispersal of settlement from the old walled towns and villages was well advanced by 1900. Kano city was also a center of manufacturing and commerce, and enjoyed a close economic interrelationship with its rural environs.

After a study of three village communities in the immediate environs of Kano (8), it was concluded that high population densities in the heart of the Close-Settled Zone appear to be maintained by natural increase, with migration playing a minor or insignificant role. The pressure of population is reflected in the virtual disappearance of fallow and the devotion of 85 per cent of the surface area to annual or perennial cultiva-

tion. Land tenure is becoming more individualized, and land sales, fostered by rising values and the influence of a commercial economy, have forced acceptance of increasingly frequent alienation. The subdivision and fragmentation of landholdings is proceeding at a greater rate than consolidation and enlargement. In the process to intensify agriculture, heavy manuring has replaced fallowing, and regular intercropping of legumes and grain crops is practised with high labor inputs (especially in perennial irrigated cultivation). There is a small, but significant deficit in food crops, largely the result of increased cultivation of cash crops. Secondary occupations, especially weaving, oriented principally toward the urban market, provide sufficient income to make up for deficiencies in agricultural production. The exchange of manure and firewood on a large scale has increased the interdependence of urban and rural communities. The close web of economic ties between town and country, which has survived from pre-colonial times, has played an essential part in the growth of the Zone.

In view of the gradation of density from the center of the Zone outward, it might be expected that some of the distinctive economic adjustments recognized in the Central Area would disappear or assume reduced significance with greater distance. A comparison between two villages in the Central Area and four outlying villages tests this possibility. The villages in the Central Area are located in Ungogo District (density 244/km²) and have densities of 370/km². Kausani, one of the four "outliers," is located in Wudil District 43 km southeast of Kano, but is still well within the limits of the Close-Settled Zone. In Wudil District the density is 207 (1962), and the rate of growth is 1.2 per cent per annum, one of the slowest in Kano State. Seasonal migration is very common among the young men, who travel to Kano, Jos, and other towns for urban employment in the dry season. Farmers from this District take up irrigated farms on the Jos Plateau, where there is a large market for vegetables among the mining population, and fishermen travel to the Hadejia River in the northeast where permanent water is to be found. These movements, which are said to affect nearly every family in Kausani, suggest the inadequacy of agricultural resources, but evidently the situation is not serious enough to provoke permanent emigration.

Masallaci, a village in Dambarta District 51 km north of Kano, lies just outside the Close-Settled Zone in an area of rapid population growth (2.3 per cent per annum). The over-all density of population in the district is 202/km². Gangaren Riji lies 72 km west of Kano within the Close-Settled Zone in Gwarzo District, which has a density of 176/km². Dry season migration to urban areas is common, but no permanent migration is reported; the population is growing at 2.2 per cent per annum. Finally, Hamburawa in Ringim District is 69 km northeast of Kano and outside the Close-Settled Zone. Ringim District has a density of 116/km² and an annual growth rate of 2.4 per cent, which is above average. Altogether some 189 compounds were surveyed in these villages for comparison with 44 family compounds in the Central Area. It should be noted, however, that only in Ringim District is the population density markedly below the general average for the Close-Settled Zone, which is about 200/km².

The Division of Land

In the Central Area of the Zone a serious shortage of agricultural land is shown by the large proportion (approximately 85 per

TABLE 23-1   LAND USE IN THE CENTER AND ON THE PERIPHERY OF THE KANO CLOSE-SETTLED ZONE

Category	% of total area	
	Central area	Hamburawa
Woodland, scrub, grazing	7.5	53.4
Annually cultivated land	79.6	45.2
Perennially cultivated (irrigated) land	4.2	—
Settlements (including some garden land)	6.0	0.6
Rock surfaces, gullies	0.4	—
Rivers	1.3	—
Roads, paths etc.	1.0	0.8
	100.0	100.0

cent) of the total area given to annual or perennial cultivation, while attempts are still made to cultivate residual marginal land. By contrast, in Hamburawa this proportion is only 45 per cent. The relative importance of the different types of land use in these two areas is shown in Table 23-1, and the patterns of land use are mapped in Figures 23-2 and 23-3.

Hamburawa preserves the appearance of a village with no shortage of agricultural land; the reserves of "bush" (woodland and grazing), which in the Central Area are almost exhausted, form a continuous belt on three sides of the cultivated land which surrounds the village itself. Much of the "bush" is long fallow which has been cultivated in the past. Scattered fields still occur in this scrub woodland. A zone of permanent woodland and grassland follows a slight topo-graphical depression along the northern boundary, where seasonal flooding renders agriculture impracticable.

The other three villages do not enjoy Hamburawa's favorable position, and in all of them land is reported to be in short supply. Woodland reserves have been almost exhausted and often farm trees have to be cut down for firewood. But nowhere are the woodlands as depleted as in the Central Area, where Kano city has stimulated an active trade in firewood. Yet the density of farm trees is greatest in this area, where their value is most appreciated.

It has been suggested that in the area closest to Kano the increasing frequency of sale is an indicator of the shortage of agricultural land. Land is regularly bought and sold in all of the villages, but most frequently in Gangaren Riji and the Central

Fig. 23-2. AVERAGE ANNUAL INCREASES OF POPULATION BY DISTRICTS IN KANO STATE, 1931-52 AND 1952-62

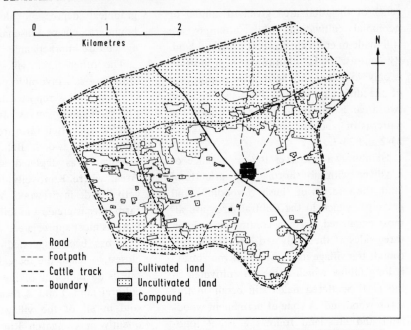

Fig. 23-3. LAND USE AT HAMBURAWA, RINGIM DISTRICT, KANO STATE

Area, where 39 and 31 per cent of the holdings (respectively) were partly or wholly purchased by their present occupiers. (Table 23-2). "Borrowing" land, with payment of rent on an annual lease, is a very common means of obtaining extra land.

The frequent purchase of land outside village boundaries is another indicator of land shortages. In the Central Area this process, aided by subdivision, has resulted in a complicated pattern of tenure in which

TABLE 23-2   KANO CLOSE-SETTLED ZONE:
PERCENTAGE OF HOLDINGS PARTLY
OR WHOLLY PURCHASED

	Number of Holdings	% Purchased
Central area	44	31
Kausani	54	11
Masallaci	45	26
Hamburawa	42	21
Gangaren Riji	48	39
Outlying villages	189	24

the village boundary no longer has real significance.

Comparison of the size of holdings is beset with difficulties. In one of the central villages an area of 180 hectares was surveyed in 1964 and found to contain between 103 and 115 separate holdings, the average size about 1.4 hectares. The uncertainty as to total number of holdings arose from the duplication of some names which could not be satisfactorily resolved afterwards. However, the frequency of landholding across village boundaries suggests that family holdings in the outlying villages may be larger. A sample of 17 holdings in these villages, representing 7.2 per cent of the families surveyed, revealed larger holdings averaging 2.6 hectares. Valid comparisons were obstructed by the occasional farmer who attempted to conceal his land holdings or by marked differences in family size from village to village.

Thus, although it is clear that cultivated

land is scarcer in the central area, where only 1.04 hectares per adult male are available compared with 1.6 hectares in the outlying villages taken together, it is not certain to what extent this has caused a reduction in the size of family holdings. But an increase in population density in the Central Area from 132/km² in 1931 to 320 in 1964 was accompanied by progressive fragmentation and subdivision. Between 1932 and 1964, the number of separately occupied plots in the surveyed area increased by 42 per cent to 185; the number of landholders also increased from 95 to about 115. During the same period the cultivated area was increased by the clearance of 10.4 hectares of "bush," mostly marginal land situated in depressions. Of all the plots registered in 1932, 41 per cent had been subdivided by 1964, while only 16 per cent had been consolidated with adjacent holdings. Thus subdivision gained at the expense of consolidation. Fragmentation is also increasing. The average plot decreased in size from 1.08 to 0.84 hectares, a decrease of 22 per cent, whereas the average holding diminished by less than 11 per cent from 1.5 to 1.3-1.5 hectares.*

Elsewhere in Hausaland, population density has been found to be related to the amount of cultivated land available per capita and to the frequency of types of tenure, a larger proportion of holdings having been inherited in less densely populated areas (10; 6). Near Zaria, Norman has shown an increase in the average size of holdings from 2.4 hectares, close to the township, to 3.5-4.04 hectares at distances of 32-40 km, to be in association with diminishing population density, and a proportionate increase in fallow land.

* This analysis was made from the records of the Kano Revenue Survey which were made available to the author by the Kano Native Authority Survey Department.

Agricultural Intensification

The most important indicator of agricultural intensification in the Central Area is the use of manure at an annual rate of 3.25 to 5.0 tons per hectare. Inputs are at a maximum close to Kano, which itself supplies much of the material. A large-scale trade exists between the city and its rural environs and about 15 out of 44 families spend money on manure. Fertilizer is also used in the outlying villages—reportedly by all farmers. In Masallaci increased input is considered an alternative to obtaining extra land, such is the effect on yields. Table 23-3 shows, however, that inputs are considerably greater

TABLE 23-3   KANO CLOSE-SETTLED ZONE:
ESTIMATED MANURE INPUTS IN
TONS PER ACRE

Tons per Acre (approx.)	Central Area	Outlying Villages
	% of holdings	
0	9	13.5
0.1—1.0	27	62.5
1.1—1.6	14	17.5
1.7 and over	50	6.5
	100	100.0

in the Central Area than in the outlying villages. These figures were obtained by adjusting the application per holding according to the average size of holdings in the measured sample, namely, 1.3/hectare in the Central Area and 2.6/hectare in the outlying villages. Manure is commonly bought in Kausani, but it is produced locally. In Gwarzo District farmers resident in the town transport manure to outlying farms and hire donkeys for the purpose, but it does not change hands in the process.

The hiring of agricultural labor, which offers a means of increasing inputs beyond the capacity of the family labor force, and provides a source of income for farmers unable to supply all of their needs, is most common in the Central Area. Farmers with larger holdings may rely extensively on hired labor during the wet season. The institution exists in Gangaren Riji and Kausani, but is rare in Masallaci.

The magnitude of groundnut production in Kano State gives some idea of the extent to which agriculture is commercialized. Judged by the relatively few non-producers and quantity of larger producers the Central Area is the most important, despite the great demand for subsistence crops imposed by the high density of population. Some 32 per cent of the families enumerated by the census produced five or more sacks of groundnuts in 1962, compared with only 9 per cent in the outlying villages taken together. This apparently paradoxical situation may be explained by the necessity to grow groundnuts in order to pay special taxes levied in the area. Also, it is probably recognized that small deficits in food crops can be met by using the proceeds of groundnut sales, with money to spare. Such a deficit is unlikely to exist in the outlying villages. Thus Kano State, with its large population, produces about half of the groundnuts exported from Nigeria. Unfortunately, the complexities of marketing are such that no broad comparison can be made between outputs and population densities.

Secondary Occupations and Rural-urban Relations

The development of secondary sources of income is undoubtedly greatest in the Central Area, where every family receives an amount varying from $1.00 to $75.00 yearly. In the outlying villages only 48 per cent of the families receive extra income, although the figure varies from 90 per cent in Masallaci to 27 per cent in Kausani. The most interesting feature about secondary occupations, beside their diversity, is their tendency to concentrate in certain villages. In the Central Area, weaving cloth for the Kano city market involves 62 per cent of the families surveyed. In Masallaci, there is an equally marked concentration of mat-making. Palm leaves are gathered in the "bush" up to 16 km away, and the finished products are sold in the large market at Dambarta. The reason that nine out of ten compounds engage in this craft is simply that it is traditional. Yet, in Kausani, only a small proportion of families benefit from such occupations—probably because of the considerable development of dry-season emigration as an alternative source of income.

Trading is important in all the villages, but is most developed in the Central Area and in Masallaci. Firewood is exchanged in Kano for manure, and is sold in Ringim by Hamburawa villagers and in Gwarzo by Gangaren Riji villagers. Groundnuts are traded in Masallaci and sugar cane in Hamburawa, where it is said that trading is specifically the resort of small farmers. All the outlying villages enjoy close economic ties with their District Headquarters, which have large markets, but none engage in direct trade with Kano, for they lie outside the range of the donkey-borne trade which plays such a large part in the economy of Kano. But the importance of secondary occupations to village communities remains considerable. The towns of the Close-Settled Zone have not taken over the provision of rural services to the extent common in "Western" economies. Furthermore, the tradition of part-time engagement in these occupations and the low costs of participation ensure a very thin spread of the economic benefits among the population.

Conclusion

Population density cannot be regarded as an isolated variable, and the treatment of the outlying villages together may be misleading because it masks differences. Soil and rainfall variations explain the differences in cropping systems and may lie behind many other contrasts which obscure the pattern. Disparities in the socio-economic structure of these communities emphasize that no two Hausa villages are the same, while the range of differentiation between the central and outlying villages is limited because all are in the areas of high population density (only Hamburawa is significantly below the average density for the Close-Settled Zone). Finally, the insufficiency and inadequacy of the data which have been used make any conclusions tentative at best.

Nevertheless, some conclusions emerge. The land-use pattern in Hamburawa shows the reduced impact of a smaller population. A somewhat reduced incidence of purchase and a greater area of cultivated land per adult male in the outlying villages reflect a less serious scarcity of land, and holdings appear to be somewhat larger. Fragmentation and subdivision have accompanied population increase in the Central Area during the last 30 years. Yet manure inputs are noticeably greater there, owing partly to the proximity of Kano city and organized trade. The hiring of labor is most common in the Central Area, and the commercial production of groundnuts is more developed despite (or because of) the limited supplies of land. Dependence on secondary sources of income, everywhere considerable, is greatest. The proximity of a large urban market for handwoven cloth and other goods has played a vital role in this development; and in one of the outlying villages (Kausani) the absence of such an outlet may lie behind the importance of seasonal emigration.

The evidence suggests that a growing density of population is encouraging not only the intensification of agriculture but also the commercialization of the rural economy; the application of a cash value to land and to agricultural inputs, the successful competition of commercial with subsistence crops for land and labor, and the development of secondary sources of income dependent on markets. Before the export of groundnuts began, the grain surplus was sold in the towns, whose growth was closely tied to the development of agriculture. There are many parallels with the beginning of the "New Husbandry" in northwestern Europe (5).

There is much in Kano to support the idea of population density as a primary determinant of rural economic systems (2), a theme which carries considerable weight in northern Nigeria (3). In such a dynamic situation the concept of a "critical population density" tied to a specific agricultural system (1) is difficult to apply. Those features of the rural economy which allow high population densities are not unknown to most of the rural communities in the Sudan zone of Nigeria, but the stimulus of a growing population is required to bring them into use. It is to be hoped that a successful transition can be made elsewhere from extensive land rotation systems, associated with densities of less than 80/km², to more intensive systems capable of supporting dense populations (11). On the other hand, it must be remembered that the Kano Close-Settled Zone evolved as the result of a favorable combination of soil conditions and historical circumstances. In this sense it is unique, and it would be rash to disregard its special advantages in seeking to encourage similar developments elsewhere.

REFERENCES

(1) W. Allan: The African Husbandman (London, 1965).

(2) E. Boserup: The Conditions of Agricultural Growth (London, 1965).

(3) A. T. Grove: Population Densities and Agriculture in Northern Nigeria, in: K. M. Barbour and R. M. Prothero, eds.: Essays on African Population (London, 1961), pp. 115-36.

(4) G. M. Higgins and K. Klinkenberg: Map of the Great Soil Groups of Northern Nigeria (Soil Survey Section, Institute for Agricultural Research, Ahmadu Bello University, Zaria, 1965).

(5) Sir J. Hutchinson: Land and Human Populations, Presidential Address delivered on August 31st, 1966 at the Nottingham Meeting of the British Association, The Advancement of Science, Vol. 23, 1966, pp. 241-54.

(6) H. A. Luning: An Agro-Economic Survey of Katsina Province (Kaduna, Government Printer, 1963).

(7) D. F. H. MacBride: Land Survey in the Kano Emirate, Northern Provinces, Nigeria, Journal of the Royal African Society, Vol. 37, 1938, pp. 75-91.

(8) M. J. Mortimore: Land and Population Pressure in the Kano Close-Settled Zone, Northern Nigeria, The Advancement of Science, Vol. 23, 1967, pp. 677-86.

(9) M. J. Mortimore: Population Distribution, Settlement and Soils in Kano Province, Northern Nigeria, 1931-62, in: J. C. Caldwell and C. Okonjo, eds.: The Population of Tropical Africa (London, 1968), pp. 298-306.

(10) D. W. Norman: An Economic Study of Three Villages in Zaria Province. 1, Land and Labour Relationships, Samaru Miscellaneous Paper No. 19, Institute for Agricultural Research, Ahmadu Bello University (Zaria, 1967).

(11) R. M. Prothero: Some Observations on Desiccation in Northwestern Nigeria, Erdkunde, Vol. 16, 1962, pp. 111-19.

ASIA AND THE PACIFIC: INTRODUCTION

Clearly any internationally based study of population-resource relationships and the pressures associated with them must give some consideration to the problems they present in Asia. In this continent, examples of these problems are to be found in their most diverse and extreme forms. The size and diversity of the continent are such that some narrowing down of attention is necessary; and within this wealth of opportunity, the subcontinent of India seems a logical choice for primary consideration. Here, over-all and in the more restricted parts of the subcontinent, some of the greatest concentrations of population in the world may be found. Here quantitative and qualitative population-resource problems occur most acutely, in both rural and urban areas.

Politically, the subcontinent has undergone major changes in the course of the last two decades, following the partition of British India and the subsequent establishment of the independent republics of India and Pakistan. Each is a major political unit, with great diversity of land and people. The act of partition led to substantial population changes to which reference has already been made (Section III). In both India and Pakistan, the problems of social and economic development have to be faced in conditions of continuing political instability, which derives in no small degree from these problems, as well as contributing to them.

Intrinsic interest and concern with the subcontinent were supported by the availability of contributors able to highlight the problems of population-resource relationships. Three are themselves from India. They view these problems from a variety of points of view and at a number of different scales.

Miss Sen Gupta and *Nath* are concerned with the country as a whole. Miss Sen Gupta draws attention to the unevenness of population distribution, such that the average density for the whole of India is no higher than for countries with no comparable population-resource problems. Rightly she points out that neither this over-all figure nor those for more limited areas (of either high or low concentrations of population) have much meaning. Her study of regional variations in rural population pressure is based on an index which attempts to relate population to utilized resources. Second, she divides the country into population-resource regions on the basis of a number of socio-economic characteristics, including population density, population-growth character, and resource potential. Third, on the basis of three categories of resource regions, she examines the possibilities for relieving population pressure in rural areas, particularly through transfer of surplus population to urban areas. As previously indicated, this is the only contribution to the Symposium which suggests that rural-urban migration may be a positive contribution to the solution of population pressure (*Kosinski and Prothero*). Inevitably, the

389

desirability and efficacy of this suggestion must be open to question in the light of evidence presented by *Brush* on the dimensions of India's urban problems, and on the urban trends observable in the country.

While also concerned with the whole of India, *Nath's* review involves a much wider time-perspective, though concentrating upon developments during the last two decades. The paper directs attention to the significant attempts made toward over-all planning for development, to try to achieve an efficiently integrated exploitation of available resources. During the course of three Five-Year Plans, advances were made during the first two, such that output was ahead of population growth, even though the growth rate was increasing. In the present decade, there has been little advance, and severe shortages of food staples led to near-disaster in parts of India in 1966 and 1967. Fortunately, recent experience has been rather more satisfactory, though there is need for a sustained increase in productivity to maintain the agricultural output necessary to meet the needs of the growing population. While maintaining that any spectacular decline in the fertility of the population is unlikely in the 1970's Nath is cautiously optimistic for the future. However, he points out the difficulties of achieving centralized planning in an essentially democratic political and administrative structure. Direction and control under these circumstances are difficult to ensure. Inevitably, future prospects for population-resource development will depend to no small extent upon the maintenance of a relatively stable political situation, irrespective of the ideology upon which it is based.

The State of Punjab presents evidence of areas which have reached saturation point in respect to existing population-resource relationships. Population growth rates have been of such magnitude as to neutralize the substantial developments in the economy and in social welfare. *Gosal* points to an internal redistribution of population which is going on in the Punjab in an attempt to adjust to available resources. The situation is complicated by ethnic differences which are now limiting the possibilities for redistribution. Satisfactory solutions to problems are to be sought through control of population growth (which is likely to be achieved only slowly), intensification of production, and diversification of the rural as well as the urban economy. Though there has been emigration from the Punjab to other parts of India and overseas, *Gosal* is quite firm in maintaining that this is not the solution to the population-resource problems of the state.

East Pakistan, which includes parts of the lower Ganges and Brahmaputra valleys, records some of the highest population densities not only in the subcontinent but in the world. The population is predominantly rural (about 95 per cent). Rice is the staple food and occupies more than 72 per cent of the cropped area. *Robinson's* empirical study is concerned with adjustments occurring under pressure of continuous population growth. These adjustments are made through "work-sharing," where the time contributed per worker is reduced below any reasonably full employment norm. Work-sharing is taking place in circumstances in which the already marginal productivity of labor units actually applied to the land is approaching zero, while the number to be fed per family unit is increasing. Increased numbers are put to work to contribute to their own subsistence, even though this means reducing the labor inputs per worker of the existing labor force.

While the Indian subcontinent provides fine examples of population pressures in the Asian context, no discussion from this part of the world would be complete without reference to Japan. Here, as *Kiuchi* shows, the problems of population pressure have not been entirely eliminated from the rural areas or from the towns. But within the rural areas, which support the highest densities in the world per unit of cultivated land, considerable strides have been made to accommodate these populations. These have been achieved through intensification and diversification of agriculture, by migration to urban areas in Japan, and also, in the past by movements abroad. Where there has been rural-urban migration, it has been to the larger towns (more than 500,000 inhabitants), which have been expanding in terms of economic opportunity and urban infrastructure. Thus, while these towns are not without serious problems they have very many fewer than the urban areas of India and parts of South-east Asia. Other facets of Japanese experience in population-resource developments during the last century are also considered. The great question that remains is the extent to which this experience is relevant to the developing countries of Asia and other parts of the world today.

Pirie's study of Samoa is on an entirely different scale, from the others in this section, both areally and in terms of population size and it is instructive in this respect (see also, *Brookfield*'s "island" examples in Section I). Its main interest is found in the impact that two different forms of government (in American Samoa and Western Samoa respectively) have made upon people originally of homogeneous culture. Population-resource problems have been approached in contrasting ways. After a period of difficulty in the 1950's, American Samoa benefited from the massive investment of U.S. capital in secondary and tertiary activities, but only at the expense of traditional agriculture. Western Samoa suffers from a growing population, a shortage of capital, and heavy reliance upon traditional agriculture, which is characterized by low productivity. Migration to New Zealand and the remittances of migrants have some impact on the economy of this relatively circumscribed community. The disparities between the two parts of Samoa are likely to increase, and the unusual circumstances of American Samoa are such that it has little relevance as a model for economic development in Western Samoa, or in other parts of the Pacific.

24. POPULATION, NATURAL RESOURCES, AND ECONOMIC DEVELOPMENT IN INDIA

V. Nath

Rapid increase of the world's population is among the most important phenomena of our time. In the underdeveloped countries the "population explosion" is accompanied by an explosion of expectations. Governments and elite groups want and expect to attain a high (Western) level of living—for themselves and for the mass of the people. Because economic development is considered the means to this goal, most underdeveloped countries have initiated economic development programs. But the relationship between population growth and economic growth is far from clear. Although the demographic sequence accompanying economic development—decline in mortality, acceleration of population growth, decline in fertility—has been described in detail and the socio-economic changes accompanying it adequately documented, there is as yet no accepted theory which relates the two, nor is it possible "to deduce the set or sets of conditions necessary and sufficient to achieve secular fertility declines" (20: 158).

In the absence of an accepted theory of population growth and economic development, two different, almost conflicting, views on the demographic prospect of the underdeveloped countries are sustained. First, there is the view that if contraceptives are made available in these countries, they will be used, with significant effects on birth rates. Indeed, Ohlin regards the development of oral and intra-uterine contraceptives as a major technological breakthrough which has "affected the prospects of fertility control the world over" (29: 8). But this belief in the "power" of new contraceptives is contested by others who place greater em-

phasis on social and economic changes as prerequisites for decline in fertility. According to this view, "the possession of advanced contraceptive technology is an incidental matter, while the truly crucial question is whether the potential contraceptors genuinely wish to achieve the small family pattern" (45: 13).

It is not impossible that both points of view are vindicated in different underdeveloped countries. The decline of fertility in India and China, countries with large populations but limited natural resources, could be significantly different from most countries of Africa and Latin America, in which the relationship between population and natural resources is more favorable. But natural resources is an area in which relationships are even less clearly understood, and there is the additional lack of satisfactory definition or measure of the relationship between population and natural resources. Measures such as density of population, man-land ratio, and cropland per capita, once used extensively are now considered inadequate or defective. The search for more adequate measures is under way.

The view is widely held among geographers that economic development of countries poor in natural resources, such as India and China, will be more difficult than in countries where the balance between population and natural resources is more favorable. Ackerman has divided the "technology-deficient" countries into the China-type (high population-resource ratio) and the Brazil-type (low population-resource ratio), and has listed for the former "continued consciousness of impending crisis and increasing pressure for attachment to foreign resources" as characteristics of the development process (1: 149). Ginsburg expresses a similar view when discussing the development prospects of China and India:

"Their greatest similarity, however, lies in the inflexibility imposed upon their development planning and policies by the necessity for increased agricultural production, not as means for capital accumulation, but simply to prevent starvation, maintain a healthier labor force and discourage rural (and therefore national) unrest. Both illustrate the degree to which high man-land ratios act as a deterrent to accelerated economic development" (14: 420). This view reflects the thinking of the classical economists who regarded scarcity of fertile land as the major limitation to economic development—Ricardo's law of diminishing returns in agriculture, for example. But concern with inadequacy of natural resources has progressively diminished as development of new lands and technological advance have made available increasing quantities of food and natural-resources-based materials or their synthetic substitutes. Moreover, economic development has taken place in countries with abundant as well as limited natural resources —Ackerman's U.S. and European types (1: 149). However, two roles of natural resources in economic development have been important in the past and remain so today. First, abundant natural resources attract capital investment. Most of the foreign investments of the European countries in the nineteenth century were either in resource development enterprises such as mines and plantations, or in railways which made resource development possible. Until recently, most of the U.S. investment in underdeveloped countries was of this type: in 1948, 59 per cent was in extractive industries and 16 per cent in public utilities (28: 84). Second, the presence of natural resources, which can be exploited without major changes in existing technology and socioeconomic structures, facilitates economic development through local means, especially in the early stages when capital, organization, and technology are scarce and society is not oriented toward change. Recent experience in India shows that increase in agricultural output was quite rapid during the 1950's, when large areas could be reclaimed for cultivation by the farmers, but has been slow in the 1960's. Such areas are no longer available and increase in agricultural output is dependent on improvements in agricultural techniques.

Economic development is a multifaceted, complex process. Many of the factors contributing to it and the relationships connected with it are inadequately understood. Some of them, such as the relationship between population and natural resources, have begun to be explored only in recent years. This study of population growth and economic development may be regarded as a case description of development under a particular relationship between population and natural resources. Comparative studies of other regions will contribute to a better understanding of the role of this factor in economic development.

The Economic Setting of Population Growth

The population of India is curently increasing at an annual rate of 2.5 per cent. As a result of the eradication of malaria and improvement in medical and public health services (6: x-xi), the rate of growth has accelerated significantly in recent years—averaging about 2 per cent in the 1950's compared with 1.0 to 1.25 per cent in the previous three decades. The current rate of increase is not high in comparison with other underdeveloped countries, but the economic setting in which it is taking place has created serious problems, principally of raising output of food. This problem, dramatized by widespread scarcity of food and local famine during the recent drought years, 1965-67, has forced Indian planners to give the highest priority to increasing agricultural output. It has also furthered the gradual recognition of rapid population growth as a handicap to adequate economic growth. The family planning program, which has existed since the 1950's, has since 1965-66 been expanded into a nation-wide effort whose objective is "reducing the birth rate from 40 per cent at present to 25 per cent as expeditiously as possible" (36: 346).

The economic setting of population growth in India may be outlined as follows:

(i) A very low level of per capita income —$69 per year in 1965, compared with an average of $100 for East and South-east Asia excluding Japan, which itself was lowest among the major regions of the world (44: 727);

(ii) Extremely low levels of food consumption, resulting in widespread malnutrition and undernutrition. Seventy-five per cent of the calories in the Indian diet are provided by cereals; consumption of foods supplying protein, fats, and minerals is very low. Average calorie intake—1970 per capita in 1961—is below the minimum requirement of 2100 calories for a tropical country, with the result that large sections of the population are chronically undernourished. The incidence of "hunger" (calorie intake below the minimum requirement) was estimated at 33 per cent for the rural population in 1961 (22: 65);

(iii) Very small agricultural holdings, presence of a large number of land-

less or near-landless cultivators, and large-scale underemployment among a predominantly agricultural and rural population.

To understand this situation fully, it is necessary to review demographic and economic trends in the half-century which preceded the beginning of planning.

The Historical Setting

POPULATION GROWTH WITHOUT SIGNIFICANT ECONOMIC DEVELOPMENT

The population of India increased by more than 50 per cent between 1901 and 1951 (Table 24-1), most of it occurring between

TABLE 24-1 POPULATION OF INDIA, 1901-61 (PRESENT BOUNDARIES)

Year	Population (000's)	Decennial variation in %
1901	236,281	
1911	252,122	+5.73
1921	251,352	−0.31
1931	279,015	+11.01
1941	318,701	+14.22
1951	361,130	+13.31
1961	439,235	+21.50

Source: *Census of India 1961, Paper No. 1 of 1962, Final Population Totals,* New Delhi 1962, p. x.

1921 and 1951. Increase from 1901 to 1921 was curtailed by a high mortality from malaria and other tropical diseases, as well as by frequent famines and epidemics. The last two years of the nineteenth century witnessed one of the severest famines in India's history; loss of life was estimated at about 3 million (5: 275). During the first decade of the twentieth century, there were a number of epidemics of bubonic plague, and in 1918-19 the influenza epidemic took the lives of an estimated 12-13 million, ef-

TABLE 24-2 INDIA. TRENDS IN OCCUPATIONAL DISTRIBUTION OF MALE WORKERS
AND GROWTH OF URBAN POPULATION, 1901-61
(PER CENT)

Year	Agriculture	Primary Sector	Manufacturing (household and factory)	Secondary Sector	Tertiary Sector	% of Urban Population
(1)	(2)	(3)	(4)	(5)	(6)	(7)
1901	65.61	70.37	11.37	12.31	17.32	10.91
1911	68.50	73.66	9.62	10.97	15.37	10.57
1921	69.87	74.54	9.33	10.51	14.95	11.38
1931	68.73	74.08	8.99	10.43	15.49	12.13
1951	66.85	69.08	9.84	11.59	19.33	17.34
1961	64.88	67.98	11.27	12.68	19.44	18.00

NOTE: Primary sector includes agriculture, livestock husbandry, forestry, fishing, and mining and quarrying (Industrial Categories I, II and III of 1961 Census).
Secondary sector includes manufacturing (household and factory) and construction (Industrial Categories IV, V and VI of 1961 Census).
Tertiary sector includes trade and commerce, transport, storage and communications, and all other services (Industrial Categories VII, VIII and IX of 1961 Census).
Source: *Census of India, 1961, Paper No. 1 of 1962, Final Population Totals,* New Delhi, 1962, p. xxvi.

fecting a net decline in population during the decade 1911-21. After 1921, however, famines and epidemics were held in check, and a period of uninterrupted population growth began. Even the Bengal famine of 1942-43, with an estimated mortality of about 1.5 million (5: 292), and the loss of life during disturbances following the Partition of British India only marginally affected population growth from 1941 to 1951. The Census Commissioner of 1951 called 1921 the year of "the great divide" in India's recent demographic history, separating a period of uninterrupted growth from an earlier period of uneven, and in the aggregate, slow growth (4: xiii).

But population growth occurred throughout the entire period 1901-51 under conditions best described as "over-all economic stagnation." Perhaps the most telling evidence of this is the absence of significant change in the occupational structure. The proportion of male workers in agriculture and other primary activities fluctuated between 70 and 75 per cent and the proportion in manufacturing (both household and factory) remained at 10-12 per cent[1] (Table 24-2). Indeed, between 1901 and 1931 changes were regressive: the proportion of male workers increased in agriculture and declined in manufacturing. Although there was considerable growth of modern industry as indicated by a fivefold increase in output between 1900-01 and 1944-45 (41: 347), the employment provided by factories was small—less than 3 million in 1951 when the total labor force was more than 142 million.

1. Male workers alone have been considered for this comparison; female workers have been excluded because the method of classifying (changes in the definition of "worker") and consequently the number of the latter has fluctuated greatly from census to census. Most female workers are women from agricultural households who do farm work in addition to

Moreover, since the factories were concentrated in a few areas, notably in and around Calcutta and Bombay, the modernizing and growth-inducing effects of industrial development were limited. On the other hand, the principal effect of contact with modern factory industry (first foreign, but later also Indian) on the village economy was a decline in local crafts. The decline, which had begun in the nineteenth century, continued throughout this period, forcing large numbers of village artisans out of their traditional occupations and into agriculture (13).

Urbanization was negligible until the 1930's. The proportion of urban population to total population remained between 10 and 12 per cent between 1901 and 1931 (Table 24-2), began to gather momentum in the 1930's, increased during the 1940's

from 13.9 to 17.3 per cent partly as a result of the exceptional conditions of war and Partition, and then slowed down in the 1950's. Brush links the slowing down of urbanization with the inability of the Indian economy to expand employment and housing rapidly enough to sustain the process of rapid urban growth (Brush, pp. 299-301). The point that Indian urbanization has not entirely been the result of economic growth, but has represented, at least in part, a transfer of population pressure from rural to urban areas has been developed by the debate between the proponents of the "pull" and "push" explanations of Indian urbanization.

Historical comparisons of national income for developing countries are limited because of lack of data. The principal difficulty in comparisons for the late British pe-

TABLE 24-3   GROWTH OF POPULATION AND CROP OUTPUT IN UNDIVIDED INDIA, 1900/01 TO 1944/45

Average of quinquennium:	Population index	Index of area cultivated	Index of average annual output			Index of crop output adjusted for population		
			Food*	Non-food*	All crops	Food*	Non-food*	All crops
1	2	3	4	5	6	7	8	9
1900/01 to 1904/05	100.0		100.0	100.0	100.0	100.0	100.0	100.0
1905/06 to 1909/10	103.1	105.8	97.5	106.8	99.6	94.6	103.6	96.6
1910/11 to 1914/15	105.1	109.8	105.6	121.7	109.1	100.5	155.8	103.8
1915/16 to 1919/20	105.6	108.8	107.2	102.8	110.5	101.5	97.3	104.6
1920/21 to 1924/25	108.0	108.9	101.8	124.7	106.8	94.3	45.5	98.9
1925/26 to 1929/30	113.6	111.8	97.3	138.7	106.3	85.7	122.1	93.6
1930/31 to 1934/35	120.5	114.8	100.3	137.9	108.5	85.2	114.4	90.0
1935/36 to 1939/40	129.2	115.3	97.9	159.1	111.1	75.8	123.1	86.0
1940/41 to 1944/45	137.9	118.4	100.9	155.3	112.6	73.5	113.2	82.1

* Food includes rice, wheat, jowar, bajra, maize, barley, and gram. Non-food includes sugarcane, sesamum, rape and mustard, linseed, cotton, jute, tea, coffee, and tobacco.
Source: Mukherjee, P. K. and Sivasubramonian, S: Agricultural Output and National Income in India: in Bhattacharjee, J. P. (ed). *Studies in Indian Agricultural Economics,* Indian Society of Agricultural Economics, Bombay 1958, p. 24.

TABLE 24-4   CHANGES IN POPULATION AND
AGRICULTURAL PRODUCTION IN BRITISH
PROVINCES OF INDIA IN
1891/92−1946/47
(annual average in %)

Population	0.67
Cropped area	0.40
Output: all crops	0.37
foodgrains	0.11
non-foodgrains	1.31

Source: G. Blyn, *Agricultural Trends in India,
1891-1947,* Philadelphia, 1966, Chapter 5.

riod of India's history was the existence of a large number of Princely States, most of whom had very inadequate and poor statistics. One of the more careful estimates, however, reports per capita income in Undivided India in the early 1940's as only 18 per cent higher than at the turn of the century, the average annual income figures being Rs. 52.2 for 1900-01−1904-05; and Rs. 61.6 for 1940-41−1944-45 (41: 340). In spite of considerable growth of manufacturing and some urbanization, the growth rate of per capita income for the period works out to less than 0.5 per cent per year, a direct result of stagnation in agriculture. The latter fact emerges from a number of

studies of population growth and trends in agricultural output. Table 24-3, based on the study of Mukherjee and Sivasubramonian, shows that during 45 years crop output increased by only 12.6 per cent, while population increased by 37.9 per cent. Output per capita declined by almost 18 per cent for all crops, and as much as 26.5 for food grains. In fact, the entire increase in crop output was due to increase in output of non-food-grain crops. It should be noted that increase in crop output was less than increase in cropped area, indicating a net decline in average crop yields.

Similar results emerge from Blyn's study, which covers the period 1891-92 to 1946-47, but is confined to the British provinces and does not include the Princely States (Table 24-4), both studies include West Punjab and Sind, now in Pakistan, where rapid increase in agricultural output followed construction of irrigation canals. If these areas were excluded, figures for the areas which now form part of the Indian Union would be less favorable. For the 1951 census an estimate of trends in population, cropped area, and irrigated area for the period 1891-1951 was made for 61 districts in the north, west, and south, representing

TABLE 24-5   INDIA. TREND OF CULTIVATION AND IRRIGATION, 1891−1951

	1891	*1921*	*1951*
In million hectares: gross area sown*	40.4	41.9	45.2
net area sown**	36.4	37.5	40.1
irrigated area	5.2	6.2	6.8
In hectares, per capita: gross area sown	0.47	0.48	0.37
net area sown**	0.42	0.43	0.33
irrigated area	0.06	0.07	0.05

* Gross area sown includes net area sown and those cropped areas which are sown more than once.
** Net area sown in the physical area under crop.
Source: *Census of India 1951, Vol. 1, Part I B. Appendices to the Census Report 1951,* Delhi 1955, pp. 48-49.

TABLE 24-6   FOODGRAINS IN UNDIVIDED INDIA: 1900/01 TO 1944/45

Quinquennium	Population (millions)	Production (million t.)		Foodgrains	Net availability for consumption (million t.)	Consumption per capita per day in g.
		Gross	Net	Net imports Net imports (+) or net exports (−)		
(1)	(2)	(3)	(4)	(5)	(6)	(7)
1900/01-1904/05	288.8	63.6	55.6	−1.1	54.6	536
1905/06-1909/10	300.4	62.0	54.2	−0.6	53.6	505
1910/11-1914/15	313.8	70.8	61.9	−2.0	60.0	541
1915/16-1919/20	315.0	70.3	61.5	−0.4	61.9	558
1920/21-1924/25	312.0	66.1	58.4	+0.8	59.2	539
1925/26-1929/30	328.4	63.3	55.6	+0.8	56.2	485
1930/31-1934/35	348.0	66.5	57.7	+1.2	58.9	497
1935/36-1939/40	373.2	63.4	55.3	+1.4	56.6	431
1940/41-1944/45	397.2	65.8	57.6	+0.5	58.2	417

Source: Bhattacharjee, J. P. and Roy, S. M.: Trend of Consumption of Food and Foodgrains in India, in: Bhattarjee, J. P. (Ed.) *Studies in Indian Agricultural Economics,* Bombay, 1958, p. 202.

about one-third of India's total population in 1951, and a similar proportion of the cropped area. Districts whose boundaries had not changed during the period and whose agricultural statistics were good were selected for this analysis. The results, summarized in Table 24-5, indicate that gross cropped area per capita declined by 21.5 per cent between 1891 and 1951, while gross irrigated area per capita declined by 12.5 per cent. These declines were not compensated by increased crop yields. On the contrary, data on yields of rice, wheat, and other crops for the period 1910-11 to 1945-46 show a decline in most cases. The one outstanding exception is rice in Madras, whose yield showed an increase of 15 per cent during the period (5: 61-71).

though India became for the first time a net importer of food grains in the 1920's (mainly rice from Burma), and progressively increased these imports (Table 24-6), per capita consumption of food grains declined by 20 per cent from 1900-01 to 1944-45. This percentage does not even include the exceptionally low figure during World War II, resulting from the interruption of rice imports after the Japanese occupation of Burma in 1942. The interruption was followed by famine in Bengal in 1943 and scarcity of food grains over large parts of South India in 1945 and 1946. Since food grains provide most of the calories in the Indian diet, fall in per capita consumption of them meant chronic undernutrition for large sections of the population.

Decline in Food Consumption

The most disturbing result of the failure of agricultural and food-grain output to keep pace with growth of population was the decline in per capita consumption of food. Al-

Small Agricultural Holdings and Widespread Underemployment

Most of the agricultural population subsisted by cultivation of very small holdings, but there were also large numbers of land-

TABLE 24-7   INDIA. CATEGORIES OF AGRICULTURAL LABOR FAMILIES

Census zone	% Agricultural labor families to total rural families	% of total agricultural labor families		% of total agricultural labor families	
		With land	Without land	Casual	Attached
North India	14.3	40.6	59.4	78.3	21.7
East India	32.7	58.0	42.0	76.1	23.9
South India	50.1	54.4	45.6	95.0	5.0
West India	20.4	43.2	56.8	90.2	9.8
Central	36.7	39.9	60.1	81.6	18.4
North-West India	9.8	28.5	71.5	69.0	31.0
	30.4	50.0	50.0	84.6	15.4

Source: Ministry of Labour, Government of India: *Report on Intensive Survey of Agricultural Labour: All India, Vol. 1,* New Delhi, 1954.

TABLE 24-8   UNEMPLOYMENT IN INDIA, 1951

Rural agricultural	30.3 million persons for 7 months
Rural non-agricultural	4.8 " " " 6 "
Urban agricultural	0.8 " " " 7 "
Urban non-agricultural	2.1 " " " 6 "

Source: B. N. Datar, The Second Five-Year Plan—Employment Approach in: *Papers Relating to the Formulation of the Second Five-Year Plan,* Planning Commission, New Delhi, 1955, p. 208.

less or near-landless agricultural laborers.

About five-sixths of all agricultural holdings were below four hectares (37: 3). "Agricultural labor" families defined as "ones in which either the head of the family or 50 per cent or more of the earners reported agricultural labor as their main occupation" accounted for 30 per cent of all rural families (Table 24-7). Half of these families cultivated small bits of land in addition to laboring for wages, but the remainder were completely landless. The existence of such large numbers of landless or near-landless agriculturalists is an indication of the extent of land hunger in India. The working members of the "agricultural labor" families averaged employment about seven months in the year. For women, the average was about 134 days. There was also widespread underemployment among the small cultivators. Datar, using the data of the Agricultural Labour Enquiry conducted by the Government of India, and sample surveys of unemployment conducted in a number of states, estimated in 1956 that 31.1 million agricultural workers were unemployed for more than half the year (Table 24-8). This number represented 28.5 per cent of the total agricultural labor force, then estimated at 109 million (10: 195, 288). Attempts have been made to estimate the surplus agricultural labor population. One, based on continuation of cultivation with human and bullock labor and the family farm enterprise, put the surplus in the 1950's at 20 million (21, quoted by 7: 116).

Paucity of Other Natural Resources

India's other natural resources do not materially alter this picture of high pressure of population upon the agricultural resource. The mineral and energy resources, while they do provide a basis for an industrial structure of adequate size and diversity, do not include any large export-revenue earning item, such as petroleum in the Middle East, which could help finance economic development. On the contrary, there are major deficiencies in fuels and minerals, the effect of which has been felt increasingly with expansion of industry. It will be felt even more in the future. Imports of minerals and fuels which accounted for 21.8 per cent of the total value of imports in 1960-61 are expected to increase to 34.2 per cent by 1975-76. In contrast, exports of minerals and fuels represented only 6 per cent of the total value of exports in 1960-61 (Table 24-9).

The principal assets of India's mineral and energy resources are large reserves of high-grade iron ore, fairly large reserves of medium-to-poor-grade coal, a substantial hydro-power potential (about 41 million kw), and sizable deposits of manganese, mica, bauxite, and thorium-bearing sands (27). The liability is the lack of nonferrous metals —copper, lead, zinc, and tin; raw materials of the chemical industry such as sulphur and rock phosphate, and most important, petroleum. The petroleum position has improved

TABLE 24-9   CONTRIBUTION OF AGRICULTURAL AND MINERAL PRODUCTS TO IMPORTS
AND EXPORTS IN 1960/61, AND PROJECTIONS FOR 1970/71 AND 1975/76,
IN INDIA

A. *Imports*	1960/61 Value* Mil Rp.	%	1970/71 Value* Mil Rp.	%	1975/76 Value* Mil Rp.	%
Agricultural products (Cereals, fibres, and vegetable oils)	3,368**	29.9	1,840	13.5	2,000	12.4
Mineral products (Metal, petroleum products, sulphur, and rock phosphate)	2,332*	21.8	4,140	30.5	5,500	34.2
TOTAL	11,216**	100.0	13,600	100.0	16,100	100.0
B. *Exports* Agricultural and animal-based products	5,092	75.8	7,224	59.0	8,503	52.4
Minerals (including coal)	401	6.0	1,713	14.0	2,300	14.2
TOTAL	6,719	100.0	12,251	100.0	16,243	100.0

* $1 = Rp 7.5
** 1961-62
Source: Planning Commission: *Notes on Perspective of Development India 1960/61 to 1975/76*, New Delhi, April 1964, pp. 164-173.

somewhat with the discovery of oil in Gujarat and may well be transformed if there are large oil finds in the Gulf of Cambay, where preliminary explorations have been promising. But excluding this area, the proved reserves have been estimated at only about 100 million tons. Although consumption of petroleum is still small—about 8 million tons in 1960-61—it is increasing rapidly and is expected to range between 45 and 65 million tons annually by 1980-81 (15: 116). India also has large reserves of nuclear fuels, especially thorium-bearing sands, which could provide almost unlimited energy if economic processes of developing them were devised. But until then, energy supplies will remain limited and expensive.

Inadequate Social Resources

Underdeveloped countries have very limited supplies of the social resources needed for development—capital, technology, and organization—and India in 1951 was no exception. Very low per capita income meant low savings (estimated at about 5 per cent of the national income in 1950-51 (34: 8), and very limited supplies of capital. In technological skills and organization, India was undoubtedly more fortunate than most underdeveloped countries. There were large numbers of educated, trained, and experienced people, especially in the cities. The administrative and technical services, which had a fair level of efficiency, had been manned predominantly by Indians for a long time. Business and industry were managed by Indian entrepreneurs, and the skilled workers were all Indians. India also had well-organized political parties headed by leaders of outstanding ability, political acumen, and stature. Large numbers of Indian civil servants, technicians, skilled workers, and traders had left to work in neighboring countries of Asia and Africa. This, and the prevalence of unemployment among the educated, seemed to indicate that the number of educated and skilled persons was in excess of the requirements of the country. But this supply of education, skill, and entrepreneurial ability, concentrated in the cities, must be viewed alongside the illiterate and apathetic mass of the Indian population if a proper measure of India's social resource endowment is to be obtained. The percentage of literate persons, even with the very liberal definition of literacy adopted in the Indian censuses, was only 16.6 per cent in 1951. In rural India the knowledge and experience of most people were limited to their village and small local area, and they had little awareness of or interest in the outside world. Modern technical skills were virtually nonexistent; except for a flour or rice mill in larger villages, or an occasional pump for irrigation, there was little use of power-driven machines. Finally, except for small groups, such as the Marwari and Gujarati traders and Punjabi Sikhs, the rural population did not show the dynamism needed to escape the local environment. Migration was small in volume—the 1951 Census showed only 3.1 per cent of the population living outside its state of birth, and most of the migrants, whether they went to other parts of India, such as the tea plantations of Assam and the coal fields of Bihar; or to foreign countries, were content to remain unskilled laborers. The dynamism of the rural population described by Gosal in his paper on the Punjab (Gosal, pp. 450-52) was rare.

Many explanations have been given for both the lack of dynamism and the prevalence of an attitude of stoic (or apathetic) acceptance of fate. They range from the value system of the Hindu religion to the effects of the monsoon. Malenbaum attrib-utes them to the rigid social system of the Indian village (23: 133-43).

A discussion of the influence of such social factors on economic development would take us far beyond the scope of this paper, but it is pertinent to add that static resource-use techniques and low levels of consumption (including food) persisting over long periods, with little visible prospect of improvement, contribute to the formation and strengthening of such attitudes. This is suggested by the dynamic attitudes and behavior patterns of villages where efficient resource use is resulting in economic improvement. For example, the development of remunerative, progressive agriculture in the canal colonies of the West Punjab produced in the 1920's a new, dynamic group of peasants (9). More recently, Scarlett Epstein has described a similar phenomenon in the Mysore villages (12).

If we are to understand fully the magnitude of India's task of economic development, we must add to this list of natural and social resource limitations her decision to use democratic methods. The choice was made consciously and deliberately, and over the years the Government of India has consistently enlarged the area of democratic action in development. In agricultural and rural development, this is best seen in the rapid expansion of co-operatives and the constitution of representative institutions for management or development programs. But development through democratic methods is harder and slower, especially in its early stages, than development through authoritarian methods. Modernization of agriculture, for instance, will have to be achieved in India by voluntary decisions of some 60 million heads of agricultural families. Most of them are illiterate and tradition-bound and too poor to take risks. These "decision-makers" require dynamic leadership and intensive education by trained personnel. But both trained personnel and dynamic leaders are desperately short in India. The pace of development could be accelerated if decision-making was concentrated in the hands of trained workers or executives of development institutions. Similarly, the utilization of surplus labor for the creation of physical capital (irrigation works, roads, schools, etc.) advocated by some economists (21) as a method of accelerating development requires organizational resources of larger magnitude and perhaps also of higher quality when the workers have to be organized on a voluntary rather than compulsory basis. China has adopted such programs on a large scale; but in India their use has been very limited. A rural manpower program aimed at utilizing surplus rural labor for construction of development works was started only in the Third Five-Year Plan (1961-66); earlier, the only opportunities for labor were through voluntary contributions. But the program was small—the target was to provide by the end of the Plan employment for 100 days to each of 2.5 million persons. This number, it will be recalled, is only 7 per cent of Datar's estimate, made in 1956 of the total number of underemployed persons in rural areas. Furthermore, achievement has been only 16 per cent of the meager target (36: 111).

Experience with Planning

The First Five-Year Plan (1951-56) was drawn up under conditions of acute stress—food shortage, disruption of the economy, and the influx of about 7 million displaced persons following the Partition. Primary emphasis was given to increasing agricultural output and to rehabilitation—of displaced persons, of the economies of Punjab and West Bengal, which had been affected most by the Partition, and of sectors, such as railways, in which equipment had been depleted during World War II. But the planners also recognized the prime need for removing the causes of long-term stagnation in the economy and initiating a "process of development" (32: 14; 33: 1).

The Plan set forth a model of long-term development, which provided for a doubling of total national income in 21 years (by 1971-72) and per capita income in 27 years (by 1977-78). The rate of population increase assumed in the model was the 1941-51 rate of 1.25 per cent per year. The model was subsequently revised in later Plans, in the light of emerging demographic and economic trends. The Second Plan (1956-61), keeping in view the favorable performance of the economy under the First Plan, brought forward the target dates of doubling national and per capita income to 1967-68 and 1973-74 respectively (34: 11). It revised the rate of population growth slightly, to 13.3 per cent per decade in 1961-70 and 14.0 per cent per decade in 1971-80. But the 1961 census revealed that the rate during the 1950's was in fact much higher than predicted—2 per cent per year, instead of 1.25—and it became clear that the earlier models of economic development would have to be revised. The Third Five-Year Plan put forward a new model of growth for the 15-year period 1960-61 to 1975-76, in which the rate of growth of national income was raised to about 6 per cent, so that after providing for the annual population increase of 2 per cent, per capita income could still increase by about 4 per cent per year (35: 27).

The period of the three Plans witnessed the beginnings of economic growth. National income increased by more than 60 per cent and per capita income rose by nearly 20 per cent (36: 419-20). In agriculture, long-term stagnation was broken

TABLE 24-10   INDIA—GROWTH RATES IN AGRICULTURE
1949/50 TO 1964/65

	(Compound growth rates in %)		
	Agricultural production	Area under crops	Agricultural productivity
1949/1950—1964/65			
Foodgrains	2.98	1.34	1.61
Non-foodgrains	3.61	2.52	1.06
All crops	3.19	1.55	1.60
1949/50—1958/59 All crops*	3.8	2.3	1.32
1955/56—1964/65 All crops*	3.9	1.1	1.9

* Growth rates calculated from annual index numbers given in Appendices 1.1 to 1.3.
Source: Economic and Statistical Adviser, Ministry of Food and Agriculture, Government of India, Growth Rates in Agriculture, New Delhi, March 1966, p. 21.

and output began to increase steadily: agricultural output was 58 per cent higher in 1964-65 than at the beginning of the First Five-Year Plan (ibid). Industrial output increased nearly 2.5 times. There was also considerable expansion of social services, the best indication of which was the near trebling of enrollment in primary schools (36: 422). By the end of the Third Plan, nearly 80 per cent of the boys and girls in the age group 6-11 years were in schools (36: 313).

Within the 15-year period, however, growth was more rapid in the first ten years than in the last five; in the latter, growth of national income was barely adequate to keep pace with growth of population:

Growth (per cent per year)	1950–60	1960–65
National income	3.6	2.6
Population	2.0	2.4
Per capita income	1.6	0.2

The slower growth rate of the 1960's was due mainly to the slowing down of growth in agriculture. The average rate of increase of agricultural output during the period 1949-50 to 1964-65 was 3.2 per cent per year (Table 24-10); but the rate for the period 1960-61 to 1964-65 was only 1.9 per cent per year, as compared with 3.6 in the earlier 12-year period. Moreover, examination of annual index numbers of agricultural output shows that during the three years 1961-62 to 1963-64 output fluctuated around the level of 1960-61 (Table 24-11). It rose by 11 per cent in 1964-65, but the high output of that year was followed by exceptionally low outputs, owing to widespread drought in 1965-66 and again in 1966-67. The year 1967-68 is reported to have been a good one, and according to preliminary indications, output will exceed the previous high level of 1964-65 by about 5 per cent. But it is clear that the steady growth of agricultural production begun in

TABLE 24-11   INDIA. AGRICULTURAL PRODUCTION, FOODGRAIN PRODUCTION
AND FOODGRAIN IMPORTS

A. Production				*B. Imports (on Government of India's account)*		
Year	*Index of agricultural production (1949/50 = 100)*	*Index of foodgrain production (1949/50 = 100)*	*Quantity of foodgrain production (million t.)*	*Quinquennial average*	*Quantity (million t.)*	*Value (million rupees)** *
				1951-55	2.46	1,166.9
				1956-60	3.46	1,347.0
				Annual		
1960/61	142	137	82.02	1961	3.50	1,295.6
1961/62	145	140	82.71	1962	3.64	1,410.9
1962/63	140	134	78.45	1963	4.56	1,830.6
1963/64	143	137	80.24	1964	6.27	2,662.5
1964/65	159	150	88.95	1965	7.46	2,903.2
1965/66	133*	121*	72.29*	1966	10*	n.a.
1966/67	132*	125*	n.a.	1967	9*	n.a.

* Provisional
** $1 = Rps 7.5
n.a. = not available
Source: Up to 1965: Economic and Statistical Advisor, Government of India, Ministry of Food and Agriculture, New Delhi, 1966.
1966 & 1967: Government of India, Ministry of Finance, *Economic Survey 1967-68,* New Delhi, 1968.

the 1950's has not been maintained during the 1960's.

Output of food grains increased less rapidly than total agricultural output—the average rate of increase during the period 1949-50 to 1964-65 being 2.98 per cent per year (Table 24-10). But like total agricultural output, output of food grains was also stagnant between 1960-61 and 1963-64 and since then has fluctuated markedly. The rate of increase of food-grain output in the 1950's, though higher than the rate of increase of population, was not high enough to terminate imports, which continued at 2 to 4 million tons per year (Table 24-11).

One reason for this was the rise in per capita consumption with increase in income: per capita availability of foodstuffs is estimated to have increased from 1759 calories per day in 1950-51 to 2145 calories in 1964-65 (36: 9). The income elasticity of demand for food grains is high in India; it is estimated at 0.81 for the rural population and 0.64 for the urban population (31: Appendix C, 14). But as domestic output began to stagnate, imports increased rapidly to 10 million tons in 1966 and decreased only slightly to 9 million tons in 1967. Large imports of food grains were necessary in 1966 and 1967 to avert famine; but they

TABLE 24-12   INDIA. PROJECTIONS OF FOODGRAIN REQUIREMENTS
AND VALUE OF EXPORTS

	Import requirement of foodgrains			Proportion of value of foodgrain imports to value of exports
Year	Quantity (million t.)	Value (billion U.S.$)	Value of Total exports (billion U.S.$)	(col. (3)/ col. (4) in %)
(1)	(2)	(3)	(4)	(5)
1965-66 (Actual)	7.46	0.62	1.69	36.41
1971	15.3	1.07	1.63	65.50
1976	24.0	1.68	2.17	77.50
1981	32.5	2.28	n.a.	—
1986	42.8	3.00	n.a.	—

Sources: 1965-66: Government of India, Ministry of Finance, 1968.
1971-86: Cols. 2 and 3: Holst W., Evaluation of Population and Food Production Problems of India, in: *The World Food Problem,* Report of the Panel on World Food Supply of the President's Science Advisory Committee, The White House, 1967, p. 687.
1971-76: Col. 4: Planning Commission, *Notes on Perspective of Development of India: 1960/61—1975/76,* New Delhi, April 1964, p. 167.

were made without drastic reduction in other imports only because a large proportion were obtained under PL 480 assistance from the United States. The value of imports of "cereals and cereal preparations" represented nearly 40 per cent of the total export earnings of India during 1965-66 and 52.2 during 1966-67. But 77.5 per cent of the imports during 1965-66 and 55.0 of those in 1966-67 were obtained under PL 480 assistance (24). In the absence of such assistance, an additional 30 per cent of the export earnings in each year would have had to be spent on imports of food grains.[2]

2. Schultz (39) has argued that supply of food grains under PL 480 assistance to India and other countries has depressed production be-

Moreover, continuation of rapid population increase and slow growth of food-grain output for any length of time will push import requirements to impossibly high levels. The Panel on World Food Supply of the Science Advisory Committee of the U.S. President has calculated import requirements of food grains in Table 24-12; the calculation is

cause it "has had the effect of reducing farm product prices below what they would have been without such forms of aid." It is true that the period of stagnation of domestic output in India has coincided with the period of heavy imports of food grains under PL 480; and the increasing difficulty of obtaining such imports since 1966 has been followed by intensified official efforts to increase domestic production of food grains.

based on the assumption that the population growth rate increases progressively from 2.42 per cent per year during 1960-64 to 2.80 in the late 1970's and early 1980's, while food-grain output increases at "no more than its 14-year (1950-64) trend line rate of 2.36 per cent per year" (16: 687).[3] The cost of the imports projected for 1971 is 65.5 per cent of the total export earnings for that year, as projected by the Planning Commission.

Even apart from the need to avoid an impossible international trade situation, rapid increase in agricultural output is essential for maintaining a satisfactory rate of economic growth. The close connection between agricultural growth and over-all economic growth is clearly indicated by the foregoing review of economic trends.

The importance of increasing agricultural output has been recognized in India's Plans. In the First Five-Year Plan, it was given top priority and as much as 36.94 per cent of the total development expenditure was on agricultural development and irrigation programs (38: 480). But the proportion fell to 22.26 during the Second Plan and 21.84 during the Third Plan (*ibid*). In both the Second and Third Plans, large investments were made in industry and there was less emphasis on agriculture and irrigation, which can be partly attributed to the steady growth of agricultural output in the 1950's and the relatively comfortable food-supplies. But stagnation of agricultural output during 1960-64 and the sharp fall during 1965-67 have again focused attention on agriculture. The draft outline of the Fourth Plan, issued in 1966, reiterated the need for giving the

highest priority to increased output (36: 30); and the Government of India adopted in the same year a "New Agricultural Strategy" for increasing output of food grains. The Strategy is a significant departure from earlier official programs. It relies heavily on use of high-yield, hybrid and dwarf seed varieties, chemical fertilizers, and pesticides —and provides for concentration of these inputs and other resources in areas with assured and adequate irrigation facilities, where such concentration will produce maximum results. By 1970-71, 25 to 30 million hectares of cropland will be brought under intensive cultivation; they are expected to produce 63.35 million tons of food grains, out of the total projected output of 120 million tons (40: 440).

Strategies of Agricultural Development

The New Agricultural Strategy is based on recognition, on the one hand, of certain natural-resource-based limitations on increasing agricultural output and, on the other, of the possibilities opened by agricultural research. These limitations and possibilities are discussed below at some length because they point to the directions that agriculture in India must take in the future. The discussion is based on a comparative analysis of three programs: the New Agricultural Strategy, the perspective plan for Development of Agriculture 1960-61 to 1975-76 drawn up by the Planning Commission in 1964 (31), and the USPSAC Panel program (16). The Planning Commission's plan represents official thinking on increasing agricultural output before adoption of the New Agricultural Strategy; the program of the Panel appears to have had a considerable influence on the Strategy. The projections of the three programs are given in Tables 24-13, 24-14, and 24-15.

3. This rate is lower than the rate of 2.98 per cent per year calculated for 1949-50 to 1964-65 by the Economic and Statistical Advisor to the Ministry of Food and Agriculture, Government of India, and given in Table 24-10.

TABLE 24-13   INDIA. PROJECTIONS OF THE PERSPECTIVE PLAN,
PLANNING COMMISSION

	1960/ 61	1965/ 66	1970/ 71	1975/ 76
Population millions)	439	492	555	625
Growth rate (% per year)				
Population		2.4	2.5	2.5
National income		5.0	7.7	7.5
Per capita income		2.6	5.0	5.0
Agricultural production		2.3	5.1	4.3
Industrial production		8.6	12.3	10.0
Gross cropped area (million ha.)	152.25	n.d.	171.66	182.19
Net sown area ” ”	132.74	n.d.	137.78	141.05
Area sown more than once ”	19.51	n.d.	33.88	41.14
Gross irrigated area ”	27.93	n.d.	45.75	55.47
Area under foodgrains ”	113.24	n.d.	127.53	134.41
Production of foodgrains (million t.)	82.0	n.d.	122.0	151.0
Consumption of chemical fertilizers (million t., NPK)	0.3	n.d.	2.45	

n.d. = no data
Source: Planning Commission: *Development of Agriculture, India 1960/61
to 1975/76*, New Delhi, January 1964 (Mimeographed) and *Notes on Perspective of Development India 1960/61 to 1975/76*, New Delhi, April, 1964.

TABLE 24-14   INDIA. PROJECTIONS OF USPSAC PANEL REPORT

	A. *Growth of population and production*				
	1964	1967	1971	1976	1986
Population (millions)	471.3	509.0	565.4	647.5	853.5
Growth rates (% per year) Population		2.52	2.66	2.75	2.80
National income		3.80	4.50	4.40	4.30 to 4.20
Per capita income		1.22	1.78	1.60	1.46 to 1.36
Agricultural production		3.33	6.8	3.4	3.6 to 2.3
Industrial production		3.4	2.6	4.8	4.8 to 5.4
Foodgrain production		3.28	6.75	3.61	3.22 to 3.03
Gross cropped area (million ha)	157.5	160.3	163.0	166.0	172.0
Gross irrigated area (million ha)	30.2	32.7	36.5	45.0	63.0
Foodgrains (million ha)	116.3	118.7	121.0	123.5	128.5
Production of foodgrains (million t.)	79.4	87.4	113.5	135.5	184.4
Consumption of chemical fertilizers (million t. NPK)	0.60	1.40	4.25	6.81	11.06

TABLE 24-14 (continued)

	B. *Intensive and general cultivation of foodgrains*							
	1967		1971		1976		1986	
	I.C	G.C.	I.C.	G.C.	I.C.	G.C.	I.C.	G.C.
Cropped area (million ha)	2.0	116.7	12.0	109.0	22.0	101.5	42.0	86.5
Production (million t.)	3.4	84.0	23.0	90.5	45.9	89.6	108.6	75.8
Yield per ha (kg)	1716	720	1916	830	2085	883	2586	876
Consumption of chemical fertilizers (NPK): Total (million t.)	0.10	0.88	0.90	2.51	1.98	3.55	5.25	3.64
Per ha (kg)	50	7.5	75	23	90	35	125	42

Source: Holst, W: Evaluation of population and food problems of India in: *The World Food Problem*. A Report of the President's Science Advisory Committee, Panel on the World Food Supply, The White House, May, 1967, p. 703-06.

TABLE 24-15   INDIA. TARGETS UNDER THE PROGRAM OF THE NEW AGRICULTURAL STRATEGY

	1970/71	
	Cropped area under foodgrains (*million ha*)	Population of foodgrains (*million t.*)
Irrigated area:		
High-yielding seed varieties	13.16	40.95
Double cropping with use of short-term varieties	12.14	22.40
Other irrigated area	7.09	9.20
Total	32.39	72.55
Unirrigated area	105.26	47.45
Grand total	137.65	120.00

Consumption of chemical fertilizers 4.1 million t. of which ¾ in areas under high-yielding and quick maturing varieties.
Source: Sivaraman, B., "The Strategy of Food Production," *Indian Journal of Public Administration,* Vol. 13, 1967, 3, p. 440.

EXPANSION OF CROPPED AREA VS.
INCREASE IN PRODUCTIVITY

During the period 1949-50 to 1964-65, the rates of increase of cropped area and productivity of croplands were almost equal (Table 24-10). But calculation of the rates for two reference decades, 1949-50 to 1958-59 and 1955-56 to 1964-65, shows that increase in cropped area was more rapid in the first decade, while increase in productivity was exactly the reverse. Rapid expansion of cropped area in the early 1950's was the result of land reform. With the abolition of feudal systems of land tenure (*zamindari* and *jagirdari*), and government adoption of policies favoring reclamation of culturable wastelands,[4] many such areas, transferred to private or village control, were brought under cultivation by the former *zamindars* and *jagirdars,* who wanted to become "cultivators," or by their former tenants, who had acquired rights in land; the process was assisted by loans and grants from the government. Also, large areas of government-owned wastelands were allotted to landless cultivators. However, as reclamation of the more marginal lands became increasingly difficult, the rate of expansion of cropped area slowed down after the middle 1950's. The "net sown area," which had increased by 12 million hectares between 1950-51 and 1956-57, increased between 1956-57 and 1962-63 by only 6 million hectares (Table 24-16).

Both the Planning Commission (31) and USPSAC Panel (16) recognize that expansion of cropped area can make only a limited contribution to the future increase of agricultural output and that most of the increase must come from increase in productivity. But whereas the Planning Commission has visualized an increase of 20 per cent in gross cropped area between 1960-61 and 1975-76 (Table 24-13) which would contribute more than one-fourth to the total increase in agricultural output in this period, the USPSAC Panel has projected only a marginal increase of 10 per cent in the cropped area under food grains during a 22-year period, 1964-86, in which total food-grain output would more than double (Table 24-14. An examination of the projection of the Planning Commission, however, reveals that most of the increase in gross cropped area will come from multiple cropping over of a larger proportion of the

4. *Zamindari, jagirdari,* and other feudal systems of land tenure were abolished in the early 1950's as part of the land reform program of the Indian Government.

cropland—increase in area sown more than once—whereas increase in cropland or "net sown area" will be small. Out of a total increase of nearly 30 million hectares in gross cropped area, as much as 21.6 million hectares will be from areas "sown more than once" (Table 24-13). Increase in these areas is to come from an expansion of irrigation—by 27.54 million hectares—and consequent second crop growth.

The possibilities of increasing the "net sown area" are in fact quite limited, even though large areas continue to be recorded as "culturable waste," "current fallows," and "fallows other than current," indicating that they could be cultivated. The total area under these categories was nearly 40 million hectares in 1962-63 (Table 24-16). "Current fallows" form an integral part of the cropping system on unirrigated lands in the low rainfall zone (below 762 mm annually) as well as on other lands of low productivity and probably cannot be reduced much; the area under "current fallows" changed little between 1950-51 and 1962-63. In the other two categories, there are large areas which suffer from soil erosion, weeds, salinity, alkalinity, or other soil defects, and are either unsuitable for cultivation or can be reclaimed only at high cost. In 1960 a team of agricultural experts investigated the possibilities of extension of cultivation into culturable wastelands and concluded that: "Ten million acres (4 million hectares) might be the upper limit of the additional area that might become available for arable farming itself out of the existing culturable waste during a period of about fifteen years beyond 1960-61" (8: 4). When considering the possibilities of extension of cultivation, one must also remember that these areas, as well as most of the areas classified as "forest," are used for grazing. The large livestock population—226.8 million bovine animals and 101.1 million sheep and goats in

TABLE 24-16   LAND UTILIZATION IN INDIA 1950/51 TO 1962/63
(IN 1,000 HA)

	1950/51	*1956/67*	*1962/63*
Geographical area	326,287	326,287	326,287
Area according to village papers	284,315	292,435	299,912
Forests	40,482	51,702	55,448
Not available for cultivation	47,517	47,024	50,308
Permanent pastures and grazing lands	6,675	12,190	14,127
Land under miscellaneous tree crops and groves (Not included in net area sown)	19,828	5,510	4,589
Culturable waste	22,943	21,846	17,971
Fallow land: Other than current	17,445	11,965	10,263
Current	10,679	11,705	10,962
Net area sown	118,747	130,493	136,244
Area sown more than once	13,146	18,582	20,492
Total cropped area	131,893	149,075	156,736
Irrigation			
Net irrigated area	20,853	22,533	25,663
Area irrigated more than once	1,710	3,174	3,935
Gross irrigated area	22,563	25,707	29,598

Source: Directorate of Economics and Statistics, Ministry of Food and Agriculture, Government of India, New Delhi, 1966.

1961—depends mainly upon grazing these lands because the area actually classified as "permanent pasture and grazing land" is very small—14.13 million hectares in 1962-63 (Table 24-16). Diversion of large areas of culturable wastelands or fallow lands for cultivation will only accentuate the problem of subsistence of livestock.

The area under forest also cannot be reduced without further reducing the supplies of wood and other forest products and exposing large areas to serious soil erosion. Supplies of industrial wood, pulp for paper and other industries, and fuel-wood are al-

ready inadequate, and the demands are growing rapidly. Production of timber and other industrial wood was estimated at 8.0 million m^3 in 1965. The demand in that year was estimated at 11.0 million m^3, and was expected to increase to 24.0 million m^3 by 1975-76 (36: 205). The demand for pulp, derived mainly from bamboo, was expected to increase more than five times, from 450,000 tons to 2,275,000 tons between 1960-61 and 1975-76 (30: 125). The demand for fuel-wood, which is the principal domestic fuel in both rural and urban areas, was expected to increase by more than 30 per cent during this period (15: 77). The Planning Commission has come to the conclusion that these rapidly growing demands can be met only by a radical change in forestry practices from the existing conservation-management to modern plantation-management (36: 205). Any large reduction in the area under forests is out of the question.

The lack of areas of culturable land which could be reclaimed by the peasants themselves is a handicap for agricultural and over-all economic development. Reclamation of such areas is the easiest and the most economical method of increasing output under the economic and social conditions of Indian agriculture. The cost is low because most of the resources are furnished by human-bullock labor which is chronically underemployed; even a part of the capital requirement is met by savings which would otherwise be hoarded or used for unproductive purposes. Output can increase rapidly because no major change from traditional agricultural practices is involved. Increase of output by increasing productivity of cropland, on the other hand, requires large external investment—in irrigation works and for production and supply of chemical fertilizers and high-yielding seed, for instance—and also involves major changes in traditional farming practices. Such changes depend in turn on an increase in knowledge among the farmers and changes in attitudes and socio-economic structures; these are slow in getting started. Increase of agricultural output in the early 1950's, to which expansion of cropped area by the farmers themselves made the major contribution, was relatively rapid and painless; indeed, it occurred faster than expected, because the targets of the First Five-Year Plan were overfulfilled. But output increase during the 1960's, which is dependent upon increase in productivity, has proved to be slower, and much more difficult; it has already led to a reappraisal of official development policies and may lead to major socio-economic changes within village society before it becomes established as a process.

Increase in productivity is linked with irrigation and improved agricultural techniques, including use of modern inputs. Concentration of resources in selected areas is a strategy, based on evaluation of the relative efficiency of application of resources in different areas.

IRRIGATION

Nearly one-fifth of the cropped area of India is irrigated (Table 24-16) but the contribution of the irrigated area to total agricultural output is much larger because average productivity of the irrigated lands is higher than that of the unirrigated lands. Average yields of rice are 58 per cent higher and those of wheat 77 per cent higher (31: Appendix 4, p. 7). Also, high-yield crops, such as sugar cane, are grown mainly on irrigated lands. Irrigation has been important in recent years: in the first three Plans, more than 40 per cent of the expenditure on agricultural development has been for extension or improvement of irrigation facilities (38: 48). The irrigated area increased from 22.56 million hectares in 1950-51 to 29.60 million hectares in 1962-63 or by 2.3 per cent annually (Table 24-16), and additional large increases are projected both by the Planning Commission and the USPSAC Panel. The Commission has projected a doubling of the gross irrigated area between 1960-61 and 1975-76; the Panel has projected a similar increase over the 22-year period 1964-68 (Tables 24-13 and 24-14). But the increase rates in both projections—4.9 and 3.3 per cent per year respectively—are much higher than the actual rate between 1950-51 and 1962-63. The rate of increase could be faster in the future —the potential of a number of irrigation projects remains to be utilized (36: 216, 232-35). But it is quite unlikely that it will be 50 or 100 per cent higher than in the recent past.

Development of irrigation has particular importance for the programs of the USPSAC Panel and the New Agricultural Strategy, because the "intensive cultivation" areas which will account for most of the increase in output must be provided with assured and adequate facilities ("100 per cent irrigation" according to the Panel). Efficient water management is an essential counterpart to use of high-yielding seed, chemical fertilizers, and other inputs. The strategy is based on experimental evidence which indicates that very high crop yields can be obtained with intensive use of these inputs under conditions of controlled and adequate moisture (16: 695). But all irrigated areas do not fulfill the condition of assured and adequate irrigation; large areas, especially those irrigated from tanks and other surface irrigation, have inadequate supplies of water which, moreover, fail during periods of drought. The USPSAC Panel has limited the ultimate extension of the "intensive cultivation" areas to 42 million hectares apparently on the assessment that not more than two-thirds of the total irrigated area of 63 million hectares will meet the exacting requirement of "100 per cent irrigation." But the New Agricultural Strategy has assumed that the requirement will be met in as much as 25.3 million out of a total of 32.4 million hectares of irrigated area under food grains by 1970-71 (Table 24-16). Against the background of widespread failure of irrigation in 1965-67 from water sources which had been considered "safe for agriculture" (40: 438), such an assumption seems quite unrealistic.

In 1961 the ultimate potential of irrigation development was estimated at 71 million hectares (35: 189). It now is being revised upward because of recent experience indicating that two or more crops can be grown each year on much of the land with the use of new, quick-maturing varieties. Sivaraman has estimated that nearly half of the irrigated land may ultimately be multiple-cropped and that the gross irrigated area may as a result reach 81 million hectares (40: 441). The latter is a little less than half of the ultimate gross cropped area of 168 million hectares he projects.

USE OF MODERN INPUTS

In development programs preceding the adoption of the New Agricultural Strategy, improvement of techniques included both the use of modern inputs and the adoption of traditional good farming practices, such as use of compost and green manure, deep ploughing, and systematic crop rotation. Considerable emphasis was given to more extensive adoption of the latter which, it was thought, could bring large gains in productivity without much capital investment. The effort itself could be considered "organization-intensive," because, apart from money spent on irrigation, land reclamation, and soil conservation, the expenditure was largely for agricultural extension and credit and supplies organizations.

This approach was continued in the Perspective Plan of the Planning Commission. Of the projected increase in output, only 36 per cent would come from use of improved seed and chemical fertilizers, while as much as 42 per cent would be contributed by "other inputs," including both traditional improvements and more efficient use of inputs (31: 24). However, both the USPSAC Panel and the New Agricultural Strategy emphasize use of modern inputs. Under the program of the Panel, two-thirds of the projected increase between 1964 and 1986 will come from chemical fertilizers and high-yielding seed; the balance will come mainly from irrigation (16: 700). Under the NAS program, the entire increase will come from intensively fertilized areas sown to high-yielding and quick-maturing varieties.

These programs were patterned after highly successful projects within India, and in Mexico, Taiwan, and the Philippines (16: 693-95). But use of modern inputs is capital-intensive and technology-intensive. It requires large investment in seed farms and factories and also agricultural research organizations staffed by qualified plant breeders, agronomists, and other specialists. These requirements have been clearly stated by the Panel, which has recommended allocation of adequate resources for their implementation. The investment needs of the program are estimated at U.S. $29 billion over a 22-year period—an average of U.S. $1.32 billion per year (16: 700-701).

Total investment in the Indian economy was estimated at U.S. $3 billion in 1965-66, and will undoubtedly increase over the 22-year period.[5] Yet it is clear that the program will take a very large share, especially in the early years (late 1960's and early 1970's) when the major investments will have to be made.

CONCENTRATION OF RESOURCES
IN SELECTED AREAS

Under the program of the USPSAC Panel, as well as under the New Agricultural Strategy, most of the increase in output will come from areas selected for "intensive cultivation." As mentioned above, the strategy is based on experimental evidence which

5. The Planning Commission estimated the national income in 1965-66 at 159,300 million rupees and the investment ratio at 14 to 15 per cent of the national income (36: 28 and 420). At the current conversion rate of US $1 = Rp 7.5, total investment is between US $2.97 million and 3.18 billion.

shows that very high yields can be obtained with intensive use of these inputs under conditions of controlled and adequate moisture. It is also implied that the possibility of increasing output in much of the unirrigated area is meager. The Panel has proposed that areas having "100 per cent irrigation" and other favorable conditions should be selected for "intensive cultivation" of food grains. It predicts a progressive increase of such areas from 2.0 million hectares in 1967 to 12.0 million in 1971, and 42.0 million in 1986 (Table 24-14). The corresponding production targets are 3.5 million tons, 23.0 million tons, and 108.6 million tons. In 1971 these areas will account for about 10 per cent of the total area under food grains but contribute more than one-fifth of the output; the corresponding figures for 1986 are 33 and 59 per cent. Also in 1986 the intensive cultivation areas will account for 59 per cent of the total consumption of chemical fertilizers for food-grain production, and average yields will be nearly three times those in the general cultivation areas (Table 24-14).

Concentration of resources and output increase has been carried even further under the program of the New Agricultural Strategy. A proposed total area of 25 million hectares for high-yielding or quick-maturing seed varieties by 1970-71 is expected to account for three-fourths of the total consumption of chemical fertilizers and to contribute more than half of the projected output of food grains in that year (Table 24-15). The unirrigated areas appear to have been entirely ignored; indeed, total output projected for them in 1970-71 is lower than the actual output of 1964-65 (40: 438, 440).

The idea of concentrating resources in favorable areas to obtain rapid increase in output is not new, although both programs present it in a more extreme form than had been done earlier. It can be traced back to the early 1950's when a number of community development blocks were located in areas having a good potential for increasing agricultural output (i.e. irrigation projects). But a decision to extend the community program to the whole country soon relegated it to the background. It was revived in 1959 by a team of American agricultural experts invited by the Government of India to review its agricultural development programs and suggest measures to increase output more rapidly. The team recommended selection of "promising areas" for increased production of wheat and rice, and seven districts (out of more than 300) were selected accordingly in 1960 for an "intensive agricultural development program" (IADP) of five years in duration. In 1962 the number of districts was increased to 15 and from that time on new areas continued to be selected until by the end of the Third Five-Year Plan (March 1966) nearly a third of the cropped area of the country was covered by either IADP districts or "intensive areas" (36: 175). Such rapid expansion could only mean dilution of effort, because trained personnel, finance, and materials were limited.

The feasibility of the principal features of both programs can be questioned. It can be argued that exclusive reliance on use of capital-intensive inputs, ignoring the possibilities of production increase through improvement in farm management and use of traditional good farming practices, unduly raises the investment requirements. It can also be argued that it will not be possible to sustain concentration of resources in limited areas for long because the same pressures which caused a retreat from it earlier will again operate in the future. Resource concentration in particular areas involves discrimination in their favor; increasing interregional and interfarm disparities

in income soon become evident. In periods of scarcity of inputs such as chemical fertilizers, reservation of large proportions of supplies for "intensive cultivation" areas is particularly resented by farmers in other areas. The pressures against resource concentration are strong.

Other difficulties arise as a result of land tenure and administrative deficiencies. The feasibility of "intensive cultivation" in areas cultivated by tenants can be questioned on the ground that these people are not sure of their status, are subject to extortionate rents, and have little incentive to increase production (19: 9). Further, because of administrative inefficiency, the performance of the existing IADP districts has been much below expectations (18: 486-87). Indeed, it can be argued that no present administrative agency is capable of carrying forward the highly intensive programs proposed by the Panel under the NAS.

Finally, the desirability of leaving much of the agricultural area in virtual stagnation may be seriously questioned. The nonintensive areas have been entirely ignored in the New Agricultural Strategy. The USPSAC Panel envisages an increase in average yield of food grains in the "general cultivation" areas of about one-third between 1964 and 1986. But they will include both comparatively well-watered areas where irrigation is below 100 per cent, and unirrigated areas in the zones of moderate to heavy rainfall (1140 mm per year and above)—as well as moisture-deficient areas. If one assumes that the well-watered areas will receive higher inputs and experience larger productivity increase than the moisture-deficient areas, it is clear that the latter will be left to stagnate. The extent of such areas is not small: in 1960-61, about 60 per cent of the total cropped area of India was unirrigated and located in zones with rainfall below 1140 mm per year. Providing for little or no growth in such a large proportion of the cropped area constitutes wasteful use of resources. Indeed, average productivity per agricultural worker will decline in these areas, unless the increase in the labor force is offset by emigration—an extremely unlikely prospect in a country with such pronounced immobility of population.

Population Growth and the Prospects of Increasing Food Output—Some Earlier Assessments

We have selected three assessments made since 1950: the 1951 Report of the Census of India (4), Coale and Hoover in 1958 (7), and Sukhatme in 1965 (42). These reports not only illustrate different points of view, but changes in thinking on the subject within a very short period. The Perspective Plan of the Planning Commission and the Report of the USPSAC Panel might also be considered here, even though their primary object is to outline programs needed to meet predetermined targets of output. Both arrive at the conclusion that increases in food output, required to meet the needs of population growth and economic development, are possible. Similar confidence has not existed in some of the earlier assessments. The Report of the Census of 1951 was particularly pessimistic. In Malthusian style, it prescribed a rigid upper limit to the possibilities of expansion of agriculture (and food) output and forecast "catastrophe" if population outgrew that limit. The difference between the pessimism of this Report and the confidence of the latest assessments, even with their forecast of much higher populations, is due to two reasons:

    (i) a much better record of increase in agricultural output during the period of the three Plans than in the previous half-century, and

    (ii) technological advance which has increased productivity of croplands.

1951 CENSUS REPORT

Based on a continuation of the 1941-51 rate of growth for the next 30 years, the 1951 Census Report forecast a population of between 527.6 million and 535.5 million in 1981 (Table 24-17). A higher rate of growth was considered possible, but no estimate was given. It was estimated that agricultural output would have to increase by 55 per cent between 1951 and 1981 to maintain the existing levels of consumption; but the possibilities of increasing output were put at a maximum of 35 per cent. This pessimistic view was based on a detailed analysis of the prospects of increasing both cropped and irrigated areas and raising productivity through improvements in techniques. It was influenced undoubtedly, by an analysis of the performance of Indian agriculture in the 60 years preceding 1951 which revealed declining cultivated and irrigated areas per capita, and stagnant or declining per acre yields. On the basis of this analysis, the Census Commissioner concluded: "Our effort to keep pace with unchecked growth of population is bound to fail at some point . . . and we should be able to go one step further and fix this point by saying that it is the time at which our total number reaches and passes 45 crores (450 million)" (4: 207). He estimated that this number would be reached by 1969.

Increase of population beyond this number could, in the view of the Commissioner, only result in catastrophe. His prescription for averting catastrophe was a nation-wide program of family planning "to limit the number of births [so] that they do not materially exceed the number of deaths and thus to achieve a substantially stationary population before our number exceeds 45 crores (450 million)" (4: 216). The birth

TABLE 24-17   SELECTED POPULATION PROJECTIONS FOR INDIA, 1961-86
(*Population in millions; Growth rate in % per year*)

Source	1961	1971	1976	1981	1986
Census of India 1951 (4)	407	464		527.6 to 535.5	
Coale and Hoover 1958 (7)					
Projection II	424.0	524.0	569.0	603.0	634.0
Projection III	424.0	532.0	601.0	682.0	775.0
Sukhatme 1965 (44)					
Projection I					
Population	438.0	535.0	585.0	630.0	
Growth rate		2.0	1.8	1.5	
Projection II					
Population	438.0	555.0	625.0	680.0	
Growth rate		2.5	2.5	2.0	
Planning Commission 1964 (30)	439.0	555.0	625.0		
USPSAC Panel 1967 (16)					
Population	439.0	565.4	647.5	734.4	853.5
Growth rate		2.4 increasing to 2.66	2.75	2.80	2.80

rate would have to fall in this period from 40 to 25 per mille and this would have to be achieved by reducing the incidence of "improvident maternity" from its present level of 40 per cent to under 5 per cent in 15 years" (4: 218). Improvident maternity was defined as "child-birth occurring to a mother who has already given birth to three or more children of whom at least one is alive" (4: 217). It is interesting to note that while the Census Commissioner did believe it possible for agricultural output to increase by 35 per cent in 30 years, he was extremely conscious of the difficulties of expanding output under conditions of peasant agriculture. He believed that Indian society could be transformed in 15 years from a stage in which few had heard about family

planning to universal acceptance of the practice.

COALE AND HOOVER (1958)

Coale and Hoover selected India as a case example of their study of the relationship between population growth and economic development. The study is concerned primarily with projection of population growth and evaluation of the prospects of economic development in India; assessment of the agricultual prospects forms part of the larger evaluation.

In making their population projections, Coale and Hoover assumed growth rates of 2.0 to 2.5 per cent during the period 1951-86. (Table 24-17). These projections were much higher than the official projections of the time, and their publication immediately effected upward revision of the latter. But all projections made in the 1950's, including the highest projection by Coale and Hoover, were proved to be too low by the 1961 census. Now projections are much higher; some of them, including the projection of the USPSAC Panel, assume increasing rate of population growth well into the 1980's (Table 24-17).

Coale and Hoover's assessment was not as detailed as the Census Commissioner's; but it was based on the food consumption data of the National Sample Survey, other rural sample surveys and the production results of the First Five-Year Plan. Their conclusion, more hopeful than the Commissioner's, stated that "India's output of food and other agricultural products can, for the next two or three decades, increase at least as fast as the maximum rate of growth of the consuming population (78 per cent in 25 years)" (7: 110). They thought that the main difficulties in increasing output were in the area of social institutions and attitudes, and that the prime need was to overcome the apathy and inertia of the rural population.

SUKHATME (1965)

Sukhatme was concerned primarily with assessing the possibilities of meeting the food needs of India's growing population. He made two projections of population growth by 1981 (Table 24-17). The higher projection was similar to the government's official projection, but the lower one assumed a decline in fertility and growth rate beginning in the late 1960's when Sukhatme felt that the government's family planning program could begin to have an effect. He was well aware of the difficulties of spreading family planning practices among a predominantly rural and illiterate population, but cited the experience of Japan and the East European

countries, where birth rates fell by one-fourth to one-third in a decade, to support his assumption of an early decline (42: 101). Sukhatme's work was notable for a very detailed assessment of existing consumption levels and the extent of "hunger" in India and the increases, quantitative and qualitative, needed to bring consumption up to minimum nutritional requirements. His estimates of food consumption were based on nutrition surveys conducted by the Indian Council of Medical Research for about 30 years, State government surveys, and the National Sample Survey. The "targets" of consumption requirements were based, similarly, on an exhaustive evaluation of recommendations of Indian and international (FAO) nutritionists. Sukhatme estimated the food requirements of the projected population of 1981 at "minimum" and "medium" targets, both of which envisaged specified quantitative and qualitative improvements over existing consumption levels. His conclusion was similar to Coale and Hoover's, namely, that it is possible to raise agricultural output sufficiently to meet "minimum target" needs, but that it is not possible to provide for any major improvement in nutrition level, such as an appreciable increase in consumption of animal products (42: 154-55).

Population Growth and the Economic Prospect

The Perspective Plan of the Planning Commission and the Report of the USPSAC Panel also constitute in a sense assessments of economic development. The Perspective Plan is based on the assumption that an annual population increase of 2.5 per cent can be combined with a growth rate of 2.5 to 5.0 per cent in per capita income (Table 27-14). The Panel has assumed a higher growth rate and a lower increase rate in per capita income; the latter falls as low as 1.36 per cent annually in the 1980's (Table 27-15). This lower rate is due only partly to assumption of a higher growth rate. The lower rate may also be the result of development strategy followed by the Panel. The subject obviously needs detailed analysis; but the implication of the low rate is clear, namely, that the effort to increase food output to meet the minimum needs of the rapidly growing population will take such large resources that economic development will be delayed for a long time. The Panel explains accelerated population growth in the 1960's and the 1970's on the ground that decline in death rate will be more than the decline in birth rate and the spread between births and deaths will increase: There can hardly be any major differences on the forecast of a decline in the death rate. The rate of 22.8 per mille calculated for 1951-60 by application of the reverse survival method to the 1951 and 1961 censuses, is very high even by the standards of the developing countries—the rates in Ceylon, Jamaica, and a number of other countries are already between 8 and 9 per mille (43: 561-63)—and should fall with further improvement in health services and communications and increase in literacy. The Panel assumes a high birth rate continuing well into the 1980's because "it is not expected that population control will have such a downward impact on growth rates much before 1985 either in India or the World as a whole" (16: 683). This view differs from official expectations and from those of Sukhatme and a UN Mission which studied India's family planning program in 1965. Reference has been made to Sukhatme's view that the family planning program could have a noticeable effect on the birth rate even in the late 1960's. The UN Mission, after examining progress of the program, stated that "population control measures could be suffi-

ciently effective by 1975 to prevent the rate of increase from accelerating, but not falling" (29: 92). The object of the family planning program officially is to reduce the birth rate from 40 to 25 per cent "as expeditiously as possible," but it is expected that the reduction will be rapid enough to affect population growth in the late 1970's.

The prospect of population growth will remain somewhat uncertain until there is more information on the progress of the family planning program. In existence since the 1950's, only during the last three years has the program been implemented as a nation-wide effort. According to the latest official report, nearly 6 million couples, out of a total of 90 million in the reproductive age group, were practicing family planning in 1967-68 (25). The practices included use of IUCD, condoms, and sterilization of both males and females. Of these, sterilization appears to be gaining in popularity, while use of IUCD has declined somewhat. The number of people sterilized during 1967-68 was 1.4 million, double the number of the previous year, while the number of users of IUCD had decreased by 20 per cent (*ibid*).

Progress of the program will depend in future on speed of change in attitudes, the resources allocated to it, and adequacy of basic medical services. It is fortunate that there is no deep-seated prejudice against family planning among the majority of the population; the main task is to propagate the attitude that something can be done about family size. The Fourth Five-Year Plan proposed to raise resource allocation to nearly four times the level of the Third Plan (36: 347). But lack of medical personnel is a serious handicap. There were fewer than 100,000 doctors in India in 1961, and two-thirds of them were concentrated in the towns (17, No. 6: 20-21). The total number of female doctors, whose role is critical in the spread of practices such as use of

IUCD, was only about 8500, and only 1082 of them were in the rural areas. The female doctor-female population ratio was as low as 6 per million in the rural areas. The number of trained nurses and midwives was equally small—about 109,000 (17, No. 5: 24). The popularity of sterilization of males frequently performed in camps organized by peripatetic medical teams, and the slow acceptance of IUCD, which requires follow-up advice and medical assistance in a percentage of cases, reflect, in our view, this shortage of medical and nursing personnel.

Economically, the recent record of stagnation and instability in agricultural output does impart a degree of uncertainty. But given continuance of adequate emphasis on increasing output, it should not be difficult to resume the steady growth of output ahead of population growth achieved during the 1950's. The resources of capital, organization, and technology are much larger now, and reappraisal of official policies to ensure more effective use of resources is well under way. Investment rates have gone up steadily—from 5.5 per cent in 1950-51 to 14 to 15 in 1965-66. The industrial base is larger and more diversified than at the beginning of the First Plan; the number of trained technicians is much higher; and further development of industry, transport and other modern sectors can be based much more on domestic resources than in the past. In agriculture, the basic extension, supplies, and credit organizations needed for modernization exist, and have only to be strengthened and reoriented. Forecasts of large increases in output within three or four years, such as the one made under the program of the New Agricultural Strategy, are possible only because of the existence of the basic organizations. The Strategy, for all its excesses and limitations, does represent an effort toward reappraisal of policies which will take into account the potential of rapidly advancing technology on the one hand and natural-resource-based limitations on the other. The rate of economic growth can be faster (than in the 1950's) with more efficient utilization of resources. Among these, particular mention needs to be made of the very large resource of underemployed manpower. We have referred earlier to the difficulties in utilization of this resource. But the difficulties are not insuperable: they can be overcome with good organization and leadership.

REFERENCES

(1) E. A. Ackerman: Population and Natural Resources, in: P. M. Hauser and O. D. Duncan, eds.: The Study of Population (Chicago, 1959), pp. 717-27. Reprinted in: I. Burton and R. W. Kates, eds.: Readings in Resource Management and Conservation (Chicago, 1965), pp. 127-52.

(2) J. P. Bhattacharjee, ed.: Studies in Indian Agricultural Economics (Bombay, Indian Society of Agricultural Economics, 1958).

(3) G. Blyn: Agricultural Trends in India, 1891-1947: Output availability and Productivity. (Philadelphia, 1966).

(4) Census of India, 1951: Vol. 1 India. Part 1-A Report (Delhi, 1953).

(5) Census of India, 1951: Vol. 1 India. Part 1-B-Appendices to the Census Report, 1951 (Delhi, 1955).

(6) Census of India, 1961: Paper No. 1 of 1962. Final Population Totals (Delhi, 1962).

(7) A. J. Coale and E. M. Hoover: Population Growth and Economic Development in Low-Income Countries—A Case Study of India's Prospects (Princeton, N.J., 1958).

(8) Committee on Natural Resources, Planning Commission, Government of India: Study on Wastelands including Saline, Alkali and Waterlogged Lands and their Reclamation Measures (New Delhi, 1963).

(9) M. Darling: The Punjab Peasant in Prosperity and Debt, 4th ed. (Bombay, 1947).

(10) B. N. Datar: The Second Five Year Plan—Employment Approach, in: Papers Relating to the Formulation of the Second Five Year Plan, Panel of Economists, Planning Commission (New Delhi, 1955).

(11) Economic and Statistical Advisor to the Government of India, Ministry of Food and Agriculture: Growth Rates in Agriculture (New Delhi, March 1966), mimeographed.

(12) S. T. Epstein: Economic Development and Social Change in South India (Bombay, 1962).

(13) D. R. Gadgil: The Industrial Evolution of India in Recent Times (Calcutta, 1942).

(14) N. Ginsburg: Natural Resources and Economic Development, *Annals of the Association of American Geographers,* Vol. 47, 1957, pp. 167-212. Reprinted in: I. Burton and R. W. Kates, eds.: Readings in Resource Management and Conservation (Chicago, 1965).

(15) Government of India: Report of the Energy Survey Committee New Delhi, 1965).

(16) W. Holst: Evaluation of Population and Food Production Problems of India, in: The World Food Problems—Report of the Panel on the World Food Supply of the President's Science Advisory Committee (Washington, 1967).

(17) Institute of Applied Manpower Research and National Institute of Health Administration and Education: Manpower Group Survey. IAMR Working Papers Nos. 5 and 6. *Stock of Nursing Personnel in India and Stock of Health and Medical Manpower* (New Delhi, 1965), mimeographed.

(18) E. A. Kieloch: Some Administrative Shortcomings of Intensive Agricultural Development Efforts, *Indian J. Publ. Adm.,* Vol. 18, No. 3, July-September 1967, pp. 484-92.

(19) W. Ladejinsky: A Study on Tenurial Conditions in Package Districts. Planning Commision, Government of India (New Delhi, 1965).

(20) H. Leibenstein: Economic Backwardness and Economic Growth (New York and London, 1957).

(21) W. A. Lewis: Economic Development with Unlimited Supplies of Labour (The Manchester School, May 1954). Reprinted in: A. N.

Agarwala and S. P. Singh, eds.: The Economics of Under-Development (New York, 1963), pp. 400-49.

(22) S. S. Madalgi: Hunger in Rural India: 1960/61 to 1964/65, *Economic and Political Weekly,* Bombay. Vol. 3, Annual Number 1968, pp. 61-67.

(23) W. Malenbaum: Prospects for Indian Development (London, 1962).

(24) Ministry of Finance, Government of India: Economic Survey 1967/68 (New Delhi, 1968).

(25) Ministry of Health, Government of India: Annual Report 1967/68 (New Delhi, 1968).

(26) Ministry of Labour, Government of India: Report on Intensive Survey of Agricultural Labour: All India, Vol. 1 (Delhi, 1954).

(27) V. Nath: Natural Resources of India, in: Gazetteer of India, Vol. II, Chapter III. (Ministry of Education, Government of India, New Delhi, in Press).

(28) R. Nurkse: Problems of Capital Formation in Under-Developed Countries (Oxford, 1953).

(29) G. Ohlin: Population Control and Economic Development (Development Centre, Organisation for Economic Cooperation and Development, Paris, 1967).

(30) Planning Commission, Government of India: Notes on Perspective of Development India: 1960/61 to 1975/76 (New Delhi, April 1964).

(31) Planning Commission, Government of India: Development of Agriculture India: 1960/61 to 1975/76 (New Delhi, January 1964), mimeographed.

(32) Planning Commission, Government of India: First Five Year Plan —A Draft Outline (New Delhi, 1951).

(33) Planning Commission, Government of India: First Five Year Plan (New Delhi, 1952).

(34) Planning Commission, Government of India: Second Five Year Plan (New Delhi, 1956).

(35) Planning Commission, Government of India: Third Five Year Plan (New Delhi, 1961).

(36) Planning Commission, Government of India: Fourth Five Year Plan—A Draft Outline (New Delhi, 1966).

(37) Planning Commission, Government of India: Reports of the Committee of the Panel on Land Reforms (New Delhi, 1959).

(38) R. Saran and H. L. Chawla: Food Production Policies and Programme since Independence: A Historical Review, *The Indian J. Publ. Adm.,* Vol. 13, No. 3, 1967, pp. 461-83.

(39) T. W. Schultz: What Ails World Agriculture? *Bulletin of Atomic Scientists,* Vol. 24, No. 1, 1968, pp. 28-35.

(40) B. Sivaraman: The Strategy of Food Production, *The Indian J. Publ. Adm.,* Vol. 13, No. 3, 1967, pp. 433-447.

(41) S. Sivasubramonian; National Income of India, 1900/01 to 1946/ 47 (Ph.D. dissertation, Delhi School of Economics, 1965).

(42) P. V. Sukhatme: Feeding India's Growing Millions (Bombay, 1965).

(43) United Nations: Demographic Year Book 1964 (New York, 1965).

(44) United Nations: Year Book of National Accounts Statistics—1966 (New York, 1967).

(45) W. Zelinsky: The Geographer and His Crowding World, *Revista Geográfica*, Vol. 65, 1966, pp. 7-28.

25. POPULATION AND RESOURCE DEVELOPMENT IN INDIA

P. Sen Gupta

About one-half of India's population lives in about one-fourth of its land area. Although the over-all density (in 1961, 138/km²) is lower than that of many European countries, population is heavily concentrated in areas where resources are easily exploited; as a result some sections of the nation swarm with humanity, while others are nearly empty. But neither a dense nor a thin concentration of population clearly reveals whether the number of persons is excessive in terms of resources. Crude density is not a scientific index for measurement of crowding. A better measure would be the economic relationship between population and resources.

Even though India possesses enough natural resources to develop a complex of industries, ranging from basic industries to consumer goods, land is the only resource to have been utilized intensively from time immemorial, with almost every square centimeter of arable land brought under the plough. Other resources—coal, hydroelectric power, oil and natural gas, iron ore, manganese, aluminium, copper, and forests are only partially exploited. About 70 per cent of the net domestic product from India's natural resources in 1961-62 was derived from the soil, and 72 per cent of the working force was engaged in agriculture and allied activities.[1] Since the population of

India is predominantly rural (82 per cent) and agrarian (72 per cent), (according to the 1961 census), the economic significance of population pressure in the country may be best expressed by the relationship between rural population and land productivity.

This study is divided into three parts: (i) It measures population pressure in terms of the economic relationship between rural population and land resources; (ii) It attempts to divide the country into population-resource regions on the basis of existing population density and dynamics, resource-potential, and levels of socio-economic development; (iii) It selects three examples of contiguous population-resource regions and examines their current and prospective ability to relieve excessive pressures in rural areas.

Pressure of Rural Population on Land Resources

The degree of population pressure on resources in rural areas ' is measured by an Index, computed according to the formula:

$$I = \frac{P - P_1}{A}$$

Where I is the Index of Population Pressure per km² of rural area, P_1 is the estimated number of rural inhabitants in a district capable of being supported by the developed land resources, assuming a constant income per person, P is the actual rural population in 1961 for each district, and A is the total rural area of the district in km².

P_1 is obtained by X/K, where X is the gross value of output for each district from the Primary Sector—agriculture, fishing, and

1. Net domestic product from natural resources at current prices is estimated at Rs 96,500 million ($20,300 million), of which Rs 68,500, million ($14,300 million) was derived from agriculture, forestry and fishery and Rs 28,000 million ($6,000 million) from mining, factory establishment and small industries. See estimates of National Income 1948-49 to 1960-61, January 1963, issued by C.S.O., Government of India.

forestry—at current prices,[2] and *K* is the constant income per person from these activities needed to obtain a slight improvement in standard of living for the rural population. The earnings from the Primary Sector per capita among the rural population for the year 1961 are estimated at Rs 192/ ($40.25), but for this study K is assumed as Rs 250/- ($52.41).[3]

I has been calculated for each of the districts. Two sets of values were observed: the positive, indicating the extent of overpopulation, and the negative, indicating underpopulation. After grouping these indices at suitable intervals into three categories—Very High (above 100), High (51-100), and Moderately High (50 and below)—all the 335 districts, including Union Territories, were symbolized by means of two patterns —cross-hatching (overpopulation), and dots (underpopulation) (Fig. 25-1).

A cursory look at the map reveals that extreme overpopulation exists in the non-

2. Gross Value of Agricultural Output, Forestry, and Fishery—the gross value of agricultural output is based on the average production during 1956-57 to 1960-61 of agricultural commodities: (a) cereals and pulses (rice, wheat, jowar, bajra, maize, ragi, small millets, barley, gram, and tur); (b) oil-seeds (groundnut, rapeseed and mustard, linseed, castor-seed, and sesamum); and (c) plantation and commercial crops (tobacco, sugar cane, tea, coffee, rubber, coconut, jute, cotton, and cashewnut). The prices used here are the simple average of wholesale prices for 1959 for some of the towns of each district. Source for the required production and price statistics is the relevant publication of the Directorate of Economics and Statistics, Ministry of Food and Agriculture.

As the district data for the output from fishery and forestry are not available, their values are calculated on the basis of their respective ratios with the gross value of output from agriculture at State level.

3. Based on the estimates of national income 1948-49 to 1961-62, published by C.S.O. in January, 1962. Total income from agricultural sector in 1961-62 was Rs 69,000 million ($14,465 million) and rural population totaled 360 million, so that per capita income amounted to Rs 192 ($40.25).

irrigated rice areas—the Ganga Plain, embracing northern Bihar and eastern Uttar Pradesh, the coastal plain of Kerala, the Hooghly basin of West Bengal, and the Mahanadi delta of Orissa. Rural population greatly exceeds the supporting capacity of the land, the main resource of all of these areas. Even if output were to increase through better care and management of the land, the probability that so large a population could raise its living standards through better organization seems improbable. Rural crowding in all of these areas demands immediate dispersal of the surplus population to prospective industrial and urban centers.

Population levels are also too high for resources in the northeastern part of the peninsular plateau that embraces the hills and plateau area of Orissa, Bihar, eastern Madhya Pradesh, and the western margin of West Bengal. In this area thin, stony soils fail to yield an output adequate for the support of a large population, though the mineral potential is unparalleled.

In the Southern Peninsula, a large compact area embracing eight districts of Telangana Plateau and four of Karnataka Plateau also show overpopulation, though the actual density per km[2] in many of these districts is below 100. Scanty and unreliable rainfall and thin, coarse soils have made this area agriculturally unproductive and incapable of supporting even the existing number of inhabitants. The southern part of Karnataka Plateau and the northern part of Tamilnad Plateau are also overpopulated. Thus the region, which embraces seven districts in Mysore, and two in Madras, is very much in need of irrigation: the scarcity of water limits its capacity to support population.

The hills and mountains of the north and east and the deserts of the west, though showing disproportionately low densities are in fact among the overpopulated sections of the country. The mountainous areas, where

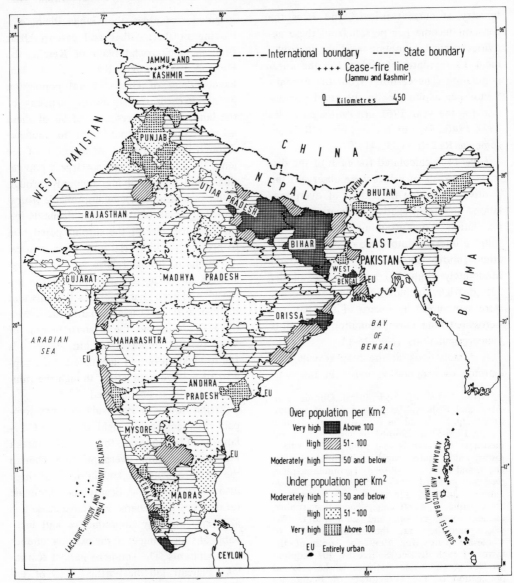

Fig. 25-1. INDIA. POPULATION DENSITY, 1961

steep slopes, stony soils, and inhospitable climate limit the extent of arable land, can support only a limited number of persons, and the deserts and semi-deserts, though the most sparsely populated parts of the country, are paradoxically overpopulated. Since water is scarce, even one or two persons per km² in desert tracts means overpopulation.

Curiously, the Punjab and Upper Ganga plains and the Krishna-Godavari and Cauvery deltas, despite their high densities, are relatively underpopulated. The use of irrigation has brought about a rationalization in the adjustment of population to resources. Given the level of efficiency in utilizing resources, it would be possible to support additional population with no drop in the per capita income of Rs 250/- ($52.41). But it is doubtful if potential resources, which consist mainly of agricultural land, can raise the income level for the expanding population—even with improved techniques for exploitation.

Another surprising feature is that districts with a predominantly plantation agriculture exhibit less population pressure, despite high densities. In fact, commercial crops such as tea, coffee, and rubber, inflate the value of agricultural output, giving rise to relatively low pressures. But the money accruing from plantation crops does not affect the income of the sedentary farmers. If yields were not taken into account in estimating gross agricultural earnings, all plantation areas such as Lakhimpur, Darrang, and Sibsagar districts in Assam; Jalpaiguri and Darjeeling districts of West Bengal; and Coorg and Chikmagelur districts of Mysore would probably be reclassified as overpopulated.

Some of the underpopulated parts of India are the Chambal Basin, the Bundelkhand Upland, the Malwa Plateau, the Narmada trough, the Upper Mahanadi Basin, and the lava plateau of Maharashtra and Gujarat. Although they are contiguous areas resembling one another in general relief features, there is some contrast between north and south. The Chambal Basin and Bundelkhand Upland in the north are rugged and harsh. Thins soils little more than a few inches in depth and even bare peneplain rock comprise much of the land surface. In places, poor grasslands and open acacia shrubs are interspersed with poor farms. As a result, southward from the Ganga Plain there is a sharp fall in population density. The present low densities imply lesser pressure on resources that are mainly agricultural.

Farther south, the lava plateaus, which embrace six districts in Gujarat, fifteen in Maharashtra, and sixteen in Madhya Pra-

desh, show less pressure. These districts may be divided into two compact areas—one in the west (Joway), a cotton and sugar-cane area, and the other in the east—a mineralized and well-watered plateau. Wide expanses of fertile plains, easy communications, and the great importance of cash crops, such as cotton and sugar cane, have fostered higher rural incomes than elsewhere in India. This region is outstanding by virtue of greater emphasis on cash crops than on food crops. Existing pressures are not too great for its resources; but further population increase may result in overpopulation. Since the region is not immune to drought, and since food crops are limited, it is difficult to imagine self-sufficiency in the production of food for a growing population.

The Central Plateau and some parts of Karnataka and Rayalaseema Plateau of the Southern Peninsula manifest a degree of underpopulation consistent with low densities.

Three conclusions may be derived from a review of the regional imbalance in population pressure described above: (i) areas of very high density (more than 200/km²) are not always overpopulated; areas with excellent irrigation systems and well-suited commercial crops, such as tea, cotton, sugar cane, etc. have proved to be underpopulated; (ii) low density areas (less than 50/km²) uniformly contain population in excess of capacity; and (iii) population pressure reaches high levels in nonirrigated rice-growing tracts—the middle and East Ganga Plain, the Bhagirathi Delta, and the Kerala coast.

Population-Resource Regions

The great inequality of population pressure in rural areas of India affords insights into the utilization of potential "social" resources (tools, capital, and the like). Areas with a strong natural resource base may be the

TABLE 25-1 INDIA. POPULATION/RESOURCE REGIONS AND THEIR LATENT CAPACITY TO SUPPORT NON-AGRICULTURAL POPULATION

No.	Name of the Region	Demographic Character		Level of Socio-Economic Development[1]	Resource-potentials, other than land resources*	Capacity for Diverting rural Population to Industrial and Urban Nuclei	
		Density 1961	Growth rate 1915-1961			In immediate future (within 10 years)	In distant future (beyond 10 Years)
1	2	3	4	5	6	7	8
A. DYNAMIC REGIONS							
A.1	W. Bengal Delta	Very High	Very High	High	Coal, hydro-power, potential forest & marine wealth	High	Low
A.2	Lava Area, embracing Gujarat & Maharashtra but excluding Kutch, Konkan Coast & Marathawada	High	High	High	Minerals, such as bauxite. petroleum, forest wealth, hydro-power.	High	High
A.3	Tamilnad Region	Very High	Low	High	Lignite, iron-ore, limestone & chromite	High	Low
A.4	Punjab Plain & Ganga-Yamuna Doab Area	Very High	High	High	Deficient	High	Low
A.5	Southeastern Karnataka Plateau	High	High	High	Gold, iron-ore, manganese, limestone & diamond	Medium	High
B. PROSPECTIVE REGIONS							
B.1	North-Eastern	Low	Medium	Low	Coal, metallic & flux minerals for iron & steel industry, mica, copper, bauxite.	Low	High
B.2	Godavari Basin	High	Medium	Medium	Ferrous minerals, forest resources, & marine wealth	Low	High
B.3	Aravalli Hills & Malwa Plateau	Low	Medium	Medium	Copper, zinc, limestone, etc.	Low	High

(*Table 25-1 continued*)

B.4 Western & Southern Karnataka Plateau including Goa Terr.	Low	High	High	Iron-ore, manganese, limestone, forest resources & hydro-power	High	High
B.5 Brahmaputra Valley	High	Very High	Medium	Forest wealth & hydro-power, oil, natural gas & coal	Low	High
C. PROBLEM REGIONS						
C.1 Middle & East Ganga Plain	Very High	Low	Low	Deficient	Very Low	Very Low
C.2 Orissa Coast	High	Medium	Low	Marine wealth	Very Low	Very Low
C.3 Kerala Coast	Very High	High	High	Forest, hydro-power & marine wealth	Low	Very Low
C.4 Laccadive, Minicoy & Amindivi Islands	Very High	Low	Low	Nil	Very Low	Very Low
C.5 N.E. Karnataka Plateau & Rayalaseema area of Andhra Pradesh, Marathawada & Konkan Coast	Low	Low	Low	Limestone, mica, iron-ore, manganese, etc.	Low	Low
C.6 Rajasthan Desert, including Kutch Peninsula	Very Low	High	Low	Building stone & salt	Low	Low
C.7 North-Western Himalayas	Very High	Low	Very Low	Copper, forest & hydro-power	Very Low	Low
C.8 Eastern Hills and Plateaus	Very Low	High	Low	Forest & hydro-power	Very Low	Low
C.9 Andaman & Nicobar Is.	Very Low	Very High	High	Forest & marine wealth	Very Low	Low

* Economically exploitable resources are taken into account as the actual reserves for each item cannot be shown in this small table.

Source: Census of India, 1961, Volume I, Part II-C (iii): Migration Tables.

Density per km.²
V.V. High = Above 500
V. High = 201-500
High = 101-200
Low = 51-100
V. Low = 50 & below

Decennial Growth Rate in %
V. High = 33.01 & above
High = 25.01-33.00
Medium = 17.01-25.00
Low = 9.01-17.00
V. Low = 9.00 & below

1 *Categories of Levels of Development*
High, Medium, Low & V. Low computed according to Levels of Socio-Economic Development on the basis of a system of statistical weights in a large number of Indices grouped under six categories—I General ecology; II Agricultural infrastructure; III Participation rate with traditional economy; IV Potential human regions; V Distribution of trade infrastructure; VI Organized industry in the modern sector.

Sources: Explained in the text and A. Mitra, I.C.S., *Census of India, 1961*, Vol. 1, Part I-A.

effective safety-valve for crowded rural areas after suitable developmental programs have been organized. In the future, migrants from overpopulated rural areas could shift to industrial and urban nuclei, which are likely to increase in number in those areas with rich potential resource bases and a high level of socio-economic development. In order to assess India's latent capacity to support population, it is necessary to divide it into population-resource regions according to the aggregate pattern of the demographic structure of the population (density and growth rate), resource-potential, and levels of socio-economic development. Each of these variables has been weighted according to value from high to low; and various combinations of the four variables were subsequently grouped into types of population-resource regions, according to the net impact of these variables on the capacity to support nonagricultural population.

Nineteen regions have been classified according to the term above (Table 25-1). They are further grouped into three characteristic population-resource regions; five as Dynamic; five as Prospective; and nine as Problematic (Fig. 25-2). *Dynamic* regions are those which support advanced industrial areas and predominantly urban populations, and have the scientific and technological resources necessary for diverting population from crowded rural areas. Where potentials are large but socio-economic obstacles to the technological transformation of resources persist, the regions are classified as *prospective*. However, a number of industrial nuclei—signs of cultural and technological advance—have cropped up in some of these regions. The *problem* regions are those which show little promise, at least for the immediate future. Some of them are overpopulated and have reached the saturation point; others have a lean natural resource base; still others face the problem of uneconomic utilization of resources due to restrictive environment, poorly developed transport systems, and a dearth of skilled workers.

DYNAMIC REGIONS

The five dynamic regions in the country are: (A.i) the deltaic plain of Ganga coinciding with West Bengal; (A.ii) the Deccan trap area embracing Gujarat State (excluding the Kutch Peninsula) and Maharashtra State (excluding Marathawada and Konkan Coast); (A.iii) the Tamilnad region identified with Madras State; (A.iv) the Punjab Plain and Ganga-Yamuna Doab area; and (A.v) Southeastern Karnataka Plateau.

Among these regions, the most powerful magnet for attracting rural population is in the *deltaic plain of West Bengal*. There is an unparalleled concentration of industries in the Greater Calcutta Region, and not far away, in the mineralized Damodar Valley, is another recently developed industrial belt.

Equally significant is the *Deccan trap area,* which has also made rapid strides in industrialization and urbanization in the last two decades. The infrastructure of transport, power, education, and health services has been strengthened in its two major industrial nucleii—Bombay and Ahmedabad—and has radiated along the transport lines to Surat, Nagpur, and Sholapur. The region has limited mineral resources; but its hydroelectric power potential along the Western Ghats and petroleum deposits at Ankleshwar have compensated for deficiencies in mineral fuels. Industrialization and urbanization in the hinterland of Greater Bombay will favor the movement of population from rural to urban areas.

The *Tamilnad region* has a high density of population, a low growth-rate, and a well-developed system of industry and commerce. Madras and its ring of satellite towns at-

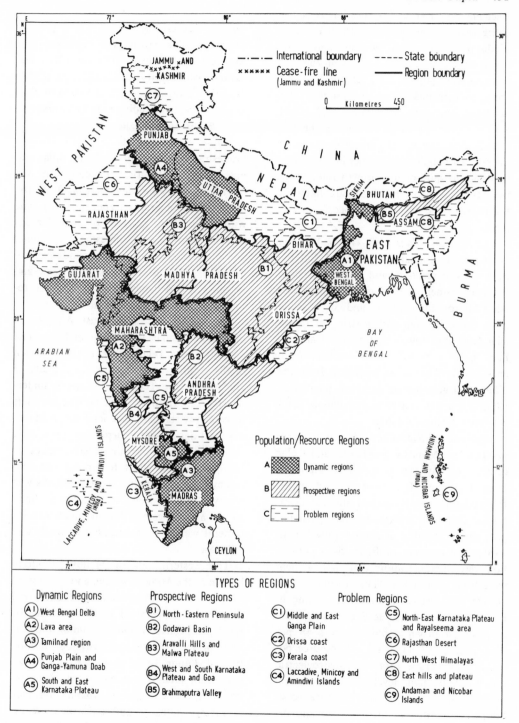

Fig. 25-2. INDIA. POPULATION/RESOURCE REGIONS

tract manpower from the rural areas of the entire region. The other industrial nucleii—Madurai, Coimbatore, Neiveli, and Tuticorin—have also played significant roles in relieving the population pressure in rural areas, as evidenced from the growth rates of urban and rural population (22.5 and 8.39 per cent, respectively) during the last decade. The paucity of natural resources is the greatest handicap to further industrialization and, in spite of low growth rates (11.3 per cent), available resources are likely to fall short of the needs of the people in this region.

The *Punjab Plain* and *Ganga-Yamuna Doab* are traditionally agricultural, but the pace of urbanization and industrialization has been rather rapid during the past decade. Metropolitan Delhi and its satellite town clusters, along with a string of industrial cities and towns that follow transport lines have attracted large numbers from crowded rural areas, as is evident from the differential growth rate of urban population (33.3 per cent) and rural population (24.1 per cent) during 1951-61.

Southeastern Karnataka Plateau, embracing Tumkur, Mandya, Bangalore, and Kolar districts of Mysore, is the fifth important dynamic region. The rapid pace of industrialization around Bangalore, the nodal center for economic growth, has had great impact on the mobility of rural population. In 1961, 42.1 per cent of Bangalore's population were migrants; more than half of them were from rural areas. Thus, during the last decade, the district witnessed a decline in rural population of some 5 per cent, while the gain in urban population was 48 per cent. Because of its significant resource potential (minerals, forests, hydroelectric power) and high level of technological progress, this region shows immense possibilities for further industrialization and urbanization.

PROSPECTIVE REGIONS

There are five *prospective* regions: (B.i) Northeastern Peninsular Plateau; (B.ii) Godavari Basin; (B.iii) Aravalli Hills and Malwa Plateau; (B.iv) Western and Southern Karnataka Plateau, including Goa Territory; and (B.v) Brahmaputra Valley.

The seventeen districts of Eastern Madhya Pradesh, six districts of Southern Bihar and nine districts of Orissa Plateau form the *Northeastern Peninsular Plateau.* It is the most richly mineralized zone in India, one with unparalleled reserves of coal, ferrous and nonferrous ores, limestone, dolomite, and mica. The region also abounds in lumberable species of trees, such as teak and sissoo, sal, and bamboo. Many of these resources still await exploitation.

The *Godavari Basin* lies just to the south of the Peninsular Plateau. It includes nine districts of the Telangana Plateau and seven of the Andhra coast. Except for the city of Hyderabad, the Telegana Plateau is underdeveloped. Centuries of feudal rule have left its economy stagnant. The land is barren and dry, and agriculture is dependent upon tank irrigation. The Nagarjun Sagar Project is, however, a new effort to remedy the deficiency in water supplies. The region has vast reserves of coal, iron ore, manganese, limestone, and asbestos, though much of this mineral wealth is inaccessible to roads and railways.

The western half of Madhya Pradesh, known as the *Malwa Plateau,* and the eastern districts of Rajasthan, including the *Aravalli Hills* and its piedmont platform, form the third prospective region. Excluding the former princely States of Gwalior, Indore, Bhopal, Jaipur, Jodhpur, Ajmer, and Rotah, the entire area is still backward, as is reflected in a low degree of urbanization, lack of factory industry, and a dearth of transport facilities and technical skill. Its unique potential lies in diverse metallic and non-metallic minerals, (copper, zinc, lead, lignite, gypsum, mica, limestone, and salt,) and places it in the forefront of regions with rich possibilities for developing chemical and metal-based industries.

Another prospective region is the *Western and Southern Karnataka Plateau,* including *Goa Territory.* It includes the Malnad area —a stretch 640 km in length and 48 to 64 km in width, in western Mysore and the southern part of Maidan area—a rolling plateau in eastern Mysore. The Malnad area and Goa Territory are endowed with forests, potential hydroelectric power, and mineral resources. Both the east- and west-flowing rivers of Mysore State have their sources in the Malnad region, and offer excellent sites for hydroelectric power. The Maidan area is dry and its agricultural potential is limited; but its richness in metallic minerals is noteworthy. The potential in ferrous and non-ferrous minerals suggests the development of iron and steel, ferro-alloy, and cement industries. At present, the area supports only one steel plant at Bhadravati and one ferro-manganese plant at Dandeli. Taken as a whole, the region offers great scope for the development of metallurgical, chemical, and forest-based industries.

The *Brahmaputra Valley* with its unique hydroelectric power potential coupled with coal, oil, and forest wealth, can look forward to the development of industries based on these resources. The great disparity between population growth and progress in resource-development has accentuated population pressure in this part of the northern plain.

PROBLEM REGIONS

The problem regions of the first category are (C.i) the middle Ganga Plain (eastern Uttar Pradesh and northern Bihar Plain); (C.ii) the Orissa Coast; (C.iii) the Kerala Coast; and (C.iv) the Laccadive, Minicoy,

and Amindivi Islands. They face the problem of bitter poverty due to overcrowding; their density of population is almost three- to fourfold that of the country as a whole.

The second category of problem regions is visible in (C.v) the Konkan Coast and the central part of the Southern Peninsula, which stretches from Marathawada through the northeastern part of the Karnataka Plateau to the Rayalaseema area of Andhra; and (C.vi) the Rajasthan desert, including the Kutch Peninsula of Gujarat. These regions show limited potential for supporting population because of their weak natural resource base.

The third category of problem regions embraces all the *hill districts,* which include (C.vii) the Northwestern Himalayas; (C.viii) the Eastern Himalayas and Eastern Hills and Plateaus; and (C.ix) the Andaman and Nicobar Islands. Rugged surfaces and shallow stony soils restrict arable lands, and potential resources—hydroelectric power, forests, and minerals—though available in quantity, can hardly be utilized, due to inaccessibility imposed by high altitude and inhospitable climate.

Three Characteristic Population-Resources Regions: Their Problems and Prospects

Three contiguous regions representing three categories of population-resource regions—dynamic, prospective, and problematic—have been selected for this study. These are the deltaic plain of West Bengal, the Northeastern Peninsular Plateau, and the Middle Ganga Plain (Fig. 25-3).

THE DELTAIC PLAIN OF WEST BENGAL—
A DYNAMIC REGION

With the historic partition of India accompanying Independence on August 15, 1947, West Bengal, which includes about two-

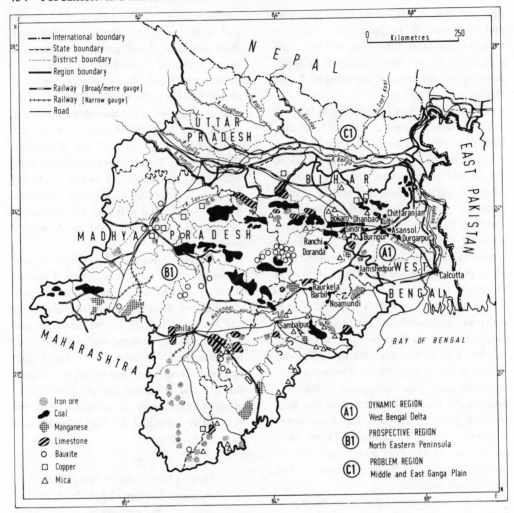

Fig. 25-3.   INDIA. REPRESENTATIVE POPULATION/RESOURCE REGIONS: WEST BENGAL; NORTHEAST PENINSULA; MIDDLE AND EAST GANGA PLAIN

fifths of the land area of the Ganga delta, came into existence. Partition brought in its wake a heavy exchange of refugees, and the abnormal burden of this population continues to be borne by the depressed economy. In addition, the state lost most of its fertile agricultural tracts to East Pakistan, a situation which created a chronic food problem. Since then, this region has been trying to develop in the face of a maladjustment of population and natural resources. There is heavy pressure on the arable lands,

clearly underlining the necessity of diverting population to industrial and urban centers.

Fortunately, West Bengal enjoyed an early start in industrialization, though extreme polarization existed. Except for the new, growing Asansol-Durgapur region, nearly all the larger industries are concentrated in Calcutta and nearby clusters of towns (Fig. 25-3). The Calcutta region has been building a strong industrial base for some decades. About 70 towns merge with one another along either bank of the River

Hooghly for a stretch of 120 km and support 71.6 per cent of the state's total urban population. Locational factors, availability of plant and services, finance, and entrepreneurial ability have stimulated the flow of population from rural areas.

The "pull" power of Calcutta and its satellites is reflected in the large share of migrants classed as rural. In 1961, 53 per cent of the total population of Calcutta were classified as migrant. Percentages for the other cities were as follows: Howrah 54, Bhatpara 61, Kamarhati 53, Baranagar 57, and Baly 70. More than 50 per cent of the migrants in each city were attracted from the rural areas (2). For several decades, there has been a steady shift of landless laborers from the overloaded rural areas of the Ganga Plain, Mahanadi Delta, and Brahmaputra Valley to Calcutta, thus forming a large urban aggregation that has come to be called the Calcutta Metropolitan Area. At first the vast adjacent, officially nonmetropolitan areas grew rather slowly. But it seems that by 1961 Calcutta was saturated with migrants and a countermovement was started toward the satellite towns. Three facts provide evidence for a "push back"—(a) a great disparity between decennial growth rates and the ratio of migrants to the total population. The city saw only an 8 per cent increase in population during 1951-61, while more than half the total population consisted of migrants. This implies that a large segment of the population may have pushed away from the city to accommodate the previous migrants; (b) the intensity of intrastate urban-to-urban migration is much higher for towns and cities adjacent to Calcutta than for those distant from the city core. For example, in the nearby cities of South Dum Dum, Baranagar, and South Suburban more than 80 per cent of the migrants took part in intrastate movements, while in Bhatpara, about 40 km from Cal-

cutta, the share of migrants was less than 50 per cent; and (c) during 1951-61, there was a fall in density gradients to towns located at increasing distances from the city core. Density gradients from the city to distances in different directions are shown by graphs for which the equation, representing the best fit, reads as follows:

$$Y_c = d_o - bx,$$

where Y_c is the log of density of towns at different distances, d_o is the log of the density of the city center, b the log of the density gradient, and x the distance. Values of the above equation were plotted graphically, and it was found that there had been a fall in the density gradient of urban population during 1951-61 in all directions from the city core. The rate of decline, however, was more marked to the east and northeast, (presumably sectors with relatively weak gravitational pull) than to the north and south. The value of b diminished from 0.10 in 1951, to 0.07 in 1961 in the northeast, from 0.13 to 0.07 in the east, and from 0.02 to 0.01 in the north and south (Fig. 25-4). In fact, cities and towns in the outer area swelled at the expense of the central core. This is indicative of an over-all decline in the gravitational pull of the Calcutta Industrial Region in recent years, a trend that should continue. Newcomers to the region outnumber the jobs available and convincing proof of this is found in the intensity of unemployment and social unrest that prevail. In 1961, about 6 per cent of the total employable population of age-group 15-59 were unemployed in the four districts of the Industrial Hooghly Region (3).

Not far from the Calcutta Region another industrial belt—the Damodar Valley—has recently materialized with major power for attracting migrants from rural areas. During 1951-61, some new towns—the steel town of Durganpur, the locomotive factory town of Chittaranjan, and the mining town of

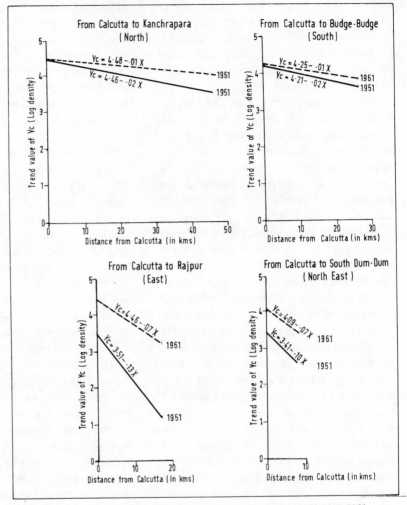

Fig. 25-4. CALCUTTA. DENSITY-DISTANCE GRADIENTS, 1951 AND 1961

Jamuria—were added to the industrial nucleus around Kulti, Burnpur, and Asansol in the district of Burdwan (Figure 25-3). During the last decade, in the wake of this growth, the district witnessed a significant movement of population from rural to urban areas. About 120,000 persons, or 20.5 per cent of its total urban population, were migrants; 69 per cent of them were from rural areas. The district is favored by its potential in mineral resources, an infrastructure for industrialization, and is capable of

generating immense power for pulling population away from overcrowded rural areas.

It should be noted that, with the exception of the Asansol-Durganpur region, all major industries are clustered in Greater Calcutta. Given limitations of space and a severe strain on transport facilities and civic amenities, Greater Calcutta has nearly reached a state of saturation. But the over-all industrial prospects for the Bhagirathi Delta are bright. Its abundant coal resources, low overhead costs, and high level of technological progress justify the current faith in its progress. A number of dispersed industrial towns with adequate economic and social resources are likely to appear in the delta in the near future. But most of the benefits accruing from increased urbanization and industrialization are likely to be dissipated by an exploding population, which will mean a limitation in the area's ability to siphon off population from nearby problematic areas.

THE NORTHEASTERN PENINSULAR PLATEAU

The Northeastern Peninsular Plateau, taking in the eastern half of Madhya Pradesh and the plateau section of Bihar and Orissa, is the largest and perhaps most promising area for industrialization and urbanization. It has a strong natural resource base, but the infrastructure for industrialization is relatively weak. The over-all population density is low (less than $50/km^2$), but land resources are used in excess of their capacity. Soils are thin and stony, and yields are poor (about 6.7 kg/hectare of rice compared with India's 9.4 kg/hectare). In addition, the primitive farming practices of tribal people (who account for more than 60 per cent of the area's population) yield a low gross value per hectare of cropped land: Rs 289 ($60.00), as compared with the national average of Rs 343 ($72.00).

The plateau area is the richest mineralized zone in the country, with unparalleled reserves of coal, ferrous and nonferrous ores, manganese, limestone; dolomite, copper, mica, and bauxite. In spite of this vast potential, there are only a few advanced industrial nuclei in this region. After three successive Five-Year Plan programs, the progress has been noted only in a belt stretching from Jamshedpur to Bhilai, including South Bihar; the northwestern part of Orissa; and the northeastern corner of Madhya Pradesh. The towns of Rourkela and Bhilai (steel),

Doranda (heavy machinery), Barbil (iron ore), Sindri (fertilizer), and the coal-mining towns grouped at Bermo are examples of the new industrial and mining centers built during the last decade. Increasing numbers of people from rural areas are being drawn to these centers. In the coal-mining district of Dhanbad, for example, the mobility of rural population in the last decade was quite significant. About 100,000, or 30 per cent of its urban population were migrants, and 81 per cent of them were from rural areas.

Given the magnitude of potential mineral reserves, industrial progress in the area is slow; and it is also confined to a narrow belt between the Damodar Valley and the Calcutta-Nagpur railway line (Figure 25-3). The dearth of skilled workers, poor transport facilities, and scarcity of capital are some of the major handicaps in the effective utilization of resources. If these problems can be overcome, the area should develop a strong pull upon the surplus populations in the problem region to the northeast.

OVERPOPULATED MIDDLE GANGA PLAIN

The crowded Middle Ganga Plain is transitional between the dry Bhangar doab of Upper Ganga Plain and the humid delta area in Bengal. The map of precipitation shows a steady decrease fom 1700 mm in the west to 1000 mm in the east. Rainfall is more reliable here than in the west, but it is sufficiently variable to introduce insecurity in crop farming. On the slopes of the Himalayas monsoon rainfall becomes increasingly heavy, causing frequent flooding. The River Kosi, noteworthy for its violent fluctuations in volume and course, has been responsible for enormous devastation by floods and micaceous sands. Fortunately, the taming of this notorious river is now in progress. Also devastating, but to a lesser extent, are the other great rivers, Gogra, Greater Gandak, Burhi Gandak, and Kamla. The entire plain faces the problem of both droughts and floods. Moreover, continuous farming by primitive methods has reduced the productivity of its lands.

Despite intensive land use, the over-all agricultural output is lower than that of the country as a whole. For example, average rice yields during 1956-61 were 6.84 kg/hectare as compared with 9.26 for the country; wheat, 5.60 compared with 7.58 kg; pulses 5.60 as against 9.31 kg. Until a few years ago, this region was the stronghold of landlords, and even now the majority of farmers hold only small, scattered, uneconomic plots (0.20 to 0.28 hectares).

The Middle Ganga Plain is industrially the least developed, and its level of urbanization is deplorably low. In many districts, such as Ghazipur, Ballia, Deoria, Pratapgarh, Basti, and Sultanpur in Uttar Pradesh, and Champaran, Saran, Sanarsa, Darbhanga, and Muzaffarpur in Bihar, more than 95 per cent of the population lives in rural areas. Since natural resources and the infrastructure for industrialization are very weak, the population pressure is quite intense. Agricultural holdings are amazingly low: in some of the districts, the per capita holding is as little as 0.18 hectares. With the decrease in size of agricultural holdings, the proportion of landless laborers has increased by 4 to 5 per cent within a span of ten years. For example, in the districts of Sultanpur, Faizabad, and Deoria, in Uttar Pradesh, the percentages of male agricultural laborers increased from 11.8, 8.0, and 7.2 in 1951 to 17.8, 13.5, and 12.1, respectively, in 1961.

In spite of two successive developmental campaigns, the economic condition of the people showed hardly any improvement, as is evident from the low per capita gross value of agricultural output in rural areas —Rs 71/($14.89) against India's Rs 117/($24.53); a low labor participation rate— 40 per cent compared to 43 per cent in India

(4), a low degree of urbanization—5 per cent of urban population compared with 18 per cent for India (5). Unemployment and underemployment, which are essentially the reflection of poverty and low productivity, seem to have pushed rural dwellers toward developed regions, while at the same time towns and cities attracted surplus rural population, promising possible freedom from poverty. The question arises as to how much mobility resulted from bitter poverty and what proportion of the rural population was removed by out-migration in the last decade.

Unfortunately, there are no direct migration data for estimating the force of "Pull" and "Push" factors in the crowded rural areas of the Plain. But indirect migration data, which are based on the number of persons enumerated in a given place as related to the place of birth, are available, though they cannot be estimated separately. Yet the extent of mobility in rural and urban communities and its effect in relieving population pressure can be approximated with the migration data for Bihar and Uttar Pradesh (Tables 25-2 and 25-3).

In Uttar Pradesh, 7.5 million or 71 per cent, represent the flow within rural areas, and in Bihar the figure is 4.7 million, or 76 per cent. A large part of this movement is confined within the state boundaries, and has no effect in reducing population pressure in the Ganga Plain. In Uttar Pradesh, again using 1961 data, 94.7 per cent of the rural-to-rural movement were within the state, while in Bihar it was 88.9 per cent.

The flow from rural to urban areas accounts for 1.8 million, or 17.2 per cent in Uttar Pradesh and 1.1 million, or 17.5 per cent in Bihar. The flow of urban migrants to towns and cities outside the states accounts for only 0.4 million, or 3.8 per cent of the total for Uttar Pradesh and 0.5 million, or 8.5 per cent in Bihar. Figures for the reverse flow—urban to rural—within the

TABLE 25-2   MIGRATIONS IN THE STATES OF UTTAR PRADESH
AND BIHAR, 1951-1961

Direction of Movement	*Uttar Pradesh*		*Bihar*		*Total*	
	Migrants	%	Migrants	%	Migrants	%
Rural to rural (Total)	7,481,744	71.0	4,701,290	76.5	12,183,034	73.0
Rural to rural (within State)	7,083,336	67.2	4,179,665	68.0	11,263,001	67.5
Rural to rural (out-migration)	398,408	3.8	521,625	8.5	920,033	5.5
Rural to urban (Total)	1,817,421	17.2	1,072,738	17.5	2,890,159	17.3
Rural to urban (within State)	1,062,528	10.1	589,581	9.6	1,652,109	9.9
Rural to urban (out-migration)	754,893	7.1	483,157	7.9	1,238,050	7.4
Urban to urban (Total)	931,095	8.8	278,724	4.5	1,209,819	7.3
Urban to urban (within State)	549,356	5.2	145,571	2.4	694,927	4.2
Urban to urban (out-migration)	381,739	3.6	133,153	2.1	514,892	3.1
Urban to rural (Total)	313,964	3.0	92,376	1.5	406,340	2.4
Urban to rural (within State)	264,761	2.5	70,095	1.1	334,856	2.0
Urban to rural (out-migration)	49,203	0.5	22,281	0.4	71,484	0.4
TOTAL MIGRANTS (internal + out-migration)	10,544,224	100.0	6,145,128	100.0	16,689,352	100.0
TOTAL POPULATION	73,746,401	14.3*	46,455,610	13.2*	120,202,011	13.9*

* Proportion of mobile population to total population.
Source: Census of India, 1961, Vol. I—Part II-C (iii)—Migration Tables.
The above data characterize population flows between towns and countryside
in both directions. From 1951-61, migrations (internal and out-movements)
accounted for 16,689,352 (13.9%) or an annual average of 1,668,935 persons
or 4% of the total population. Uttar Pradesh showed a slightly higher population mobility (14.3%) than did Bihar (13.2%), indicating that the intensity of
movement was slightly more in the western half than in the eastern half of the
Ganga Plain.

TABLE 25-3   NET MIGRATORY LOSS, RURAL COMMUNITIES OF
UTTAR PRADESH AND BIHAR, 1951-1961

| | Gain | | Loss | | | Rural Population | | |
| | | | | | | | | |
State	In-migration	Migration urban to rural within state	Out-migration	Rural to urban within state	Net migration	Actual population 1961	Hypothetical pop. as a result of natural increase (natural pop.)	Per cent loss
Uttar Pradesh	278,249	264,761	1,153,301	1,062,528	−1,672,819	64,266,506	65,939,325	−2.54
Bihar	235,220	70,095	1,004,782	589,581	−1,289,048	42,541,690	43,830,738	−2.94

states are 0.26 million, or 2.5 per cent in Uttar Pradesh and 0.07 million, or 1.1 per cent in Bihar. There was some addition of rural population through immigration—0.28 million in Uttar Pradesh and 0.24 million in Bihar.

The figures above indicate that rural communities in Uttar Pradesh experienced a migration loss of 1.67 million, or 2.5 per cent; in Bihar a loss of 1.38 million, or 2.9 per cent. Together, the two states recorded a net loss from rural communities of 3.0 million, or 2.7 per cent, within a period of ten years, or 0.27 per cent per year by migration.

These findings indicate that the urban "pull" factor was probably not strong enough to reduce population pressure in rural areas within the Middle Ganga Plain in the past decade. The basic factors responsible for this slow movement of rural population are—(i) the number of industrial towns and cities is very small; (ii) all the "million" cities and important industrial belts of the country which draw surplus population from the countryside are located outside the Middle Ganga Plain. Other than the Damodar Valley region, the Calcutta industrial region, and the Delhi Metropolis, all "million" cities are situated far away from the Middle Ganga Plain; and (iii) the poverty of the rural people has discouraged long-distance migration to "million" cities or industrial nuclei, even though a strong "push" of the villagers toward cities is present.

The solution to the problem of overpopulation in the Ganga Plain is to be found in the development of its economy through industrialization, and in stimulating emigration through organized efforts to utilize the potential natural wealth of regions to the south.

ACKNOWLEDGMENT

My warmest personal thanks to Shri Asok Mitra, Registrar General, Shri A. Chandra Sekhar, Additional Registrar General, India, who have given me the fullest facilities for undertaking this Research Paper. I take great pleasure to acknowledge my particular debt to:

Shri C. P. Vasudeva, Statistical Assistant; Shri Kailash Chander, Computor; Shri I. P. Singh, Computor; and Shri R. N. Verma, Assistant

Compiler, for collecting and processing the data. I am also indebted to:
Shri P. T. Deshpande, Junior Artist; Shri N. K. Roy, Junior Artist, who
have drawn the maps and charts. I am also indebted to S/shri Harcharan
Singh and P. D. Likhyani who typed a long and difficult manuscript.

REFERENCES

(1) A. Mitra, ICS, Reg. Genl., India: Census of India, 1961: Volume
I. pp. 10-14. Levels of Regional Development in India. Part I-A (i).

(2) A. Mitra, ICS, Reg. Genl., India: Census of India, 1961: Volume
I. Part II-C (iii).

(3) A. Mitra, ICS, Reg. Genl., India: Census of India, 1961: Volume
XVI, West Bengal. Part II-B (i) and (ii).

(4) A. Mitra, ICS, Reg. Genl., India: Census of India, 1961: Part
II-A (ii) Vol. 1.

(5) A. Mitra, ICS, Reg. Genl., India: Census of India, 1961: Part
II-A (i) Vol. 1.

26. DEMOGRAPHIC DYNAMISM IN PUNJAB AND INCREASING PRESSURE ON ITS RESOURCES

Gurdev Singh Gosal

Few problems in population geography are as defiant of satisfactory solution as the problem of direct, quantitative measurement of population pressure on resources. This impasse results from the spatial and temporal dynamism of both population characteristics and resource appraisals. Moreover, several of the variables involved in determining population pressure are qualitative and thus cannot be subjected to mathematical calculation. Nevertheless, inferences from the study of related phenomena do lead to some judgments on this vital problem.

No other social phenomenon has proved to be so alarming to both the experts and the general public as the accelerating growth of population and increasing pressure on physical and social resources in "underdeveloped" countries in recent decades. If not checked in time, this trend is likely to tax the limited resources of several of these lands to a disastrous degree. In some cases, the problem is already enormous enough to frustrate the planner and the administrator in their ameliorative efforts. Even though there is no dearth of literature dealing with the problem of population and resources in general terms, very little detailed spatial analysis of the problem in local areas has been accomplished. The importance of such regional studies, however, hardly needs to be emphasized.

For the present study, the choice of Punjab as politically defined in 1961 has been made for three reasons: the writer's experience in studying its population and economic geography; the recent attempts by its government and people at reactivating and mobilizing its resources in the face of a staggering increase in population; and the avail-ability of detailed and reliable census data, even by individual villages, for 1951 and 1961.

Distribution and Density of Population

A brief account of patterns of distribution and density of population may be useful in understanding the spatial aspects of demographic change and its implications in Punjab.

With an arithmetic density of 166/km² (as against an average of 142 for India as a whole), Punjab is one of the more densely populated parts of the country. However, in an area where 80 per cent of the population lives in villages and where 75 per cent of the rural working force is directly engaged in agriculture, nutritional density (number of persons per km² of net area sown) provides a more sensitive index of the pressure of population on land resources. According to 1961 data, Punjab has a nutritional density of 271/km².

There are marked contrasts in distributional pattern and density of population within the state itself. As is evident from Fig. 26-2, sparsely populated mountainous and hilly areas in the southwest and north stand in contrast to the plains, where concentration of population is generally quite heavy.

In the arid, mountain-locked Lahaul and Spiti district, the distributional pattern of population, like that of its drainage, is dendritic as the settlements are strung almost exclusively along river valleys where patches of level cultivable land and water are available. Elsewhere, slopes are too steep and water supply too scarce to permit cultiva-

Fig. 26-1. PUNJAB: ADMINISTRATIVE DIVISIONS, 1961

443

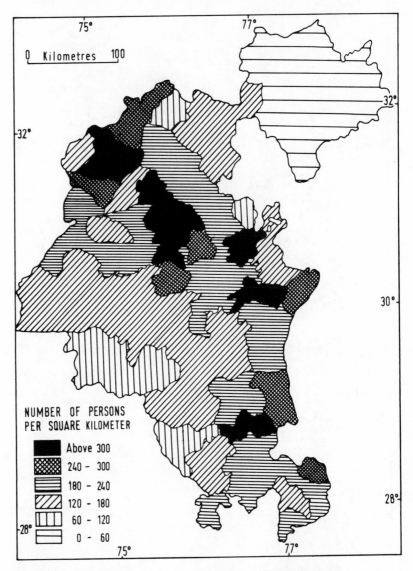

Fig. 26-2.   PUNJAB: DENSITY OF POPUATION, 1961, BY **TAHSILS**

tion. Much of the land surface is rocky and devoid of vegetation. Although this area has the state's lowest arithemetic density (2.3/km²) it has one of the highest nutritional densities, exceeding 849/km² (Fig. 26-3). This is because only a fraction of the area is under cultivation. Mountainous Simla district with a nutritional density of 1213/km² presents a still more difficult situation. Simi-

larly, in large parts of the hilly and mountainous Kangra district, where the arithmetic density is also low (between 15 and 144), the nutritional density ranges between 386 and 926.

In the Kangra and Simla districts, where slopes are less steep, growing seasons longer, and rainfall far heavier, population is more evenly distributed than in Lahaul and Spiti.

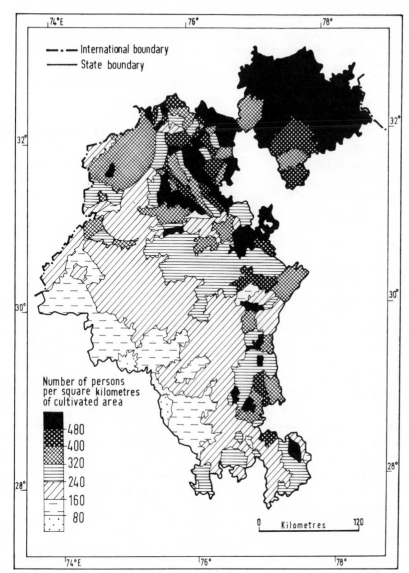

Fig. 26-3.   PUNJAB: DENSITY OF POPULATION PER SQUARE KILOMETER
OF CULTIVATED LAND, 1961, BY ASSESSMENT CIRCLES

Nonetheless, river valleys and adjoining gently sloping areas provide the most favorable locations for settlement. An overemphasis on hand labor in cultivating the land and the prevalence of vegetable culture have caused unusual concentration of population along the valleys, in sharp contrast to the sparsity of population on the steeply sloping lands. A deeper understanding of the locational patterns of population in these areas of hilly terrain can be obtained by mastering the details of their physical setting, minutiae of economy, broader lineaments of cultural and social structures and history of their populations.

Another area of low to medium arithmetic

density is the southern and southwestern belt of Punjab, where it is 77 to 154/km². These areas suffer from arid and semi-arid conditions, rendering farming without irrigation uncertain. To ensure adequate production, the farmers have brought every cultivable piece of land under the plough, and they sow the maximum area wherever rains permit. Over most of this belt, more than 80 per cent of the land is under cultivation, so that the nutritional density is not much higher than the arithmetic density. In some less favorable localities, however, it falls below the level of 77.

Sandwiched between the relatively sparsely populated mountainous areas on the northeast and the arid and semi-arid areas on the southwest is the densely populated Punjab plain where the arithmetic density ranges between 154 and 569. In parts of the Upper Bari Doab and the Bist Doab, even rural densities approach 310/km². Generally, the agricultural productivity of the land has been the chief determinant of population density, particularly in less urbanized areas. The amount of water supply (from rains, irrigation, or both) is the single most important co-variant, followed by soils. The predominantly sandy areas, as in Kapurthala and Samrala *tahsils,* and the hard clayey belts, as in parts of the Karnal district, are less densely populated than areas having loamy soils. Intricately intertwined with these physical determinants are a variety of other factors causing variations in density of population. They relate to regional history, period of settlement, land-tenure, and other social and cultural characteristics.

The rainier eastern and northern parts of the Punjab plain were under direct occupation by the British, and have higher nutritional densities (231 to more than 772) and more urban population than the southwestern parts, comprised largely of the erstwhile native states (nutritional density ranging between 154 and 231), where a kind of feudal system characterized by large landholdings prevailed before Independence. The northern and northwestern parts of the Karnal district have agricultural potential but low densities, which may be attributed in part to political conditions during the late eighteenth century. The post-Independence years, however, have brought considerable numbers of land-hungry migrants to the area.

Even within the heavily settled eastern and northern parts of the Punjab plain, there are local contrasts in population density. The flood plains of the Jamuna, Sutlej, Beas, and Ravi rivers are only sparsely populated, in marked contrast to the wheat-culture area of upland plains where the pressure is everywhere acute. This pattern is a reversal of that found in the lower Ganges plain, where the rice culture areas of flood-plains are characteristically more crowded than the upland regions.

Also in parts of the Hoshiapur district and Pupar subdivision, population densities are higher where the proportion of Sainis, who commonly have small landholdings and are known for intensive cultivation, is relatively high. Examined at still closer levels, "accidents" of history and differences in the qualities of individuals are likely to emerge as important factors in determining density of population.

Thus, with an above-average density of population in the national context, Punjab displays marked variations in the man : land ratio at regional, subregional, and local levels which are related to physical and cultural factors alike.

Population Growth

A vigorous growth in the population of Punjab in recent decades has given rise to enormous increases in numbers, especially during the period 1951-61.

TABLE 26-1   STATEWISE GROWTH OF POPULATION IN INDIA,
1951-1961

State	Density per km² in 1961	*Percentage increase during 1951-61*	*Change in Density of Population, 1951-61*
Andhra Pradesh	131	15.65	+18
Assam	97	34.45	+25
Bihar	267	19.18	+44
Gujarat	110	26.88	+24
Jammu & Kashmir	D.N.A.	9.44	D.N.A.
Kerala	435	24.76	+87
Madhya Pradesh	73	24.17	+14
Madras	258	11.85	+27
Maharashtra	129	23.60	+24
Mysore	123	21.57	+22
Orissa	113	19.82	+19
Punjab	166	25.86	+34
Rajasthan	59	26.20	+12
Uttar Pradesh	251	16.66	+36
West Bengal	398	32.79	+98
India	142	21.50	+22

Source: Census of India, 1961, Paper No. 1 of 1962, pp. 320-21.

During this time Punjab's population increased by 25.9 per cent (16,134,890 to 20,306,812) as against the national average of 21.5. This increase was unprecedented in the recorded history of population growth in Punjab. In fact, the rate would have been still higher but for an excess of out-migration (including emigration) over in-migration of about 350,000 persons during the decade. Yet even when allowance is made for this loss, the rate of natural increase was about 28 per cent—immensely high for a region already densely populated.

For the full significance of this growth rate, it must be seen in its historical perspective. The paucity and nonreliability of population data for the pre-twentieth-century period, however, restrict our analysis to the present century. Figures in Table 26-2 reveal two distinct periods in the history of population growth in Punjab and in India during the present century. The first two decades (1901-21) were marked by famines and epidemics and there was a net decrease in population from 13,265,860 to 12,465,009. During the next forty years, by contrast, growth rates accelerated and in 1961 the population stood at 20,306,812. Thus, for Punjab, as for India, the year 1921 represents a significant demographic divide (1:87; 2:53).

The population of Punjab suffered a decrease of 9.96 per cent during 1901-11, and during the following ten years the increase was no more than 4.35 per cent. However, from 1921 onward, the rate of increase started to spiral. In the wake of the Partition of Punjab in 1947, emigration exceeded immigration, resulting in a net increase of only 0.21 per cent during the period 1941-51, despite a natural increase of about 16 per cent. The increase rate shot upward during the following ten years to an all-time high of 25.86 per cent in 1961.

TABLE 26-2   POPULATION GROWTH IN PUNJAB: 1901-61

| | | Punjab* | | | India** | |
| | | % Decennial Change | | | | % |
Year	Population	Total Popu-lation	Rural	Urban	Population	Decennial Change
1901	13,265,860				236,281,245	
1911	11,945,019	−9.96	−9.7	−11.2	252,122,410	+5.73
1921	12,465,009	+4.35	+4.0	+7.2	251,352,261	−0.31
1931	13,666,876	+9.64	+7.4	+26.2	279,015,498	+11.01
1941	16,101,189	+17.81	+15.0	+36.1	318,701,012	+14.22
1951	16,134,890	+0.21	−4.5	+27.0	361,129,622	+13.31
1961	20,306,812	+25.86	+24.1	+33.3	439,235,082	+21.50

Sources: * Census of India 1961, Vol. XIII, Part II-A, General Population Tables, p. 62
** Census of India 1961, Paper No. 1 of 1962, Final Population Tables, pp. 8-9.

For a comprehension of past and present trends of population growth in Punjab and to visualize the trend likely to emerge in the near future, it is necessary to look into the determinants of demographic growth in the state. Except at the time of Partition, migration played a rather minor part so that for all practical purposes the growth during the sixty years reviewed above was largely determined by the difference between birth and death rates. The birth rate, which has remained high and has shown no signs of decreasing, is not the chief determinant of population growth in Punjab. Instead, it is the death rate, which has been easily susceptible to change and has consequently controlled the dynamics of population in the state, as elsewhere in the country.

During the early years of the nineteenth century, when famines and epidemics (plague, influenza, etc.) were rampant, both birth and death rates were high (each being well above 40) and one cancelled the other, giving only marginal rates of increase or decrease. But after 1921, the birth rate remained at virtually the same level, while the death rate plummeted from more than 40 to 15 (1961). The decline was particularly spectacular during 1951-61, when it dropped from 26 to 15. This dramatic decline in mortality was accomplished through a vigorous campaign against epidemic and endemic diseases, in which plague and malaria have been practically eradicated. However, smallpox and cholera, though quickly contained wherever detected, still occasionally harass the people. In addition, successful efforts have been made (i) to increase agricultural production through extension of irrigation, reclamation of waste lands, use of better seeds, etc.; (ii) to improve and extend transport facilities for the movement of food supplies to areas of need; and (iii) to start welfare departments for organizing relief. The combined effect of all these measures has been a rapid decline in death rate during the last four decades. Thus, the recent history of population growth in Punjab is essentially a narration of the changing pattern of mortality rates. Yet it should be noted that changes in the rate of accidental and premature deaths resulting from catastrophic events are responsible for the lowering of the death rate in general. There has been but slight change in the rate of "normal deaths," for problems of general sanitation and hygiene continue to remain unsolved in many areas. The lack of potable water and a deficiency of protective foods still render the population vulnerable to diarrhea, dysentery, and typhoid.

In sum, while the state has almost won the spectacular half of the battle—saving the population from deaths resulting from catastrophe, the slow, undramatic half—solving problems of sanitation, hygiene, and nutritional deficiencies—still remains. Thus, there is ample scope for further reduction in Punjab's mortaility rate, and if present efforts in this direction continue, the rate is likely to fall below 10 before long. After passing through a similar history, the crude death rate in Ceylon declined to 8. If there is no appreciable change in birth rate in the next few years, the declining mortality will by itself accelerate the rate of natural increase. Thus, with a continuing high birth rate and a fast declining death rate, demographic change in Punjab is bound to assume still more serious proportions.

In terms of absolute increase as well as the rate of growth, the decade 1951-61 is exceptionally significant. During this single decade, the increase of 4,171,922 persons was far in excess of the increase of 2,869,-030 during the preceding fifty years. There are several Latin American countries, such as Brazil, Venezuela, Ecuador, Colombia, Paraguay, Panama, Honduras, Guatemala, El Salvador, and Costa Rica, with equally high or even higher rates of growth. But in these countries high rates do not present so serious a problem because of a relatively small increase in actual numbers and the existence of potential resources. In Punjab

even a modest rate of growth means a massive increase in absolute numbers because of the existing heavy base of population. If the actual increase of 4,171,922 persons during 1951-61 is equally distributed throughout the state, it represents an increase of as many as 34/km² as against the corresponding figure of 22 for India. The average density in the United States is 23/km²—the result of continuous growth during the past two centuries.

The unmistakable implications of the recent growth in Punjab's population form a depressingly long list. In the first place, it has neutralized agricultural development to a considerable extent. Even though most of the waste lands have been reclaimed, increasing the net sown area by more than 0.8 million hectares, the per capita net sown area declined from 0.42 hectares in 1951 to 0.36 in 1961. Again, although the double-cropped area increased by 75 per cent during the decade, the per capita total cropped area declined from 0.49 hectares in 1951 to 0.47 in 1961 (Table 26-3).

Seventy-five per cent of the increased cropped area has been devoted to food crops—a fact which underlines the increasing pressure of population. Nevertheless, cash crops accounted for accelerated growth of urban population in certain areas, as will be seen in later discussion.

In the context of Punjab's predominantly agricultural economy—one still based on a backward technology—the race between farm production and population growth represents a case of the Malthusian trap. Even though one might cavil at Malthusian arithmetic, one who has seen poverty and its concomitants in some of the rural areas certainly cannot doubt the reality of Malthusian checks.

In terms of literacy, Punjab recorded remarkable progress: in 1951 16.47 per cent of the total population were literate, by 1961

TABLE 26-3   PUNJAB. CHANGES IN PER CAPITA NET SOWN
AREA AND TOTAL CROPPED (IN HECTARES): 1951-61*

District	Per Capita Net Sown Area		Per Capita Total Cropped Area	
	1950-51	1960-61	1950-51	1960-61
Hissar	0.97	0.73	1.07	0.97
Rohtak	0.41	0.32	0.53	0.45
Gurgaon	0.45	0.37	0.50	0.46
Karnal	0.36	0.36	0.44	0.52
Ambala	0.28	0.24	0.33	0.31
Simla	D.N.A.	D.N.A.	D.N.A.	D.N.A.
Kangra	0.21	0.18	0.34	0.30
Hoshiarpur	0.32	0.23	0.32	0.30
Jullundur	0.24	0.21	0.27	0.26
Ludhiana	0.28	0.26	0.37	0.32
Ferozepur	0.61	0.48	0.69	0.56
Amritsar	0.24	0.21	0.33	0.28
Gurdaspur	0.26	0.21	0.33	0.29
Patiala	0.39	0.37	0.46	0.51
Sangrur	0.56	0.47	0.70	0.61
Bhatinda	0.65	0.56	0.73	0.66
Kapurthala	0.26	0.32	0.32	0.36
Mahendragarh	0.56	0.52	0.69	0.84
Punjab	0.42	0.36	0.49	0.47

* Calculated from data in Statistical Abstract of Punjab, 1961.

the proportion had risen to 28.77 per cent. The actual number of literate persons rose from 2.65 to 5.84 million, an increase of about 120 per cent. If allowances are made for mortality, the growth of literacy would be still more impressive. Yet, thanks to the staggering growth in population during the decade, the number of illiterates increased by about one million.

It may further be noted that the percentage of population in the 0-14 age group increased from about 42 in 1951 to 44 in 1961, which has created additional complications by increasing the fraction of the nonworking age groups. Now, far greater efforts are needed in educational, medical, and other fields of welfare activity to maintain even the present level of social well-being. Within the working age groups, unemploy-

ment and underemployment are assuming alarming proportions, despite the expansion of new employment avenues, under the first two Five-Year Plans.

Patterns of Out- and In-Migration

The demographic dynamism of Punjab, particularly during the post-Independence period, is not only reflected in the phenomenally high rate of its population increase but also in the sizable migration of its inhabitants to other parts of the country and overseas, and considerable redistribution of population within the region (6: 107).

OUT-MIGRATION
The place-of-birth data collected by the 1961 Census reveal that 1,318,456 persons (685,-

123 males and 633,333 females) born in Punjab were enumerated in other states of India. The corresponding figure in 1951 was 676,712 (365,856 males and 310,856 females), giving a net migration of 641,714 persons (319,267 males and 322,447 females) during the decade. Apart from this, thousands of Punjabis left for other countries, particularly the U.K. It is noteworthy that the net migration equaled the number of all surviving migrants from Punjab up to 1951. This extraordinary tempo synchronizes with the two *Five-Year Plans* which undoubtedly opened up diverse avenues of employment to the Punjabis. The push for migration has also been provided by the rapidly increasing pressure of farm population. Seventy-one per cent of the migrants were born in rural areas, and a large majority of them are from districts with the highest density of agricultural population. This leads us to the obvious inference that the growing inadequacy of the farm economy to support the rapidly increasing rural population is in part responsible for the large exodus of people to other states of India and abroad. However, this inadequacy is frequently relative, for what appears to be "insufficient" to the Punjabis may be sufficient to people in other parts of the country. Also, what is sometimes referred to as the adventurous or the enterprising spirit of the Punjabis in general and the Sikhs in particular seems to be a trait of their culture. In this connection it is clear that any attempt to evolve a uniform standard for measuring pressure of population on resources in areas of diverse culture by multiplying the statistical data for each area by some constant factor can only be highly subjective.

It is of interest to note that the main areas of out-migration are also those of high percentage of literacy, and that among migrants a majority are from among the Sikhs. Their population increased by only 21.8 per cent compared with the state's increase of about 28 during the decade. The population of the Hindus, on the other hand, increased by 30.8 per cent.

An analysis of the place-of-birth data reveals that (i) migration from Punjab is largely of a short-run type; (ii) agriculture decreases in importance as a motive as the radius of migration increases; (iii) migration becomes more and more male-selective with increase in distance; and (iv) much of the migration, especially to rural areas, has been from among the Sikhs.

The intimate connection of migration with the pressure on land is also revealed by the fact that a majority of the migrants are native to the state. Among the Pakistanis who settled in Punjab after Partition, and who were presumably less exposed to the normal types of rural population pressures, there was no appreciable movement to other states during 1951-61, though there has been a lot of redistribution of these persons within Punjab.

IN-MIGRATION

Punjab, with a predominantly agricultural economy, a practically nonexistent mineral resource base, meager potential for large-scale manufacturing industries, an increasing surplus of sturdy labor, and fast intensifying pressure of population, does not offer much attraction for in-migration. By far the bulk of its cultivable land is already under the plough. Arid waste lands which remained unoccupied till recently are now being filled up by settlers from areas suffering from acute pressure of population. New industries are mostly cottage types, developed from household establishment. Local genius, labor, and capital, therefore, have played the important role in industrial development, rather than the inflow of these commodities from other states of India. A priori, one would not expect considerable migration to Punjab, yet the magnitude during 1951-61 (177,061 males) was remarkable. Though the numbers in themselves are not very impressive, they are significant because they equal the total number of migrants to Punjab surviving to 1951.

Most of the people migrating to Punjab are unskilled and semi-skilled laborers engaged in construction work on roads and buildings. In addition large numbers of domestic servants and rickshaw-pullers are attracted to Punjab's growing cities. With about 86 per cent of the male in-migrants during 1951-61 having been born in adjoining states (a majority of them in Uttar Pradesh), the radius of in-migration is smaller than that of out-migration.

Regional Analysis of Population Growth in Punjab

Thus far we have been examining the growth of population in Punjab as a whole. Yet our analysis of demographic dynamism is bound to remain incomplete if we do not pay equal attention to its spatial aspects and to differences in growth of the rural and urban populations.

Although the total population in Punjab has experienced a persistently accelerated growth since 1921, increases in rural and urban numbers have followed different trends. A perusal of the vital rates for the last four decades suggests that the rate of natural increase for both has remained practically unchanged. But in terms of actual increase, rural population has been growing at a regularly accelerated rate since 1921, while urban population has been increasing at a nearly uniform rate. The latter, however, is far higher than its rural counterpart. The rural-urban differential which was very large in 1921-51, narrowed considerably during 1951-61 when the rural growth rate reached

its all-time high. Urban population represented 19 per cent of the total in 1951; in 1961 the corresponding proportion was 20.1. (Fig. 26-4) The rate of natural increase of both rural and urban population for the decades 1921-31, 1931-41, 1941-51, and 1951-61 has been estimated at 10, 15, 16, and 28 per cent, whereas the urban population increased by 26, 36, 28, and 33 per cent. These figures suggest that rural-urban migration, a significant factor in urban growth from 1921 to 1951, lost some of its importance during the period 1951-61. Assuming that Punjab's urban population increased by about 28 per cent during 1951-61, and making allowance for the migration of urbanites to other states, it appears that about 80 per cent of the increase was natural and only about 20 per cent was due to rural-urban migration.

Although the increase in urban population by 28 per cent during 1951-61 may be considered high enough in itself, it appears rather small when compared with the manifold growth of industries and commercial enterprises during the same period. Among the factors that contributed to this growth were the introduction of labor-saving devices to the manufacturing industries, and the development of fast, efficient transport, which has made it possible for many laborers to commute to the factories daily from rural residences.

Even in those cities and towns where population increased phenomenally during 1951-61, massive rural-urban migration was not necessarily involved. In fact, in many cases the unusual increase is partly attributed to movement from other towns where population had reached a kind of a saturation level for the nature and magnitude of their particular functions.

Of the actual increase of about four million persons in Punjab during the last dec-

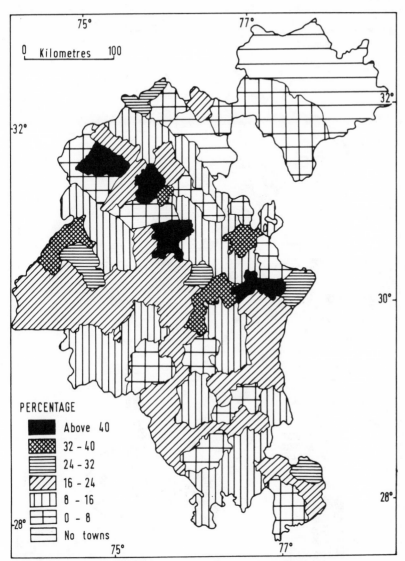

Fig. 26-4. PUNJAB: URBAN PUPULATION AS A PERCENTAGE OF TOTAL POPULATION, 1961, BY **TAHSILS**

ade, urban areas accounted for about one million, and the already crowded rural areas took the burden of the remaining three million souls, resulting in increasing pressure on the farm land. This is in marked contrast to Japan, where recently most of the population increase has taken place in urban areas.

REGIONAL ASPECTS OF GROWTH OF URBAN POPULATION, 1951-61

Marked regional contrasts characterized urban population growth in Punjab during the decade 1951-61 (Fig. 26-5). Although, as a rule, the process of urbanization follows development of industry and commerce, and the multiplication of service functions, there

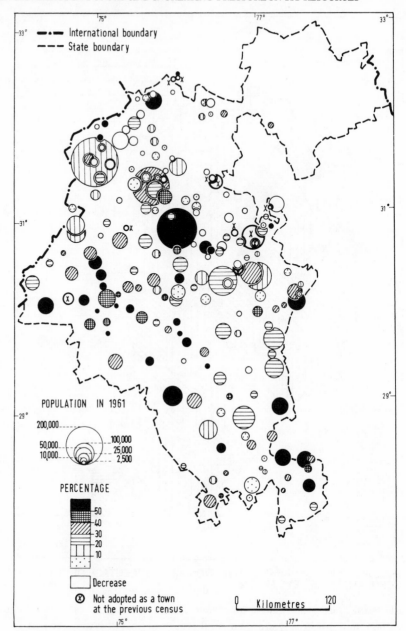

Fig. 26-5. PUNJAB: CHANGES IN URBAN POPULATION, 1951-61, BY IN-DIVIDUAL CENTERS

are certain fairly contiguous regions that have developed characteristics of their own in this process (5: 110-11).

The process of urbanization was extremely slow throughout much of the sub-mountainous zone and the region bordering on West Pakistan. Not only was the growth in many towns below the rate of natural increase, indicating out-migration; a number of them suffered an actual decrease. The slack growth of towns in the submountainous zone is coincident with its backward stage in economic development, the only exceptions being Chandigarh, Mani Majra, Nangal Township, Naya Nangal, and Pathankot. Tertiary functions, the development of which stimulates the process of urbanization, are largely lacking in this zone. In the belt along the border of West Pakistan, on the other hand, feelings of insecurity rising from proximity to an unfriendly neighbor impede development of industry and commerce and, consequently, the growth of towns. Before the Partition this insecurity did not exist, and many of the towns in this belt were growing rapidly. Further, the Partition caused a reduction in the service areas of many of the urban centers situated along the border. In the Bist Doab, Phagwara and Jullundur City are the only two places where the growth was considerable during 1951-61 —in Phagwara because of the vast expansion of industrial activity and in Jullundur City because of gradual growth of small-scale industrial establishments, commerce, and miscellaneous services.

Most of the Haryana tract reflects little more than natural increase. Exceptions are those areas adjoining the Union Territory of Delhi, where a number of towns have experienced phenomenal growth in the wake of development of small-scale industries and facilities for commuting to Delhi for work.

Maximum increase in urban population took place in a wide belt of southwestern Punjab comprising large parts of the districts of Ferozepur, Bhatinda, Sangrur, and Hissar. Most of the towns of this region, which belong to small and medium-size categories, increased by more than 40 per cent, nearly half of which was attributable to migration —generally from the surrounding rural areas. Most of these towns are situated along the main railway line connecting Ferozepur with Delhi, and their fast growth may be attrib-

uted to the development of processing industries and commercial activities dependent upon cash crops such as cotton and oilseeds. The fast growth of Ludhiana, Gobindgarh, and Yamunangar is mainly due to the expansion of industry, while Khanna owes much of its extraordinary growth to diversity and increase in its commerical functions. In this region land planted in cotton has greatly increased, and long-staple cotton has replaced the old shorter variety to a large extent. Commercial farming has been stimulated by improvements and additions to the regional irrigation systems. As is evident from their names, most of the towns in this region are primarily agricultural markets or *mandis*—Jakhal Mandi, Rampur Phul Mandi, Jaiton Mandi, Mandi Dabwali, and Abohar Mandi, for instance.

PATTERNS OF GROWTH OF
RURAL POPULATION

The rural population of Punjab increased by more than 24 per cent during 1951-61. But in a state as large as Punjab (122,261 km²) where various parts differ considerably, not only in their physical resource-base but also in social, economic, and political history, differences in distribution, density, and growth of population are but natural. Figure 26-6, which shows percentage growth of rural population during 1951-61, reveals three types of areas: (i) rapid growth with more than 30 per cent increase; (ii) relatively slow growth with less than 20 per cent increase; and (iii) moderate growth with 20 to 30 per cent increase.

(*i*) *Areas of Rapid Growth of Rural Population.* The greatest increase in rural population took place in the central belt of the state, which extends northeast to southwest. It includes large parts of the Patiala, Karnal, Sangrur, Bhatinda, and Hissar districts. In the Sirsa and Fatehabad *tahsils* of the His-

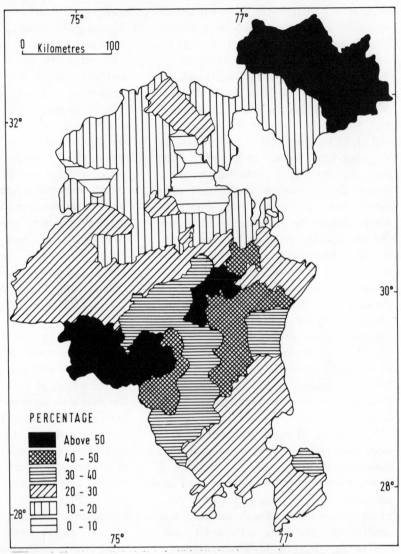

Fig. 26-6.   PUNJAB: CHANGES IN RURAL POPULATION, 1951-61, BY
TAHSILS

sar district and in the Patiala *tahsil,* rural
population increased by 73.2, 55.1 and 59.7
per cent respectively during the decade. Undoubtedly more than 50 per cent of this increase is due to migration from other parts
of the state. In the Hissar, Kaithal, Thanesar,
Jind, and Rajpura *tahsils,* the increase
ranged between 40 and 50 per cent. Making
allowance for the natural increase, 40 to 50

per cent of the total growth of rural population of these areas is directly attributable to
inmigration. In the remaining areas within
the belt, the rate of increase ranges between
30 and 40 per cent—still a very high rate.

These are the areas where cultivable
wastelands were extensive. Some of them
were in areas where landholdings were large
and landlordism was the prevalent system of

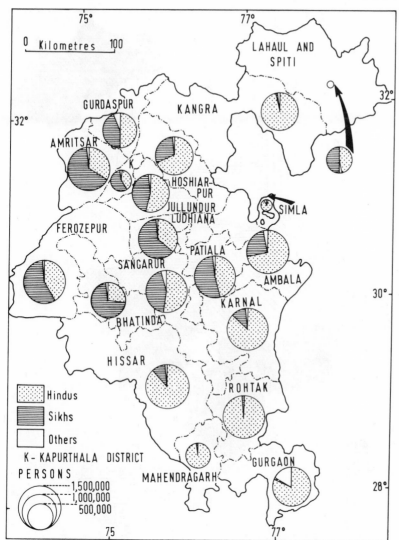

Fig. 26-7.   PUNJAB: RELIGIOUS COMPOSITION OF POPULATION, 1961, BY DISTRICTS

tenure, as in parts of the Patiala and San-grur districts. In the northern half of the Karnal district, which had remained un-developed in the pre-British period, settle-ment was extended only gradually. The Pehowa sub-*tahsil* was an especially thinly settled area. In the Thanesar *tahsil,* where the villages are still of predominantly small size, settlements on former waste-lands are

of relatively recent origin with considerable areas awaiting reclamation and proper utili-zation. In the Sirsa, Fatehabad, and Hissar *tahsils* of the Hissar district, on the other hand, semi-arid conditions had rendered the otherwise fine land of little value.

The implementation of the 30-acre ceiling on the size of landholdings and the introduc-tion of canal irrigation from the new Bhakra

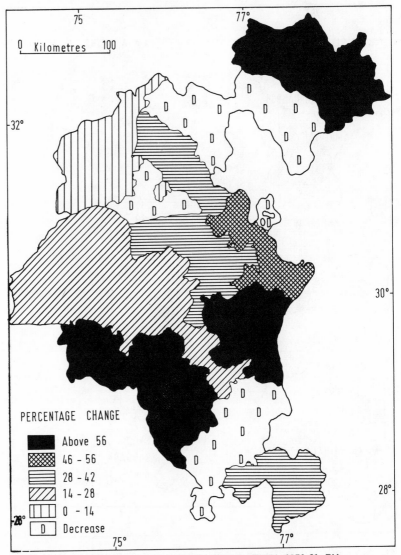

Fig. 26-8. PUNJAB: CHANGES IN SIKH POPULATION, 1951-61, BY DISTRICTS

canals in nearly all of these areas attracted streams of migrants from other districts of the state during the ten-year period preceding 1961.

In the Karnal district, in-migrants were (i) ex-service men, particularly from Ambala district, whom the state had granted 4.05 hectares of land each; (ii) persons from the water-logged areas of the Amritsar, Gurdaspur, Kapurthala, and Jullundur districts, and Dasuya *tahsil* of the Hoshiarpur district; and (iii) peasants who had taken land on 20-year leases. The densely populated and partly water-logged Amritsar district was the single largest exporter of migrants, most of whom went to the newly reclaimed and canal-irrigated Pehowa sub-*tahsil*. The number of males born in other

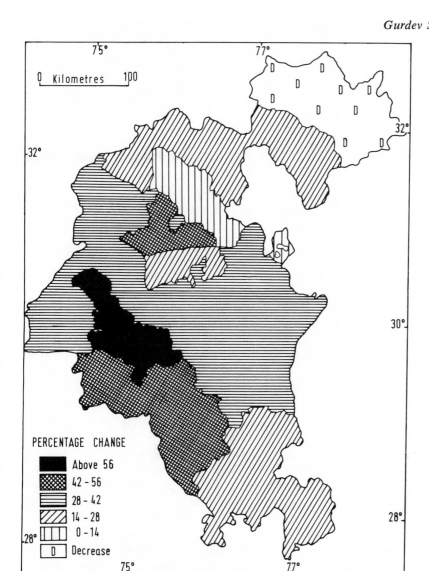

Fig. 26-9. PUNJAB: CHANGES IN HINDU POPULATION, 1951-61, BY DISTRICTS

districts of the state, but enumerated in the Karnal district increased from 13,720 in 1951 to 40,712 in 1961. Similarly about 20,000 Pakistanis migrated to Karnal district from other districts, mostly to the northern rural areas. In the Thanesar and Karhal *tahsils,* the newly developed tube-well irrigation has enabled peasants to move from larger villages to smaller villages hav-

ing surplus land that had not previously been irrigated.

With a preponderance of Sikh peasants among the in-migrants, the religious composition of the Karnal district has changed. The Hindu population increased by 32.8 per cent, while that of the Sikhs by no less than 84.7 per cent. As a result, the proportion of the Sikhs to the total population of

Karnal increased from 8.9 per cent to 11.9 from 1951 to 1961 (Figs. 26-7, 26-8, 26-9).

In parts of the Patiala district, particularly in Patiala, Sirhind, and Rajpura *tahsils,* the clayey soils, which were proving too hard for plough cultivation, have revealed great agricultural potential with the advent of canal and tube-well irrigation. This prospect has brought thousands of families from the densely populated districts of Amritsar, Ludhiana, Ambala (mostly from the Rupar and Kharar *tahsils*), and Jullundur. Apart from the newly extended irrigation facilities, the distribution of surplus land from large holdings that had once dominated the rural scene in erstwhile Patiala state, was also a big incentive to farmers, especially those from Amritsar, who comprise the largest group of in-migrants.

Still another area of significant in-migration is the Hissar district where, in the Sirsa and Fatehabad *tahsils,* the rural population increased at the phenomenal rates of 73 and 55 per cent respectively during the last decade. The Sirsa subdivision, where extensive areas were lying unproductive because of arid conditions, suddenly became a dynamic frontier with the arrival of canal irrigation from the Bhakra scheme. In the Neli assessment circles along the Ghagger River, where the soils are fine clayey loams and where the villages were small and rather widely spaced, the population growth has been most explosive. An overwhelming majority of the villages in this belt have experienced more than 100 per cent increase in population. The per-square-kilometer increase in density during the ten years was as much as 100 persons. Migrants to these areas include persons from within the Hissar and other districts, and Pakistanis who had earlier settled elsewhere. During the decade, as many as 40,000 Pakistanis may have migrated from other parts of the state to areas of new canal irrigation in the Hissar district. Sim-

ilarly, the number of males born in other districts but enumerated in the Hissar district increased from 12,372 in 1951 to 55,756 in 1961. Three-fourths of the increase took place in the rural areas, and as many as 22 per cent were from the adjoining district of Ferozepur alone. These migrants include (i) those who had small landholdings in their home districts and who, finding the price of land rather low in the Sirsa subdivision in the early 1950's, purchased land in areas awaiting irrigation from the new canal; (ii) those in whose native areas waterlogging was posing a serious problem; and (iii) Kambo tenants who had been ejected by their landlords.

The Amritsar district is the second largest contributor to this in-migration, followed by Bhatinda and Jullundur. Some of the migrants from the Amritsar district are those whose landholdings were too small to provide a living, while the others have come from areas where the menace of water-logging is becoming serious. As in the Karnal district, an overwhelming majority of migrants to the rural areas of the Hissar district are Sikh peasants. Although it continues to be a Hindu-majority district, the proportion of Sikhs, whose population has increased by 89.9 per cent, rose from 7.7 to 9.9 per cent during 1951-61 (3: 119-124). Thus all these areas of rapid growth of rural population, which are invariably those of low or moderate densities, have shown strong inverse correlation between density and growth, and in many instances, in-migration has proved a vital factor in the unusually high rate of increase.

This significant movement from the densely populated rural areas to the thinly or moderately settled parts of the central belt represents a process of readjustment to the changing agricultural resources.

(*ii*) *Areas of Slow Growth of Rural Population.* The trans-Sutlej tract, the Ludhiana district, and Rupar subdivision of the Ambala district are areas where the increase in rural population has been relatively meager and far below the state average of 24.1 per cent. Coincidentally, they have the highest density of rural population in the state: 173 to 309/km² (Fig. 26-2). As a result of the heavy base of population and accelerated rate of natural increase, the cultivated land per capita in nearly all of these areas has declined to between 0.16 and 0.24 hectares—less than half of the corresponding figure for most of the other areas of the state. A large proportion of the rural population is dependent on agriculture for a livelihood. Thus, under the impact of increasing pressure of population, declining cultivated area per capita and deteriorating subsistence farm economy, this region has become an important source of out-migration. The net effect of out-migration from this region is also reflected in a low percentage of working population to total population (4: 4).

Despite a high rate of natural increase—28 per cent—rural population in the Tarn *tahsil* of the Amritsar district increased by only 4.7 per cent. This indicates an exodus of almost a quarter of the rural population during the ten-year period. In the sub-hilly *tahsils* of Garhshankar and Una (Hoshiarpur district), where the *chos* (seasonal streams originating in the Siwalik hills) have damaged the cultivable land, and in Nawanshahr *tahsil* (Jullundur district), the corresponding growth was 5.8, 7.1, and 9.7 per cent respectively, and presents a similar phenomenon. Increase in other areas of this type is everywhere below 16 per cent.

This region is not only the main source of migration to the developing central belt of Punjab, but also the major area sending people to other states of India. In addition, many thousands of workers, skilled and semi-skilled, have gone abroad, particularly to the U.K. Almost three-fourths of the state's total male migration is from this region, with the Jullundur district the single largest contributor.

Because a large majority of the migrants were Sikhs, the rate of increase among them during 1951-61 was far lower than the rate of natural growth. In fact, in the Jullundur district the Sikh population decreased by about 9 per cent. In the Amritsar, Kapurthala, and Gurdaspur districts the increase was only 2.6, 6.6, and 6.9 per cent respectively (Fig. 26-8). By contrast, the Hindu population has increased at the natural, if not a higher, rate of growth.

Knowing the growing inadequacy of the farm economy in this rural tract of out-migration, we cannot help seeing a causal connection between the two. There are about 386/km² of cultivated land, and because of progressive increase in rural population over the last four decades, the cultivated land per capita has fallen markedly despite extensive migration. In addition to the acute pressure of population, numerous farming areas in this region have been facing an increasing menace from water-logging of soils. In the Hoshiarpur district, the *chos* have wrought havoc upon the agricultural land. All these factors have prompted peasants to migrate to the agricultural frontiers in Punjab, Rajasthan, Uttar Pradesh, and Madhya Pradesh, and to towns and cities throughout the country where possibilities of employment seem bright. Those who left earlier for the U.K., Canada, East Africa, and elsewhere have continued to encourage more and more of their friends and relatives to follow. Another factor which seems to have encouraged migration is the high percentage of literacy among the people of this region.

In the Amritsar and Gurdaspur districts, proximity to the border with an unfriendly country has also induced both rural and urban groups to pull out gradually. The moderate or low rates of increase in the rural

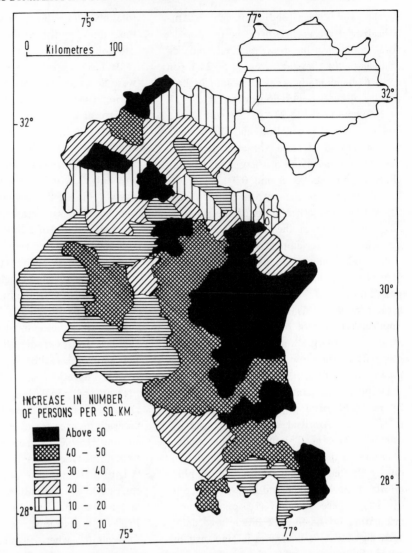

Fig. 26-10.   PUNJAB: CHANGES IN POPULATION DENSITY, 1951-61, BY
TAHSILS

population should not mislead one into thinking that the absolute increase has been
identical. For example, in the Amritsar, Ferozepur, Jullundur, and Ludhiana districts
increases were as much as 23 to 46/km^2
(Fig. 26-10).

In conclusion, the areas of slow growth
and significant migration are those where (i)
the density of rural population is very high;

(ii) the problem of water-logging has rendered extensive areas unfit for cultivation;
and (iii) a considerable proportion of the
population is literate. The phenomenon of a
relatively low rate of population increase is
not new to these areas. In the earlier decades also, migration and meager growth
have gone hand in hand. Thus, all these
features—the continuing migration, the slow

growth of population, the prevailing subsistence farm economy, and the small amount of cultivated land per capita—provide some indication that a saturation level is being reached. It seems certain that unless methods of farm production are vastly improved and a sizable proportion of the farm population is diverted to nonagricultural pursuits such as small-scale and cottage industry, these areas will find it difficult to support additional numbers even at the current low level of living.

(iii) *Areas of Moderate Growth.* Areas belonging to this category include large parts of Ambala, Ferozepur, Bhatinda, Sangrur, Rohtak, Gurgaon, and Mahendragarh districts, where rural population increased by 20 to 30 per cent during 1951-61, a level close to the estimated rate of natural increase. In Rohtak, Gurgaon, and Mahendragarh districts, as many as 90 per cent of the rural male inhabitants are enumerated at their place of birth. The corresponding figures for Ambala and Sangrur districts range between 80 and 90 per cent. These figures are convincing proof that there is little migration toward the countryside and that rural population growth there is almost totally due to natural increase.

The migration from these southern districts to other areas in Punjab or India has also been negligible. The immobility of the population is correlated with lack of education, lack of willingness to leave ancestral homes, and a rudimentary stage of economic development. With the overspilling of industrial activity from Delhi to adjoining areas in Gurgaon and Rohtak districts, however, the *tahsils* of Ballabgarh, Rohtak and Sonepat have started to show signs of demographic dynamism. As already noted, with increasing demand for labor in the fast growing industries within the Union Territory of Delhi, there are large numbers of workers of this area who commute daily to the city, thanks to the development of quick and efficient transport.

Problems and Prospects

Recent acceleration in the growth of Punjab's population, caused by dramatic declines in mortality rates and by high birth rates, has given rise to numbers unprecedented in the region's demographic history. The ample scope for further reduction in death rate will further quicken the pace of population growth. The implications of this trend are manifold and frightening, for it has neutralized to a considerable degree recent remarkable achievements in agricultural development, literacy, employment, and social welfare. The inescapable conclusion is that economic development without population control will be meaningless. There is an immediate need to retard population growth substantially by perfecting the implementation of family planning programs, and to consider even more direct and effective measures.

The fast disappearance of taboos against population control, as revealed in recent rural as well as urban surveys, is a helpful factor. This change in attitude stems from: (i) decreasing size of landholdings which are already uneconomical in many cases; (ii) rapidly improving survival rate of children; (iii) increasing desire for higher levels of consumption; and (iv) growing unemployment. The landless scheduled castes— the so-called "untouchables"—however, are a significant exception to this change, since they have been less affected by recent socioeconomic change.

Yet despite the general willingness of the people, progress in family planning is likely to be slow because of the shortage of the trained personnel, funds, and readily usable techniques for converting parents to a new reproductive pattern. Furthermore, whatever success is achieved through sustained

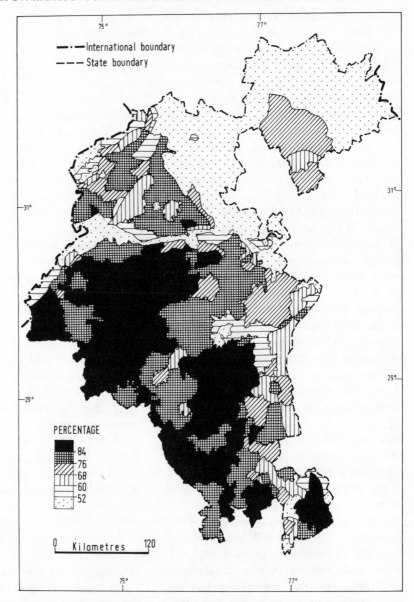

Fig. 26-11.   PUNJAB: NET SOWN AREA AS A PERCENTAGE OF TOTAL AREA, 1961, BY ASSESSMENT CIRCLES

efforts at family planning is likely to be neutralized by (i) the youthfulness of the region's population, 43.8 per cent of which is below 15 years of age; (ii) the fast declining rate of maternity deaths; (iii) the improving health of the population; and (iv) the increasing of remarriage of widows. It would appear, therefore, that all attempts at population control at best can only prevent further acceleration in the growth rate in the next few years, and only after that will positive results become visible.

The spatial analysis of the growth of rural population, revealing a strong inverse correlation between density and growth rate, brings to light a process of redistribution which is essentially a readjustment to changing land resources. Under the existing economy and technology, the densely populated areas, where the economy is predominantly agricultual and landholdings are small, and whence a sustained, sizable migration to other parts of the country and abroad has been going on, seem to have approached a kind of a saturation level. The development of water-logging in some of these areas has further aggravated the problem, although the extension of irrigation and reclamation of arid and semi-arid land, on the other hand, have stimulated in-migration. Similarly, the newly reclaimed flood plains have experienced rapid growth of population. But this process of redistribution seems to be nearing culmination. Most of the arable land has already been cultivated (Fig. 26-11). With recent attempts at extension of cultivation to the maximum limits, the wastelands have shrunk; and the possibilities of further development of irrigation are becoming more and more limited. The recent linguistic reorganization of the region into Punjabi and Hindi-speaking states might adversely affect the future possibilities of internal redistribution, as the most densely populated areas are in Punjab (the Punjabi-speaking state) and the wastelands that do remain are in Haryana (the Hindi-speaking state). In other states, also, the agricultural frontiers are practically closed. In fact, even to maintain the present cultivated area in Punjab is a problem. Tens of thousands of hectares of good farm land have been lost to cultivation in recent years because of encroachment by growing towns and villages, new canals, roads, industrial, and commercial establishments, new educational institutions, and a variety of other nonagricultural uses. Extensive areas have been water-logged. All these developments have neutralized to a considerable degree the expansion of cultivated area brought about through irrigation and reclamation of land. Unfortunately, the land around towns and villages encroached upon by cultural uses is often of better quality than the newly cultivated lands. Thus, hectare for hectare, there is generally a net loss in this exchange. If this deplorable trend is not to be perpetuated, the towns and villages must expand *vertically* to accommodate the increasing population and economic activities. If horizontal expansion seems unavoidable, only low-grade agricultural land should be used. In addition, the land already under cultivation must be re-energized through consistent application of the principles of conservation of land resources.

There is no doubt that agricultural yields are continually improving, but to rely on this measure alone cannot provide a lasting solution to the population problem. Thus, agriculture must be diversified to the fullest extent. The development on every farm of poultry and piggery, which do not require much space, will go a long way toward improving the quantity and quality of food supply. Further, a diversification of the rural economy, which would involve a substantial transfer of the agricultural population to nonagricultural activities, is necessary. If the change is to be successful, the object must be decentralized, rather than city-oriented industrial development, so that the villagers do not have to migrate to urban areas to seek new employment. By diverting industrial activity to the countryside to the greatest possible extent, it should be possible to avoid many of the problems that arise from rapid urbanization. Moreover, this kind of a decentralization would not only assimilate the industrial activity in the rural economy but would also mean a fair distribution of wealth among the people, a desirable goal from the demographic, economic, social, and political points of view.

In conclusion, the solution for the fast increasing pressure of population on social and physical resources in Punjab in the wake of its vigorous demographic growth must be sought in (i) effective population control, (ii) intensification and diversification of agriculture, (iii) diversification of rural as well as urban economy, and (iv) consistent application of the principles of conservation of resources. Out-migration is not the answer to the population problem confronting the region.

REFERENCES

(1) G. S. Gosal: Regional Aspects of Population Growth in India, *Pacific Viewpoint,* Vol. 3, No. 2, Sept. 1962, pp. 87-99.

(2) G. S. Gosal and B. S. Ojha: Pattern of Population Growth in Punjab, 1951-61, *Research Bulletin of the Punjab University,* Vol. 15, Parts I-II, June 1964, pp. 51-68.

(3) G. S. Gosal: Changes in Religious Composition of Punjab's Population: 1951-61, *The Economic Weekly,* Vol. 17, No. 4, Jan. 23, 1965, pp. 119-24.

(4) G. S. Gosal and Gopal Krishnan: Occupational Structure of Punjab's Rural Population, 1961, *The Indian Geographical Journal,* Vol. 40, Nos. 1-2, Jan.-June, 1965, pp. 1-12.

(5) G. S. Gosal: Urbanization in Punjab (India), 1921-61, *Tijdschrift voor Economische en Sociale Geografie,* Vol. 57, May-June 1966, pp. 104-12.

(6) G. S. Gosal: Redistribution of Population in Punjab during 1951-61, in: Ashish Bose, ed.: *Patterns of Population Change in India 1951-61* (New Delhi, 1967), pp. 107-29.

27. POPULATION CHANGE AND AGRICULTURAL PRODUCTIVITY IN EAST PAKISTAN, 1951-1961

Warren C. Robinson

"Disguised" or "hidden" unemployment in agriculture is often given a key role in explanations of economic backwardness and in showing how future economic development can occur (6; 12; 19). At the conceptual level, "disguised" unemployment has been rather well worked-out, but the empirical content remains uncertain. This paper makes an effort to cast more light on the matter by looking at the macro-economic relationship between changes in output (in constant prices) and agricultural labor force per hectare during the period 1951-61 for the province of East Pakistan. The results in general support the notion that the marginal product of agricultural labor is strikingly low or even zero in some districts, and that the labor surplus has been growing over time. There is also indirect evidence that growing population pressure on resources affects the economic behavior of the cultivators. Specifically, it leads to a declining average product per worker, but due to concomitant reduction in hours worked per worker, marginal product per worker is not driven to negative values.

"Disguised Unemployment" as a Concept

Evidently, the term "disguised unemployment" was first used by Joan Robinson in 1936. According to Mrs. Robinson:

> a decline in demand for the product leads to a diversion of labor from occupations in which productivity is higher to others where it is lower. The cause of this diversion, a decline in effective demand, is exactly the same as the cause of unemployment in the ordinary sense, and it is natural to describe

the adoption of inferior occupations by dismissed workers as *disguised unemployment* (18:84).

Since this early usage, the concept has evolved into a phenomenon in which the marginal productivity of labor is not reduced because of a temporary shift in demand (Mrs. Robinson's definition) but approaches zero as a normal, equilibrium event. Disguised unemployment of this type is considered typical of the agricultural sector of underdeveloped areas. Its existence implies a substantial waste of labor. Nurkse says: "Even with unchanged techniques of agriculture a large part of the population engaged in agriculture could be removed without reducing agricultural output" (12: 32). For Nurkse, disguised unemployment also exists in developed areas and sparsely populated underdeveloped areas, but is not characteristic of them. Disguised unemployment is an important phenomenon in the overcrowded and heavily agricultural underdeveloped areas of the world (12: 35).

The rather stringent constraint of Nurkse's "unchanged techniques of agriculture" has led to further refinement and extension of the definition. Rosenstein-Rodan divided the concept into a static and a dynamic formulation (19: 1). The static formulation is essentially Nurkse's and refers to the quantity of agricultural labor which could be removed from agricultural production, "without any change in the method of cultivation" and without any change in agricultural output.

> the second and quite different concept is the dynamic one which refers to that amount of population ("potential surplus") which can be removed from

467

agriculture *without its output falling,* assuming change in the method of cultivation. . . . It is convenient to distinguish at least two degrees of dynamic ("potential") surplus: (i) assuming a minor change of method of cultivation obtained merely through a rearrangement of work with but small additions of circulating capital, and (ii) the true dynamic surplus, with the assumption of thorough change, including additional use of both fixed and variable capital.

The same notion of labor withdrawal without affecting output is enunciated by Chiang Hsieh (9) in his concept of "visible employment." He calls the dynamic concept "potential unemployment."

There is the further complication that agriculture is typically a seasonal occupation with peak periods of productive activity. Underemployment is often incorrectly represented by statements such as: "in Burma the landless agricultural laborers are employed only five months per year or in Ceylon they are unemployed for four months per year" (9: 719). Such chronic, seasonal unemployment cannot be considered "disguised" unemployment by most of the definitions above because it is visible and easily measured. Leibenstein (10: 602) attempts to deal conceptually with this problem. Another type of disguised unemployment, he says,

is involved in the case where a subtraction of a portion of the labor force will yield a smaller output no matter what sort of reorganization of the smaller force takes place. Similarly, an addition to the labor force would result in a higher total yield. The sense in which we can have disguised unemployment in this case is that with additional resources or means of creating additional employment opportunities *of the right kind, more effort* could be obtained from the existing labor force. This type of unemployment is due to the seasonal nature of the production process in

agriculture, coupled with the fact that there is a lack of alternative employment outlets.

Thus labor has a productivity greater than zero because there is no unemployment during peak periods (such as harvest time) when all labor is productively employed. Unemployment at other times results from a lack of resources such as handicraft industries, which could employ workers during slack times and thus raise total productivity per worker per year.

Finally, there is some ambiguity concerning labor inputs when the marginal product of labor is said to have fallen to zero. Whereas the theory of production is couched in terms of man-hours, the measurement of the labor force typically deals with numbers of workers employed or unemployed, with perhaps only a lower limit to the number of hours which a worker must work to be classified as employed (and sometimes not even that). Thus, it is not clear that a zero marginal product of labor (in man-hours) implies a zero marginal product for additional laborers; nor can we be sure that the marginal product per additional man-hour of input is necessarily zero, even when the addition of more workers to the land brings no increase in total product.

Strictly speaking, the stringent case outlined by Nurkse in which workers may be removed with no loss of production would imply that either (i) some workers actually contribute zero hours to production and are thus in fact totally (if covertly) unemployed; or (ii) workers may be removed with no loss in total man-hours of input due to a rise in the average time worked by those remaining in agriculture.

Viner and others have pointed out that it is not likely that the marginal product per labor hour of input will actually become negative. For to continue to apply inputs when they actually had begun to have an adverse effect on total output would imply an extreme irrationality. However, in an extended family situation, where the "cost" of added workers is zero, then workers, if not man-hours, may be added almost indefinitely.

In any given situation the actual amount of man-hour inputs which could be usefully employed will vary with the size of the plots, with the techniques employed, and with the availability of capital and other inputs. If capital is mostly draft animals, the use of which replaces human labor, then the more capital the cultivators possess the more quickly the marginal product of labor man-hours would tend to fall to zero. However, if the capital means increased irrigation, or better seed, or more fertilizer, then the added capital may entail a complementary rise in the demand for labor man-hours. In the end (and particularly in densely settled areas such as East Pakistan), one could argue that the crucial factors affecting the requirements (or the potential maximum usefulness of labor in man-hour terms) will be the size of plots and the cultivation techniques employed. As Mrs. Boserup has pointed out, to speak of the "right" amount of labor inputs per unit of labor assumes a type of cultivational practice (3). Given highly intensive, double-cropped annual agriculture in which little or no capital is employed, a very substantial amount of labor man-hours may be absorbed before zero marginal product per unit is reached.

It is thus possible to imagine a situation in which small-scale peasant cultivators engaged in labor-intensive agriculture are able to absorb an increase in population without changing numbers of hours worked. Additional members of the extended family unit are "employed," even if only during harvest, without affecting the pattern of work and duties of the "senior" members of the family labor force. The margin product per man-

hour is still positive. The additional workers are thus employed seasonally and "unemployed" visibly or disguisedly the rest of the year, depending upon one's definitions. The marginal product (in an annual sense) per worker will be positive, but it is clear that adding these workers will have the effect of lowering the average product of labor considered on a per worker basis. Ultimately, the addition of further workers, when the marginal product per man-hour is approaching zero, would result in a diminution of the average number of hours worked by all members of the labor force, thus reducing the average product per worker even while having no effect on the product per man-hour of labor. (This phenomenon may be called "work-spreading" and is well documented.) Thus, marginal product per worker and per man-hour would still be positive. Only if the number of workers added were to become so large that it would be possible to "spread" the work any more thinly (when average product per worker is approaching the marginal product and both are very low), would zero marginal product per worker begin to appear. At this point visible unemployment of workers would appear and consumption per capita would fall sharply, since the added workers would be consuming, yet producing nothing.

East Pakistan: Physical and Socio-economic Background

SETTING AND HISTORY[1]

East Pakistan lies in the eastern part of the Indo-Pak subcontinent. Except for about 275 km of border with Burma, the area is surrounded on three sides by Indian territory. To the south is the Bay of Bengal. The

1. This entire section is based on the material of the 1961 Census of Pakistan, Volume 2, East Pakistan (15). See also the authoritative work of Ahmad (1).

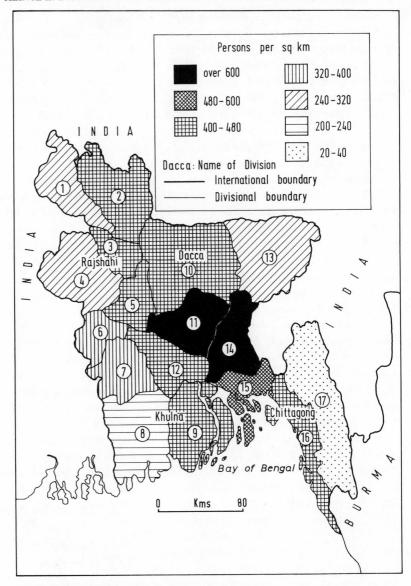

Fig. 27-1. EAST PAKISTAN: POPULATION DENSITY

total length of the land and sea boundary is 4714 km and the total area is 142,776 km² including large rivers and 134,476 km² excluding large rivers and foreshores.

East Pakistan was created on August 14, 1947, when the old British Indian Province of Bengal was partitioned. The newly created province comprised the larger part of East Bengal and some 13,000 km² (the major portion of the present district of Sylhet) from the Indian province of Assam. Named East Pakistan in 1956, the area is organized as a province, with an appointed Governor and an elected state legislature. The administrative hierarchy runs from Union Council (village or urban ward), through Thana

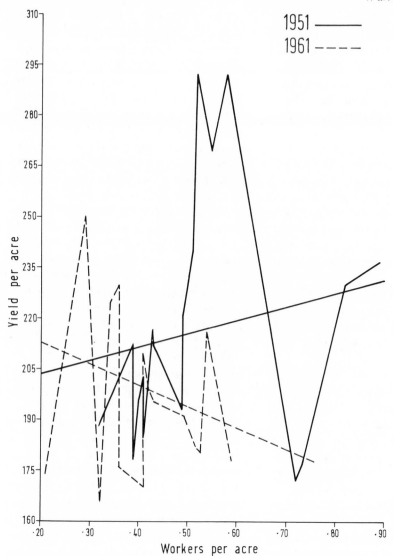

Fig. 27-2. EAST PAKISTAN: YIELD PER ACRE/WORKERS PER ACRE IN 1951 AND 1961

(police district), subdivision, district, and from division to province. In 1961 there were 17 districts (Fig. 27-1) in East Pakistan and these units form the basis for our analysis.

PHYSIOGRAPHY AND CLIMATE

East Pakistan is a vast plain built by the enormous alluvial deposits of the Ganges,

the Brahmaputra, the Meghna, and their innumerable tributaries and distributaries. The major physiographic types are the Tertiary Hill, the Pleistocene Terraces, and the Recent Flood Plains.

The Recent Flood Plains, a major part of the province, cover most of the district of Comilla and parts of Sylhet and Noakhali districts. Adjacent is a piedmont plain, which comprises most of Dinajpur, and a portion of Rajshahi and Bogra. The climate is tropical monsoon, with warm wet summers and cool dry winters. Winter temperatures do not usually fall below 15.5°C. Due to its nearness to the sea, small area, flat surface, vegetation cover, and the presence of numerous bodies of water in the form of rivers and marshes, the area's climate is generally equable. About 80 per cent of the annual rainfall is received during the monsoon season (June to early October) with no place receiving less than 1270 mm normally. Two regions, the Chittagong coast and the Sylhet district, get more than 2540 mm. During the monsoon, much of East Pakistan is inundated, becoming a vast lake dotted with artificially raised settlements and natural highlands. Except for a few hilly regions in the east, most of the land is flat and covered with rich alluvial soils which are renewed every year (Fig. 27-2).

ECONOMY AND AGRICULTURE
East Pakistan has more than 40 per cent of the total agricultural land of the country, yet only 15 per cent of the total land area. The climate, soils, and topography favor cultivation of relatively large areas and production of two or more crops yearly. Less than 2.2 per cent of the cultivated land is irrigated, mainly during the dry winter months in the western part of the Province. In general, the crops produced are those requiring a hot wet climate, such as rice, jute, tea, and tropical fruits.

More than 72 per cent of the cropped area, or 8,903,278 hectares, is given to rice, with an average of more than 259 million *maunds* (10 million tons) produced annually. Jute is the most important cash crop, dominating the economic structure of the province. A total of about four million bales earns more than 1000 million rupees ($200

million) of foreign exchange annually. East Pakistan's crop, which is cultivated on about 10 per cent of the agricultural land, represents about 60 per cent of the total world production. Tea and sugar cane are also important cash crops. About 32,000 hectares in tea produce a yearly average of 27.3 million kg, of which nearly half is exported, and about 113,000 hectares in cane produce some 360,000 tons of crude sugar. Other crops include tobacco, pulses, oil seeds, betel leaf, fruits, and minor food crops.

As one might expect, most of the civilian labor force (84 per cent) are cultivators and other agriculturalists. Females represent only about 14 per cent of the total, indicating their less important role—even in agriculture. Most of the cultivators either own their own land or work for no pay on family-owned land (36 and 33 per cent respectively). A smaller fraction own some land and rent more (10 per cent), while only about 20 per cent are wage-laborers or sharecroppers. Agriculture seems to be a full-time pursuit, since only about 5 per cent of agricultural laborers indicated any subsidiary occupation in the 1961 census.

POPULATION SIZE AND CHARACTERISTICS
The population of East Pakistan in January 1961 was 50,840,235 (excluding non-Pakistanis) of whom 26,348,843 were males and 24,491,392 were females. The total represents an increase of 21.2 per cent over the 1951 figure. Although the registration of vital events (births and deaths) is seriously deficient, there is substantial evidence from surveys and special registration areas that the rate of population growth has been accelerating. Recent estimates place the annual increase at 3 per cent or more, a balance between a birth rate of 50°/oo and a death rate of 20°/oo (6). The true growth rate may even be considerably higher than

this. Although the province is largely Muslim (80 per cent), Hindus, Buddhists, Christians, and other minor sects are represented.

In spite of rapid urbanization in recent years the province is still overwhelmingly rural and village-oriented. Some 78 towns had come into existence by 1961, and their population accounted for 5.2 per cent of the total of the Province. In 1961, only 4 of the towns (Khulna, Dacca, Narayanganj, and Chittagong) had populations of more than 100,000, together accounting for 45 per cent of the total urban population. Rural dwellers, representing some 95 per cent of the population, reside in nearly 65,000 villages.

Following the Partition, there was a substantial interchange of population between East Bengal and West Bengal (India)—largely a movement of Indian Muslims to East Pakistan and Hindus to India. The extent of such movements, which continue from time to time on a much-reduced scale, is known to have been large—seven millions is the estimate for both East and West Pakistan in the period 1947 to 1951—but precise estimates are lacking. However, in over-all terms, the impact on the population of East Pakistan had by 1961 become slight. In that year in Dinajpur, Rajshahi, and Kushtia (districts immediately adjacent to West Bengal) only 3 per cent of the population returned themselves as having been born outside the Province. Even allowing for children born to immigrants since 1947, it seems clear that the population resulting from such migrations is only a small fraction of the total.

Fertility rates are high in East Pakistan, where some 45 per cent of the people are under age 15. The social and cultural backgrounds which explain this phenomenon are familiar ones in this part of the world. Females marry very early, at about 15, and marriage is almost universal (by age group 20-24 some 96 per cent of the females have been married). Fertility is virtually unchecked, since contraceptive knowledge and practice is unknown to all except a small fraction of the educated urban elite. The sex ratio (males per 100 females) reflects the excess mortality that the risk of constant pregnancy and child-bearing imposes upon females. In 1961 there were 930 females for every 1000 males, far below the ratios found in most Western countries and even considerably below Latin America and other nations of Asia.

The population of East Pakistan is mainly illiterate. Even by the most generous definition of literacy ("reading with understanding"), only about 21 per cent of the population over 5 years was literate in 1961. Males constituted about four-fifths of this total; thus female literacy is near zero outside the educated upper strata concentrated in the urban areas. Of the literate groups, more than 70 per cent had completed barely four years of formal schooling in 1961. Only about 5 per cent of the entire population had a matriculate degree (roughly equivalent to an American high school diploma) or better.

DENSITY

Densities per square km are among the highest in the world, 2535/km², if inhabitable areas are excluded. Of the 17 districts, 11 have a density of well over 2600 and two of them have more than 3885/km². Dacca and Comilla with 4579/km² and 4359/km² respectively may be among the most densely settled areas of the world. Eight other districts, Noakhali, Faridpur, Mymengsingh, Chittagong, Bogra, Pabna, Rangpur, and Bakerganj, are also above the provincial average. The rather low densities of Khulna, which contains large uninhabitable mangrove swamps, and the Chittagong Hill tracts, Dinajpur, Rajshahi, and Sylhet districts, where jungle-covered hill country prevents dense habitation, explain the range around the provincial mean.

Thus, in sum, East Pakistan is inhabited for the most part by illiterate, backward peasant cultivators who own their own land, live in small villages, and grow rice and jute primarily by their own labor. The area is already densely settled and population is growing very rapidly. If "disguised" unemployment, labor input in the form of owner and family cultivation, and lack of alternative sources of employment are assumed to be a feature of densely settled small holdings in south and southeastern Asia, it is clear that East Pakistan meets all of these conditions. Disguised unemployment is particularly in evidence.

Approach Employed

Cho (15), in discussing previous empirical efforts to verify the existence of disguised unemployment, says that the approaches taken are either direct or indirect. By direct, he means field surveys in which day-to-day work experience is recorded or observed and an estimate of the amount of unused labor time, relative to some average or normal figure, is arrived at. Such surveys are expensive and time-consuming, and there are also the usual and serious problems of response error and bias encountered as well as problems in the construction of the sample.

Indirect approaches include use of data collected for other purposes but nonetheless useful in estimating the marginal productivity of labor. Most, if not all, previous efforts have been of this sort. Briefly, our data, which also falls into this category, consist of: (i) figures on the agricultural labor force by districts for 1951 and 1961; (ii) constant price (1959-60) value of output for all major crops, by district for 1951 and 1961;

(iii) total cropped acreage by districts for 1951 and 1961. These three series make possible a cross-sectional analysis of the relationship between output and the two major inputs, land and labor. By expressing the output and the labor inputs in terms of per hectare figures, it is then possible to trace with some exactness the marginal relationship between labor and output, land held constant.

The approach we are using attempts to approximate a production function for East Pakistan from cross-sectional data. In other words, each district for 1951 (or 1961) is taken as an observation of the province-wide production function. This approach is a fairly familiar one in empirical studies of the production function (7).

There are some limitations to our data. Figures for the labor force come from the censuses of 1951 and 1961, and there are problems of coverage and definition between the two. We have attempted to adjust for these. The data on cropped area are estimates compiled by the Department of Agriculture and may include many rough estimates. The series on value of output are reached by recording the value of marketed output for all major crops separately and for minor crops as a group, multiplying them by appropriate farm wholesale prices, and then deflating them to constant 1959-60 prices, using the index of change in wholesale prices compiled by the Central Statistical Office. These data, too, are rough and undoubtedly contain many errors. Because of the dominance of rice, jute, and a handful of other crops, the output figures we employ consistently represent 95 per cent or more of the cropped area in use. There does exist a small residual component made up largely of minor food crops, but it is not part of the total output value and seems to account for a very small fraction of the cultivated acreage.

TABLE 27-1   YIELD PER HECTARE, 1951 AND 1961, BY DISTRICTS
OF EAST PAKISTAN

			1951			1961	
Code	Districts	Cropped Area (ha)	Gross Value of Output*	Yield Per ha in Rupees	Cropped Area (ha)	Gross Value of Output*	Yield Per ha in Rupees
1	2	3 ×	4 ×	5	6	7	8
–	East Pakistan	10,623,107	5,503,000	518	11,165,951	6,620,000	593
1.	Chittagong	351,032	154,085	439	405,290	176,195	435
2.	Chittagong H.T.	107,554	48,613	452	101,975	43,338	425
3.	Comilla	749,257	399,788	533	835,355	489,357	586
4.	Noakhali	434,725	194,236	447	384,615	218,333	568
5.	Sylhet	781,654	368,207	471	838,519	559,244	667
6.	Dacca	752,059	339,617	452	706,693	509,336	721
7.	Faridpur	640,533	314,470	491	772,089	353,652	458
8.	Mumensingh	1,564,606	757,414	484	1,653,948	1,195,428	723
9.	Barisal	883,110	372,773	422	1,006,439	503,762	501
10.	Jessore	554,203	277,959	502	545,306	264,032	484
11.	Khulna	594,590	258,383	434	479,789	239,036	498
12.	Kushtia	341,665	147,056	430	335,803	154,384	460
13.	Bogra	369,746	202,391	547	382,376	204,260	534
14.	Dinajpur	474,305	268,352	566	489,323	256,384	524
15.	Pabna	467,816	289,376	618	433,291	191,210	441
16.	Rajshahi	697,452	285,269	409	875,166	458,246	524
17.	Rangpur	858,793	488,831	569	919,972	501,416	545

* Thousands of 1959-1960 Rupees ($1.00 = Rs 4.72 different from 1968 rate of exchange)
Sources: Directorate of Agriculture, East Pakistan, Dacca; Central Statistical Office, Karachi.

THE QUESTION OF CAPITAL INPUTS

A major conceptual weakness of our approach could be the absence of a figure for capital stock or investment annually. However, this weakness is not so serious as might be supposed. Capital, for the most part, consists of draft animals and simple agricultural tools such as plows and hoes. The latter are related directly, perhaps even in a fixed way, to labor inputs, since laborers require many hand tools. If labor inputs increase, one could argue that capital inputs are also likely to increase. In this case, one could then argue that when land is held constant (by working with output and input per hec-tare), one is measuring the changes in output per hectare associated with changes in the inputs of a labor-capital dose. (This is precisely the way in which Ricardo and other classicists stated the conditions for diminishing returns.) Yet is also possible that simple hand tools are not truly part of capital and that in the absence of mechanical equipment and expensive fertilizer and seed, draft animals represent the only real capital input. Animals are likely to be used in a fixed relationship to the land—so many yoke of oxen or buffalo per hectare. Presumably, increased labor will not affect this, since labor does not replace animals; nor does an increase in labor mean that it is more eco-

TABLE 27-2   AGRICULTURAL WORKERS PER CROPPED HECTARE, 1951 AND 1961,
BY DISTRICTS OF EAST PAKISTAN

		1951			1961		
Code	Districts	Cropped Area (ha)	Agricultural Labor Force[1]	Workers Per Cropped ha	Cropped Area (ha)	Agricultural Labor Force[2]	Workers Per Cropped ha
1	2	3	4	5	6	7	8
–	East Pakistan	10,623,107	10,715,467	1.01	11,165,951	14,336,496	1.28
1.	Chittagong	351,032	514,335	1.47	405,290	735,634	1.82
2.	Chittagong H.T.	107,554	86,834	.81	101,975	182,185	1.79
3.	Comilla	749,257	993,487	1.33	835,355	1,827,152	2.19
4.	Noakhali	434,725	563,007	1.30	384,615	780,230	2.03
5.	Sylhet	781,654	948,416	1.21	838,519	1,129,362	1.35
6.	Dacca	752,059	944,083	1.26	706,693	915,630	1.30
7.	Faridpur	640,533	658,566	1.03	772,089	785,118	1.02
8.	Mymensingh	1,564,606	1,665,411	1.06	1,653,948	2,384,721	1.44
9.	Barisal	883,110	888,414	1.07	1,006,439	1,017,250	1.01
10.	Jessore	554,203	425,692	.77	543,306	543,227	1.00
11.	Khulna	594,590	524,840	.88	479,789	582,831	1.21
12.	Kushtia	341,665	180,403	.53	335,803	269,637	.80
13.	Bogra	369,746	310,363	.83	382,376	404,452	1.06
14.	Dinajpur	474,305	356,319	.75	489,323	520,590	1.06
15.	Pabna	467,816	334,424	.71	433,291	420,278	.97
16.	Rajshahi	697,452	560,055	.80	875,166	713,953	.82
17.	Rangpur	858,793	760,818	.89	919,972	1,124,246	1.22

Sources:
[1] Census of Pakistan, 1951, Vol. 8, East Pakistan, Tables, pp. 1-3, (Karachi, Manager of Publications).
[2] Population Census of Pakistan, 1961, *Census Bulletin No. 5, Economic Characteristics,* pp. 40-78. (Karachi, Manager of Publications.)

nomic to use more animals. If this kind of reasoning is accepted, then it may be said that holding land area constant for the purposes of our analysis also has the effect of holding constant major capital input, so that changes in output can be associated with change in labor output, land and capital being held constant.

Our analysis is macro in approach. We deal in terms of district-wide averages and totals, and are not able to look at or control regional institutional, social and economic variations. Our defense on this point is that the province is a relatively small homo-

geneous region, and that our data do not lend themselves to any other approach.

Tables 27-1 and 27-2 present the important economic relationships contained in the basic data—output per hectare and workers per hectare. Table 27-3 presents a similar series on output per worker.

According to Table 27-1, the average value of yield per hectare was about 210 rupees in 1951 and 593 rupees in 1961. Within these averages, there was a wide range of values for particular districts. Between 1951 and 1961, yields per hectare in eleven districts increased, but dropped in six

TABLE 27-3 OUTPUT PER WORKER, 1951 AND 1961, BY DISTRICTS
OF EAST PAKISTAN

			1951			*1961*	
Code	Districts	*Agricultural Labor Force*	*Gross Value of Output**	*Productivity Per Worker***	*Agricultural Labor Force*	*Gross Value of Outputs**	*Productivity Per Worker***
1	*2*	*3*	*4*	*5*	*6*	*7*	*8*
–	East Pakistan	10,715,467	5,503,000	514	14,336,496	6,620,000	462
1.	Chittagong	514,335	154,085	300	735,634	176,195	240
2.	Chittagong H.T.	86,834	48,613	560	182,185	43,338	238
3.	Comilla	993,487	399,788	402	1,827,152	489,357	268
4.	Noakhali	563,007	194,236	345	780,230	218,333	280
5.	Sylhet	948,416	368,207	388	1,129,362	559,244	495
6.	Dacca	944,083	339,617	360	915,630	509,336	556
7.	Faridpur	658,566	314,470	478	785,118	353,652	450
8.	Mymensingh	1,665,411	757,414	455	2,384,721	1,195,428	501
9.	Barisal	888,414	372,773	420	1,017,250	503,762	495
10.	Jessore	425,692	277,959	653	543,227	264,032	486
11.	Khulna	524,840	258,383	492	582,831	239,036	410
12.	Kushtia	180,403	147,056	815	269,637	154,384	583
13.	Bogra	310,363	202,391	652	404,452	204,260	505
14.	Dinajpur	356,319	268,352	753	520,590	256,384	492
15.	Pabna	334,424	289,376	865	420,278	191,210	455
16.	Rajshahi	560,055	285,269	509	713,953	458,246	642
17.	Rangpur	760,818	488,831	643	1,124,246	501,416	446

* Thousands of 1959-60 Rupees ($1 = 4.72 Rs).
** Rupees
Sources: See Tables 27-1 and 27-2.

of them, because of decreases in cropped area.

Table 27-2 shows that the ratio of workers per cropped hectare increased from 1.01 in 1951 to 1.28 in 1961. Variations in the districts around the provincial mean were less great in this ratio for both 1951 and 1961 than for yield per hectare and the increase between the two dates more uniform, with fifteen of the seventeen districts showing a higher ratio in 1961 than in 1951, one district a slightly lower ratio, and one with an unchanged ratio. In only one district was there an apparent decrease in the agricultural labor force.

Correlation and Regression Results

Using the data from Tables 27-1, 27-2, and 27-3 as inputs, it is possible to judge precisely the degree of statistical association among the important series through the use of correlation and regression analysis. The effect of change in area on output can be eliminated by working in terms of per hectare output and labor inputs. In so doing, we also eliminate the most significant source or explainer of variation revealed by correlation and regression analysis. Substantial variation remains, however, in the yield per hectare data as shown in Table 27-1. Our

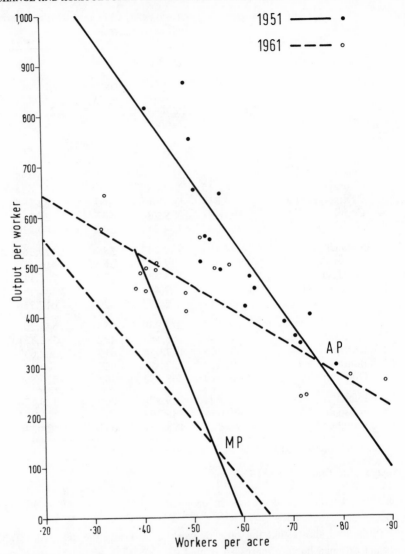

Fig. 27-3.   EAST PAKISTAN: OUTPUT PER WORKER/WORKERS PER ACRE IN 1951 AND 1961

correlation and regression analysis of this variation reveals the following results:

	1951	1961	*Change from 1951 to 1961*
$x_{1.2}$	—.226	+.190	+.127

where

x_1 = constant price value of output per cropped hectare

x_2 = agricultural workers per cropped hectare[2]

Interpreting these results, one is first struck by the fact that all the associations shown are rather weak and uncertain. The 1951 negative relationship between agricultural workers per cropped hectare and value of output is explained by the presence of

2. Density of population shows, as one might expect, a strong relationship to workers per hectare, but it adds very little to a joint explanation of variation in output per hectare or per worker.

TABLE 27-4   ACTUAL AND ESTIMATED OUTPUT PER WORKER,
1951 AND 1961, BY DISTRICTS OF EAST PAKISTAN

District Code	Workers Per ha (Y)	Actual Average Output Per Worker*	Estimated Average Output[1] Per Worker* (X)	Estimated Marginal Output Per Worker*
1	2	3	4	5
12)	.53	815	803	803
15)	.71	865	687	383
14)	.75	753	673	253
10)	.77	653	658	225
16)	.80	509	644	195
2)	.81	560	630	166
13)	.83	652	615	138
11)	.88	492	586	94
17)	.89	643	586	94
9)	1.01	420	514	−74
7)	1.03	478	499	−94
8)	1.06	455	485	−123
5)	1.21	388	398	−224
6)	1.26	360	379	−85
4)	1.30	345	355	−894
3)	1.33	402	326	−427
1)	1.47	300	253	−528
East Pakistan	1.01	514		
12)	.80	573	565[2]	565
16)	.82	642	559	400
15)	.97	455	523	320
10)	1.00	486	517	310
7)	1.02	450	511	300
9)	1.02	495	511	300
13)	1.06	505	499	250
14)	106	492	499	250
11)	1.21	410	463	200
17)	1.22	446	463	200
6)	1.30	556	445	167
5)	1.35	495	428	150
8)	1.44	501	410	100
2)	1.79	238	326	75
1)	1.82	240	320	50
4)	2.03	280	266	−166
3)	2.19	268	224	−270
East Pakistan	1.28	452		

1951 — (brackets districts 12) through East Pakistan 1.01 514)

1961 — (brackets districts 12) through East Pakistan 1.28 452)

[1] $X = 110717 - 1447.40 \, (Y)$ * 1959-1960 Rupees ($1 = 4.72$ Rs).
[2] $X = 756.93 - 598.85 \, (Y)$ Source: Tables 27-2 and 27-3.

479

several pairs of observations which deviate sharply and by large magnitudes from the expected sort of relationship. If these are taken to be spurious and are eliminated, the sign and the approximate value of this correlation is similar to 1961.

One could conclude that labor inputs per hectare are associated in a consistent and statistically significant way with value of output, both cross-sectionally in 1961 and also over time for the same in areas. Thus indirect (although not compelling) statistical evidence indicates that in the recent past incremental labor inputs were associated with positive changes in output.

The relationship between changes in output and workers per hectare is also worth showing graphically (Fig. 27-3). In 1951, there is an apparently negative relationship indicating that output actually declines as additional workers are added. This would be consistent with negative marginal product per worker per hectare. (This relationship is not very pronounced, however, and if one removes only two or three of the extreme observations, a mildly positive association between output and workers emerges.) The 1961 data present a more straightforward positive relationship between the two. The table below summarizes the least-squares functions fitting these relationships, as they are shown in Fig. 27-3.

$$1951 \ x = 218.0 \ - 53.517 \ (Y)$$
$$1961 \ x = 194.26 + 42.094 \ (Y)$$

where x = output per hectare
y = workers per hectare

$$1951\text{-}61 \ x = 27.737 + 28.980 \ (Y)$$

where x = change in output per hectare
y = change in workers per hectare

AVERAGE AND MARGINAL PRODUCTS

Since we lack any measure of labor in man-hour units, our measure of marginal labor product must be changes in the output per worker as changes occur in average number of workers per hectare. In view of the rather small number and wide dispersion of available observations, we resorted to a "smoothing" technique in an effort to bring to the fore the underlying relationships.

The actual output per worker for each district was known (Column 3 of Table 27-4). A linear least-squares estimation equation then made explicit the relationship implied by the paired observations of outputs per worker and workers per hectare. Computed next were estimated output per worker for different levels of workers (Column 4 of Table 27-4), and total output values corresponding to the estimated average output per worker (estimated average per worker times worker per hectare). Changes in total output, as more workers were added, was then computed (not shown in Table 27-4), and by dividing this change by the change in the ratio of workers per hectare, our estimated marginal output per worker (Column 4 of Table 27-4) was obtained.

Thus, our average and marginal products are, in effect, "smoothed" estimates of these variables based on the raw data, with more weight given to the mean values of the distribution shown by the raw data and less to the extreme cases.

The results (Table 27-4 and Figs. 27-5 and 27-6) suggest that for 1951 and 1961 average and marginal products per worker fall continuously and rather sharply. Comparing 1951 and 1961, the average product seems to have fallen from about 514 rupees to 452 rupees, while workers per hectare rose from about 1.01 to 1.28. Within these over-all changes there are some interesting differences. In 1951 the range of marginal products was from about 384 to a minus 528. Marginal product became negative at about 550 average product and when about

.16 workers per hectare were employed. In 1961 both the average and marginal functions flattened out and shifted slightly to the left, with the result that the marginal product function had less range (from about 400 to a minus 270) and fewer negative values. The marginal values became negative when some 2.00 workers per hectare were employed or when the average product was about 300 rupees per worker.

In view of the incomplete nature of our underlying data, we must be careful not to attach too much importance to the apparent shift in the average product curve of labor between 1951 and 1961. It may very well be a statistical artifact. Moreover, it is not inconsistent with our expectations of what might have been going on in agriculture during this period. What the shift could mean is simply that a reorganization of agricultural tasks occurred, to the extent that work was shared more evenly, thus increasing the contribution of some, but lowering the contribution of others. In other words, the existence of a negative marginal product for a large share of the labor force in 1951 may have evoked "work-sharing" changes in the use of land and capital. The result was the "employment" of a larger share of the labor force in 1961 (in that their marginal products were positive) but also to lower the average product per labor. This interpretation is also consistent with the earlier findings that the relationship between yield and workers per hectare became more positive in 1961 than in 1951. The number of man-hours of labor input thus probably remained relatively constant per hectare or perhaps increased slightly from 1951 to 1961.

Turning to the 1961 figures on average and marginal product, one can make some estimates of the extent of "disguised" unemployment in agriculture in that year. First, if the 1951 relationships between labor inputs and output per worker (the average

and marginal product per hectare) had also held for 1961, then the actual ratio of workers per hectare in 1961 (1.28) would have resulted in a province-wide average product per worker of about 360 rupees and a total output of about 5200 million rupees, or a drop of about 20 per cent from the actual 1961 total output. This means that as the labor force increased between 1951 and 1961, and had no shift in the average and marginal product functions occurred, workers would have become so redundant as to cause a total output to fall sharply from the 1951 figure. The marginal product per worker would have been strongly negative.

Also, had it been possible to hold constant the ratio of workers per hectare for 1951 (1.01), the increase in cropped area of 485,625 hectares between 1951 and 1961 would have called for an increase of about half a million workers. Since the actual increase was 3.7 million, the difference of 2.2 (15 per cent of the 1961 work force) can be considered "surplus." This is an incremental measure of "surplus," and it is possible that even in 1951 a substantial amount of it existed. If this is true, the ratio of workers in 1951 did not represent an optimum, and lowering it would have brought more than proportional increases in average product per worker. However, there is evidence that this ratio of workers per hectare had prevailed for a considerable time in Bengal. If a "surplus" existed, it had become a rather stable one and one which was already deeply institutionalized prior to 1951.[3]

The number of workers with negative marginal products decreased between 1951 and 1961. The fact that average product also fell strongly suggests that "unemploy-

3. Thus, for greater Bengal, Blyn (2: 207) shows the following worker per hectare ratio:

1901	.951
1911	.966
1921	1.025
1931	.979

ment" was simply converted into a lower average contribution per worker to total output. This reorganization, coupled with actual increases in man-hours employed (due to a fall in average farm size) and slight increases in area, explain the increase in total output.

Summary and Conclusions

Some very tentative conclusions based on the foregoing analysis may now be offered.

First, changes in the number of workers per hectare have recently been associated with positive changes in the output per hectare. However, in some districts, particularly densely settled ones, this has not been true. Correlation and regression analysis of workers per hectare and output per hectare support a moderate positive relationship between these variables. Population pressure itself, by reducing the average size of farm, may explain part of this increase in total man-hours required and output forthcoming, since smaller farms tend to be cultivated more intensely.

Second, average and marginal products per worker showed considerable variation by districts in 1951 and 1961. In general, average product per worker fell, while at the same time, the marginal product curve shifted, reducing the number of districts showing negative marginal product. The best interpretation of these results seems to be that increasing pressure of population, coupled with the small-peasant owner-cultivator tenure pattern, has resulted in an absorption of increasing numbers of workers but only with a decline in the hours worked per worker and in average output. This can be seen as a rational, albeit unconscious, response of cultivators to growing population pressure.

Third, between 1951 and 1961 "disguised" unemployment increased by about 15 per cent of the 1961 labor force. This estimate does not take into account the decline in average hours worked per worker which we are suggesting has occurred since 1951. Thus, in terms of man-year equivalents, or some other input measure relating workers to man-hours, the extent of disguised unemployment would presumably be even greater.

In closing, we should note that while the period of 1951-61 was one of relative stagnation in agriculture, remarkable changes have occurred since 1961, due chiefly to increased flows of nonhuman inputs (water, fertilizer), which tend to increase yields.[4] It may well be argued that the presence of the labor "surplus," which was readily available, has thus proved a favorable factor for growth in total product more recently.

4. See especially Falcon and Gotsch (5).

REFERENCES

(1) Nafis Ahmad: An Economic Geography of East Pakistan (London, 1958).

(2) George Blyn: Agricultural Trends in India, 1891-1947: Output, Availability and Productivity (Philadelphia, 1966).

(3) Ester Boserup: The Conditions of Agricultural Growth (Chicago, 1966).

(4) Yong Sam Cho: "Disguised Unemployment" in Underdeveloped Areas (Berkeley and Los Angeles, 1963).

(5) Walter Falcon and Carl Gotsch: Agricultural Development in Pa-

kistan: Lessons from the Second Plan Period (Paper prepared for 1966 Conference of the Howard Development Advisory Service, Bellagio, Italy).

(6) John C. H. Fei and Gustav Ranis: Development of the Labor Surplus Economy (Homewood, Ill., 1964).

(7) Zvi Griliches: Estimates of Aggregate Agricultural Production Functions from Cross-Sectional Data, *Journal of Farm Economics,* Vol. 45, 1963, pp. 419-28.

(8) Sultan S. Hashmi: Main Features of the Demographic Conditions in Pakistan. Country Background Paper for the Asian Population Conference, 1963 (Karachi, Central Statistical Office, 1963).

(9) Chiang Hsieh: Unemployment in Asia: Nature and Extent, *International Labour Review,* Vol. 65, No. 6, 1952, pp. 703-25.

(10) Nurul Islam: Concept and Measurement of Unemployment and Underemployment in Developing Economies, *International Labour Review,* Vol. 89, No. 3, 1964, pp. 240-56.

(11) Harvey Leibenstein: Economic Backwardness and Economic Growth (New York, 1957).

(12) Ragnar Nurkse: Problems of Capital Formation in Under-Developed Areas (Oxford, 1953).

(13) Government of Pakistan, Census Commissioner: Census of Pakistan, 1951, Volume 8, East Bengal Tables.

(14) Government of Pakistan, Census Commissioner: Census of Pakistan, 1961, Bulletin No. 5.

(15) Government of Pakistan, Census Commissioner: Census of Pakistan, 1961, Vol. 2, East Pakistan.

(16) Government of Pakistan, Department of Agriculture: Land and Crop Statistics of Pakistan, Fact Series III, Revised and Enlarged, June 1962.

(17) Government of Pakistan, Central Statistical Office: Pakistan Statistical Yearbook, 1963.

(18) Joan Robinson: Essays in the Theory of Employment (New York, 1937).

(19) P. N. Rosenstein-Rodan: Disguised Unemployment and Underemployment in Agriculture, *Monthly Bulletin of Agricultural Economics and Statistics,* FAO, Vol. 6, Nos. 7/8, July/August, 1957, pp. 1-7.

(20) Jacob Viner: Some Reflections on the Concept of Disguised Unemployment, *Indian Economic Journal,* Vol. 38, July 1957, pp. 17-23.

(21) Doreen Warriner: Economics of Peasant Farming (Oxford, 1939).

28. POPULATION PRESSURE IN JAPAN

Shinzo Kiuchi

Japan has the highest density of population per unit of cultivated land in the world (Table 28-1).

TABLE 28-1 DENSITY OF POPULATION
ON CULTIVATED LAND IN
SELECTED COUNTRIES

Japan	1,539/km^2
Taiwan	1,221
S. Korea	1,216
Netherlands	1,105
Belgium	967
Great Britain	719
W. Germany	624
Indonesia	538

Source: *Population of Japan*, 1960. p. 50.

If a country is isolated and has limited trade, the population density per unit of land area may be a useful index of population pressure. As most countries today are not in this position, density alone does not necessarily measure population pressure. Still it should be considered, for even in a developed country regional imbalance in population in relation to economic development may give rise to population pressure.

Japan has been modernized since the Meiji Restoration in 1860. Western culture and industries were imported and established at first in and around large cities. Rural areas were modernized later; their traditional way of living—peasant agriculture based on the family unit—was preserved, with drastic changes occurring only very recently. Urban-rural contrasts are very sharp. Population pressures in rural areas push people toward urban centers. Under a feudal regime that existed before the 1860's, the villages of Japan regulated their population by themselves, which gave rise to "static population pressure." But today, metropolitan development demands labor from the rural areas and people are attracted by the cultural and social amenities of cities. This "pull" factor has resulted in a big change in the distribution of population, which in recent years has given rise to "dynamic population pressure."

Underdeveloped Rural Areas of Japan

The Japanese census has recognized the "densely inhabited district" (D.I.D.) since 1960.[1] The former *shi* (city)-*cho* (town)-*son* (village) classification has become inadequate because of wide amalgamation of administrative units and urbanization since 1955. The statistics for D.I.D. relate to truly urbanized districts and those for non-D.I.D. to the unurbanized districts (Table 28-2).

TABLE 28-2 POPULATION OF JAPAN, 1965

	Population	Area (km^2)	Density/ km^2
D.I.D.	47,261,455	4,605	10,263
Non-D.I.D.	51,013,506	365,172	140

Part of the non-D.I.D. population is engaged in various nonfarming occupations, that is in trade, manufacturing, education, administration, and other services to the rural population. The non-D.I.D. population density on cultivated land in 1963 was 852/km^2. A typical village located on the plains in Central Japan has a density of 300-400/km^2 within its administrative boundary, which usually includes 50 per cent or more of nonfarmland. The high density of the

1. A contiguous census unit with more than 5000 inhabitants at a density of more than 4000/km^2.

484

rural population is also shown by the fact than an average farmer works on 1.05 hectares of farmland, which includes very little grazing land (Table 28-3). Comparisons

TABLE 28-3   FARM SIZE IN JAPAN, 1965

Size in Ha.	% in Size Category	% of these farms on which farming is a subsidiary occupation
<0.3	20.4	90
0.3-0.5	17.0	90
0.5-1.0	31.3	82
1.0-1.5	16.9	78
1.5-2.0	7.3	60
>2.0	7.0	53
	100.0 (5,665,000 farms)	

with other countries show that the number of agricultural workers per unit area of cultivated land is unusually high in Japan (Table 28-4).

TABLE 28-4   AGRICULTURAL WORKERS PER HECTARE OF CULTIVATED LAND IN SELECTED COUNTRIES

Japan (1963)	2.55
India (1961)	0.81
Switzerland (1963)	0.66
Netherlands (1963)	0.45
Italy (1963)	0.35
Canada (1961)	0.02

These data give some indication of overcrowding in rural areas. But in spite of this, good harvests are achieved with intensive cultivation—combining diligent labor, rotation of crops, irrigation, use of fertilizer (Table 28-5), mechanization, and other improvements. Postwar agricultural reform to abolish large land owners has had an important effect in increasing crop production. Productivity per hectare of cultivated land is about $600, that is five times greater than

TABLE 28-5   APPLICATION OF CHEMICAL FERTILIZER IN KILOGRAMS PER HECTARE OF CULTIVATED LAND IN SELECTED COUNTRIES (1964/65)

	N	P_2O_5	K_2O
Japan	120	82	98
Netherlands	301	114	142
West Germany	93	94	141
Great Britain	78	73	59
U.S.A.	23	17	14
U.S.S.R.	8	6	6
India	3	1	0

Source: Yano Memorial Foundation: Nihon Kokusei Zue (Japan Statistical Year Book 1967)

the United States average, and twice as high as that of Italy and Thailand; in contrast, labor productivity per capita is about $170, which is comparable with Thailand, 50 per cent of Italy's average, and only 6 per cent that of the United States.

How have the Japanese solved the problems of surplus labor in rural areas? In part by migration to urban areas or abroad,[2] or by finding employment outside of farming,[3] but largely through making better use of the land. The latter might be called "the Japanese solution" for crowded rural areas. The Japanese farmer is not in so miserable a situation as the former description may have suggested. Japanese governments throughout the centuries have pushed forward policies for agricultural improvements to reclaim lands and to support the prices of farm products. The production of rice has been particularly important in the development of the economy, sometimes even serving as a substitute for money, and today it supplies 44 per cent of all the food calories consumed in Japan. Against this national

2. In prewar days to the Americas, Manchuria, Korea, Taiwan, Sakhalin, and Pacific islands. In the postwar period there has been no considerable emigration.
3. Seasonal employment in forestry, carpentry, fishing, metal-working, trade, etc.

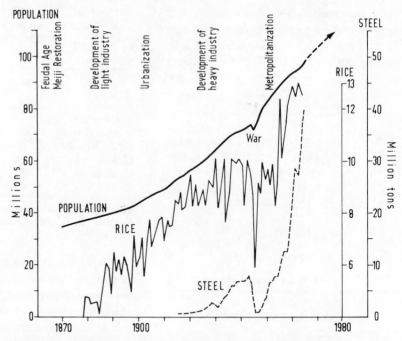

Fig. 28-1.   JAPAN: POPULATION GROWTH AND THE PRODUCTION OF
RICE AND STEEL, 1870-1960

background, the farmers of each district have improved their farming.

Two opposing opinions on the economic development of developing countries exist today; one stresses industrialization to solve the problems of surplus population and the other emphasizes the importance of agriculture. From Japanese experience during the past century the writer inclines to the latter.

Since the 1870's, the Japanese population has increased 2.7 times. The production of rice has risen between two and three times (Figure 28-1), and annual fluctuations due to climatic conditions have been largely eliminated. The increase resulted from expansion of cultivated areas and the rise in production per unit area—from 2.0 tons per hectare in the nineteenth century to 3.8 tons today. Postwar agricultural reform, technical improvements and governmental controls have favored the national food situation.

Under the policy of food control, a farmer sells most of his rice crop at a relatively high price to the government, which then sells it to the consumer at a lower price. With these various measures, it has been possible to maintain high population densities in the rural areas, which in turn have supported industrialization.

In parts of rural Japan numerous small-scale family industries—brewing, textile, paper, porcelain, and metal manufacture—were established in feudal days. These were located near raw materials and were supported by seasonal surpluses in the labor force. Some of them still preserve their old styles, but others have grown into modern industries, particularly with the development of communications. Their share of the total Japanese industrial population is today less than 10 per cent, but they represent bases of Japanese industrial development. These additional occupations have also made

TABLE 28-6   JAPAN. THE INCREASE OF "SUBSIDIARY" FARMS,
1950-1965

	Non-Subsidiary Farms (%)	"Subsidiary" Farms (%)		Total (thousands)
		Type 1	Type 2	
1950	50.0	28.4	21.6	6,176
1960	34.3	33.6	32.1	6,057
1965	31.5	36.8	41.7	5,665

Source: Ministry of Agriculture and Forestry, Japan: Agricultural Census Report 1965.
Note: A subsidiary farm has at least one family member engaged in a non-farm job.
Type 1: Where income from farm products is larger than that from non-farm jobs.
Type 2: Where income from farm products is less than non-farm jobs.
Various non-farm jobs are classified into: (a) seasonal or permanent; (b) in-village or in-town; (c) blue or white collar; (d) primary, secondary, or tertiary industries; (e) modern or traditional industries.

it possible for rural areas of Japan to support an extraordinarily high density of population.

Population pressure in rural areas has been the main "push" factor in rural-urban migration, while metropolitan development has provided "pull." Since 1955, extensive depopulation has been going on in areas throughout Japan, with the exception of the great metropolitan regions. In areas remote from the cities, young people merely move out, while in rural areas adjacent to the cities the number of commuters has tended to increase.

There has been a tremendous increase of "subsidiary" farms in recent years; Type 2 of this group, depending mainly upon non-farm income, has doubled in proportion to the total, (Table 28-6). "Subsidiary" farms of Type 2 are becoming more and more dependent on the labor of women and older men in the family, resulting in a loss of production through more extensive use. Increased incomes from nonagricultural employment may help to solve rural population pressure but only at the expense of delays

in the modernization of agriculture and a consequent loss of resources. It may be asked whether farming should be maintained in this way. Traditionally, people prefer to keep their own food supplies, which saves money since the cost of their own labor is not counted. Also, land is regarded as the most valuable property in Japan—if it is not cultivated, it is not recognized as farmland and is subject to a high property tax.

Case Studies in Japan

Japan has experienced two great periods of social change in her recent history. The first was the Meiji Restoration (1860) and the Industrial Revolution that followed, the second was that of postwar reforms in the agricultural system which were linked with heavy industrialization and rapid urbanization.

Since World War II, death rates and birth rates have been drastically reduced (Table 28-7), and national income has increased as a result of the sensitivity of vital trends to economic conditions (Table 28-8). The gen-

TABLE 28-7   NATURAL INCREASE OF POPULATION IN JAPAN,
1925-1964

	Birth Rate (%)	Death Rate (%)	Natural Increase (%)	Increase in 1000's
1925	35.0	20.3	14.7	872
1930	32.4	18.2	14.2	909
1935	31.7	16.8	14.9	1022
1940	29.4	16.5	12.9	924
1947*	34.3	14.6	19.7	1541
1948*	33.5	11.9	21.6	1731
1949*	33.0	11.6	21.4	1751
1950	28.1	10.9	17.2	1433
1955	19.4	7.8	11.6	1037
1960	17.2	7.6	9.6	899
1961	16.9	7.4	9.5	894
1965	18.6	7.1	11.4	1123

* Postwar baby boom
Source: Ministry of Health and Welfare, Japan: Vital Statistics 1966.

eral pattern of reproduction and migration has long been one of high natural increase in rural areas, balanced by migration to metropolitan centers. Since 1955, demand

TABLE 28-8   DEMOGRAPHIC ELASTICITY
COEFFICIENT IN JAPAN,
1925-1960

	(a) Real national income growth rate	(b) Demographic growth rate	a/b
1925-30	5.9	1.5	3.9
1930-35	3.8	1.4	2.7
1935-40	3.9	0.8	4.9
1950-55	8.7	1.4	6.2
1955-60	9.4	0.9	10.4

Source: M. Tachi. Forecasting manpower resources, population and labour force: some experiences in Japan. Inst. Pop. Problems, English Series, No. 55, 1962.

for labor in great cities has acted as a tremendous force in attracting population from rural villages; consequently, it is only the great cities that have shown population in-

creases, and most parts of Japan have lost people to them.

A recent survey of Tsushima, an island located on the Korea Strait, demonstrated a change in the population situation from one of static balance to dynamic migration. Under the feudal system the village of Tsushima was not allowed to expand. Its lands were limited and communal organization strictly controlled family size. Before the 1890's, abortion and infanticide were widely practiced and the maximum number of children in each family was two or three. But by the turn of the century, communications had begun to improve, making it easier to seek work in the northern Kyushu coalfields, to emigrate to Korea and Manchuria, or to engage in commercial activity. Eventually, communal organizations began to break down, and the number of children per family began to increase; four or five were not unusual, sometimes there were more than ten.

Iwate prefecture, situated in the northern part of the mainland (Honshu), has been one of the most underdeveloped regions in

Japan. Most of its area, 15,275 km², is occupied by mountains. The average annual temperature of Morioka, the capital, is 9.5° C, but surrounding mountainous areas have averages of 5° or 6° cooler than this and repeatedly suffer from crop failure due to shortage of sunshine and lower summer temperatures. The Kitakami valley bottom, where Morioka is located, is the main agricultural area, especially for paddy rice. Land in the mountains is in forest and grazing, with small patches of cultivated land for local food supply, mostly *hie* (*Panicum Crus Galli*), beans, and a little paddy rice. The prefectural population in 1965 was 1,411,188, with a density of 92.4/km², which is next lowest after Hokkaido.

Notwithstanding low population density, the Iwate prefecture experiences considerable population pressure. Its average per capita income in 1960 was about 84,000 yen —37 per cent that of Tokyo, which is the highest in Japan. Through regional development it has increased now to 178,000 yen,[4] 43 per cent of the per capita income of Tokyo. Physical conditions, poor communications, and especially *Nago,* the feudalistic social relationship between the large land owner and agricultural workers, which had been continued up to the end of World War II, have hindered economic growth. High natural increase has been balanced by emigration and low agricultural income is supplemented by subsidiary employment.

4. Including a slight change in the value of money.

Postwar social reforms, improvement of rice cultivation, the breeding of dairy cattle, and other agricultural techniques have resulted in the development of Iwate. The Kitakami Valley Project, one of 19 districts in Japan authorized in 1950, has contributed particularly to industrial and population development. Now, Iwate prefecture crops an average of 4430 kg of paddy rice per hectare, higher than the national average (3900 kg); and income level has also risen. Up to 1955, more than 60 per cent of all the employed population was engaged in primary industry; but in the last ten years, secondary and tertiary industries have increased in importance.

This change of industrial structure is reflected in the areal pattern of population growth; Morioka and ten other cities and towns in the prefecture have increased in numbers, while the other 52 towns and villages have decreased. Also, migration has accelerated through demands for labor force in Tokyo and adjacent regions (Table 28-9).

Population Pressure in Metropolitan Regions of Japan

The migration of people to metropolitan regions has increased population pressure wherever planning and public investment are too late or too little to meet the rising living standards and enormous demands of increasing numbers.

Since 1955, the economic development policy of the Japanese Government, in ad-

TABLE 28-9   NATURAL AND SOCIAL INCREASE OF IWATE PREFECTURE, 1950-1965

	Natural Increase	Social Increase	Balance
1950-55	124,891 (9.3%)	−44,522 (−3.3%)	80,369 (6.0%)
1955-60	92,048 (6.5%)	−70,628 (−4.9%)	21,420 (1.5%)
1960-65	77,911 (5.4%)	−115,310 (−8.0%)	−37,399 (−2.6%)

TABLE 28-10   JAPAN. CHANGES IN RURAL/URBAN POPULATION,
1950-1965

	Shi (*urban municipality*)		Gun (*rural municipality*)		Densely Inhabited District	Non-D.I.D.
	(1,000's)	%	(1,000's)	%	(1,000's)	
1950	31,203	(37.5)	51,996	(62.5)	n.d.	n.d.
1955	50,288	(56.1)	38,988	(43.7)	n.d.	n.d.
1960	59,333	(63.5)	34,084	(36.5)	40,830	51,014
1965	66,919	(68.1)	31,356	(31.9)	47,262	52,589

n.d. = No data.

dition to the efforts of individuals and companies, has stimulated rapid metropolitan growth. As a result, Tokyo, especially, attracts migrants, and there has been an increase of its crude birth rate because young married couples now form a higher percentage of the total population. Consequently, the metropolitan population has continued to grow, currently reaching more than 11 million—a fivefold increase in the past sixty years. The economic development policy has resulted in greater regional income dispar-

ities. People in the underdeveloped regions, where the prefectural income in one-third that of the Tokyo prefecture, have been encouraged to move to Tokyo, Osaka, Nagoya, and their adjacent areas.

Though the postwar food shortage has been solved, another type of man-land or man-resource pressure has developed. It is manifested in housing shortages, abnormal rises in land values, traffic congestion, water and air pollution, and the lack of many other public amenities. And in remote and

TABLE 28-11   JAPAN. SIZE OF MUNICIPALITIES, 1965,
AND THEIR GROWTH 1960-1965

Size Group	Number	Population (*in 1,000's*)	Growth Rate (*in %*)
More than 1,000,000	7	19,398,000	9.1
500,000-1,000,000	5	3,405,000	24.6
300,000-500,000	15	5,582,000	13.9
200,000-300,000	27	6,417,000	14.8
100,000-200,000	77	10,923,000	16.9
50,000-100,000	170	11,431,000	8.4
40,000-50,000	110	4,862,000	3.7
30,000-40,000	167	5,781,000	1.1
20,000-30,000	267	6,607,000	−0.8
10,000-20,000	1,006	13,957,000	−4.2
5,000-10,000	1,144	8,663,000	−8.3
2,000-5,000	320	1,181,000	−13.2
Less than 2,000	52	70,000	−17.2
Total	3,376	98,275,000	5.2

isolated villages which have lost population, it is difficult to maintain public services such as medical care, education, and transport (Tables 28-10 and 28-11).

Towns and villages with less than 30,000 inhabitants experienced absolute losses of population during 1960-65; those of 30,000 to 50,000 have decreased relatively. Suburban areas of cities with more than a million inhabitants and independent great cities of more than 500,000 have shown the highest rate of population growth.

Around Tokyo and Osaka, most new housing areas are located more than an hour's journey by overcrowded commuting trains from the civic centers. This is because the Public Housing Corporation has been forced to seek cheaper land to meet the demand of middle- or low-income dwellers. Closer to the urban core, private developers seek to maximize the economic yield of their high-priced properties, dividing them minutely and in some cases illegally. But even suburbs are often crowded with small houses and with resultant high population density. Throughout these metropolitan areas, residential and industrial developments are intermixed and have been promoted without consideration of physical conditions. But overcrowded slums and an industrial-residential land use are most frequently located adjacent to the central business district. The population density of the Taito and Sumida districts, wards in downtown Tokyo, is 70,000 to 100,000/km^2. Thus it may be concluded that population pressure is not solely the problem of rural and underdeveloped areas—urban and developed areas are in different, but comparably serious, situations.

REFERENCES

(1) E. A. Ackerman: Japan's Natural Resources and Their Relation to Japan's Economic Future (Chicago, 1953).

(2) The Asahi Press: One Hundred Years of Japanese History (Tokyo, 1965). [In Japanese]

(3) Bureau of Statistics, Office of Prime Minister: The Population of Japan (Tokyo, 1960).

(4) Bureau of Statistics, Office of Prime Minister: Population Map of 1960, 1:1,000,000. (Absolute distribution map with a dot of 200 persons.)

(5) Bureau of Statistics, Office of Prime Minister: 1965 Census of Japan.

(6) Bureau of Statistics, Office of Prime Minister: Census Report of Iwate Prefecture.

(7) Geographical Survey Institute: Land Utilization of Japan (Tokyo, 1950). [In Japanese]

(8) Geographical Survey Institute: Population Density Maps of Japan by Landform Regions.

(9) P. M. Hauser and O. D. Duncan, eds.: The Study of Population (Chicago, 1959).

(10) A. Hawley: Human Ecology. A Theory of Community Structure (New York, 1950).

(11) S. Kiuchi, S. Yamaga, K. Shimizu, and S. Inanaga, eds.: Urbanization of Japan (Tokyo, 1964).

(12) Kyugakkai Rengo (Association of Nine Human, Social, and Natural Science Societies): Tsushima Island. Its Nature and Culture (Tokyo, 1952). [In Japanese]

(13) R. Minami and others: Population Encyclopaedia (Tokyo, 1957). [In Japanese]

(14) R. Minami and M. Tachi, eds.: Theories and Analysis of Urbanizing Population (Tokyo, 1965). [In Japanese]

(15) M. Tachi: Formal Demography (Tokyo, 1960). [In Japanese]

(16) I. B. Taeuber: The Population of Japan (Chicago, 1958).

(17) I. Yano, ed.: Illustrated Almanac of Economic Affairs (Nihon Kokusei Zue, 1966). [In Japanese]

29. SAMOA: TWO APPROACHES TO POPULATION AND RESOURCE PROBLEMS

Peter N. D. Pirie

Since 1900, when the Samoan group was divided, its two parts have been influenced by different administering nations and subject to different forms and varying rates of development. Both suffer severe demographic and resource problems, but their nature and the ways in which they are approached contrast. Today the two Samoas constitute small models evolved from a uniform cultural base, but with strikingly different physical, political, and economic forms. Since cultural vaiables are commonly least amenable to quantitative approaches, these models provide an unusual opportunity to test the numerical effects of different methods of administration and economic development. In this paper the contrasting situations relating to population and resources are to be examined and some of the principles isolated.

Eastern Samoa includes Tutuila and the Manu'a group of islands; Western Samoa includes Upolu and Savai'i. Both parts differ physically and at the time of partition were in all ways unequal. The eastern area, taken over by the United States, was small, steep, poor, and politically unimportant compared with the area seized by Germany. The western islands, although only 2823 km² (1090 square miles) were the center of the traditional political organization and are still of much greater intrinsic value.

American interest in Samoa was initially strategic and military, and a naval station was constructed at Pago Pago on Tutuila. Interest in the rest of the area, only about 197 km² (76 square miles), was slight, and direct interference with the Samoans was avoided. On the western side, the potential economic resources were recognized as much greater. The German administration fostered commercial plantations and regulated the customary agriculture of Samoan villages, demanding expansion and modified operating methods. Since the objectives of the German Empire and the traditional Samoan political structure conflicted, the latter was severely restricted and modified by the colonial administration. Repression of the ancient Samoan political organization persisted until 1914, when troops from New Zealand occupied Western Samoa. The results were contrary to those anticipated: Samoan political structure congealed and persisted, acting as a bulwark against social and economic change. Movement toward the disintegration of Samoan custom was much freer in American Samoa, yet Western Samoa has been independent since 1962 and the colonial status of the former shows little sign of being altered.

Population Growth

Before foreign intervention, the Samoan population was one and, although data are almost nonexistent, there is no reason to believe that significant differences existed between the eastern and western islands. Contact with alien diseases introduced by explorers, traders, and missionaries began a population decline which persisted until about the middle of the nineteenth century, yet the decline was less drastic, and was halted earlier than in most other South Pacific island groups.

The first population survey with a breakdown by islands was made in 1839, when

493

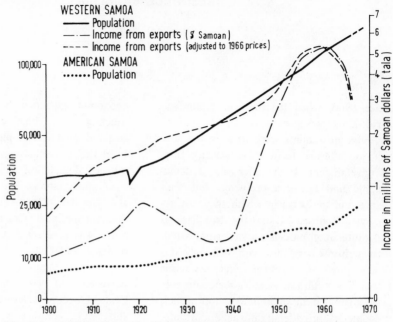

Fig. 29-1. WESTERN SAMOA: POPULATION GROWTH AND INCOME FROM EXPORTS. AMERICAN SAMOA: POPULATION GROWTH

Commodore Wilkes, of the U.S. Exploring Expedition, estimated 47,000 persons for western Samoa, and 10,000 for eastern Samoa. These figures were derived from the early missions, and cannot be regarded as very reliable. Whatever the population at this date, a "census" taken by the London Missionary Society (L.M.S.) enumerated only 40,000 for the whole group in 1845. In 1853 another island by island count, probably the first reliable one, indicated a total of 29,237 persons in western Samoa and 4664 in the eastern islands. Political conditions were extremely turbulent in western Samoa, but eastern Samoans avoided most of the violence, and from 1843 on, their numbers are said to have gradually increased. In Manu'a an average annual increase of 1.5 per cent was recorded between 1853 and 1862. In one of these years, 1854-55, a careful count was kept by a resident missionary, who noted a crude birth rate of 42°/₀₀, and a crude death rate of 20°/₀₀. The

2.2 per cent rate of increase, although based on a very small population and noted over a short time span, implied that even then a substantial increase of population was feasible given missionary guidance and freedom from epidemic disease and civil disorder. By about 1860, population decline in western Samoa seems to have been arrested, and a tendency to increase becomes evident.

By the time of partition eastern Samoa's population had increased to 5,679. In western Samoa, the figure was about 34,500, including significant part-Samoan and "European" components, and more than 800 Melanesians working as indentured laborers on commercial plantations. Both populations had increased between 1853 and 1900, but in spite of the addition of several alien groups into western Samoa, the more completely Samoan population on the eastern side had increased more quickly—22 compared to 18 per cent over the 47 years or 0.43 and 0.35 per cent per year respectively.

Modern medical care was introduced to Samoa in the 1860's when a doctor from the London Missionary Society began work in the western islands. Missions continued to play the most important role in fostering public health (and subsequent population growth) until well into the twentieth century, although both the American and German navies had established public health facilities for the Samoans by the early 1900's. The Americans located services on Tutuila and Manu'a, while the Germans established two hospitals, one the gift of a philanthropist, in Apia. Vital statistics for this period are highly unreliable, but accelerating population increase in both territories indicated that contact with foreign concepts of health and hygiene were increasingly effective.

From 1900 to 1918, the population of Western Samoa increased to about 42,500, and that of American Samoa to about 7800, an average annual rate of 1.1 and 1.8 per cent respectively. This was a significant acceleration from the previous period, but the discrepancy between the eastern and western isles was, if anything, greater, in spite of the influx of more than 1500 Chinese laborers into Western Samoa between 1903 and 1918. In Western Samoa the growth rate for Samoans was only about 0.5 per cent, and the greater success of the U.S. Navy in applying modern medical techniques to their small area is apparent.

The year 1918 saw a pandemic of virulent influenza sweep the world. The disease was introduced into Western Samoa by ship from New Zealand and the ensuing epidemic is reported to have taken 20 per cent of the total population in a seven-week period, bearing heavily upon adults of reproductive age, particularly males. The disruptive effect of this epidemic was an unfortunate beginning for the New Zealand administration, at this time just becoming organized since

their take-over in 1914. Forewarned, the authorities in Pago Pago successfully quarantined American Samoa, which became one of the few areas in the world to escape the pandemic: Western Samoa showed a rate of mortality not exceeded anywhere.

By this time public health was well advanced in American Samoa, and naval medical officers were stationed not only in Pago Pago but also in rural centers, including Manu'a. Vaccination had been a regular procedure for nearly two decades. Hookworm had been the subject of an eradication campaign, and the outhouses built on stilts over the beaches, now characteristic of the Samoan landscape and providing for simple and effective sanitation, first made their appearance in American Samoa in 1909. Gonorrhea, previously a problem, had been controlled. Pure water had been supplied to a large number of villages in the mistaken idea that it would reduce filariasis; it did greatly assist in the control of genuinely water-borne diseases. Pneumonia, tuberculosis, typhoid, and dysentery remained major health problems; but within the limits of contemporary medical knowledge, American Samoa was a model of tropical public health.

On the New Zealand side, the new administration began its public health program under a cloud—the odium persisting after the 1918 epidemic. But in 1921, a program similar to that instituted in American Samoa was initiated, and much effort went toward its success. Under the program, Samoans were enlisted to do most of the work involved in public health education, treatments, and in nursing and routine inspections. "Women's Committees" were established among the leading women of each village, an innovation which fostered strong interest in the project. The work of the administration was notable for introducing up-to-date medical techniques, reducing environmental and epidemic diseases and lowering mortality. Lambert, an American doctor working for the Rockefeller Foundation in the South Pacific, described the program in 1926 as "unexcelled in the tropics," and public health authorities throughout the tropical world noted that similar programs might be successfully applied to other areas.

Infant mortality was reduced from more than 200°/$_{oo}$ live births before 1924 to a mean rate of 79°/$_{oo}$ between 1926-30. The crude death rate was reduced from an average of 35°/$_{oo}$ between 1906 and 1917 to 13°/$_{oo}$ by 1927. Although the levels cannot be calculated, expectation of life obviously increased, and the proportion of death over ten years as a proportion of total deaths rose from 29 to 48 per cent. Population growth exceeded 3 per cent annually between 1924 and 1927.

Just how fragile such success can be was demonstrated in Western Samoa between 1927 and 1936 during the "Mau," a civil disobedience movement in which a large proportion of the Western Samoans refused to co-operate with the New Zealand administration. The sources of contention were mainly political and economic; but the work of the Health Department was greatly hindered and inspection, control, and registration in the affected districts virtually ceased. After 1931, infant mortality resumed an average level of more than 100°/$_{oo}$ and in 1936, an epidemic year, the rate rose to 292°/$_{oo}$. Thereafter, political conditions mended, and the effectiveness of the Health Department expanded again. Mortality control was steadily improved. At the outbreak of World War II, infant mortality was back to an average of 77 for three years centering on 1939 and to 65 annually by 1945.

Throughout the period preceding World War II, population growth was maintained at a high level, and between 1920 and 1940 in spite of the disturbances and interrup-

tions to peaceful administration, Western Samoa showed a mean annual rate of 2.7 per cent, exceeding American Samoa's rate of 2.4 per cent.

After World War II, the administrations of the two territories began to diverge more widely in methods and aims. A United Nations Trusteeship replaced the New Zealand administration in Western Samoa and presaged a movement toward independence. But the American side suffered increasing neglect. World War II had demonstrated the peripheral location of the naval base at Pago Pago, and in 1951, American Samoa joined Guam and the New Trust Territory of the Pacific Islands as a responsibility of the Department of the Interior. The base was closed, and the principal economic resource of the area thus vanished. Over a thousand Samoans followed the Navy to Hawaii in 1952, alternative economic opportunities for former naval employees being virtually nonexistent.

Between 1950 and 1960, population growth in American Samoa fell to 0.6 per cent annually. A special census taken in 1956 showed that even the small growth recorded was concentrated in the first six years of the decade since between 1956 and 1960 the population actually declined. Throughout the period, fertility remained extremely high, and the stagnation was entirely due to emigration to Hawaii, the U.S. mainland, and even Western Samoa.

Since 1960, the American Samoan population has resumed its growth. The most recent figures (1967) show a total of 24,513 persons, a growth rate of 2.9 per cent annually. Although an influx of American administrators and technicians recruited to initiate government programs has swollen the population, the increase is due largely to a slowing down of emigration in response to improved economic conditions and better employment opportunities, and immigration from Western Samoa.

In 1948, a United Nations report on the population of Western Samoa found that its growth rate was one of the highest recorded during the last few decades in any country in the world; yet at that time the truly spectacular nature of the Samoan ability to grow in numbers was scarcely apparent. The average annual increase between 1945 and 1956 was 3.3 per cent in spite of some net emigration. Between 1956 and 1961, emigration, mainly to American Samoa and New Zealand, began to deplete the population significantly; but the intercensal rate remained at 3.3 per cent annually, and the natural rate rose to 3.9. Preliminary results for the 1966 census show that while the natural rate was still climbing (by then it had risen to 4 per cent annually), migration had become a major element in determining population numbers locally. Between 1961 and 1966, nearly 7500 people left the country; 4500 migrated to New Zealand alone. The actual population in Western Samoa, 131,-379, showed the average annual growth rate reduced to 2.7 per cent.

The course of population growth in the two parts of Samoa reflects the differential working of several forces:

(i) The success of colonial administrations in maintaining law and order, providing public amenities, and fostering economic development. The degree of success is strongly reflected in the rates of population growth.

(ii) Decreasing mortality as medical services have increased in intensity, distribution, and effectiveness.

(iii) The relative immunity of the Samoan population to factors which could lower fertility.

(iv) The availability of opportunities for overseas emigration.

While there remains room for improvement in the control of mortality in both American and Western Samoa, and the trend toward lowered rates will undoubtedly continue, the persistence of extremely high rates of natural increase has focused attention on the present and future relationships between population and the physical and social resources locally available. In the early 1950's, both administrations became increasingly concerned with economic development, in American Samoa because of the abrupt removal of the Navy payroll, in Western Samoa because of impending independence.

Economic Development: American Samoa

The physical resources of both groups are very limited, and of the two, American Samoa has the least. Its total land area is only 19,900 hectares (49,200 acres), of which Tutuila, the largest island, comprises 13,700 hectares (33,900 acres). Of this area, only 5700 hectares (14,000 acres), or 28 per cent of the total area, is used for agriculture. About 2250 hectares (5,600 acres) are permanently planted in coconut palms, the rest mainly in subsistence crops, particularly banana, taro, and breadfruit.

The only significant agricultural cash product is copra, of which 720 tons was exported in 1964, an average year. The value was only $5.60 per capita. Production ran at about 2000 tons annually in the first decade of American administration and rose to 3000 tons in the years immediately following World War II, but since then has declined and is now even less than in 1900, the first year in which copra was exported for tax purposes.

The decline in agricultural cash cropping after 1945 is typical of American administered territories in the Pacific. There may be token efforts at bolstering traditional systems through agricultural extension and education, but the effect of alternative opportunities in employment at relatively high wages proves overwhelming. Recently, efforts of the Department of Agriculture have been strictly commercial: truck crops and livestock and poultry raising, using scientifically based systems developed in Hawaii. Such activity is almost completely foreign to traditional Samoan agriculture, but it does seem to offer the only economically feasible and durable way of utilizing agricultural land.

At present, American Samoa does not grow enough food for its own population and must import from Western Samoa and Tonga. The main deficiency is in taro, and it is estimated that only half of the necessary quantity is produced locally. This and other subsistence foods are being increasingly supplemented by imported products, such as bread, which must now be classed as a staple.

Alternatives to customary subsistence agriculture began with opportunities for employment in the U.S. Navy and the local administration. In 1951 when the Navy moved from American Samoa, the new civil administration faced a grave economic crisis. Improvement came slowly, but a turning point was reached in 1954 when a tuna-canning factory and a base for the attendant fishing fleet were established in Pago Pago. Local transportation improved, an air service from Hawaii was established, and ships began calling more frequently. While one of the consequences of an improved transport system was an exodus from American Samoa, economic conditions in the territory generally improved, and the inward flow of money increased.

A major economic revolution began in 1962, when under the threat of an impending international meeting, the Fifth South Pacific Conference, the government of American Samoa sprang into sudden action.

A general cleanup was started and a jet runway, a large auditorium, a power plant, and a new highway connecting the airport with Pago Pago were completed with a speed not previously experienced in the territory. The "grant-in-aid" by the U.S. Government rose to nearly $9.5 million in 1962. The previous year the grant had been $2.1 million, and had only reached this level after a steady increase from less than $600,000 in 1952, the first year of civil administration. The current level of Federal subsidy is approximately $18 million annually, or $730 per capita. With such a resource, a South Pacific territory scarcely needs any other. However, much of this capital has been invested in areas which will promote economic growth. In a revolutionary approach to rapid and massive improvement, the entire educational system was built around television. The method has been in use since 1965, and is still in a pioneering stage; but the indications are that it will be successful in its aim to enable Samoans to compete on terms of equality in the modern world. Although officially described as "an extension of the 'Samoa for the Samoans' policy to education," the revised system, which emphasizes the English language, will help those who migrate to adjust more easily to their new surroundings. Many of the social and economic problems confronting migant groups in Hawaii and the U.S. mainland stem from inadequate educational preparation in American Samoa.

Public works have also absorbed large amounts of capital since 1962. Most schools have been replaced by elaborate structures suited to the local climate. A large modern hospital is being built. The road system has been extended, asphalt-coated, and brought up to high-speed standards. Electricity and water supplies have been greatly expanded. The telephone system was redesigned and a sewerage system installed in the Pago Pago

Bay area. Government housing was built to quarter the incoming stateside employees in the manner to which they are accustomed. An attractive international jetport was completed. The new television system entailed the building of studios and a central facility as well as a transmitting station situated on one of the prominent peaks towering above Pago Pago harbor. The aerial tramway slung across the Bay to provide access to the site is now a tourist attraction and provides one of the more spectacular, if alarming, rides in the world. A destructive hurricane in 1966 was the pretext for a government scheme replacing a large part of traditional Samoan housing (*fales*) with modern permanent structures designed to withstand high winds.

Other major developments that have affected the economy were the opening of a second fish cannery and a can manufacturing plant in 1963. The export of canned tuna and fish byproducts now bring in between $400 and $500 per person annually, even though the catch is made by more than 1500 foreign fishermen, mainly Japanese, Korean, Okinawan, and Nationalist Chinese. The canneries employ some 800 local persons, and are among the largest employers, second only to the government. Fish prod-

ucts now account for about 98 per cent of all export income.

An industry which promises major economic benefits not only for American Samoa, but for several other neighboring groups, particularly Tonga and Western Samoa, is coconut processing. Construction of a new plant was started in 1964, but the project failed because of technical and financial difficulties. The concept of linking the islands of West Polynesia in a joint commercial enterprise remains a good one, however, and deserves to be revised.

American Samoa has also begun to expand its tourist industry, and a large new hotel, catering to "carriage-trade" tourists, has been operating now for two years with growing success. The hotel is owned by local Samoan investors and provides employment for more than 100 persons. The tourist industry is in its initial stage and will undoubtedly grow into a major employer and earner of overseas revenue. During its first year of operation, the hotel drew nearly $1 million into the islands, and the tourist numbers are showing a spectacular increase.

The nature of economic development in American Samoa has caused much of the income flowing into the territory to flow swiftly out again, without circulating or do-

TABLE 29-1   AMERICAN SAMOA: CHILD-WOMEN RATIOS, 1930-1967

	No of Children 0-4	*Women 15-44 No. of*	*Ratio*	*Standard Error*
1930	2,059	2,129	967	22
1940	2,705	2,686	1,002	19
1950	4,301	3,951	1,089	16
1956	3,734	4,108	909	16
1960	3,709	3,964	936	16
1967	3,680	4,955	743	14

Source: Department of Medical Services, American Samoa.

ing much good for the inhabitants. Nevertheless, this surge of governmental and commercial activity has caused employment oportunities to expand and now one person in five is in paid full-time employment. Given the American Samoan population with a median age below 20, it is probable that at least 90 per cent of Samoan males in the working-age range have paid employment. Thus, traditional agriculture is no longer a significant component in the economy, although only a decade ago it was the principal form of employment for all adult Samoans.

In the past American Samoa was a classic example of retarded economic development compounded by remoteness and miniscule size. In 1952, when over-all population density was 102/km^2 and inhabitation density (agriculturally used land per person of total population) was less than 0.32 hectares, it appeared that an extreme case of excessive population pressure on a totally and permanently inadequate resouce base existed. But a sudden, massive infusion of outside capital and technical assistance has propelled the territory toward prosperity, sustained economic growth, and eventual self-support at a high level.

The doubts that Samoans may have about retaining their traditional culture under the pressure of material progress are seldom voiced, even by the younger people. Eco-

nomic activity has increased to at least twelve times the level of 1952—a difficult basis for dissent.

The demographic trends caused by development are still not very obvious. Public health has greatly improved and the crude mortality rate—7.1°/$_{oo}$—is very low for a tropical country with an infant mortality rate that approximates 30°/$_{oo}$. These characteristics continue the long-time trend. Fertility continues to be extremely high in spite of recent economic progress and increasing monetization of the local economy. Although there appears to be a decline in fertility, particularly among women in the 15-24 age range, the trend is recent and has not yet attained a level of statistical significance. A program sponsored by the Health Department toward family limitation, using the I.U.D., has been underway since 1965 on a small scale.

The child-woman ratio has shown some decline since 1950, but since 1960 the pace has accelerated. This decline, although significant statistically, is related in part to the decreasing number of women in the 25-34 age range. To be convincing, the implied decline in fertility needs to be reflected in the age-specific fertility rates. In the past, annual rates have not shown a significant or consistent downward trend. Nevertheless, a lowering in the child-woman ratio may be expected, since economic development in

TABLE 29-2   WESTERN SAMOA: CHILD-WOMEN RATIOS, 1951-61

	No. of Children	No. of Women	Ratio	Standard Error
1951	15,286	17,937	852	7
1956	18,809	19,417	969	7
1961	23,232	21,840	1,064	7
1966	25,903	23,851	1,086	6

Source: P. Pine: *The Population of Western Samoa: A Preliminary Report Based on the 1956 Census* (The Australian National University). Multilithed.

American Samoa is typically urban and there are indications that the fertility rate is lower among urban dwellers. The metropolitan area of Pago Pago contains a population of approximately 8500 persons (or 35 per cent of the total); but the opportunities for paid employment extend over a much wider area.

Economic Development:
Western Samoa

As an example of economic development along traditional lines, Western Samoa provides a striking contrast to the fast-developing American territory.

The economy of the area has always been heavily agricultural, and in contrast to American Samoa, this characteristic seems likely to continue indefinitely. The original subsistence activities of the villages, mainly growing taro and coconuts, have been expanded into a semicommercial organization whereby coconut, cacao, banana, and taro are grown for export as well as subsistence. Other crops are also produced, but on a very small scale.

Of the total area of Western Samoa, 284,000 hectares (702,000 acres) about 142,000 (350,000 acres) are cultivable, of which 69,500 hectares (171,500 acres) or nearly half are already in agricultural use (1965). This represents an increase of 17,000 hectares (41,500 acres), or 32 per cent since 1956 when a land-use survey, using air-photographs as a base, established the exact extent of land under cultivation. Since the methods of measuring later areal expansion have not relied on aerial photography, they are likely to be less precise. The bulk of this land is cultivated according to Samoan village custom, but 11,300 hectares (28,000 acres) are in commercial agiculture, mainly coconut and cacao plantations or cattle ranches. Around the vil-

lages, land-use patterns tend to be extremely irregular, with each *aiga* or extended family holding several plots, usually widely dispersed, and in different crop zones.

Of the total area cultivated, about 41 per cent is in coconut palms (0.18 hectares or 0.45 acres per person)—nearly double the equivalent area in American Samoa. The yearly production of approximately 11,000 tons of copra has remained virtually static since the 1920's. Within the village systems, the return from copra is only $14 annually per capita, the most stable and most widely distributed income from customary agriculture. Coconut is also an important subsistence food and Samoans consume about 30 per cent of all the coconuts gathered.

Cacao is a more recently introduced crop and although it has been produced commercially since before 1900, significant village production did not begin until World War II. The crop returns an average of only $10 per capita annually under the village system. A greater proportion of the crop—about 40 per cent—is grown on commercial plantations which have somewhat higher yields, and a much greater per capita income. Cacao prices fluctuated widely in the postwar years, and have been depressed in the past few years. Only a small part of the crop is consumed within the country—virtually all of it is exported. Cacao is often planted with banana (the latter helps to shade the former), and it is impossible to separate them in land-use studies. Approximately 0.10 hectares (0.25 acres) per person are in cacao and banana plantings. The return from banana exports has also fluctuated, reaching $28 in 1958, but declining to $13 per capita in 1965. The total return per hectare from cacao and banana, presently the most profitable crops, is between $222 and $234 annually ($90-$95 per acre).

In early 1966, a hurricane devastated the banana crop in Western Samoa and seriously damaged the cacao. The production of cacao recovered within the year, but the banana industry was still producing at less than a one-tenth of the normal rate a year later. The hurricane only completed a well-advanced process of decline caused by bunchytop, a virus disease which first appeared in 1956. By 1959, production had been curtailed in several districts, notably those on the south coast of Upolu, where production had been highest. The disease spread inexorably and by 1965 there was a marked decline in banana exports. The current problem is to re-establish the industry under conditions which will permit the disease to be controlled. The new plantings tend to be larger, more carefully selected stock planted in regular rows, which allow better control and at least some mechanized care. Bananas are a major staple, and an increasing proportion of the crop is consumed locally.

The only other crop exported in significant quantity is taro. This is a recent development, for only since Samoans and other Pacific islanders started to migrate to New Zealand was there a market for the product. The decline of subsistence agriculture and advancing economy in American Samoa should create another permanent market. Other potential outlets are Hawaii and the U.S. mainland, but the lack of direct shipping is a major problem. Possibilities for greater expansion depend on the solution of transportation and marketing difficulties. At present the trade is small, bringing only about $2.60 per capita in 1965. Other minor agricultural crops exported include papaya, avocado, mangoes, capsicums, kapok, and whole coconuts.

Livestock raising is not well developed although considerable potential exists on land higher and wetter than the land currently used for agriculture. Samoan villagers keep pigs and poultry and cows on a sub-sistence basis, but livestock raising is not encouraged by the present village land tenure system. The only really successful cattle raising takes place on a few enclosed ranches operated by non-Samoans. The raising of poultry for eggs and meat for the local market has begun on a small scale and shows promising development.

Although agricultural soils of Western Samoa are of high initial fertility, being derived for the most part from recent basaltic parent material, with a rich and varied mineral assemblage, there is some question of their continued use under the present system. The growing of taro and even bananas for export using shift and fallow techniques has led to depleted fertility and, in some cases, actual exhaustion (27). The pattern of village agriculture has a strong centrifugal tendency, leading in many villages to the destruction of most, and in a few cases, such as Mulifanua, all reserve forest land. The agricultural system replacing such natural cover often is not stable, and the area reverts to grasses and creepers. Meanwhile the land planted permanently to coconut and cacao also shows signs of exhaustion. These soils have been cultivated longer than any others in Western Samoa, and have now been seriously overused, so that along the northeast coast of Upolu, for instance, the land is almost devoid of plant nutrients. Inland, the new soils being cleared are of progressively lower initial fertility as rainfall and altitude increase.

Crop yields are tending to decrease. It is becoming apparent that the extensive system of soil utilization relying on natural fertility is inherently unstable; and to persist in following the system to produce export income is an extravagant use of precious resources. A change toward more intensive, perpetual methods of agriculture on the stable lowland soils is urgently necessary.

The Western Samoans grow all their main

staple foods, but import significant quantities of flour, rice, sugar, canned fish, and canned meat, to the value of about $18 per capita annually. The amounts imported are increasing at a rate above that of population growth, except for meat, which has declined —a reflection of its high cost and increasing domestic production. Canned fish imports, however, have increased very rapidly. Because the resources of the Samoan reefs are largely depleted, the people have turned increasingly to low-cost canned fish from South Africa and American Samoa.

Lumber-milling has never been a large-scale activity, and although small amounts are produced for local consumption, exports are negligible. This could change greatly as the Western Samoan Government has recently signed a contract with an American concern to mill on a large scale on Savai'i. The area selected contains the only extensive stand of large tropical lumber in the country, and it could be quickly exhausted. The development could, however, be extremely beneficial in opening up a remote but valuable part of Savai'i and inducing a permanent improvement in transport facilities. The scheme is likely to develop slowly and returns may not be significant for several years, but substantial investment capital should begin flowing in shortly. An export value of about half a million dollars annually within three years, rising to a maximum of about one million dollars thereafter, is anticipated.

The primary industries, in spite of Western Samoa's utter dependence on them, generally do not receive adequate attention or investment in any component—labor, capital, or administrative effort. With one exception, the banana-export scheme—recent governmental attempts at economic development have tended to be peripheral. At first, the Mau rebellion—a response to early attempts at reform by the New Zealand administra-

tion—was responsible for much of this inertia. This specter scarcely applies today, however, and the main reason now seems to be that projects in village agriculture that interfere with existing patterns inevitably provoke opposition and have a high risk of failure.

It has been shown by Fairbairn that the average time spent by male village workers in agriculture is scarcely more than three hours daily (6). Fertilizer and insecticides are both lightly and erratically used; less than 0.65 kg per capita of fertilizer and 57 kg of insecticides are applied each year. The Department of Agriculture, from which leadership in the primary industries must come, has never been accorded adequate attention, finance, or staffing. Only about 8 per cent of all government expenditures are devoted to the Department, thus expenditures do not exceed $4.70 per capita annually. This, however, is an increase of $3.85 from only a decade ago.

Village agriculture, which produces approximately 80 per cent of all export produce, is presently short of labor, although an increase in hours worked per man would solve this problem. The proportion of male growers is low, only 13 per cent of the total village population, and is falling as more attractive alternatives become available elsewhere.

In many rural districts, economic stringency appears to be extreme, although subsistence needs continue to be met. But monetary income has been reduced by hurricane damage, plant diseases, particularly bunchy-top in bananas, and soil depletion to levels forgotten by all but the older Samoans. While many aspects of this depression are undoubtedly temporary, it has shaken the confidence of villages in the future of agriculture as a way of life.

One burgeoning aspect of Western Samoa's monetary income are remittances from overseas emigrants to relatives at home. It is estimated that nearly $1,500,000 annually comes from New Zealand and is of major assistance to the territory in meeting its overseas payments. But New Zealand, with acute balance of payments problems of its own, has recently taken measures to stem the flow. The New Zealand Government continues to give direct aid to Western Samoa, but the amount is not large.

The Department of Economic Development, recently created by the government through concern over declining revenue, has been active in fostering secondary and tertiary industries which have been notably weak in Western Samoa. Tourism has received particular attention, after a reversal of the government policy opposing a tourist industry on the ground that it would pollute the quality of Samoan life. The lack of a direct overseas air connection is a disadvantage, but the home-based airline now has daily flights to American Samoa, which does have such service. Direct connections with Fiji and Tonga assist the stop-over tourist seeking a South Pacific tour. The large-scale tourist promotion generated by the resort hotel in American Samoa should greatly assist the Western Samoan industry, as it should occur to all but the most docile tourist, once lured down to Pago Pago, that Western Samoa is considerably more interesting—and cheaper. Existing tourist accommodations which still have some way to go to meet international standards, are being improved rapidly, and the construction of new facilities is encouraged by tax holidays of up to five years and duty-free import of materials.

Tax exemptions are also available to secondary industry, and since 1965 incentives have been extended to four food-processing companies, two small garment factories, and a sawmill. The provisions of the investment incentives scheme are very liberal, and should attract overseas capital if publicized.

Other industries already established include soap-making, furniture manufacturing, and Samoan handicrafts which are handled by a government corporation that controls design, marketing, and export of the products. The growth of handicraft export has been impressive in recent years, but still remains on a small scale.

The proportion of the work force with paid employment stayed the same between 1956 and 1961, 36 per cent at both censuses, but within the group there were significant shifts in the proportions engaged in different divisions. Commercial agriculture declined in importance while construction, manufacturing, entertainment, and other service industries all increased rapidly. The work force engaged in transportation and the professions increased at approximately the same rate as the total population. Progress since 1961 is considered modest.

The future economy of Western Samoa, even granted the success of planned developments, will be hampered by extremely high population growth and disproportionate numbers in dependent groups. While actual increases have been lowered by emigration, the 4 per cent annual level attained by natural increase is ominous. Emigrants from Western Samoa will have to number over 10,000 in the next five years, if the rate of actual growth is to be maintained. Since 1965, the Government of American Samoa has restricted the entry of Western Samoans, and, as long as a wide economic differential exists between the two areas, the limitations are likely to remain. The continued immigration of Samoans into New Zealand at the current volume is also in question. One can qualify for entry with a knowledge of English, approved housing and employment in New Zealand, and the patience to withstand the administrative bottleneck in Apia. But adverse economic conditions in New Zealand could bring the existing free entry policy into review. It is in the interests of the Samoan Government to maintain this emigrant flow even though it will inevitably mean the loss of persons educated at considerable government expense, whose talents are in short supply. Net migration is only about one-third of total migration, so that the benefits of overseas contact are spread much more widely than the net figures alone would indicate. Between 1961 and 1966, approximately 9 per cent of all Western Samoans spent some time in New Zealand; the pool of permanent migrants comprised only 3 per cent of the total population. The return benefits of migration can be considerable, Samoans are extremely mobile, and many return periodically with additional education, both formal and infomal. They are also very loyal, and send back substantial amounts of money to their families.

The alternative possibility of slowing population growth and reducing fertility does not appear very likely. Fertility remains extremely high, particularly in rural areas, and is probably still increasing. The child-woman ratio has increased at each count since age data were first taken in 1951, although the most recent increase is much smaller than previous counts.

Registration of vital statistics has fallen off recently and statistics are now less reliable. The 1956 crude death rate, as derived from registration, is only $5.5°/_{oo}$, but the estimated rate, $8.0°/_{oo}$, is likely to be nearer to the truth. The registration of both births and infant deaths is so unreliable that infant mortality, officially $40°/_{oo}$ live births, is very suspect, More sure is the fact that the rate, whatever it is, has been rising since 1962, when it was officially $20°/_{oo}$—an extremely improbable level. In the absence of reliable data, an exact description of fertility and mortality characteristics cannot be made; but it seems certain that fertility is static or has increased only slightly since 1956. Deterioration in the standards of rural public health in the last five years, a falling off in the quality of registration, and the somewhat flimsy evidence of increasing infant mortality are used here as indications that mortality, although low by regional standards, is increasing slightly in Western Samoa. The prospect is for continued levels of extremely high population growth which could rise to 4 per cent annually, unless mitigated by continued migration. The concepts of family limitation have not dispersed far, particularly outside Apia. The Health Department has no policy on family planning, and little is being done to prepare the ground for one. Only one of the problems to be dealt with is the considerable prejudice against the idea of limiting family size, something considered to be contrary to tradition by Samoans of all religious persuasions.

The processes of monetization and urbanization, so conspicuous in American Samoa, are moving much more slowly in Western Samoa, and are less likely to affect the fertility levels of the population. Apia, the only town, has about 25,500 persons, and is about 3.2 per cent annually—only a modest rate. The proportion of Western Samoans living there increased only from 19.0 per cent in 1961 to 19.3 per cent in 1966.

The U.S. Peace Corps intends to send more than 100 volunteers into Western Samoa in 1967 and to continue the program for several years thereafter. This form of assistance could be very effective, but preliminary plans suggest that the main emphasis will be in the areas of health and education with public works and agriculture taking a lesser role. While all these areas can usefully be improved, it seems as though the peripheral nature of past attempts is to be repeated. The core of resource-population problems is in agriculture, and it is in this field that the first solutions must be found. The manpower characteristic of the Peace Corps seems favorably suited to elementary agricultural demonstration and technique dispersal, which are the most pressing needs.

Conclusion

Western Samoa's resource problems are not yet as weighty as those of American Samoa were after the U.S. Navy departed in 1951. Habitation densities are still much lower, and about half the cultivable land, but the poorer half, remains to be developed. Yet the present depressed condition after hurricane, bunchytop disease, and low commodity prices does bear many parallels to the situation of American Samoa at that time.

American Samoa has not provided a model of economic and demographic development that Western Samoa, or any other developing country at a similar stage, has any real hope of emulating. Its continuing connection with the United States, evidenced by the latter's recent willingness to supplement expenditures so generously, is undoubtedly the territory's major resource.

The rate of development should be viewed as a demonstration of the inherent power of capital investment and government spending to overwhelm traditional social, political, and economic barriers. The scale and speed involved are not likely to be duplicated elsewhere, although other American territories —Guam, the Trust Territory of the Pacific Islands, and even Puerto Rico—have already been exposed in a lesser way to this type of approach. These areas stand to benefit even further if the American Samoan development model is applied to them. The effect of the nuclear testing site at Muroroa on French Polynesia shows relevant similarities. Further examples of small populations that have received exceptional economic assistance from local resources are those of Kuwait and Nauru.

Western Samoa lacks almost entirely the prospect of such advantages. Investment capital is always short and is likely to remain so; the prospect that government expenditure, currently about $7,000,000, might equal the $90,000,000 invested in American Samoa seems extremely unlikely. External capital has also been difficult to secure, as shown by the failure of the government to secure a $1,000,000 loan from U.S. sources in 1966. In the absence of better opportunities, it appears that the government of Western Samoa is moving along a wisely chosen course, stimulating investment in tourism, lumber, and small-scale manufacturing. It has certainly shown itself to be more flexible and enterprising in economic development planning than the Trusteeship administration it replaced. This strategy could be criticized as one that benefits most those who need enrichment least—the urban business elite, most of whom are of part-European ancestry. It remains true that the government is not devoting enough attention to the more mundane problems of agriculture. The needed changes, including radical new techniques of intensive commercial agriculture, and modification of the land tenure system, will require considerable educational preparation. The same is true of family planning.

Of great possible significance is a change in policy forced, ironically, by the bunchytop disease, which has recently caused a disastrous decline in banana production. Under the New Zealand administration, the traditional system of land tenure, characterized by ownership of an extended family, flexibility, and loose definition, has been progressively modified toward greater rigidity and individualization. The model of the family farm lay in the minds of most New Zealand administrators whenever they considered policies for improving agricultural land-holding systems. In Samoa, such a trend, which is admittedly still in its early stages, eventually implies a depressed peasant-type of agriculture based on units subject to subdivision by inheritance. The results of such a descending spiral may be observed in the agrarian populations of Asian countries where excessive densities have built up, creating problems of economic development.

One of the major factors promoting the trend toward small-holdings in Western Samoa was the banana-producing scheme—one of the more successful and useful innovations of the New Zealand administration. Yet if the banana industry is to survive, a village-wide, profit-sharing system based on incorporated units, employing modern methods of production, and supervised by a Department of Agriculture and Marketing, must be established. The advantages of this system may extend to cacao and other crops.

Western Samoa has been lucky twice before. The lateness of her submission to European colonialism permitted her to receive most of the better effects of this form of government and few of the worse. When independence came, experience accumulated from the same processes elsewhere ensured that the Samoan transition would be uncommonly smooth. It is possible that preservation of the archaic, communal form of landholding and agriculture would be a concealed blessing. Such a system is easier to convert to modern forms of controlled, relatively large-scale agriculture than is the rigid small-holding pattern.

Many opportunities are available to Western Samoa for intensification of agriculture —as a supplier of tropical produce for New Zealand, or as a source of subsistence foods for Samoans throughout the Pacific. But in the short term, the future of the country seems all too clear; a continued dependence on agriculture of generally low productivity. The production of a small number of tropical export crops, vulnerable to market fluctuation, pests, diseases, and occasional weather disasters, will continue to be the major characteristic of the economy. Any advances will be won in the face of continued excessive rates of population growth. The slowness of development, when compared with the induced prosperity across the strait in American Samoa will become a source of bitterness, that the feeling of pride in Samoan culture and independence may not fully compensate.

REFERENCES

(1) American Samoa, Department of Medical Services: Annual Report, Fiscal years 1964-65 and 1965-66 (Pago Pago).

(2) Ward Barrett: Agriculture of Western Samoa (Ph.D. dissertation, University of California, Berkeley, 1959).

(3) Chamber of Commerce of Western Samoa: Fourteenth Annual Report, (year 1945) (Apia, 1946).

(4) B. L. Clare: A Review of Social, Labour and Economic Conditions in Western Samoa (Government of Western Samoa, Apia, 1964), mimeographed.

(5) John Cole Cool: Census of American Samoa September 25, 1956, Government of American Samoa (Pago Pago, 1957 ?).

(6) Ian J. Fairbairn: The National Income of Western Samoa, 1947-1958, (Ph.D dissertation, Australian National University, 1963), microfilm.

(7) Bryan Farrell: Perspective on Land Use—American Samoa, *Journal of the Graduate Research Center*, Vol. XXXIV, No. 3, June 1965, Southern Methodist University, Dallas, Texas.

(8) The Governor of American Samoa: Annual Report to the Secretary of the Interior, 1952-64 (Washington, D. C.).

(9) John A. C. Gray (Capt.): Amerika Samoa: A History of American Samoa and its United States Naval Administration (Annapolis, 1960).

(10) Kathleen Jupp: Report on the Population Census 1956 (Apia, 1958).

(11) S. M. Lambert: A Yankee Doctor in Paradise (Boston, 1941).

(12) O. Lemieux: U.N. Advisor to Government of Western Samoa on 1966 Census of Population. Personal Communication.

(13) B. A. Lockwood: A Study of the Apia Market, unpublished (Australian National University, 1966 ?), mimeographed.

(14) Norma McArthur: Introducing Population Statistics, South Pacific Commission and the Australian National University (Melbourne, 1961).

(15) Norma McArthur: The Populations of the Pacific Islands, Pt. IV, Western Samoa and the Tokelau Islands and Pt. V, American Samoa (The Australian National University, Canberra, 1956).

(16) New Zealand: Report by the New Zealand Government to the General Assembly of the United Nations on the Administration of Western Samoa, 1956-1961, Paper A-5 (Wellington, New Zealand).

(17) Peter Pirie and Ward Barrett: Western Samoa: Population, Production and Wealth, *Pacific Viewpoint*, Vol. 3, No. 1, 1962, pp. 63-96.

(18) Peter Pirie: The Geography of Population in Western Samoa (Ph.D. dissertation, Australian, National University, 1964), multilithed.

(19) P. Pine: The Population of Western Samoa: A Preliminary Report Based on the 1956 Census (The Australian National University, Canberra, 1960), multilithed.

(20) V. D. Stace: Economic Survey of Western Samoa, South Pacific Commission Technical Paper, No. 91 (Noumea, 1955).

(21) J. J. Van der Goes: Report to the Government of Western Samoa on Processing and Marketing of Agricultural Products, Report No. 2030, F.A.O., United Nations (Rome, 1965).

(22) Western Samoa, Bureau of Statistics: *Statistical Bulletin,* 3rd Quarter, July-September, 1966.

(23) Western Samoa Census Commissioner's Office: Western Samoa Population Census, 1961 (Wellington, New Zealand, 1962).

(24) Western Samoa, Department of Agriculture, Forests and Fisheries, State of Western Samoa: Annual Report, 1960-1964 (Apia, Western Samoa).

(25) Western Samoa, Department of Health: Annual Report 1963 (Apia, 1964).

(26) Western Samoa, Department of Economic Development: Western Samoa's Economic Development Programme, 1966-1970 (Apia, 1966).

(27) A. C. S. Wright: Soils and Land Use of Western Samoa, Soil Bureau Bulletin 22, New Zealand Department of Scientific and Industrial Research (Wellington, 1963).

LATIN AMERICA: INTRODUCTION

Zelinsky reviews comprehensively the nature and circumstances of population pressure in Central America and the Caribbean islands, drawing upon the extensive literature that exists for these regions, and making reference to the relevant symposium papers (*C. G. Clarke, Sandner,* and *Vogt*). Growth rates are among the highest in the world, and not only have death rates declined to influence them, but there has been an upward trend in birth rates. In Cuba there has been a resurgence in the birth rate following a period of decline. Such upward trends are not common in the developing world, and the explanation for them in Middle America is not clear. Notwithstanding the problems arising from such growth the attitudes toward it throughout the area are at best *laisser faire,* with only tentative moves being made toward accepting the principle of population control.

The evidence for population pressure is largely indirect and is manifest, for example, in movements of population from certain West Indian islands to the United States and Britain (*C. G. Clarke*), and from parts of Central America to the United States. There is also rapid urban expansion, particularly in the largest cities, and especially in metropolitan and state capitals. Urban growth in Costa Rica is concentrated on San José (*Sandner*); and by 1970 the city of São Paulo in southeast Brazil will contain more than 40 per cent of the population of the state of São Paulo. While there is some evidence to show that urban life may induce a slight decline in fertility, the pressures on urban facilities are clearly evident in the spread of shanty towns in and around all the major cities (*C. G. Clarke*).

The over-all view of population pressures in Middle America "cannot help but be gloomy," and in particular instances there are islands and insular and mainland republics which are entering "pathological stages of acute population pressure" (*Zelinsky*).

From Costa Rica, *Sandner* illuminates more specifically the points put forward by *Zelinsky*. The country provides evidence of "the classical cycle of the demographic explosion." Within it are contrasts in population distribution, which are both cause and effect of growing intensification of regional variations in various social and economic factors. Simultaneously, there are areas in which *minifundism* is spreading to provide employment for additional labor, others from which there is emigration of surplus population, and marginal areas undergoing unorganized colonization. *Sandner* draws attention to the development of social tensions, associated with the economic frustrations experienced by large numbers of the population as a result of pressures. Any attempts to alleviate pressures must therefore consider not only food production, but also a much wider range of factors involved in regional development, including social resources and amenities, needed to ensure social stability.

Bonasewicz outlines the major areas of population concentration in Brazil in the introduction to his study of the state of São Paulo. One of these areas, the Northeast, is considered by *Webb* in Section III. Southern Brazil is economically the most advanced part of the country, with a history of successive migrations dating to the sixteenth century contributing to its development. Today modern and traditional sectors of the economy exist side by side, and over-all there is the economic and social dominance of the city of São Paulo. Not surprisingly, *Bonasewicz* is critical of the plantation as an organization for production. He sees improvements for the population being effected particularly through changes in the social system, with land reform playing an important role. Like *Rościszewiski* (Section IV) he is concerned with the need to remove insituational barriers to achieve the relief of population pressures.

30. THE RACE BETWEEN POPULATION AND RESOURCE DEVELOPMENT IN CENTRAL AMERICA AND THE WEST INDIES: A REVIEW OF CURRENT KNOWLEDGE AND SPECULATION

Wilbur Zelinsky

This is an attempt to explore the nature and implications of current and prospective pressures of human populations upon resources in a region of both extraordinarily rapid increases and of highly varied physical, political, cultural, and social milieux. This is a provisional statement derived from a still ongoing analysis of documents (including the contributions of C. G. Clarke, Sandner, and Vogt to the present volume), statistics, and field notes. It will be useful, however, to make explicit the rather less obvious assumptions and definitions that underlie the pages that follow.

The subject matter is viewed through the eyes of a geographer with an abiding, unbounded curiosity about the total nature of places, not merely their demographic dimensions, one who has strayed, perhaps rashly, far into the field of demography with hardly a twinge of conscience. A fairly broad background knowledge of the geography, history, and demography of the study area is assumed of the reader, so as to dispense with the usual briefing. For reasons of operational convenience, the study area consists only of Central America (including Panama) and the West Indies (including the Bahamas and the Netherlands Leeward Islands)—or Middle America minus Mexico. Regrettably, it has been necessary to exclude not only Mexico but also the Guianas and the Venezuelan and Colombian islands, even though their population-resource experiences are quite relevant.

The study area is not considered as a monolithic whole. Instead, a sharp cultural-economic dichotomy must be recognized, following Wagley (117) or, more specif-ically, Augelli (8): an Hispanic-aboriginal "Mainland," and a "Rimland," largely Negroid in race and plantation in economic orientation, an area also including the Caribbean fringe of the continent along with the Antilles. Although space is lacking for detailed regional analysis, the latter area may be split for some purposes into an Iberian component (Puerto Rico, Cuba, and the Dominican Republic) on the one hand and the remaining territories on the other; but this process could carry us beyond our present purpose down to the minute pluralities of culture and society in such places as Trinidad, the Caymans, or Saba.

It is always helpful to know precisely what one is talking about; but the concept of "population pressure upon resources" (or that related, unfortunately loaded term "over-population," herein scrupulously avoided) eludes easy capture and exact definition. The geographic, demographic, and economic literature tends to be evasive or to assume, incorrectly, that the idea is axiomatically obvious. (Fortunately, the "resource" concept has been explored vigorously and fruitfully from a variety of angles.) For the moment, the brief definition of "underdevelopment" offered by Lacoste is quite serviceable and substitutable for "population pressure":

"Fundamentally, the condition of underdevelopment within a country can be defined as a situation characterized by a persistent imbalance ["distorsion"] (or a tendency toward such an imbalance) between a relatively high rate of demographic growth and a relatively weak increase in those resources effectively available to the population (69: 188).

511

This notion of a persistent imbalance between demographic and economic growth, with the latter lagging seriously behind the former, implies close interconnection within the unholy triad: Population Pressure, Poverty, and Underdevelopment. Going a step further, this means that PPR, on any significant spatial or temporal scale, is, like underdevelopment, highly time-specific, a phenomenon appearing and becoming widespread only within reecnt decades, and also one that cannot persist indefinitely on anything resembling its current scale. The poor may have been with us always, in fairly advanced societies, but normally in the past in approximately stable number and equilibrial symbiosis with privileged groups. But now the amount of deprivation, real or perceived as such, and the number of those considered poor are growing rapidly in the "developing" lands through the combined effects of demographic process and an ascending level of material aspiration.

It is suggested that three major questions be examined briefly in the light of available evidence: (i) Does a significant degree of population pressure now exist in Central America and the West Indies? (ii) If so, what are its symptoms and effects? (iii) And what reactions and strategies have been generated by these symptoms and effects? The answers to these could furnish raw material for two more difficult inquiries: How similar or dissimilar are the two major subregions, i.e. Mainland and Rimland? And what universal postulates or questions of wider relevance can be drawn from the relationships of population to resouces in Central America and the West Indies?

Does Population Pressure Exist in Central America and the West Indies?

The fact of extremely rapid population growth, currently, in the recent past, and in the near future—an average annual increment for the region of perhaps 3 per cent—is beyond dispute. The dynamics and immediate causes of a growth rate equaling or exceeding anything observed in other extensive regions has attracted the interest of a number of scholars (including 5; 28; 36; 81; 101); and some have drawn alarming conclusions from the simple velocity and mass of change. Here, as elsewhere in the Underdeveloped World during the twentieth century, the chief mechanism for rapid increase has been a rather abrupt, major reduction in mortality (104). The variable, but consistently negative, net movement of interregional migrants has helped neutralize reproductive increase only to a minor degree. The truly extraordinary, and unexpected, factor in the explosive population gain has been a strong upward trend in birth rates in most of the countries in question. This inflation of an already quite high fertility pattern began as early as the 1920's in some places or as late as the 1940's or 1950's in others; but everywhere it seems to represent a genuine change in age-specific fertility, not merely in crude birth rates, and is not at all a statistical artifact (16; 24). Although the facts now appear indisputable, the explanation for this turn in events and the theoretical implications are obscure (57; 91; 106). In effect, then, a population basically European (if pre-modern European) in culture has proved quite receptive to innovations resulting in death control, but, unlike most other underdeveloped regions today, has responded to the initial phases of modernization with a greater production of infants than ever before. The available population projections for 1980 or later (such as 1; 43; or Miró's, quoted in Vogt, p. 173) are arithmetically startling, but will very likely prove to have been conservative.

HISTORICAL TRENDS IN NUMBERS

The bare fact that the number of people in the area under review has more than doubled in the past forty years and is likely to do so again in less than twenty-five years is quite inconclusive in its implications regarding population pressure. The statistics must be evaluated in the context of social capacities, of expansion in resources and economic output. It is also profitable to frame the present era within the perspective of demographic history. Such an exercise sets the Rimland in the sharpest contrast to the Mainland, and also summons up some fascinating problems concerning the ecological and population implications of differing cultures.

The initial size of the aboriginal population encountered by the European explorers and conquerors in either Central America or the West Indies is a question that promises to stay forever in the realm of controversy. The more cautious interpretations (the most important of which are 67 and 95) indicate numbers and densities well below those recorded currently. But I am increasingly impressed, if not wholly convinced, by those inclined to take at face value the figures of contemporary chroniclers and the roughly coincident results of reckoning the population-supporting capacity of the land in terms of aboriginal technology. Thus the claims by Vivo Escoto (119:199) and Wagner (119:244-45) of a generally dense population in Central America, including settlement in forested and lowland tracts now virtually deserted, do merit a hearing, as does Sauer's implicit acceptance of a figure of 3,000,000 for Hispaniola in 1492, values of the same order for Jamaica and Puerto Rico (100:68), and for some 2,000,000 aborigines in Panama (100:284). If these are valid figures and if the Amerindians were able to sustain large, dense populations in more or less stable fashion with little, if any, degradation of the physical environment, the fact has major theoetical implications, but offers little solace in coping with current problems and solutions in Latin America.

A categorically different demographic era began with the European intrusion into the Caribbean; and it was then that the seeds of twentieth-century distress were sown. Since the very first decade of Spanish exploitation, the Antilles have experienced chronic, often acute, demographic crises, but of a highly inconsistent character. By 1519 at the latest, the Arawak peoples of the larger islands were on the verge of extinction; and a severe labor shortage was met with the introduction of African slaves, a strategy subsequently followed by British, French, Dutch, and other European planters. The nineteenth-century abolition of the slave trade and, shortly thereafter, of slavery itself, brought about changes in labor recruitment areas without solving the 300-year-old problem of preserving population and the work force at adequate levels. Instead, the importation of East Indians, Chinese, free Africans, Filipinos, and Madeirans and other Europeans (92; 93) simply added further ethnic and racial complications to an already vexed social scene. By the late nineteenth century, however, the manpower gap was, in fact, slight or illusory in terms of the actual self-supportive capacities of the islands or the ability of the world market to absorb their commercial products. With the decisive downturn of mortality around the turn of the century, the persistently buoyant, even rising, fertility, and thus a rapid acceleration in population growth, the strain upon local resources was immediately obvious in all areas (Cuba and the Dominican Republic excepted). The West Indies had thus entered an era of incipient population pressure, moving beyond an earlier period in which effective territorial saturation was being achieved. Recognition and response to the facts were necessarily urgent, with the consequences noted below.

In Central America, the advent of the Spanish was somewhat less calamitous for native peoples than in the Antilles. If the Indians were almost wholly eliminated in eastern Panama and nearly all of Costa Rica, they did survive, after numerical losses of unknown extent, in much of highland Guatemala and in less accessible areas elsewhere. From central Guatemala southeast through Nicaragua and in central and western Panama, aboriginal groups were grievously decimated but managed to rebound later in hybrid European-Indian form, so that Mestizo populations came to dominate these lands, at least in terms of simple numbers. From a post-Conquest low, possibly around 1600, there has been an almost uninterrupted quantitative and territorial expansion of the Central American peoples (95). In geometric terms, this expansion has involved a gradual, localized filtering into the empty spaces separating sporadic clusters of settlement, or the building up of densities in well-established central nodes simultaneously with their steady oozing outward, a process probable in Nicaragua and one amply documented for Costa Rica (85; 96). Thus some three centuries of population growth and short-distance migration under pre-modern conditions merged so imperceptibly with the present period of accelerated growth that it has been difficult to realize that population numbers may be outstripping the creation and use of resources. As in much of South America, the psychology of the frontier and of wide open spaces may have outlived its usefulness.

CHANGES IN ECONOMIC PRODUCTION AND CONSUMPTION

Thus far the question of the genuine existence of population pressure in Central America and the West Indies has not been confronted except by hinting that a great increase in inhabitants within a region never notorious for general affluence offers grounds for some healthy suspicion. Although we have indirect evidence aplenty to support the thesis of significant and worsening population pressures, *direct* proof is hard to come by. This is mainly a matter of the scarcity or unreliability of the relevant data. It is only quite recently, for example, that acceptable figures for total national population have been published for some of these countries, and earlier values and trends can at best be only approximated. The spatial and temporal dimensions of other population characteristics are usually even hazier. The situation is even less satisfactory for data on national or per-capita production, income, or consumption, or realistic measures of unemployment, or underemployment. But certainly more could be done with the fragmentary evidence at hand; and systematic work in this direction is only just beginning.

In any event, the isolated bits of testimony do point, on balance, toward the existence of a worrisome degree of population pressure. In their careful statistical treatment of Central America, Ducoff and Bowles find "a heavy piling up of young men entering the labor supply during the 1950-60 decade—much in excess of job vacancies created by death or retirement from the labor force" (44:475); and Ducoff's projections through 1980 of supply and demand for jobs or for cultivated land in the same area (43) offer a quite gloomy outlook, with needs far outrunning prospective opportunity. An equally depressing report is Cumper's analysis of "Employment in Barbados" (33), one that fully documents the seriousness of unemployment, both chronic and seasonal, among young adults, the grave difficulties in finding solutions—considering the structure of economy and society—and which strongly implies a progressive deterioration of the situation. The same ill tidings emanate from Trinidad and Tobago. In his contribution to this Symposium, C. G. Clarke paints a stark, minutely detailed picture of metropolitan joblessness in Kingston and a marked intensification of the problem, at least since 1946 (C. G. Clarke, p 305 ff. ; also 23). One could wish, all too quixotically for the present, that a comparably fine-meshed study could be made, by sub-national areal units through recent decades for large parts of the study area.

The dearth of hard quantitative fact concerning levels of living and changes therein is disheartening. The prevalence of very low per-capita GNP is obvious (54:18-19). Its implications, however, are much less clear. Nonmonetary income may, of course, be grossly underrepresented in such statistics; and if severe poverty is indicated, there is no way of telling whether it results from recent population pressure or is simply a continuation of a deeply ingrained pre-modern pattern.

Such recent statistics as there are on changes in per capita product would seem to belie any suggestion of a growing disproportion between population and resource exploitation.

Index Number of Per Capita Product at Constant Prices
(1958 = 100)

Guatemala	108 (1963)	Panama	108 (1961)
Honduras	104 (1962)	Puerto Rico	138 (1963)
Jamaica	107 (1960)	Trinidad and	
Nicaragua	106 (1962)	Tobago	120 (1961)

Source: U.N. Statistical Office, 1965.

Upon more critical reflection, however, these figures lose much of their rosy hue. The values themselves may be somewhat suspect in view of the problems of accurate data collection in this particular region; their interpretation is open to all the standard caveats prevailing anywhere as to their implications for the welfare of that mythical being, the average citizen; and no allowances are made for probable changes in definitions of, or aspirations toward, minimally accept-

able levels of material well-being. Even taken at face value, these figures indicate that five of the seven countries trail behind other "developing" nations in the world as a whole, for whom an over-all statistic of 118 is reported for 1962 (again with the 1958 value = 100), and even more so with respect to the "developed" countries (121 in 1962). Only Puerto Rico and Trinidad and Tobago seem to have been keeping pace with, or beginning to catch up with, other parts of the world. What is truly disturbing is the possibility that an average per capita product statistic for a nation conceals more than it reveals, that, in actuality, the rich are getting richer while the poor are getting poorer and more numerous, with the former process slightly overbalancing the latter. Indeed, it is more likely than not that where one finds a dualistic economy, the rapid growth of manufacturing—largely for the small affluent segment of the population able to buy the product—and increase in the export of mineral, forest, marine, and agricultural products may have been greatly boosting the income of a very few domestic and alien investors, while the real incomes of most small farmers and wage earners has receded or, at best, held steady. Firm proof or disproof of this contention awaits the sort of patient, incisive probing of time series of data by industry, region, and socio-economic class that is hardly feasible as yet, except perhaps for Puerto Rico where it is least needed. In the meantime, general observation and reading render credible the suggestions that such a standstill or retrogression in the lot of the common man does indeed prevail in at least El Salvador (112), Guatemala (27), Jamaica (32; C. G. Clarke, personal correspondence, Dec. 20, 1966), or even in Central America as a whole (Vogt, p. 174).

Another line of evidence—statistics on production and consumption of foodstuffs—can be equally ambiguous. Again the basic numbers are wobbly, and it is difficult to detect genuine trends in food intake through time. It has been claimed that per-hectare, and hence per-capita, production of maize and rice has been dropping in parts of Central America (27; Vogt, p. 174). Certainly any general region-wide improvement in the cultivation and use of the basic staples seems highly unlikely; and one might claim conservatively that "the expansion of agricultural production has scarcely kept pace with the rapidly growing population" (31:1). In any case, whether levels of nutrition are rising, stable, or declining, there is little evidence of serious *quantitative* inadequacies as yet or—with the ominous possible exception of Haiti—of more than the most local or temporary threat of outright famine. In this respect Middle America still rates above sections of Tropical Africa or South Asia. The easily substantiated fact of malnutrition, i.e. of unbalanced diets, with a notable deficiency of animal protein in particular, may reflect genuine population pressure, but just as plausibly may result from culture and tradition (2).

ECOLOGICAL CHANGES

It is widely acknowledged that the impact of man upon the ecology of the West Indies and Central America has been destructive and that the rate of change may have been accelerating in recent years, except perhaps in a few relict aboriginal tracts, e.g. eastern Panama (12). Yet one cannot safely equate the degradation of biota, soils, and hydrology with population pressure—in the past at least—or use the amount of ecological mischief as a measure of such pressure. This statement does not foreclose the strong probability that in the near future the further deterioration of the physical habitat will contribute markedly to population pressure, and vice versa. In concluding his careful study of

man-induced changes in the biota of Antigua, Barbuda, and Anguilla, David Harris prognosticates that "if the increase [in population] continues unabated, and if neither nonagricultural development nor emigration provides a considerable outlet for surplus rural population, then the trend of ecological change in the islands will be toward further impoverishment" (56:131). But his analysis clearly indicates that, even if there has been acceleration in soil erosion on Antigua, most of the harm was committed long before any population surplus appeared. Similarly, Merrill reports deleterious changes in the ecology of St. Kitts and Nevis starting rather early in the post-Conquest history (77); and Johannesen chronicles a deterioration of grasslands and forest in the still lightly settled savannas of interior Honduras that began long ago (164).

Following the argument advanced by Blaut and associates for a central Jamaican community (13), soil erosion and similar ills may have been endemic within the study area for quite a while for reasons related more to social and economic organization (or disorganization?) or to cultural patterns than to the simple crush of people upon the land. There is also the simple factor of cultural maladjustment—of the inadvertent transfer of inappropriate techniques (not to mention exotic plants and animals) from one ecosystem to another—on the broadest scale from Old to New World or, more locally, as from the temperate tropical uplands to the wetter, warmer lowlands of Central America (111). Furthermore, field observations in the most crowded sections of the Guatemalan highlands, Costa Rica's Meseta Central, or the Masaya upland of Nicaragua indicate that, after centuries of intensive occupation, there is, at worst, only incipient sapping of their population-supporting capacities, while much greater havoc has been wrought in extensive pastoral zones with few inhabitants. Evidence adduced below will argue that growing population pressure can indeed generate the most regrettable ecological results; but one cannot uncritically accept environmental degeneration as clear proof of population pressure. Too many other factors are at work.

AWARENESS OF THE PROBLEM

One final, but hardly conclusive, method whereby the existence of population pressure might be tested is to look for some general awareness of a general problem among the populace. This is quite aside from an individual's realization, conscious or otherwise, of pressures obliging him to alter his work or occupational pattern or his place of residence. Setting Puerto Rico apart in a special category of its own, we find general unawareness or indifference to the problem among the rank and file, while, among the intellectuals, what articulate opinion there is seems to lean toward a pro-natalist position for a variety of historical, political, and cultural reasons (107). These prevalent attitudes seem much the same as those reported for both opinion-makers and the general population in Mexico (30; 31). Insofar as any overt official cognizance of population problems may be concerned, the dominant tone, until quite recently, has been an insouciant one, or the matter has been demurely swept under the rug. To take a few examples, an elaborate quasi-official program for Nicaragua's future development takes no real notice of its galloping rate of population increase (63); a spokesman for the Dominican Republic appears confident that the development of bountiful physical resources will circumvent a Malthusian crisis (53:viii); there appears to be absolute nonrecognition by government officials of any demographic distress in Guadeloupe (70:1018-1022), an island very likely teeming with present and potential problems; and

a U.N. observer in Jamaica, Barbados, and Trinidad-Tobago reports apathy or the mildest of interest in the need for family planning among all strata of society (75).

Even more sobering, considering its impact on the governments in question, is the attitude of the more "enlightened" members of the United States business community interested in Central American investment and development who seem to find nothing at all disagreeable about demographic trends (26) or an occasional scholar denying outright the existence of a problem (50). Rather belatedly, however, and despite many inhibiting factors, there have been some tentative steps by local governments and scholars toward noting the need for population control. Usually the concern has been with symptoms rather than with the basic dilemma for "the stirrings of public interest in population policy now visible in the region seem to owe more to a widening awareness of such consequences of high fertility in rapidly urbanizing low-income groups [abortion, child abandonment, family desertion] than to acceptance of the more general theses on the dangers of over-rapid population increase" (74:3).

Thus far a skeptical posture has been struck, almost that of devil's advocate, in reviewing arguments and evidence directly testing the existence of significant population pressure in Central America and the West Indies. Although on balance the available facts do seem to support the hypothesis, their weight is not precisely overwhelming. It is quite possible, however, that the preceding statement tells us more about the frailty of the statistics, the difficulty of devising simple, but sensitive, measures of population pressure, and perhaps the need for a better operational definition of the concept than it does about its Middle American manifestation. Nonetheless, largely on the basis of hunch and the presumed *indirect* effects discussed below, one may argue that, with the exceptions noted, the entire study area is subject to varying degrees of population pressure, from well-disguised situations such as those in Nicaragua or British Honduras to the painfully obvious crises of Haiti and many of the more minute Antilles. The areas that must be excluded, by virtue of resource expansion that exceeds population growth for the time being, are Aruba and Curaçao, the Canal Zone and a few even smaller enclaves, and, above all, Cuba. (One must waver in the case of Puerto Rico; but the signs of persistent population pressure seem too strong to ignore.) Cuba's unique position is a long-standing one. As a large, thinly occupied territory with obvious and significant economic potential, it has been a consistent net importer of migrants and laborers, at least until 1959. Since the latter part of the nineteenth century, the process of modernization and general socio-economic development appears to have been under way, if not spectacularly, at least rapidly enough to push resource development ahead of population gain. The situation today, of course, is obscure, in view of a sharp rise in fertility (89: 100-101) and a radical restructing of the economy.

The Effects of Population Pressure

If population pressure does exist in Central America and the West Indies, that fact should ultimately emerge in data on employment, income and consumption patterns, various educational and social characteristics, nutrition, and disease and mortality patterns. But this will take time, better data, and closer observation. In the meantime, some notes on indirect clues strongly suggesting pressures that are serious and, in almost every instance, worsening. Let us begin with the rural population and economy, and proceed to the urban scene.

INTERNAL MIGRATION

Accelerated expansion of the area being cultivated or grazed has occurred, particularly in Central America (99), the Dominican Republic, and Trinidad. This might be taken as a sign of healthy economic growth as in the frontier epochs of Canadian, Australian, or Siberian history, *if* the newly cleared tracts were being effectively integrated into the national economy and were contributing materially to the net worth of the country. Such a sanguine prospect is suggested, for example, for northern Honduras (87). In reality, however, the process as currently observed seems to be analogous to the multiplication of yeast cells within a nutrient medium: an impressive gain in the bulk of living protoplasm, but no semblance of a stronger more elaborate organism. As Richard Adams says of highland Indian intrusions into northern Guatemala, "la extensión à El Petén de la misma economía dual que tradicionalmente ha caracterizado al resto del pais, aumenta el problema, no lo resuelve" (3:26). The movement is clearly one induced by the squeeze on land and employment in older regions, and often sheer desperation. Thus a map showing the rates of out-migration by small areas would be a reasonably good surrogate for a map of rural population pressure.

When, as so often happens, the pioneering—haphazard and without official guidance—is the work of the ecologically ignorant in fragile, unfamiliar environments, the results can be catastrophic. Sandner has painstakingly documented the creation of a hollow frontier in Costa Rica as the highland rim of the Meseta Central has been quickly cleared, despoiled, and abandoned by onward-moving pioneers (96; 97; 98; Sandner, p. 546). The same story is told for the rest of Central America as impoverished frontiersmen drift downslope into areas that are soon severely damaged without any meaningful gain for individuals or nation (18; 111).

The outlook is somewhat less bleak for the limited number of officially planned and organized colonization projects. Frost's general conclusion in his study of pioneer colonies in Guatemala's Pacific Lowland (49) is that the projects represent appreciable progress for the individual *parcelaros*. My own limited observations lead to the suspicion that this progress is quite temporary, in view of the simple shifting downslope and automatic replication of all the acute social and economic contradictions of the crowded uplands, and that any contribution by these colonies to the national welfare is infinitesimal. An equally lugubrious verdict has been reached for the Sebol Region efforts on the other side of the country (78). Two recent studies of guided land settlement schemes in the Antilles find little reason for optimism, except perhaps in Cuba (14; 59); but Augelli finds that some of the agricultural colonies in the Dominican Republic, especially those near the Haitian border, have fared reasonably well or have at least helped in slum clearance and in slowing country-to-town movement (9). In sum, however, it appears that expanding settlement frontiers are more often symptoms of a deep-seated pathology than signs of general vigor. At the best, they are defective safety valves.

Within fully settled areas, we have only a few accounts of changes in land-use that may be prompted by increasing population pressure. Thus in highland Guatemala, strips of land between properties or along roads are being incorporated into neighboring fields, and forested or pastured slopes are giving way to patches of wheat and corn as farmers search out every available bit of land (60: 164). Tricart comments on "minifundia" as an aspect of population pressure in El Salvador (113); and the continuing fragmentation and parcelization of usable land in Haiti is well attested (122:17-19). The phenomenon is probably quite widespread by now, even though inadequately studied; but nowhere does such miniaturization of landholdings seem to have led to what might have been anticipated on theoretical grounds. It is difficult to find any upward escalation into a different mode of land-use or agricultural economy yielding a greater product per unit area, at the cost of greater labor input, a process postulated for agricultural societies with slowly growing populations (15). Neither does there seem to be any "agricultural involution" in the Javanese manner, with an ever intenser application of traditional techniques within smaller plots of land, so that yield per worker remains nearly constant as output per unit area rises steadily (51). The scattered, rather questionable figures suggest that noncommercial crop yields remain steady or have been declining somewhat, but certainly have not advanced appreciably. Indeed a mounting volume of food imports into countries such as El Salvador may be predicted (11:1, 12).

One obvious response to local inadequacies in agricultural output or job opportunities is short-distance seasonal migration to farm jobs within the country. This movement appears to be growing steadily each year in Guatemala (60), El Salvador (112: 312-15; 113), and probably elsewhere as well. Such peon transhumance does not seem to improve the lot of the migrant, but is only another interim tactic for staving off starvation. Another highly revealing phenomenon—one that cries out for careful geographical study—is the set of recent changes in rural settlement patterns: the growth of dispersed, or very loosely clustered, farm settlement; "line settlements" strung out along roads; and various types of squatter settlement (120:18-23; 121:4-5).

Despite previous warnings concerning the ambiguous meaning of ecological devastation, there have been several careful accounts clearly indicating that population pressure can be the prime cause of severe damage to the habitat, whether through the misuse of land long since in production or the local extension of cultivation or herding into marginal tracts. The situation is most dramatic in Haiti (71:268-71; 80:114-21), where the destruction has been intense and widespread; but such demographically induced vandalism is also noted for Central America in general (58:175-76; 117) and in Costa Rica (115), El Salvador (120:308-9), and Antigua (6:365) in particular.

EMIGRATION

Local population pressure has made its impact felt far beyond the shores and boundaries of individual countries as emigrants have left their homes for other lands, either briefly or permanently. Except for Cuba and Puerto Rico, places which attracted large numbers of South European immigrants during the late 1800's and early 1900's, the volume of in-movement has been slight and normally far outweighed by the continuing exodus to other parts of the world. This fact would seem to be diagnostic of poor resource development and employment opportunities, which, in turn, reflect population pressure. The subject of international migration and, particularly, emigration has generated a large literature—much larger than the few citations here would suggest—largely because of the social and political impact upon the host countries.

Within the Caribbean region, interisland and interterritorial movement has been in large part short-term or seasonal, a condition probably reflecting the precarious economic situation in both sending and receiving areas. A few growth points, temporary or otherwise, have attracted the great bulk of migrants: Aruba and Curaçao, the Canal Zone, Trinidad, the American Virgin Islands (usually as a stopover en route to the United States), the American World War II military bases, banana districts along Central America's Caribbean coast, well-developed plantation districts in the Antilles during their harvest seasons, e.g. Cuba or Guadeloupe, and, now increasingly, the major tourist centers. Some of the smaller islands have become absolutely dependent on the constant circulation of migrants and their remittances as, for example, the Cayman Islands (42:177), the Netherlands Windward Islands (65:154-60), or the British Virgin Islands, where almost the entire cash income derives from neighboring American St. Thomas—plus the sales of postage stamps and receipt of money orders from emigrants on the North American mainland (7:52). For the larger islands, the export of people to Europe, North America, or, to a much lesser degree, Venezuela has been essential for maintaining any semblance of balance between population and resources (35; 90; 94) or, in the case of Puerto Rico, its great leap forward toward modernization (48). Internal pressures are beginning to spark outward movements even in places like Guadeloupe (70:1023-26), where they had been insignificant until quite recently. That these movements have been selective as to characteristics of migrants and effect on the residual population is quite obvious and has been a topic carefully scrutinized by various scholars (e.g. 83; 109), but one beyond our immediate concern.

Less visible than the numerous departures from the West Indies is the increasing volume of persons moving among the Central American republics or beyond their borders to the United States, Mexico, and elsewhere. Nonetheless, there has been a sizable movement of Salvadoreans (largely illicit and unrecorded) to Honduras, Nicaraguans and

Panamanians into pioneer zones of Costa Rica (103), or Guatemalans into Chiapas. The last two population censuses in the United States record a sharp rise in the number of persons born in the study area (aside from Puerto Rico, the Virgin Islands, and the Canal Zone), and arriving from Central America as well as the Antilles. One can only speculate as to the processes of selection operating in these movements.

RESIDENTS OF THE UNITED STATES
BORN IN STUDY AREA, 1950 AND 1960
(exc. U.S. possessions)

	West Indies	Central America	Total
1950	53,210	22,295	75,505
1960	196,702	46,169	242,871

The cumulative weight of these facts of migration and other putative symptoms of population pressure leaves no reasonable doubt that there is a serious and worsening imbalance between population and resources in Central America and the West Indies.

Reactions and Strategies

The perception of population pressures, whether clearly articulated or not, has helped initiate a number of programs and policies that might sooner or later correct the situation. Our approach to these various strategies is complicated by the fact that both motivation and effect are mixed in nature. Seldom is an ameliorative process prompted solely by dread of population pressure; and never is the outcome confined entirely to slowing population growth or augmenting resource creation. We have already seen how private and public awareness of an impending crisis has generally lagged well behind the actual facts. Consequently, most attitudes seem to stem from ignorance, indif-

ference, or a blithe confidence in the abundance of the country's natural wealth or the benevolence of supernatural forces. Nonetheless, the belated governmental organization of agricultural colonization in a few countries and a general, at least tacit, encouragement of emigration already noted, reveal a dawning knowledge of the dimensions of the problem. But what else is being done?

THE STRATEGY OF URBANIZATION
Quite spontaneously, the pressures of an inadequate rural economy are propelling migrants to nearby cities. Rapid urbanization is now a universal phenomenon, of course, and one compounded from many causes; but here one may argue that the push of agrarian poverty is rather more real than the pull of metropolitan advantage, and the rush to town perhaps more headlong than in most other underdeveloped areas (45; 102). In any event, the recent trend has been for the larger cities—and the capital most particularly—to grow more swiftly than the smaller ones, especially in Central America and Puerto Rico. The result is a top-heavy urban hierarchy, a further reinforcement of that metropolitan primacy which has been so widespread in Latin America (17). This domination of the country by a single large city—not alone in simple population size, but even more in terms of social, economic, and cultural function—is a familiar heritage of early Spanish colonial practice in much of this area (38), but is much more recent in the British and French islands, where it postdates the disappearance of plantation slavery.

An apparently endless controversy rages as to whether the macrocephalic primate city is parasitic upon the national economy or whether it represents an efficient response to the problems of organizing society and economy in the small, underdeveloped country (76; 82:22-24). Most observers are distressed by the large, highly visible accumulations of human misery growing around the edges of many Latin American cities (23; 82; 113); but there are some dissenting opinions. Caplow found Guatemala City's growth consonant with that of the country in general, at least up through the 1940's (19), and also reports a dominant note of economic and psychological satisfaction among a random sample of the citizens of San Juan, Puerto Rico (20); but, admittedly, the latter metropolis is an unusually privileged one among those of Latin America. The present Cuban regime has been sufficiently fretful over Havana's excessive size to take apparently effective steps to retard its growth and to stimulate the development of medium-sized centers (89: 107-108)—in striking contrast to the failure of similar policies in the U.S.S.R. and China. Much the same program of regional city development has been put forward for El Salvador (113) and Guatemala (55), but so far to no effect. One of the more dreaded consequences of collecting so many of the unemployed, poorly paid, and generally disaffected into a single place is the setting off of political conflagration (41; 113; 118). But aside from the Ras Tafari movement in Kingston (C. G. Clarke, p. 319), this has not occurred as yet; and, paradoxically, the successful Cuban revolution and the incipient one in Guatemala have germinated in the most intensely rural settings imaginable.

As a strategy in bringing about a better balance between people and resources, rapid urbanization is only modestly successful insofar as it induces a slight decline in fertility (124). What we really do not understand is whether the material and social welfare of the country-to-town migrants improves, deteriorates, or stays essentially the same. Neither is it clear whether the intense concentration of so much demographic, financial, and social capital in metropolises is an aid or deterrent to the general development of the country that is the only acceptable long-term solution to population-resource problems. Serious research on both questions is necessary.

ECONOMIC DEVELOPMENT

All the governments within the study area that have thought seriously about present or future problems of national welfare have recognized the desirability of accelerated economic development. But they differ widely on the precise goals or the means of implementation. In a few cases, simple intensification of traditional agricultural enterprise has been counseled as adequate, as in the Dominican Republic (53), Nicaragua (47), Honduras (87), Costa Rica (Sandner, p. 551) or Central America in general (58). Whatever the merits of such a policy for the places specified, it is manifestly unworkable in smaller or more crowded territories with long-standing problems of land tenure, little space for expanded cultivation, and with severe social and cultural inhibitions blocking agricultural development of any sort. Thus we have some quite pessimistic forecasts of agricultural production, for either domestic or foreign markets, as a ready answer to impending economic troubles in Trinidad and Tobago (11; 75:18-19; 84). Enthusiastic claims for the general benefits of the rapid development of agricultural and mineral export for Jamaica (123) and El Salvador (88) are countered by equally credible statements (113) that the income derived thereby is most unlikely to seep down into the pockets of the general population. Analyses of the situation in the West Indies in general (14; 35; 46) agree that land tenure systems, the nature of the social and economic systems, and general attitudes toward farming make agriculture a most unlikely device for their general salvation.

Along less conventional lines, one of the more hopeful possibilities for alleviating unemployment and earning developmental capital is the tourist industry. There has been a notable increase recently in the number of visitors and their expenditures not only in the West Indies, but, in lesser degree, in Central America as well. In fact, the Bahama Islands and some of the Antilles have based much of whatever prosperity they have on tourism (34; 86). Although the general economic effect may have been salutary, there may be drawbacks, as pointed out by Niddrie, writing on Tobago: "unfortunately, whenever established, [tourism] leads to a rise in the cost of living, a reduction in local food production, inflated wages and transport costs, and varying degrees of parasitic beggary" (84:17). To what degree the rapid socio-economic development of a country can be based on income from tourism is a question of considerable practical and economic importance and one that obviously calls for investigation.

There seems to be much logic behind the argument that genuine economic development requires not only further efforts with agricultural expansion for the home market and for export, the exploitation of mineral, forest, and marine resources, the promotion of tourism, and the building up of the infrastructure of transport, education, and social services, but also a significant degree of industrialization (61; 63). This is the strategy that has been followed, with much fanfare and considerable immediate success, in Puerto Rico, while there have also been some strides in this direction in Curaçao, Jamaica, and Cuba. Yet even where the rise of manufacturing has been most spectacular, as in Puerto Rico, it is all too clear that the millennium is not yet at hand. The fact that 11.3 percent of the Puerto Rican labor force was classed as unemployed in 1963 is indicative of the durability of poverty on that

island. The tidings from Jamaica are also rather disquieting. It has proved much more difficult to increase employment there than to raise production (23:5; 63:173-75); and, for El Salvador, Tricart argues that the traditional laissez-faire mode of industrialization has hindered rather than aided the general advancement of the country (112:306-307). A basic difficulty seems to be the inability of an expanding industrial economy to soak up more than a fraction of the current entrants into the labor force. In the cases of Jamaica and Puerto Rico, much of whatever progress has been registered may well be attributed to the removal through emigration of a major portion of open or disguised unemployment (48:2). It is logical, then, to consider whether it is feasible to aid in resolving population-resource problems through the sharp reduction in rates of population growth either before or during the process of significant socio-economic development. How useful is a direct assault upon population numbers?

POPULATION CONTROL

One obvious possibility is the further encouragement of emigration. But this strategy depends upon having receptive destinations, specifically the United Kingdom, the United States, and, increasingly, France, or such proposed settlement areas as the Guianas or British Honduras. It seems unlikely that the United States can very much longer accept Puerto Rican newcomers at the rates prevailing in the 1940's and 1950's; and indeed in recent months the net flow seems to have reversed its direction. The flow of British West Indians to Great Britain during the 1950's was quite heavy; but, since 1962, the outlook is much less promising. Even were the absorptive capacities of other areas unlimited, there is some doubt about the merits of emigration as a general solution. The partial depopulation of Montserrat seems to

have had a depressing effect on social conditions (73); and Roberts and Mills raise the
question of whether the removal of large
numbers of the relatively skilled and well
educated is "an unqualified advantage to a
country crying aloud for industrial development" (94:124).

An even more crucial question, not only
for Middle America but for the underdeveloped world in general, is whether it is
possible to induce voluntary reductions in
fertility *in advance* of appreciable socio-
economic development. The evidence, here
as elsewhere, is still scanty and equivocal.
As late as 1963, one analyst could write
that the only Latin American country making any official gesture toward fertility limitation was Chile (52:34-43). Since then,
Barbados, Jamaica, and Honduras have
taken limited official action. In addition,
there has been much activity by private
individuals and organizations in Puerto Rico,
Jamaica, and Barbados. But in many of the
countries in question, the matter has hardly
reached the stage of public discussion. As
far as results are concerned, the only claim
for measurable success—and one hedged
with many cautious reservations—is a statement regarding Barbados (25). Surveys
elsewhere, e.g. San José and Panama City
(79) or Jamaica (68; 105:311; C. G.
Clarke, p. 324) indicate at most a willingness
to consider the idea of smaller families,
while various factors still seriously inhibit
its implementation. Exhortation, subsidy,
and other means of persuasion may effect
some lowering of birth rates among relatively poor parents still living within a traditional type of society; but such a program
would entail major investment of talent and
money for a highly uncertain payoff.

It is tempting, then, to shop around for
various shortcuts that will engender, or at
least create a receptive mood for, the small-
family pattern—some sort of partial modernization without going through the long,
elaborate agony of full development. A frequent suggestion is a crash program in education, in keeping with the widely observed
fact that amount of school and fertility are
inversely related (21; 108). The results of
such an effort would indeed be interesting;
but, a priori, it seems likely that Carleton
is correct in concluding "that none of the
various ways in which education can affect
fertility is completely independent of progress in economic development" (107:5),
i.e. that educational progress far out of
phase with advances along other fronts
might be fruitless. Another popular one-shot
approach to rapid development is the building of modern transport systems in undeveloped areas; but in his analysis of Guatemala's Atlantic Highway, whose developmental results have been disappointingly
meager, Klein finds that "transportation improvement may serve as an effective catalyst
for development in other sectors, but if it is
to perform this function other elements
must also be present" (66:86).

One is left, then, with the only generally
certified method for engineering a low-fer-
tility pattern: the setting off of a major
decline in birth rates a certain number of
years *after* structural changes have been
effected in a community through massive,
general socio-economic advance. Or at least
that has been the experience thus far, without exception, in European and neo-European countries, Japan, Taiwan, and Hong
Kong. Is this classic model of the Demographic Transition being followed in Latin
America? Apparently only if we modify the
model quite a bit. In his careful analysis of
recent fertility trends in all the O.A.S. nations, Collver found a marked upward movement in nearly all, including some, like Mexico and Venezuela, reputed to be well along
in the developmental cycle, and concludes
that "to date none of the countries covered in

this study has either spontaneously developed its own birth control movement or borrowed it from abroad without its being carried by massive immigration (24:55). A similar finding is reported by Ridley, namely: "Several of the Caribbean and Central and South American countries currently present a puzzle to the demographer. Contrary to demographic theory, birth rates for several countries have been increasing" (91:152). And in their statistical approach to areal differences in Latin American fertility, Heer and Turner report an unanticipated positive correlation with indices of economic development (57).

Despite an enormous amount of research on Puerto Rico, obviously the guinea pig country within our study area, it is still not altogether clear whether a genuine downturn in age-specific fertility rates or size of completed family has begun there—largely because of complications injected by massive emigration of young adults. The claim that such a change is now well under way can be met by the skepticism of others who claim that "we are witnessing a slow, but steady congruence of all the influences making family planning an accepted part of society" (10:576), the prelude, so to speak, without family planning having quite caught on as yet (105:311). Then there is also the intriguing case of Cuba which, after having apparently entered the final stages of the Demographic Transition during the early decades of this century and achieving one of Latin America's lowest birth rates, is now experiencing a rapid rebound to a crude birth rate between 35 and 38, in what appears to be a burst of revolutionary euphoria (89:101-2). In Mexico, a land offering close analogies to Central America, trends within the most progressive regions and among the *nouveaux riches* fail to support the thesis that significant development leads quickly to smaller families (31), or

to the wiping out of poverty. It must be suggested, then, that if modernization is ultimately conducive to lowered fertility within Latin America, it may be only after some considerable delay and a period of much higher than traditional birth rates.

A Summing Up

It must also be suggested that the prize of an advanced, prosperous society (eventually enjoying low mortality balanced by low fertility) cannot be won easily. The obstacles are numerous, and they are serious. The small territorial extent of these twenty-odd quasi-sovereign entities and, paradoxically, the smallness of their population makes it difficult to launch successful development programs. But these countries are not all so small that poor transportation and communications are not a serious drag on progress. The limited amount and variety of physical resources, the meagerness of human skills, and the shortage of risk capital (and much of that consumed in providing bare subsistence and rudimentary social services for a swiftly multiplying population) make it mandatory to effect regional consortia and/or to turn to large affluent patrons in North America and Europe for cash, equipment, personnel, and ideas. But the perennial political instability of the region (compounded by racial divisions in at least two countries) and the failure to date to institute much more than token regional integration (4; 72) render somewhat fanciful any hope for massive imports of money or technicians or the steady carrying through of well-made plans. There is also a formidable array of cultural and social factors to thwart both rapid development and plans to deflate high fertility rates, too long a list, in fact, for specification here. Finally, as grave a problem as any is the absence of any proved, locally adaptable model of successful development—unless the paths being followed by Mexico, Puerto Rico, and Cuba lead to a full socio-economic consummation as yet highly uncertain.

The general mood of this paper cannot help but be gloomy. Despite the weakness or absence of much data one would like to have, it is highly probable that population pressure, disguised or overt, is prevalent in almost all parts of Central America and the West Indies in highly variable, but definite degree, that it appears to be intensifying, and that it will produce some highly undesirable effects upon both society and the physical habitat. The twofold approach of augmenting resources and reducing population growth is splendid in theory but extremely difficult in practice. The initiation

and successful execution of general socio-economic advance is beset by a host of problems, some of them perhaps insoluble; and such advance will lead to sharp declines in fertility and the general eradication of poverty only after a long, awkward waiting period. Any immediate assault on high fertility has yet to be proved effective in practice, and, in any case, would be costly in terms of money, organization, enthusiasm, and technicians. We can hope for the unexpected, but must be braced to observe, with clinical detachment, a variety of interesting geographic symptoms as the varied islands and republics of Middle America shortly enter the advanced, pathological, stages of acute population pressure.

REFERENCES

(1) George C. Abbott: Estimates of the Growth of Population of the West Indies to 1975; Two Projections, *Social and Economic Studies,* Vol. 12, No. 3, 1963, pp. 236-45.

(2) Richard N. Adams: Food Habits in Latin America; a Preliminary Historical Survey, in: Iago Galdston, ed.: Human Nutrition, Historic and Scientific (New York, 1960), pp. 1-22.

(3) Richard N. Adams: Migraciones Internas en Guatemala; Expansión Agraria de los Indígenas Kekchíes hacia El Petén (Estudios Centroaméricanos No. 1, Seminario de Integración Social Guatemalteca and Institute of Latin American Studies, University of Texas, Guatemala, 1965).

(4) Alvar Antillón-Salazar: Problemas y Caracteres de la Integración Regional en Centro América, in: Actas del XXXIII Congreso Internacional de Americanistas, San José, 20-27 Julio 1958, Tomo I (San José, 1959), pp. 361-72.

(5) Jorge Arias B.: La Situación Demográfica en México y Centro América (Paper presented before Fourth Conference, I.P.P.F., Western Hemisphere Region, April 18-27, 1964), mimeographed.

(6) John P. Augelli: Patterns and Problems of Land Tenure in Lesser Antilles: Antigua, B.W.I., *Economic Geography,* Vol. 29, 1953, pp. 362-67.

(7) John P. Auguelli: The British Virgin Islands: a West Indian Anomaly, *Geographical Review,* Vol. 46, 1956, pp. 43-58.

(8) John P. Augelli: The Rimland-Mainland Concept of Culture Areas in Middle America, *Annals of the Association of American Geographers,* Vol. 52, 1962, pp. 119-29.

(9) John P. Augelli: Agricultural Colonization in the Dominican Republic, *Economic Geography,* Vol. 38, 1962, pp. 15-27.

(10) Kurt W. Back, Reuben Hill, and J. Mayone Stycos: Population Control in Puerto Rico: the Formal and Informal Framework, in: Population Control, Summer, 1960 issue, *Law and Contemporary Problems,* Vol. 25, No. 3, 1960, pp. 558-76.

(11) G. L. F. Beckford: Agriculture in the Development of Trinidad and Tobago, *Social and Economic Studies,* Vol. 14, No. 2, 1965, pp. 217-22.

(12) Charles F. Bennett, Jr.: The Bayano Cuna Indians, Panama: an Ecological Study of Livelihood and Diet, *Annals of the Association of American Geographers,* Vol. 52, 1962, pp. 32-50.

(13) James M. Blaut, Ruth P. Blaut, Nan Harman, and Michael Moerman: A Study of Cultural Determinants of Soil Erosion and Conservation in the Blue Mountains of Jamaica, *Social and Economic Studies,* Vol. 8, No. 4, 1959, pp. 403-20.

(14) Helmut Blume: Die Gegenwärtigen Waundlungen in der Verbreitung von Gross- und Kleinbetrieben auf den Grossen Antillen, *Schriften des Geographischen Instituts der Universität Kiel,* Vol. 20, 1961, pp. 75-123.

(15) Ester Boserup: The Conditions of Agricultural Growth; the Economics of Agrarian Change under Population Pressure (Chicago, 1965).

(16) J. Bourgeois-Pichat: Recent Trends of Fertility in Underdeveloped Areas (Paper prepared for the Conference on Demographic and Economic Trends in the Developing Countries, New York City, October 10-12, 1963), mimeographed.

(17) Harley L. Browning: Recent Trends in Latin American Urbanization, in: Kingsley Davis, ed.: A Crowding Hemisphere: Population Change in the Americas, *Annals of the American Academy of Political and Social Science,* Vol. 316, 1958, pp. 111-20.

(18) Gerardo Budowski: Middle America: the Human Factor, in: F. Fraser Darling and John P. Milton, eds.: Future Environments of North America; Transformation of a Continent (Garden City, 1966), pp. 144-55.

(19) Theodore Caplow: The Social Ecology of Guatemala City, *Social Forces,* Vol. 28, 1949, pp. 113-35.

(20) Theodore Caplow, Sheldon Stryker, and Samuel E. Wallace: The Urban Ambience; a Study of San Juan Puerto Rico (Río Piedras, 1964).

(21) Robert O. Carleton: Fertility Trends and Differentials in Latin America, in: Clyde V. Kiser, ed.: Components of Population Change

in Latin America, *Milbank Memorial Fund Quarterly,* Vol. 43, No. 4, 1965, Part 2, pp. 15-35.

(22) The Effect of Educational Improvement on Fertility Trends in Latin America (United Nations World Population Conference 1965, WPC/WP/152), mimeographed.

(23) C. G. Clarke: Population Pressure in Kingston, Jamaica: a Study of Unemployment and Overcrowding, *Institute of British Geographers, Transactions and Papers,* Publ. 38, 1966, pp. 165-82.

(24) Q. Andrew Collver: Birth Rates in Latin America: New Estimates of Historical Trends and Fluctuations (Berkeley, Cal., 1965).

(25) G. T. M. Commins, H. G. Lovell, and K. L. Standard: Population Control on Barbados, *American Journal of Public Health,* Vol. 55, No. 10, 1965, pp. 1600-1608.

(26) Committee for Economic Development: Economic Development of Central America; a Statement on National Policy by the Research and Policy Committee of the Committee for Economic Development (New York, 1964).

(27) Conservation Foundation: La Conservación Humana en Centro América; Resumen de Discusiones (Guatemala, 1966).

(28) Robert C. Cook: The West Indies: New Bottle, Old Wine, *Population Bulletin,* Vol. 14, 1958, pp. 17-34.

(29) Arthur F. Corwin: Contemporary Mexican Attitudes toward Population, Poverty, and Public Opinion (Gainesville, Fla., 1963).

(30) Arthur F. Corwin: Mexico Resists the Pill, *The Nation,* Vol. 198, No. 20, 1964, pp. 477-80.

(31) Mary S. Coyner: Guatemala; its Agricultural Production and Trade (U.S. Department of Agriculture, Economic Research Service, ERS-Foreign-14, Washington, 1959).

(32) Raymond E. Crist and Huge Popenoe: Jamaica and Martinique: Contrasting Aspects of Folk Agriculture and Non-Folk Agriculture (Paper presented at annual meeting, Association of American Geographers, 1966), mimeographed.

(33) G. E. Cumper: Employment in Barbados, *Social and Economic Studies,* Vol. 8, No. 1, 1959, pp. 105-46.

(34) G. E. Cumper: Tourist Expenditures in Jamaica, 1959, *Social and Economic Studies,* Vol. 8, No. 3, pp. 287-310.

(35) Edmund H. Dale: The Demographic Problem of the British West Indies, *Scottish Geographical Magazine,* Vol. 79, No. 1, 1963, pp. 23-31.

(36) Kingsley Davis, ed.: A Crowding Hemisphere: Population Change in the Americas, *Annals of the American Academy of Political and Social Science,* Vol. 316, 1958.

(37) Kingsley Davis: Recent Population Trends in the New World: an Overall View, in: Kingsley Davis, ed.: A Crowding Hemisphere:

Population Change in the Americas, *Annals of the American Academy of Political and Social Science,* vol. 316, 1958, pp. 1-10.

(38) Kingsley Davis: Colonial Expansion and Urban Diffusion in the Americas, *International Journal of Comparative Sociology,* Vol. 1, No. 1, 1960, pp. 43-66.

(39) Kingsley Davis: Las Causas y Efectos del Fenómeno de Primacia Urbana con Referencia Especial a América Latina, in: Instituto de Investigaciones Sociales: Decimotercer Congreso Nacional de Sociología (Coyoacán, Mexico, 1962), pp. 361-79.

(40) Kingsley Davis: The Place of Latin America in World Demographic History, *Milbank Memorial Fund Quarterly,* Vol. 42, No. 2, Part 2, 1964, pp. 19-53.

(41) William G. Demas: The Economics of Development in Small Countries, with Special Reference to the Caribbean (Montreal, 1965).

(42) Edwin B. Doran, Jr.: A Physical and Cultural Geography of the Cayman Islands (Ph.D. dissertation, University of California, Berkeley, 1953).

(43) Louis J. Ducoff: Human Resources of Central America, Panama and Mexico, 1950-1980, in Relation to Some Aspects of Economic Development (United Nations, 1960).

(44) Louis J. Ducoff and Gladys K. Bowles: Tasas de Reemplazo de la Mano de Obra Disponible en Los Païses Centroaméricanos, *Estadística,* 1960, pp. 475-501.

(45) John D. Durand and Cesar A. Peláez: Patterns of Urbanization in Latin America, in: Clyde V. Kiser, ed.: Components of Population Change in Latin America (New York, 1965), pp. 166-96.

(46) Herman J. Finkel: Patterns of Land Tenure in the Leeward and Windward Islands and their Relevance to Problems of Agricultural Development in the West Indies, *Economic Geography,* Vol. 40, No. 2, 1964, pp. 163-72.

(47) Food and Agriculture Organization: Report of the FAO Mission for Nicaragua (Washington, 1950).

(48) Stanley L. Friedlander: Labor Migration and Economic Growth: a Case Study of Puerto Rico (Cambridge, Mass., 1965).

(49) Melvin J. Frost: Pioneer Settlements in the Pacific Lowland of Guatemala (Ph.D. dissertation, University of Florida, 1964).

(50) Robert H. Fuson: Land Tenure in Central Panama: a Case Study of an Aspect of the *Latino* Mythology, *Journal of Geography,* Vol. 63, No. 4, 1964, pp. 161-68.

(51) Clifford Geertz: Agricultural Involution; the Process of Ecological Change in Indonesia (Berkeley and Los Angeles, 1963).

(52) Harold L. Geisert: The Control of World Population Growth (Washington, 1963).

(53) Ing. Juan Ulises Garcia Bonnelly: Consideraciones Generales, in:

República Dominicana, Dirección General de Estadística y Censos: Quinto Censo Nacional Agropecuario 1960 (Datos Preliminares), Segunda Parte (Santo Domingo, 1962), pp. i-xiii.

(54) Norton Ginsburg: Atlas of Economic Development (Chicago, 1961).

(55) Guatemala, Dirección General de Cartografía: Atlas Preliminar de Guatemala, 1964).

(56) David R. Harris: Plants, Animals, and Man in the Outer Leeward Islands, West Indies; an Ecological Study of Antigua, Barbuda, and Anguilla (Berkeley, 1965).

(57) David M. Heer and Elsa S. Turner: Areal Differences in Latin American Fertility (Paper presented at 1964 meeting of the Population Association of America), mimeographed.

(58) Karl Helbig: Zentralamerika; Natürliche Grundlagen, ihre Gegenwärtige und Künftig Mögliche Auswertung, *Petermanns Geographische Mitteilungen*, Vol. 108, No. 3, 1964, pp. 161-81.

(59) Theo Hills: Land Settlement Scheme—Lessons from the British Caribbean, *Revista Geográfica*, No. 63, Tomo 35:2, 1965, pp. 67-82.

(60) Oscar H. Horst: The Specter of Death in a Guatemalan Highland Community, *Geographical Review*, Vol. 57, No. 2, 1967, pp. 151-67.

(61) Bert F. Hoselitz: Economic Development in Central America, *Weltwirtschaftliches Archiv*, Vol. 76, 1956, pp. 267-308.

(62) International Bank for Reconstruction and Development: *The Economic Development of Jamaica* (Baltimore, 1952).

(63) International Bank for Reconstruction and Development: *The Economic Development of Nicaragua* (Baltimore, 1953).

(64) Carl L. Johannessen: Savannas of Interior Honduras, *Ibero-America*, No. 46, 1963.

(65) John Y. Keur and Dorothy L. Keur: Windward Children: a Study of Human Ecology of the Three Dutch Windward Islands in the Caribbean (Assen, 1960).

(66) Martin S. Klein: The Atlantic Highway in Guatemala, in: George W. Wilson et al.: The Impact of Highway Investment on Development (Washington, 1966), pp. 55-86.

(67) Alfred L. Kroeber: Cultural and Natural Areas of Native North America (Berkeley, 1939).

(68) G. J. Kruijer: Family Size and Family Planning; a Pilot Survey among Jamaican Mothers, *West-Indische Gids*, Vol. 38, Nos. 3-4, 1959, pp. 144-50.

(69) Yves Lacoste: Géographie du Sous-Développement (Paris, 1965).

(70) Guy Lasserre: La Guadeloupe; Etude Geographique (Bordeaux, 1961).

(71) James G. Leyburn: The Haitian People (New Haven, 1941).

(72) David Lowenthal: Levels of West Indian Government, *Social and Economic Studies*, Vol. 11, No. 3, 1962, pp. 363-91.

(73) David Lowenthal and Lambros Comitas: Emigration and Depopu-

lation; Some Neglected Aspects of Population Geography, *Geographical Review,* Vol. 52, 1962, pp. 195-210.

(74) José Antonio Mayobre: Economic Development and Population Growth in Latin America (United Nations World Population Conference 1965, A.10/I/E/151), mimeographed.

(75) Robert T. McMillan: Demographic and Socio-Economic Correlatives of Fertility in Trinidad and Tobago (Office of International Training, Agency for International Development, Washington, 1964), mimeographed.

(76) Surinder K. Mehta: Some Demographic and Economic Correlates of Primate Cities: a Case for Revaluation (Paper read at 1963 annual meeting of Population Association of America), mimeographed.

(77) Gordon C. Merrill: The Historical Record of Man as an Ecological Dominant in the Lesser Antilles, *Canadian Geographer,* No. 11, 1958, pp. 17-22.

(78) Clarence W. Minkel: Colonization of the Sebol Region in North-Central Guatemala (Paper read at annual meeting of Association of American Geographers, 1966), mimeographed.

(79) Carmen A. Miró and Ferdinand Rath: Preliminary Findings of Comparative Fertility Surveys in Three Latin American Cities, in: Clyde V. Kiser, ed.: Components of Population Change in Latin America, *Milbank Memorial Fund Quarterly,* Vol. 43, No. 4, Part 2, 1965, pp. 36-68.

(80) Paul Moral: Le Paysan Haïtien (Paris, 1961).

(81) Paul Morrison: Middle America, Land of Too Many and Too Little, *National Council for Geographic Education,* Professional Paper No. 21, 1961, pp. 112-20.

(82) Richard M. Morse: The Social and Demographic Setting for Latin American Urban Planning, mimeographed.

(83) George C. Myers: Migration and Modernization: the Case of Puerto Rico, 1950-60 (U.N. World Population Conference 1965, WPC/WP/161), mimeographed.

(84) David L. Niddrie: Land Use and Settlement in the Caribbean; a Contribution to the Historical and Social Geography of the Lesser Antilles with Special Reference to the Ceded Islands and in Particular to Tobago (Ph.D. dissertation, University of Manchester, 1965).

(86) Robert E. Nunley: The Distribution of Population in Costa Rica (Washington, 1960).

(86) Carleen O'Laughlin: Problems in the Economic Development of Antigua, *Social and Economic Studies,* Vol. 10, No. 3, 1961, pp. 237-77.

(87) Organization of American States: Informe Official de la Mision 105 de Asistencia Tecnica Directa a Honduras sobre Reforma Agraria y Desarrollo Agricola (Washington, 1963).

(88) James J. Parsons: Cotton and Cattle in the Pacific Lowlands of

Central America, *Journal of Inter-American Studies,* Vol. 7, No. 2, 1965, pp. 149-59.

(89) Juan Perez de la Riva: La Population de Cuba et ses Problèmes, *Population,* Vol. 22, No. 1, 1967, pp. 99-110.

(90) Malcolm J. Proudfoot: Population Movements in the Caribbean (Port-of-Spain, 1950).

(91) Jeanne Clare Ridley: Recent Natality Trends in Underdeveloped Countries, in: Mindel C. Sheps and J. C. Ridley, eds.: Public Health and Population Change; Current Research Issues (Pittsburgh, 1965), pp. 143-73.

(92) George W. Roberts: Immigration of Africans into the British Caribbean, *Population Studies,* Vol. 7, No. 3, pp. 235-62.

(93) G. W. Roberts and J. Byrne: Summary Statistics on Indenture and Associated Migration Affecting the West Indies, 1834-1918, *Population Studies,* Vol. 20, No. 1, 1966, pp. 124-34.

(94) G. W. Roberts and D. O. Mills: Study of External Migration Affecting Jamaica, 1953-1955, *Social and Economic Studies,* Vol. 7, No. 2, Supplement, 1958.

(95) Angel Rosenblat: La Población Indigena y el Mestizaje en América (Buenos Aires, 1954).

(96) Gerhard Sandner: Agrarkolonisation in Costa Rica; Siedlung, Wirtschaft und Soziolgefüge an der Pioniergrenze (Kiel, 1961).

(97) Gerhard Sandner: Das Valle General; Landeskundliche Skizze eines Jungen Rodungsgebietes in Costa Rica, *Schriften des Geographischen Instituts der Universität Kiel,* Vol. 20, 1961, pp. 125-65.

(98) Gerhard Sandner: Die Ungelenkte Bauerliche Urwaldkolonisation in Costa Rica, *Verhandlungen des Deutschen Geographentages* (Köln, 1961), Vol. 33, 1962, pp. 202-10.

(99) Gerhard Sandner: Die Erschliessung der Karibischen Waldregion im Sudlichen Zentralamerika, *Die Erde,* Vol. 95, No. 2, 1964, pp. 111-31.

(100) Carl O. Sauer: The Early Spanish Main (Berkeley and Los Angeles, 1966).

(101) Alfred Sauvy: La Population des Pays d'Amerique Latine, *Population,* Vol. 18, No. 1, 1963.

(102) T. Lynn Smith: Un Análisis Comparativo de la Migración Rural-Urbana en Latino-América, *Estadística,* Vol. 16, 1958, pp. 436-53.

(103) T. Lynn Smith: Migration from One Latin American Country to Another, in: International Union for the Scientific Study of Population, Vienna 1959 (Vienna, 1959), pp. 695-702.

(104) George J. Stolnitz: Recent Mortality Declines in Latin America, Asia and Africa: Review and Reinterpretation (Paper prepared for Conference on Demographic and Economic Trends in the Developing Countries, New York City, October 10-12, 1963), mimeographed.

(105) J. Mayone Stycos: Experiments in Social Change: The Caribbean

Fertility Studies, in: Clyde V. Kiser, ed.: Research in Family Planning (Princeton, 1962), pp. 305-16.

(106) J. Mayone Stycos: Needed Research on Latin American Fertility; Urbanization and Fertility, in: Clyde V. Kiser, ed.: Components of Population Change in Latin America, *Milbank Memorial Fund Quarterly,* Vol. 43, No. 4, Part 2, 1965, pp. 299-323.

(107) J. Mayone Stycos: Opinions of Latin-American Intellectuals on Population Problems and Birth Control, *Annals of the American Academy of Political and Social Science,* Vol. 360, 1965, pp. 11-26.

(108) J. Mayone Stycos: Education and Fertility in Puerto Rico. (U.N. World Population Conference 1965, A.6/I/E/236), mimeographed.

(109) Irene B. Taeuber: Migration and Transformation: Spanish Surname Populations and Puerto Ricans, *Population Index,* Vol. 32, No. 1, 1966, pp. 3-34.

(110) John Thompson: Studies in the Food Supply of El Salvador (Department of Geography, University of California, Berkeley, 1961).

(111) Joseph A. Tosi, Jr. and Robert F. Voertman: Some Environmental Factors in the Economic Development of the Tropics, *Economic Geography,* Vol. 40, No. 3, 1964, pp. 189-204.

(112) Jean Tricart: Aspects de la Géographie de la Population du Salvador, *Bulletin de la Faculté des Lettres de Strasbourg,* Vol. 39, No. 6, 1961, pp. 297-311.

(113) Jean Tricart: Un Ejemplo de Desequilibrio Ciudad-Campo en una Economia en Via de Desarrollo: El Salvador, *Cuadernos Latinoaméricanos de Economía Humana,* No. 13, 1964, pp. 229-55.

(114) U.N. Statistical Office: Statistical Yearbook 1964 (New York, 1965).

(115) William Vogt: The Population of Costa Rica and its Natural Resources (Washington, 1946).

(116) William Vogt: A Brief Reconnaissance of Resource Use, Progress, and Conservation Needs in Some Latin American Countries (New York, 1963).

(117) Charles Wagley: Plantation-America: a Culture Sphere, in: Vera Rubin, ed.: Caribbean Studies: a Symposium (Seattle, 1960), pp. 3-13.

(118) Philip L. Wagner: Political Implications of Rapid Urbanization in Caribbean Countries (Typescript).

(119) Robert C. West, ed.: Natural Environment and Early Cultures; Handbook of Middle American Indians, Vol. I (Austin, Tex., 1965).

(120) Marshall Wolfe: Rural Settlement Patterns and Social Change in Latin America: Notes for a Strategy of Rural Development (CEPAL, Social Affairs Division, Santiago (?), 1964), mimeographed.

(121) Marshall Wolfe: Some Implications of Recent Changes in Urban and Rural Settlement Patterns in Latin America (U.N. World Population Conference 1965, A.8/I/E/66), mimeographed.

(122) Harold A. Wood: Northern Haiti: Land, Land Use, and Settlement; a Geographical Interpretation of the Département du Nord Toronto, 1963).

(123) B. S. Young: Jamaica's Bauxite and Alumina Industries, *Annals of the Association of American Geographers*, Vol. 55, 1965, pp. 449-64.

(124) Alvan O. Zarate: Fertility in Urban Areas of Mexico: Implications for the Theory of the Demographic Transition (Paper presented at annual meeting of Population Association of America, 1966), mimeographed.

31. POPULATION PRESSURE UPON RESOURCES IN COSTA RICA

Gerhard Sandner

Costa Rica is a small but complex and dynamic country. The internal diversity, the extreme economic, social, and regional mobility of the predominantly rural population, and the simultaneity of highly divergent social and economic developments are reflected in the present essay.

PPR (Population Pressure upon Resources) is here understood as a situation finding expression in processes occurring in the real world and one that can only be fully comprehended in its specific relationship to scale and space. In contrast to demographers and economists, geographers can see population pressure within the geographic dimensions of small regions, and realize that as areal scale varies, so too the problems and results of a study. In order to find out what PPR means in Costa Rica, we must first of all forget about the country as a national unit and focus on minor, i.e. functional, units. A comparison of alternative developments in small regions within a country can tell more about PPR than a highly generalized analysis of large spaces.

Beside dynamics, scale, and regional diversity, Costa Rican conditions force us to take into account another factor, which is even more difficult to grasp. A study of the processes and changes induced by PPR reveals a sequence of adaptations and readaptations reflecting an autochthonous, sometimes almost automatic, reaction to changes in the man-space relationship. Population pressure may grow for some time before reaching a critical stage at which maladjustment between the resources of a community and its population leads to change and action. It is very important to analyze this critical stage, its consequences, and the resulting forms of adjustment.

Basic Demographic Facts

Costa Rica has a very high percentage of rural population of Hispanic origin. An orientation toward agriculture and the high value accorded to land ownership have slowed the trend toward urbanization and caused strong internal migrations and colonization processes. The social structure of Costa Rica is marked by a well-developed middle class and comparatively weak social barriers.

The crude birth rate attained levels between 47 and 50 during the period of 1952 to 1962. During the same period, mortality dropped below 10. The following diagram shows that these figures, as well as the high crude reproductive rate, cannot be generalized but represent a special phase in the demographic development of the country. Only the future will reveal whether the decrease of birth rates after 1954, and particularly after 1963, will continue and terminate a very rapid cycle of "demographic explosion." The decrease in birth rates since 1963 is at least partly due to the census methods. Many births are recorded only after a delay of several years. The diagram is based on corrected data compiled by Jiménez (27: 35) representing the most exact figures which can be obtained at the present time.

The pattern of population distribution i principally characterized by the contrast between a densely settled central highland and thinly populated marginal areas. In 1864 85 per cent of the population lived in th Central Highland. With the settlement of th marginal parts of the country, this per centage had declined by about one-third i

535

TABLE 31-1   COSTA RICA, BASIC DEMOGRAPHIC FACTS

| | Area, 1963, km² | | | Population | | | | | |
| | Total | Farmland | Productive Agricultural Area | Total | | | Rural | | |
				1950	1963	1950-1963	1950	1963	1950-1963
Costa Rica	50,900	26,580	15,251	800,875	1,336,274	+66.8%	432,589	875,731	+66.4%
Central Highland	4,500	3,581	2,587	413,214	760,202	+84.0%	255,799	406,111	+58.9%

| | Percentage of Rural Population | | Population Density, 1965 (Number of persons per km² of total area) | | | | Population Density, 1965 (Number of persons per km² of productive agricultural area) | |
| | | | Total | | Rural Population | | Total | Rural Population |
	1950	1963	1950	1963	1950	1963		
Costa Rica	66.5	65.5	16	26	11	17	105	57
Central Highland	61.9	53.4	92	169	57	90	294	157

Sources: Censo de Población 1950 and 1963; Censo Agropecuario 1963.

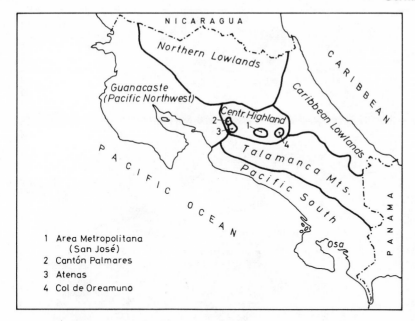

Fig. 31-1. COSTA RICA: MAJOR REGIONS

1945, but since then has been slowly rising. Numerous districts of the central region have population densities of over 200 persons per km². In the marginal parts of the country, we find unsettled forest areas surrounding small clusters of population, some of which have very high densities. A high degree of mobility and strong internal migrations are causing rapid changes in the distribution and density of population in these marginal zones.

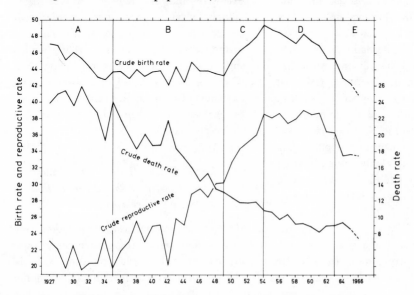

Fig. 31-2. COSTA RICA: CRUDE BIRTH, DEATH, AND REPRODUCTION RATES, 1927-66

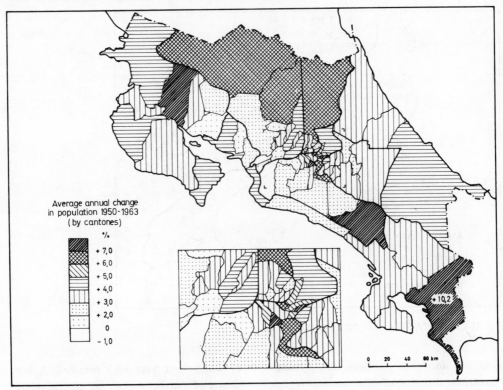

Fig. 31-3.   COSTA RICA: AVERAGE ANNUAL CHANGE IN AGGREGATE POPULATION, 1950-63, BY CANTONES

Immigration and emigration across the Costa Rican boundaries have had little importance for the distribution and development of population. Between 1950 and 1965, the total balance of international migration amounted to only 2702 persons. More important is the unregistered immigration of Panamanians into the southern Caribbean and Pacific Lowlands and the immigration of Nicaraguans into the Northwestern Lowlands. About 80 per cent of the population of the large, but still thinly settled districts of Upala and Los Chiles in the Northern Lowlands are immigrants from Nicaragua. They do not appear in the statistics of migration, but are in part recorded by the population censuses. There is no considerable uncontrolled emigration from Costa Rica. The internal migrations of the native

Costa Rican population are, however, very extensive and of great importance. Individual pioneer colonization is a characteristic of the Costa Rican scene. It was confined to the Central Highland until 1880, but has since been invading the marginal lowlands. There has been a steadily increasing internal exchange of population, so that in 1963 only 66 per cent of the population lived in their native districts.

The Relations Between the Socio-economic Structure and Population Pressure

In many cases, increasing population pressure is immediately responsible for changes in the socio-economic structure. On the other hand, changes in the socio-economic structure may cause growing population pressure on the natural resources, a process which is intensified by extreme population growth. Costa Rica offers a wealth of good information and source material from which the following conclusions can be drawn.

The transformation of the population structure started between 1840 and 1860 and passed through several phases. During the first, the rapid expansion of coffee cultivation in the eastern part of the Central Highland, which was already densely settled by 1840, and in 1864 reached population densities of as much as 50-100 persons per km² by district, brought about a reorientation of agriculture. Subsistence agriculture receded, land prices rose, and large coffee farms formed in the core of the highland. Peasants who clung to the traditional forms of agriculture began to emigrate to the marginal sections of the highlands. Simultaneously, commerce and export developed under the influence of foreign merchants and entrepreneurs.

After 1880, there was a rapid rise in the birth rate; and at the same time plantations, farms of wealthy city people, and small farm holdings began to appear in the marginal zones. Within a few decades, the highland area had been separated into specialized agricultural regions, each with a specific economic structure. Before 1840 the population consisted almost exclusively of independent farmers, but by the end of the century a large class of farm hands and small farmers who occasionally worked as hired laborers, as well as some large landowners were in existence. A strong social differentiation had developed, but the contrasts and barriers between different social strata remained weaker in Costa Rica than in other Latin American countries. The group of small, independent farmers remained predominant, however, though their economic importance was diminished by the spread of plantations

and haciendas. They continued to regard the possession of land primarily as a guarantee for independence and security for the family, and only secondarily as an economic enterprise.

This group was the catalyst for a major expansion of the settled area after 1880. The preference for land ownership and self-sufficiency persisted, though intensively managed farms and haciendas developed and exerted some influence on the peasant population even in the marginal area. Since 1910-20, however, these areas have been characterized by two contrasting structural types: stable agricultural regions with nucleated settlements and relatively intensive land use; and extensively used areas of colonization with strongly dispersed settlement and a highly mobile population.

In the last decades, only a very few stable agricultural areas have formed on virgin land, but the extensive form of colonization continues. It is supported by a highly mobile population, consisting largely of *minifundistas* with supplementary employment as farm laborers, and has become increasingly distinct from the peasant population of the highland and well-developed marginal areas. More than ever middle-class farmers regard their properties as economic enterprises and more than a means of social security. Their initiative for improved marketing, better techniques, and increased sales, and improvements in the standard of living have augmented not only the stability but also the potential of the country. Yet population in these areas is increasing faster than the opportunities for employment, and the organized colonization projects now being developed offer an appropriate alternative to undirected and extensive squatter settlement. There have also been changes in the attitude of the agricultural population toward the government. Automatic actions and self-help in the subdivision of land, in settlement, and in economic orientation are now often replaced by group organization and by demands on the government. Changes in the socio-economic structure and in attitudes toward land ownership, as well as the existence of a large class of peasants and an equally large group ranking between the farm laborers and small farmers, have had a strong influence on population development and have compensated for the growing population pressure through internal migration and agricultural intensification.

The Impact of Increasing Population Pressure in the Central Highlands

The rapidly increasing population densities in rural areas have had very different results in terms of land use, land tenure, and struc-

ture of settlement. Even in the densely settled highland, there are many different types of development side by side, as will be shown by three representative samples.

The Canton of Palmares, with an area of 45 km², is situated in a basin of the Western Highland. It was already densely settled by the end of the last century. In all of the marginal areas of the country, there are colonies of Palmarenos, who are regarded as the best, hardest working, and most successful farmers in Costa Rica. The population of this district rose by 55 per cent from 1950 (7934) to 1963 (12,283), representing an increase in density from 176 to 273/km². Increasing population pressure brought about a rapid intensification of agriculture. Tobacco culture was extended and improved, coffee growing was greatly ex-

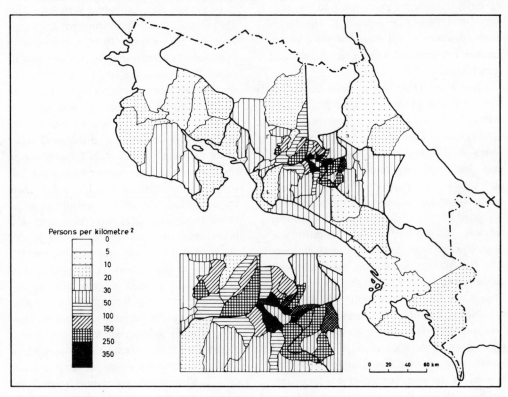

Fig. 31-4. COSTA RICA: RURAL POPULATION DENSITY (TOTAL AREA), 1963, BY CANTONES

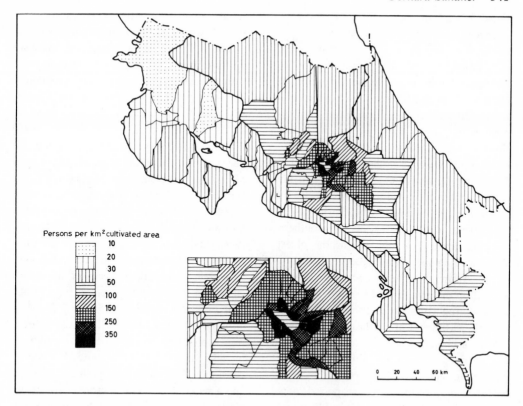

Fig. 31-5. COSTA RICA: RURAL POPULATION DENSITY (CULTIVATED AREA), 1963, BY CANTONES

panded, corn culture and cattle raising were reduced, modern methods, such as contour-plowing and use of fertilizers, were generally introduced after 1949, and the most intensively used area was increased through the reclamation of steep slopes by means of modern techniques. The first agricultural cooperative of the country was founded in Palmares in 1946. Today there are 32 cooperatives.

The intensification of agriculture was accompanied by a reduction of soil erosion, increased immigration from neighboring areas, and decreased emigration. The tendency toward dispersed settlement has augmented, and the small town of Palmares (2500 inhabitants) shows only little development. The economic development of the region is directed primarily toward a maximum carrying capacity for population on the basis of constant economic returns per family and stable conditions. The adaptation of economic activity to increasing population pressure is therefore determined primarily by efforts to maintain a stable standard of living. The strong pressure on the land is shown by the extreme land prices of $700 to $2000 per hectare. As yet intensification of agriculture and emigration of surplus population have altered in an irregular rhythm. Because further intensification is hardly possible at present and because there is little initiative on the part of the peasant community for development of trade, handicrafts, and local industry, an increase in emigration is to be expected in the future. The occupational effects of emigration have already changed, however. A considerable fraction of the emigrants choose professional careers (a disproportionately high percentage of the University students are Palmarenos). It is too early to say whether reflux of capital and family allowances will change the agricultural structure or conserve present conditions.

In other areas, population increase has led to minifundism and finally a loss of the land by the poor without causing strong emigration. An example is the district of Cot de Oreamuno (14 km²) on the southern slope of Irazu Volcano, one of the oldest settlements in the country. Because wealthy people from the nearby city of Cartago bought up the land around Cot, there was an extreme fragmentation and shortage of land as early as the end of the last century, even though a cholera epidemic in 1856 had reduced the population by almost half. The population increased 38 per cent from 1950 to 1963, and, during the same period, density rose from 127 to 198/km². More and more people had to work temporarily, then permanently, on larger farms, even though agriculture was intensified at a rate parallel with the increase of population, and the minifundias grew mostly crops of high value, such as vegetables, flowers, and potatoes, with perhaps two or three harvests per year. Today, only a very small part of the fields belongs to the members of the community, and many people possess only 0.1 to 0.5 hectares of land. Cot has become a typical example of a rural slum, and the population pressure finds expression in a steadily decreasing standard of living and in social problems. An attempt by the government to resettle part of the population in an agricultural colony was unsuccessful. Considerable individual emigration is lacking because the people cling to their minifundias and, in their frustration, have lost all personal initiative. Poverty here exceeds the stage at which self-help can be generated.

The problems of increasing minifundism in consequence of growing population pressure are made particularly clear by detailed, representative investigations in the Canton of Atenas in the Western Highland. In 1959, 24 per cent of the farmers in this area were the sons of peones. On the other hand, 42 per cent of the landless peones were the sons of farmers. Seventy-five per cent of the farmers of the parent generation had subdivided or sold their properties to distribute the money among the heirs (on an average seven heirs per farm). This caused minifundism and the percentage of leased land to increase. Seventy per cent of the fincas cultivated less than 3.5 hectares and 20 per cent cultivated between 3.5 and 7 hectares although the minimum area necessary for a return of 10,000 colones per year (approximately $1500) was 11 hectares. In spite of considerable increases in permanent crops and a reduction of annual crops, most of the yields were barely sufficient to afford a low standard of living to families that averaged 6.3 persons. Growing population pressure promotes greater mobility of properties and an increase of minifundism. At the same time, the percentage of land in large farms is increasing (1950-55: land in farms of 0.7 to 10 hectares—12 per cent; in farms of 10 to 35 hectares—6 per cent; in farms over 33 hectares—25 per cent). On larger farms, the area of permanent and annual crops is being reduced, while the percentage of pasture is strongly increasing. This reduces the availability of employment for the minifundistas and usually lowers the intensity of land use. The alternating development of minifundios and large farms increases population pressure proportionately to the number of small farms, though the typically Costa Rican mobility between different forms of land ownership and the tenacious fight of the minifundista for more land are always tending toward an equilibrium.

A comparative investigation of the greatly different agricultural regions of the Central Highland shows that growing population pressure leaves the following alternatives:

i. expansion of the cultivated area
ii. intensification without fragmentation of property (increase of labor intensity, and/or increase of productivity)
iii. intensification connected with fragmentation of properties and an increasing need for additional employment
iv. emigration

In most of the regions of the highland, a further expansion of cultivated land is not possible. Seventy-two per cent of the total area is already intensively used. An increase in capacity depends decisively on the relation between size of property, intensity of land use, and availability of labor. Many of the small farms can only survive because the owners accept temporary work on larger farms, and with growing fragmentation of property the amount of such work can only increase. This system, which is not restricted to the coffee zone, is disturbed if the larger farms introduce changes in land use or if employment and the leasing of small lots are limited by some other factor. In 1963, 52 per cent of the farm laborers in the Central Highland were at the same time owners of small farms. Beside the 22,000 *fincas* of over 0.7 hectares, there were 31,000 properties under 0.7 hectares, a large part of which were in coffee. High soil fertility, favorable climatic conditions, and intensive land use facilitate the preservation of minifundism, as long as temporary employment is available. On the other hand, the reduction of small *fincas* to the minimum of existence impedes their social and economic progress and promotes mobility.

Minifundismo, a major problem for agrar-

ian reform, is an adaptation of the rural population to increasing population pressure on the basis of intensive land use. It creates an unstable equilibrium between size of property (the population density being inversely proportional to property size) and intensity of land use, which is determined by the minimal demands of standard of living. Within the Central Highland, however, there are strong differences of population density and capacity, a result of the predominant culture, conditions of land tenure, and physical setting. Close adaptation to natural conditions and increasing fragmentation of property has allowed an increase of population density in the most favorable areas. Since the end of the last century, however, there has also been colonization in the surrounding mountain areas, where the limiting factor was not land but labor. The land was therefore used in an extensive form, resulting in soil impoverishment, erosion, and subsequent emigration. In the strongly dissected mountain areas on the western and southern margin of the highland, there developed a degraded landscape, which today has only a small population-carrying capacity.

Regional Aspects of the PPR in the Marginal Areas

The peripheral parts of the country show a basically different situation. Here, we have to differentiate between the plantation zones, the dry lowland of Guanacaste with its large cattle ranches and great numbers of farm laborers, and the area of unorganized agricultural colonization, where an expansion of cultivated land, accompanied by extensive forms of economy and a very low population density predominate. The colonization movement was initially influenced little or not at all by the natural potential and ecological capacity of the land. As long as there were

TABLE 31-2   COSTA RICA. INTERNAL MIGRATION BY REGIONS, 1963[1]

Region	Number (1000)	% of Total Pop.	Urban Pop. %	Internal Migrations Between Regions In % of Population			
				In the Region	Immigrants	Emigrants	Balance
Northwest[2]	214	16	21	12.5	14.0	17.2	−3.2
Northern and Caribbean lowlands[3]	105	8	25	8.1	23.8	16.8	+7.0
Southern Pacific[4]	153	11	11	12.7	31.3	13.5	+17.8
Western Highland[5]	105	8	13	4.4	12.4	41.3	−28.9
Area Metropolitana[6]	341	26	76	19.4	23.3	11.1	+12.2
Other highland areas	418	31	24	10.4	11.9	19.0	−7.1

[1] Census data by cantones.
[2] Prov. Guanacaste and Cantones Puntarenas, Esparta, Montes de Oro.
[3] Prov. Limón and Cantón San Carlos.
[4] Cantones Turrubares, Tarrazú, Leon Cortés, Dota, Aguirre, Pérez Zeledón, Buenos Aires, Osa, Golfito.
[5] Cantones Puriscal, Mora, Acosta, San Mateo, Atenas, Orotina, Palmares, San Ramón.
[6] Cantones San José, Escazú, Desamp, Goicoechea, Alajuelita, Tibás, Moravia, Montes de Oca, Curridabat.

ulation density, but even more so on social conditions, farm size, intensity of agriculture, and agricultural specialization. In stable agricultural regions with small or medium-size farms, the flow of migrants is much more important than in areas where properties change hands frequently or small farms are interspersed with large ones.

The greatest mobility is found in marginal areas of recent colonization and extensive agriculture. Illegal occupance and the lack of legal protection of property are opposed to stabilization. Many of the small, continuously growing population clusters in these areas are, despite extensive land use, characterized by strong population pressure; and the negative effects of isolation and lack of transport facilities may rapidly result in emigration. In the marginal mountain areas of the highland, erosion, soil exhaustion, and communication problems have often effected a decrease in population density within a few years. The pioneer phase of

settlement is usually followed by the development of large and relatively extensively used farms.

The map of the balance of migration shows that immigration predominates around the Area Metropolitana and the peripheral parts of the country, while emigration is predominant in the mountain areas surrounding the highland regions. Exceptions are the dry lowland of Guanacaste with its large cattle-haciendas and the Canton of Osa in the south, where abandonment of the banana plantation of Palmar was the reason for emigration. This special structure is made more clear by Table 31-2. During the past few years, centrifugal migration has decreased, and individual pioneer colonization has lost its importance as a way of relieving the overpopulated agricultural regions of the highland. There are several reasons for this. The land-seeking population no longer seems to be willing to endure the hardships of pioneering in distant, undeveloped areas. Easy marketing, good traffic connections, and grouping have achieved higher value. Virgin lands of good quality have become scarce and are to be found only in very distant areas. Moreover, colonization by individual squatter was outlawed by 1963. In the same year the state-controlled "Instituto de Tierras y Colonización" (ITCO) started several colonization projects, and in rapid sequence founded a number of small agricultural colonies. This was an important move, and many potential squatters who applied for lots in new colonies are now awaiting their turn. The decrease of individual squatter colonization will lead to still higher population pressure in the highland.

The Growth of the Area Metropolitana

The trend toward urbanization is comparatively weak in Costa Rica. The population of the Area Metropolitana of San José increased by 77 per cent from 1950 to 1963; but there is not that disequilibrium between immigration and employment opportunities which in other Latin American cities leads to the formation of slums. The adjustment of immigration to the employment opportunities of the city is facilitated by two phenomena; the strong affiliation of the population, even of the poorest strata, to their land, and to the rural way of life; and the location of the capital city in the core of a rural area with high population density and very intensive agriculture. In Costa Rica 52 per cent of the population lived within a radius of 50 kilometers from the capital city in 1963, as compared with 40 per cent in El Salvador, 24 per cent in Nicaragua, and 21 per cent in Guatemala, 9 per cent in Honduras, and 8 per cent in Panama. A large part of the population is familiar with the city of San José, and there is no aliena-

tion between city and country as in Panama or even Guatemala.

A considerable number of city-bound migrants settle in the coffee zone on the margin of San José and try to acquire a traditional small *finca* as a base for entering the process of urban life and work. Forty-four per cent

TABLE 31-3   THE AREA METROPOLITANA OF SAN JOSÉ

	San José*	Area Metropolitana
Population		
1927	62,053	91,240
1950	111,820	180,651
1963	168,938	320,431
Population development in %		
1927-1950	+80.0	+98.0
1950-1963	+50.4	+77.3
% of total population		
1927	13.2	19.3
1950	14.0	22.5
1963	12.6	24.0
Immigrants in % of population		
1950	41.5	44.8
1963	34.8	42.7
Balance of migration 1963		
Immigrants	58,811	79,611
Emigrants	57,625	37,986
Balance	+1,186	+41,625

* Cantón Central San José

of the approximately 10,000 farmers in the Area Metropolitana are immigrants, and in 1963, there were more than 7000 minifundios of less than 0.7 hectares—a total of 840 hectares, 440 of which were in coffee. The city has fingered out into the coffee zone, incorporating many rural settlement clusters, which have maintained their character to a large degree. Urbanization is strongest to the east and south, because small farms pre-

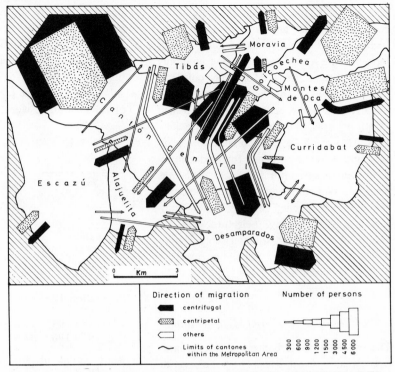

Fig. 31-7. SAN JOSE MEROPOLITAN AREA: INTERNAL MIGRATION UP TO 1963

dominate there. Large coffee *fincas* in the west impede the expansion of the city in that direction. There are no extensive urbanized areas and no slums. This partly agrarian marginal zone, which has the highest rates of growth within the Area Metropolitana, produces a considerable part of the farm wage laborers whose mobility and persistent ties to agriculture create an intermediate stage in which urban and rural life cease to appear as insurmountable contrasts.

The strong mobility within the Area Metropolitana and considerable emigration of population from the partly agricultural suburbs into rural areas indicate a high degree of adjustment to existing employment opportunities. Only 717 of the emigrants from the Canton of Palmares lived in the Area Metropolitana in 1963, but 634 people had migrated from the Area Metropoli-

tana to Palmares. From the Canton of San Carlos in the Northern Lowlands, an area of recent agricultural colonization, 820 people (14 per cent of the emigrants) had gone to the Area Metropolitana, but 1027 people came to San Carlos from the Area Metropolitana. On the other hand, the slow progress of urbanization and psychological barriers against life in the big city favor the development of rural slums. In Costa Rica, urbanization is not a measure for economic and social pressure on the agricultural sector.

General Aspects of PPR in Costa Rica

Judged by the national balance as shown in Table 31-4, the growing population pressure in Costa Rica does not seem to be an insoluble problem, at least as far as food

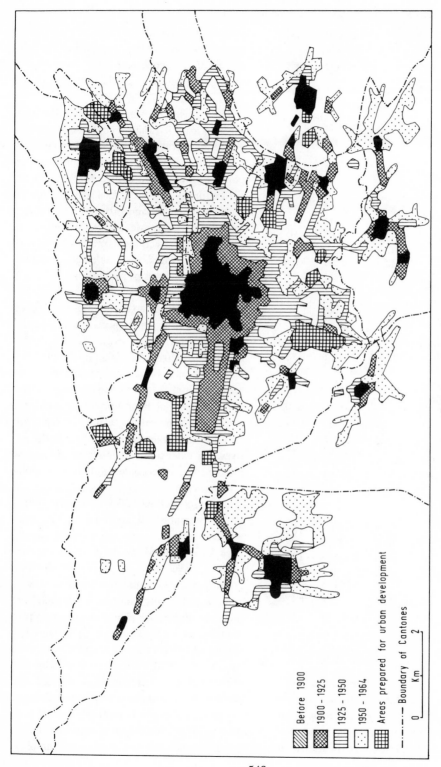

Before 1900

1900 - 1925

1925 - 1950

1950 - 1964

Areas prepared for urban development

— Boundary of Cantones

0   Km   2

Fig. 31-8. SAN JOSE: URBAN GROWTH

TABLE 31-4   COSTA RICA. POPULATION AND
LAND USE, COMPARATIVE DATA

Item	1955	1963	1955-1963 %
Population	969,640	1,336,274	+37.8
Farms (over 0.7 ha)			
Number	47,286	64,621	+36.7
Areas (1,000 ha)			
Total	1,851	2,667	+44.0
Productive	1,160	1,543	+33.0
Annual crops	111	167	+50.5
Permanent crops	155	201	+29.7
Pasture	722	935	+29.5
Secondary brush	134	279	+108.0
Forest	542	821	+51.5
Farms, in %			
0,7-10 ha	54.2	52.6	+33.1
10-100 ha	40.3	40.8	+38.0
100-1,000 ha	5.2	6.2	+62.5
over 1,000 ha	0.3	0.4	+51.2
Principal crops (1,000 ha)			
Coffee	56	81	+44.5
Corn	50	53	+6.2
Rice	25	51	+99.2
Beans	33	44	+31.1
Sugar Cane	19	25	+49.2
Principal crops (1,000 t of production)			
Coffee	26.5	53.5	+101.9
Corn	46.8	55.4	+18.4
Rice	17.4	39.9	+129.2
Beans	10.7	16.0	+49.5
Sugar Cane	595.2	1,083.8	+81.8
Cattle (1,000)	705	1,051	+49.0
Imports of food and food products in U.S. ($1,000,000)	12.3	11.4	−7.3

production is concerned. The area of cultivated land, agricultural production and
yields have increased more than population.
The table does not show that the number of
uneconomic minifundios has increased in

numerous parts of the highland, and that
many farms have been depressed to the minimum of existence and can survive only
through "stagnation" of the standard of living.

The growing problems of population pressure in Costa Rica are recognized by farmer
and administration alike; but they are still
principally seen as a disequilibrium between
population and land and as pressure on the
agriculturally used area. As a social factor the
high valuation of land property has led to a
dualism characteristic of Costa Rica. Until
recently, the government promoted individual pioneer colonization as a chief solution
to population pressure; today that system is
causing considerable problems and high social costs. Simultaneously, densely settled agricultural areas experienced an intensification and a formation of *minifundios,* which
resulted in extremely high population pressure. The necessity for intensification, the
growing number of uneconomic small farms,
and extremely high land prices have effected
a much better use of the natural resources
than in the marginal areas. But both alternatives, i.e. extension and intensification, have
proved to be inadequate solutions to population pressure.

In densely settled agricultural areas, population pressure will continue to rise even
without further numerical increase, simply
because aspirations toward a higher standard
of living have appeared, the market situation
is being changed by the development of large
commercial farms, and because there are
nonagricultural jobs. The influence and productivity of large farms are increasing. The
system of small farm co-operatives which is
simultaneously developing has a stabilizing
effect, but can increase the economic and
demographic potential only insignificantly.
Population pressure is primarily regarded as
an economic problem, as a result of the relation between population numbers, employ-

ment, and returns per family. But in the peripheral areas with shifting cultivation and latifundism, the pressure of population on natural resources and the land is immediate, and becomes apparent much in advance of the intensification and full utilization of the ecological potential.

Land tenure reform would bring no permanent relief on the national scale, because there are too many minifundios that would have to be eliminated. The economically oriented demand for "reasonable" farm sizes and for an increase in productivity is contrary to the social necessities and to the tradition of guaranteeing security, employment, and a minimum standard of living to as many small proprietors as possible. Much more important is regional adjustment between overpopulated and underpopulated areas, which is effected by stabilization and regional development in the marginal areas. This development, however, is impeded by economic problems, such as overproduction of basic agricultural products, low market capacity, and the economic weakness of the traditionally operated small farms, as compared with the modernized large farms.

The increasing problems of growing population pressure in Costa Rica should primarily be seen as results of problems in the economical and regional structure and only secondarily as results of the extremely high reproductive rate. The combination of three elements makes this pressure particularly troublesome: high valuation of private land rooted in a strong peasant tradition; lack of nonagricultural jobs, together with an insufficient increase of employment opportunities; and a common striving for a higher standard of living. This last factor is of particular importance in Costa Rica, where the standard of living is fairly high because of relatively stable political and social conditions. Just as a self-sufficient peasant economy with strong social orientation toward the *finca* has

evolved toward higher productivity and standards of living combined with an "economization" of values, growing population pressure has brought about a disintegration of traditional structure. Social and economic contrasts and tensions among different groups and regions are increasing. Some observers of the Costa Rican scene regard this diversification and the growing concentration of population as a necessary prerequisite for higher economic and social development. We cannot share this optimism because over-all economic problems are growing and the frustration gap of the active, intelligent Costa Rican farmers is increasing. On the other hand, reasonable economic development of the marginal areas and an improvement of the structure in the highland offers many possibilities for a compensation of growing population pressure during the next two to three decades. Sufficient funds for far-reaching structural improvement are not available, however; and essential changes will continue to occur in an empirical manner and by half-automatic self-regulation. In the long run, the only chance for Costa Rica will be a considerable reduction of the present birth rates and a basic improvement of the economic structure by the creation of nonagricultural jobs and an increase in productivity.

Elements of National Individuality

The general aspects of the PPR in Costa Rica are made particularly clear by comparing it with the other Central American countries. On the national scale, Costa Rica is by no means representative of the Central American situation. Its specific national characteristics include the predominance and importance of the peasant community and the peasant structure. The feudal structure of the hacienda and peon system is only of local importance. The strong mobility and agility of the agricultural population finds expression not only in strong internal migrations, but also in rapid changes of the occupational structure, the forms of land tenure, the farm sizes, and even the social situation. The existence of large reserves of virgin land, the mobility of population, and the agricultural policy of the government made possible a strong internal colonization, mainly in the form of squatter settlement, which effectively reduced the population pressure of the highland for a long time. There is a strong intercommunication between the areas of different structure in the highland and in the marginal areas. Still, the regional contrasts in the economic and social structure and in the consequences in terms of PPR are increasing.

On the regional scale, Costa Rica appears less unique. In particular, the marginal areas reveal many problems and characteristics of regional structure typical of Central America and Latin America as a whole. The dynamic forces of development, however, are particularly intensive in Costa Rica. The Central Highland as a whole cannot be compared with other Central American regions; but some of the regional units share certain characteristics with them. Considering the basic regional units within the larger functioning reality, Costa Rica despite its national individuality, exhibits some, if not all, of the representative traits of the Central American situation. Its dynamic development and wealth of different types of adaptation to the process of PPR make Costa Rica an excellent area for studying and recognizing the actual operation in small areas.

REFERENCES

(1) Richard N. Adams: Cultural Surveys of Panama, Nicaragua, Guatemala, El Salvador, Honduras (Panamerican Sanitary Bureau, Scientific Public. No. 33, Washington, 1957).

(2) AID Resources Inventory Center: Atlas Costa Rica, Analisis Regional de Recursos Físicos (Washington, D.C., 1965).

(3) Daniel E. Alleger: Estudios sobre Problemas Agro-Económicos en Costa Rica (Minist. de Agric. e Indust., San José, 1960).

(4) Luis Barahona: El Gran Incógnito. Visión Interna del Campesino Costarricense (San José, 1953).

(5) Oscar Benavides: Estudio Agrícola-Económico de la Cuenca Media del Río Grande (Inst. Costarricense de Electricidad, San José, 1956).

(6) Ester Boserup: The Conditions of Agricultural Growth; the Economics of Agrarian Change under Population Pressure (Chicago, 1965).

(7) Gerardo Budowski: Middle America: the Human Factor, in: F. Fraser Darling and John P. Milton, eds.: Future Environments of North America; Transformation of a Continent (Garden City, 1966), pp. 144-55.

(8) O. Andrew Collver: Birth Rates in Latin America: New Estimates of Historical Trends and Fluctuations (Berkeley, Cal., 1965).

(9) Conservation Foundation: La Conservación Humana en Centro América. Resumen de Discusiones (Guatemala, 1966).

(10) M. Córdoba: Estudio Agroeconómico de 22 Fincas de Zaragoza de Palmares (San José, 1958).

(11) Kingsley Davis, ed.: A Crowding Hemisphere: Population Change in the Americas, *Annals of the American Academy of Political and Social Science,* Vol. 316, 1958.

(12) William G. Demas: The Economics of Development in Small Countries, with Special Reference to the Caribbean (Montreal, 1965).

(13) Dirección General de Estadística y Censos: Censo de Población 11.5.1927 (San José, 1960).

(14) Dirección General de Estadística y Censos: Censo de Población 22.5.1950 (San José, 1953).

(15) Dirección General de Estadística y Censos: Censo de Población 31.3.1963 (San José, 1966).

(16) Dirección General de Estadística y Censos: Censo Agropecuario de 1955 (San José, 1959).

(17) Dirección General de Estadística y Censos: Censo Agropecuario de 1963 (San José, 1965).

(18) Dirección General de Estadística y Censos: Areas Demográficas de Costa Rica (San José, 1959).

(19) Dirección General de Estadística y Censos. Anuario Estadístico (San José, annually).

(20) Wolf Donner: Entwicklung and Entwicklungspolitik in Zentralamerika: Costa Rica (Forschungsinstitut für Wirtschaftsfragen der Entwicklungsländer, Bonn, 1965).

(21) Louis J. Ducoff: Human Resources of Central America, Panama and Mexico 1950-1980, in Relation to some Aspects of Economic Development (United Nations, 1960).

(22) Joe C. Hayes and Milford J. Wiltbank: Costa Rica, Toward Rural Security (International Development Services, New York, 1960).

(23) George W. Hill, Manuel Gollás Quintero, and Gregorio Alfaro: Un Area en Desarollo, sus Problemas Económicos y Sociales en Costa Rica (Instituto Universitario Centroaméricano de Investigaciones Sociales y Económicas (San José, 1964).

(24) Instituto de Tierras y Colonización: Tenencia y Uso de la Tierra en Costa Rica (San José, 1964).

(25) Eduardo Jenkins Dobles: El Desarollo Económico y Social de Costa Rica (San José, 1962).

(26) Wilburg Jiménez Castro: Migraciones Internas en Costa Rica (Pan American Union, Washington, D.C., 1956).

(27) Ricardo Jiménez Jiménez: Proyección de la Población de Costa Rica por Sexo y Grupos de Edad 1965-1990, *Revista de Estudios y Estadísticas,* No. 8, 1967, pp. 3-76.

(28) Ricardo Jiménez Nuñez: La Alimentación de Nuestros Campesinos, *Revista del Instituto de Defensa del Café de Costa Rica,* Vol. 10, No. 72, 1940-41, pp. 229-57.

(29) Clyde V. Kiser, ed.: Components of Population Change in Latin America, *Milbank Memorial Fund Quarterly*, Vol. 43, No. 4, 1965.

(30) Charles P. Loomis and R. M. Powell: Sociometric Analysis of Class Status in Rural Costa Rica. A Peasant Community Compared with a Hacienda Community, *Sociometry*, Vol. 12, No. 1-3, 1949, pp. 144-47.

(31) Charles P. Loomis: Turrialba: Social Systems and the Introduction of Change (Glencoe, Ill., 1953).

(32) P. Luros: Aspectos Biodemográficos de la Población de Costa Rica (Secretaria de Salubridad Pública y Protección Social, San José, 1940).

(33) Joao Lyra Madeira: Evalucão Demografico de Costa Rica. *Revista Brasileira de Estadistica*, Vol. 17, No. 65, 1956.

(34) J. F. Montoya and L. A. Reuss: Estudio Comparativo de los Cambios en Occupación de los Individuos y Tamaño de las Fincas de los Padres y sus Herederos, Cantón de Atenas, Provincia de Alajuela, 1959 (Minist. de Agric. e Industr., San José, 1960).

(35) M. A. Muños: Breve Estudio Agro-Económico del Cantón de Grecia, *El Agricultor Costarricense*, Vol. 1, 1943, pp. 245-52.

(36) Helmut Nuhn, et al: Estudio Geográfico Regional, Zona Atlántico Norte de Costa Rica (Instituto de Tierras y Colonización, San José, 1967).

(37) Robert E. Nunley: The Distribution of Population in Costa Rica (Nat. Acad. of Science, National Research Council Publ. 743, Washington, D. C., 1960).

(38) Oficina de Planificación: Plan de Desarollo Económico y Social de Costa Rica (San José, 1966).

(39) N. W. Painter and P. C. Morrison: Rural Population Stability, Central District of Turrialba Canton, Costa Rica, *Rural Sociology*, Vol. 17, No. 4, 1952, pp. 356-66.

(40) L. E. Peterson: Agricultural Development Prospects for Costa Rica (Report of the Inter-American Development Commission, Washington, D.C., 1947).

(41) Hans Polakowsky: Die Bevölkerung von Costa Rica, *Petermanns Geographische Mitteilungen, Ergänzungsheft*, Vol. 101 (Gotha, 1889).

(42) L. A. Reuss and J. F. Montoya: Tipo y Tamaño de Finca en el Cantón de Atenas, 1959 (Minist. de Agric. e Industr., San José, 1960).

(43) M. Rodriguez and A. W. Peterson: Capacidad de Producción Económico-Agricola de Dos Areas del Cantón de Turrialba, Costa Rica, *Turrialba*, Vol. 1, 1950-51, pp. 234-39.

(44) Eugenio Rodríguez Vega: Apuntes para una Sociología Costarricense (San José, 1953).

(45) José Manuel Salazar N.: Tierras y Colonización en Costa Rica (Publicaciones de la Universidad de Costa Rica, Serie Tesis de Grado No. 15, San José, 1962).

(46) René Sánchez Bolaños: Proyecciónes de Población de la República de Costa Rica para los Años 1960, 1965, 1970 (San José, 1962).

(47) Gerhard Sandner: Turrubares. Estudio de Geografía Regional, Problemas Sociales y Económicos de la Expansión Agrícola en Costa Rica (San José, 1960).

(48) Gerhard Sandner: Aspectos Geográficos de la Colonización Agrícola en el Valle del General (San José, 1961).

(49) Gerhard Sandner: El Concepto Espacial y los Sistemas Funcionales en la Colonización Espontánea Costarricense, *Informe Semestral,* Instituto Geográfico de Costa Rica, Julio a Diciembre 1962.

(50) Gerhard Sandner: La Colonización Agrícola de Costa Rica (Instituto Geogr. de Costa Rica, San José, Vol. 1, 1962, Vol. 2, 1964).

(51) Gerhard Sandner: Cot de Oreamuno, Herencia Colonial, Uso de la Tierra, Problemas Socioeconómicos (Instituto Geogr. de Costa Rica, San José, 1964).

(52) Gerhard Sandner: Die Erschliessung der karibischen Waldregion im südlichen Zentral-Amerika, *Die Erde,* Vol. 95, No. 2, 1964, pp. 111-31.

(53) Gerhard Sandner: Costa Rica, Allgemeine Statistik des Auslandes, ed. (Statistisches Bundesamt, Wiesbaden, 1966).

(54) Gerhard Sandner: Die Hauptstädte Zentralamerikas. Wachstumsprobleme, Gestaltwandel und Ausstrahlung der Gross-stadt in tropischen Entwicklingsländern (Heidelberg, in press).

(55) T. Lynn Smith: Un Análisis Comparativo de la Migración Rural-Urbana en Latino-América, *Estadística,* Vol. 16, 1958, pp. 436-53.

(56) Pierre A. D. Stouse Jr.: Cambios en el Uso de la Tierra en Regiones Ex-Bananeras de Costa Rica (Instituto Geográfico de Costa Rica, San José, 1967).

(57) Bernardo Augusto Thiel: Mongrafía de la Población de Costa Rica en el Siglo XIX (Revista de Costa Rica en el Siglo XIX, San José, 1902).

(58) William Vogt: La Población de Costa Rica y sus Recursos Naturales (Pan American Union, Washington, D.C., 1946).

(59) Ernst Wagemann: Menschenzahl und Völkerschicksal. Eine Lehre von den optimalen Dimensionen gesellschaftlicher Gebilde (Hamburg, 1948).

(60) Philip L. Wagner: Nicoya. A Cultural Geography, *Univ. of California Publ. in Geography,* Vol. 12, No. 3, 1958.

(61) Leo Waibel: White Settlement in Costa Rica, *Geographical Review,* Vol. 29, 1939, pp. 529-60.

(62) Wilbur Zelinsky: Population Growth in Central America and the West Indies; Prospects and Problems, *Mineral Industries* (The Pennsylvania State University), Vol. 35, No. 6, 1966, pp. 1-7.

32. POPULATION PRESSURE IN THE STATE OF SAO PAULO, BRAZIL

Andrzej Bonasewicz

General Characteristics of the Demographic Situation in Brazil

Brazil is one of those countries now experiencing a "demographic explosion." The rate of natural increase is growing year by year (9; 21; 22); see table below.

During the years 1950-60, the population rose from 51,976,000 to 71,117,000, an increase of 19 million persons. By 1966, the total had reached 85 million—a growth of 14 million within six years. Natural increase and immigration have been responsible for the growth, although the importance of the latter has decreased considerably during the last decade. In the period 1950-60, about 580,000 immigrants came to Brazil, most of them from Portugal, Italy, and Spain (4).

The population of Brazil is a young one: in 1960, 42.3 per cent of the country's population belonged to the 0-14 age group and 55.0 per cent to the 15-64 age group. Only 2.7 per cent were over 65 (21). Families with many children are numerous. On the average, there are 661 children per 100 white women. For other races, the indices are lower; including women of all age groups there are 643 children per 100 mulatto

women, 581 children per 100 Negro women, and 456 per 100 Asian women (23).

Women marry early: 24 per cent of all married women are under 20. At the same time there is a high percentage of illegitimate children: about 42 per cent of unmarried women over 35 have children. No family planning campaign is conducted in Brazil, and contraceptives are not officially used. This is largely due to the attitude of the clergy and to the great difficulties of carrying out such a campaign in almost inaccessible regions.

On the other hand, the cost of maintaining children is low in Brazil. In rural areas they either help on their parents' farm or are hired as workers on neighboring farms. Their needs are modest: a bowl of manioc or beans a day and a single dress or suit is enough. The situation does not essentially differ in towns: children are employed as domestic servants and parents do not have to spend anything on their upkeep.

In recent years, mortality has dropped considerably, the average life span has been prolonged, and the reproduction potential of the population has greatly increased, thanks to progress in the medical sciences.

Population distribution in Brazil is very

Years	Average birth rate (per 1000)	Average death rate (per 1000)	Natural Increase (per 1000)
1891/1900	46.0	27.8	18.2
1900/1920	45.0	26.4	18.6
1920/1940	44.0	25.3	18.7
1940/1950	43.5	19.7	23.8
1959/1961	40.0–43.0	11.0–13.0	29.0–31.0

uneven. The interior is sparsely populated and the great majority of people live in the coastal zone in three large agglomerations that have existed since colonial times. The oldest is the northeastern region which played the predominant role in the colonial period, and is now subject to the strongest population pressure. Unfavorable environmental conditions in the so-called "polygon of drought" (*poligono das sêcas*) have resulted in continuing migration from the area. In the coastal zone the density of population is as much as 100/km², but drops to 25 and even 20/km² west of the 36th meridian. The income per capita is much lower than in the other regions.

The second region of population concentration, a belt with densities exceeding 25/km², extends past the 44th meridian and encompasses the central and eastern parts of the country. It is the most compact and uniform of the densely populated areas, and includes the southern part of Espirito Santo, eastern Minas Gerais, Rio de Janeiro, Guanabara, and São Paulo. This area, comprising 11 per cent of the territory of Brazil, accounted for 44 per cent of the population in 1960. The region shows various trends in migration: on the one hand, there is an outward movement to the south, mostly Paraná, on the other, an influx of people from the northeastern provinces.

The third agglomeration, not so large as the other two, but the most uniform in racial composition, encompasses the three southern states of Brazil. Here the density of population surpasses 25/km² only in a few areas; but the rate of growth is particularly high as a result of immigration, both from other parts of the country and abroad. This region is demographically the most dynamic.

In addition to the three major agglomerations, a few smaller ones are found in the southern part of Goias, northeastern Para, and northern Maranhão.

The rapid growth of urban population is a characteristic feature in Brazil. In the decade 1950-60, the number of city dwellers increased by 70 per cent. In 1950, 36.2 per cent of the population lived in cities and towns, as against 45.1 in 1960 (4). The surge from the countryside to urban areas has been and still is the most important migrational trend. Cities with a population of more than 20,000 are increasing at a particularly rapid rate. The number rose from 96 in 1950 to 172 in 1960, and their combined population increased from 10.3 million to 19.2 million during the same period. As of 1960, 67.3 per cent of the urban population of Brazil was living in cities with a population of more than 20,000 (4).

The average density of population in Brazil is but 10/km², yet population pressure exists in the country. The average per capita income was $182 in 1950; it increased at a rate of 5.7 per cent to reach $233 in 1960 (4). Population growth during that period was 3.6 per cent. Thus by 1963 the rate of income growth had dropped to 2.1 per cent, while population growth rose to a higher level than in the previous period. There are great differences in the distribution of national income in various sectors of the economy. In 1956, each person employed in agriculture received an average of $110, those in industry, $440. The regional distribution also varies greatly—in 1960 per capita income in the richest state, Guanabara, was $624, and only $57 in the poorest—Piaui (4).

Characteristics of the State of São Paulo

The present study is aimed at analyzing population pressure in one of the twenty-two states of Brazil, São Paulo. It is situated in the southeastern part of the country, between the 20th and 25th parallels and occupies 247,898 km² or 2.91 per cent of the area of the country. In 1960 it was inhabited by 12,947,000 persons representing 18.33 per cent of Brazil's population. The average density was 52.3/km². Physically, São Paulo is a plateau: only 8 per cent of its area is under 300 m; 52 per cent is from 300 to 600 m, and as much as 40 per cent from 600 to 1500 m (1). There are no sharp differences of altitude, which is conducive to the development of agriculture. The climate is tropical in the coastal zone, with average temperatures from 21° to 22°C. and annual rainfall totals of more than 2000 mm; in the center it is subtropical with temperatures of 16° to 18° and rainfall of 1300 to 1800 mm. Tropical forests cover 76 per cent of the area, savanna 15 per cent, and prairies 9 per cent. Of São Paulo's many rivers, the Paraná (which marks the border of the state) and its tributaries the Rio Grande, Rio Pardo, Tiete, and Paranapanema are particularly rich sources of water, as is the river Paraíba, which flows directly into the Atlantic Ocean. These rivers are a source of power, and many hydro-electric power plants have been built along them, notably Furnas (150,000 kW), Ibitinga (140,000 kW), and Chavantes (400,000 kW); and some very large hydro-electric power plants are currently being built at other points in these river basins: Ilha Solteira (3 million kW), Três Lagoas (1.2 million kW), and Sete Quedas (10 million kW). These hydro-electric resources constitute a base for the development of industry.

São Paulo has no important mineral resources, but the lack is compensated for by deposits in neighboring states, especially Minas Gerais. On the other hand, there are fertile soils everywhere—terra roxa, massape, and others—all excellent for coffee plantations. The state is also able to maintain direct contact with the United States and Europe because of its coastal location. Thus, conditions for the development of agriculture and industry in the region are generally good.

São Paulo is the most economically advanced state in Brazil. In 1960 it employed 970,000, or 58.8 per cent of the country's industrial workers and produced 18.3 per cent of the national income. It also supplied 52.35 per cent of the electric power produced in the country: 3,780,267 kW. The engineering, chemical, and textile industries are well developed, and the state's network accounts for one-quarter of the total railway mileage in Brazil. The agricultural output of São Paulo is also considerable. It contains one-fourth of all the arable land in Brazil and farms occupy 190,076 km², or 76.6 per cent of the area of the state. Coffee, cotton, and sugar cane are the main marketable products, while rice and maize are the most important crops grown for consumption. An analysis of the yields of these crops in 1950 and 1965 shows an absolute growth of production with a simultaneous drop of the state's share in the total national output (4):

Crop	Output of the state of São Paulo (1000 tons)		Percentage of national output	
	1950	1965	1950	1965
coffee	469	993	43.8	27.1
cotton	610	626	52.3	31.5
sugar cane	6,914	29,476	21.2	38.9
rice	993	1,095	30.8	14.4

Although minerals contribute little to the economy of the state, in 1965 São Paulo provided 73 per cent of Brazil's total output of apatites, and 32 per cent of its dolomites. It also produced small amounts of talc—7 per cent of the total—and about 6 per cent of the lead ores mined in Brazil (4).

São Paulo was originally settled by the

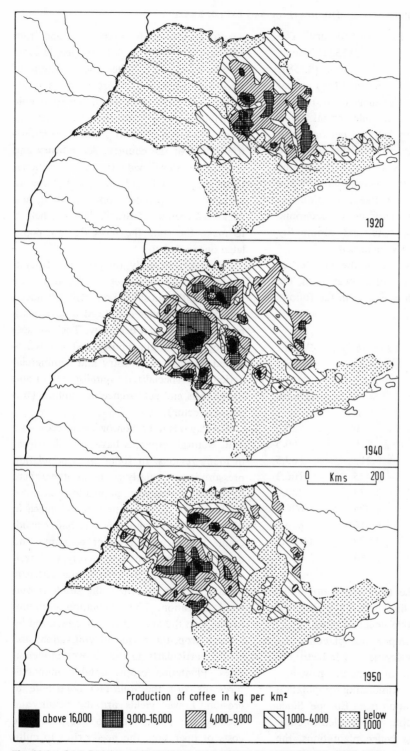

1920

1940

0   Kms   200

1950

Production of coffee in kg per km²

■ above 16,000   9,000–16,000   4,000–9,000   1,000–4,000   below 1,000

Fig. 32-1.   SAO PAULO: EXPANSION OF COFFEE PLANTATIONS, 1920, 1940, 1950

Portuguese in the sixteenth century. The first colonies—São Vicente (1532), Santos (1545), São Paulo de Piratinga (1558), Nossa Senhora de Itanhaem (1561), and São João Batista de Caneneia (1600)—were located in the more accessible coastal zones. By 1797, only about 158,000 persons lived in the state, and its role in the economic life of the country was only a minor one (19). But during the second half of the nineteen century the coffee plantation became an important factor in the economic development of the state, and commodity production was greatly increased.

The relationships among the number of inhabitants, the extent of railway lines, the number of coffee trees is seen in the following table: (11)

Year	Population	Length of railway lines in km	Coffee shrubs, in millions
1860	695	0	26.8
1870	830	139	60.5
1880	1,107	1,212	69.5
1890	1,395	2,425	106.3
1900	2,280	3,375	220.0
1910	2,800	4,825	696.7
1920	4,592	6,616	826.6
1930	7,161	7,099	1,188.1
1950	9,314	7,594	1,094.7

It appears from the table that until 1930 there was a close link between population growth and the development of coffee plantations. Later, the importance of coffee decreased and the development of industry became the main factor of economic growth.

Another factor stimulating population growth was immigration from Europe. Since more and more people were needed to cultivate the developing coffee plantations, the state negotiated contracts with various European organizations for manpower, and from 1870-1900 as many as 806,000 people came to São Paulo (2). After the abolition of slavery in 1889, even more immigrants arrived, especially from Italy. These people contributed much to the growth of agriculture and were the first to promote the industrialization of the country. As industry and agriculture developed further, additional labor was needed, and the state became an attraction for people from the poor and backward regions of Brazil. This too helped to make the state the most densely populated one in Brazil.

In the present study, the problem of population pressure has been analyzed in the context of the most economically advanced and densely populated state of a developing country with a dual economy. The two sectors operate simultaneously and are represented by modern industry and commercial agriculture (specialized capitalist sector) and handicrafts and subsistence agriculture (traditional sector).

São Paulo is not a homogeneous economic unit. Natural resources have been destroyed in many regions. In some areas population pressure is particularly acute, in others there has been a dynamic population increase. Various parts of the state were colonized in different periods, and this has had considerable influence on type of economy and density of population. For each type of agricultural economy, there is a characteristic density; if it is exceeded, the result is outward migration. The population optimum depends on the amount of labor required by a given crop, the period of cultivation, and yields, particularly in the case of monocultures. Plantation crops, notably monocultures, exhaust the soil, and contribute to erosion. Lower yields are the result, and because the plantations do not repay the costs of operation, the need arises to cultivate food crops or to turn to stock-breeding.

Some people, however, migrate to new areas and set up plantations in "pioneer colonization" zones. In this way various crops wander, as it were, from one region to another, and the people travel with them, making it difficult to pinpoint the relationship between type of economy, density of population, and rate of population increase within the state.

Determining these relationships becomes more and more urgent as the state's share in the total population of Brazil increases. The following data illustrate the percentage of the country's population living in São Paulo since 1872 (4).

In the years 1950-60, the population increased by 4.2 per cent with a natural increase of 2.3 per cent. In absolute figures there were 3,840,300 additional persons or 20.2 per cent of Brazil's total increase in

Year	Per cent
1872	8.43
1890	9.66
1900	13.08
1920	15.00
1940	17.41
1950	17.59
1960	18.28
1965	18.64
1970	19.00

population. Immigration from overseas and from other states played an important role in this growth. In 1950, the population included 1,080,400 persons born in other states, of whom 512,700 were from Minas Gerais; 62,700 from Pernambuco; and 56,100 from Rio de Janeiro (2). In the years 1950-59, the immigration pattern was as follows: (13)

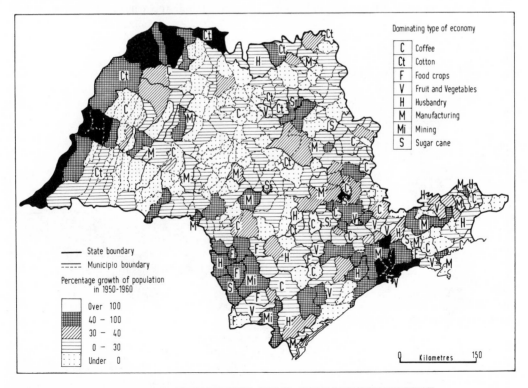

Fig. 32-2.   SAO PAULO: POPULATION GROWTH, 1950-60, AND DOMINANT TYPES OF ECONOMY

1950	100,100	1955	88,500
1951	208,500	1956	86,400
1952	249,600	1957	44,000
1953	110,600	1958	101,800
1954	94,300	1959	121,000

During these years, most of the newcomers were from Bahia, Minas Gerais, Pernambuco, Alagoas, and Ceara, and the share of immigrants from abroad decreased considerably, as shown in the table below: (19; 20).

Year	Per cent
1872	3.5
1900	21.0
1920	17.9
1940	10.6
1950	6.9

In 1950, 700,000 foreigners, most of them Italians, Portuguese, Spaniards, and Japanese lived in São Paulo, and represented the great majority of foreigners who have settled in Brazil.

The growth of population has been accompanied by an increase in the number of industrial workers. The table below shows workers of São Paulo as a percentage of all industrial workers in Brazil (4; 12).

| 1920 | 29.1 | 1950 | 38.6 |
| 1940 | 34.9 | 1964 | 58.8 |

The combination of population growth and increased employment brought about a 12 per cent increase in per capita income—from $340 in 1950 to $381 in 1960. Yet during the same period, the national average increased by 22 per cent. The lower rate in São Paulo may be explained by the high percentage of population increase, for in the same period, the percentile growth of per

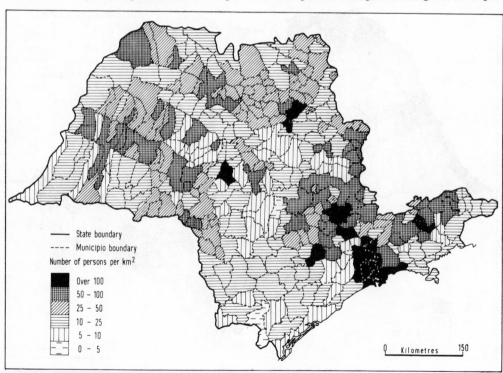

State boundary
Municipio boundary
Number of persons per km²

Over 100
50 – 100
25 – 50
10 – 25
5 – 10
0 – 5

Kilometres

Fig. 32-3.   SAO PAULO: POPULATION DENSITY, BY MUNICIPIO, 1960

capita income was higher in areas of emigration in northeastern Brazil.

Although average per capita income in the state is relatively high, distribution varies greatly. As a rule it is more in towns than in the countryside, with particularly high incomes in the city of São Paulo. In 1960 urban population accounted for 62.81 per cent of the whole population; the national average was 45.08 per cent. These figures are higher than the actual number of urban dwellers indicates, because in Brazil the capital of each administrative unit is a town only if it has more than 150 inhabitants. In 1966 there were 3958 administrative units of secondary rank, or *municipios,* in Brazil; and the capital of each was a town, according to Brazilian statistics. In spite of this, it should be acknowledged that in comparison to other Brazilian states the percentage of urban population in São Paulo is relatively high.

Population Pressure in São Paulo

São Paulo is divided into municipios, which in turn are composed of districts. The number of municipios increases each year; local authorities tend to set up ever more new administrative centers in order to get a share of the state budget. Their number in various years since 1938 is shown below (4):

1938	270
1950	369
1960	504
1963	502
1966	573

This very large number of administrative units makes general orientation difficult. To

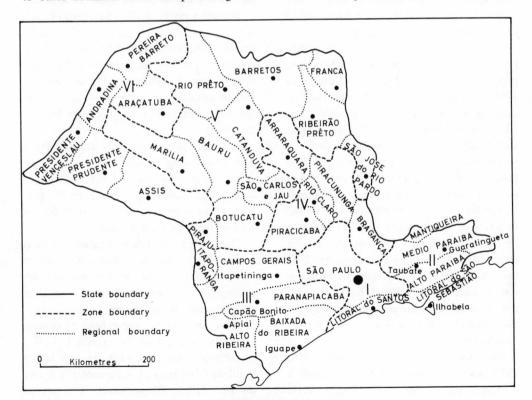

Fig. 32-4. SAO PAULO: REGIONS AND PHYSIOGRAPHIC ZONES

Type	Region	I	II	III	IV	V	VI	Total
Coffee		–	–	1	2	57	13	73
Coffee and other crops		2	4	3	19	76	13	107
Cotton		–	–	–	–	3	9	12
Cotton and other crops		–	–	–	2	9	13	26
Fruit		2	–	9	–	–	–	11
Fruit and other crops		4	2	3	3	–	–	12
Sugar cane		–	–	–	–	–	–	–
Sugar cane and other crops		2	2	1	3	5	–	13
Food crops		1	–	6	–	–	–	7
Stock-breeding		–	3	–	–	–	–	3
Stock-breeding and other		–	13	9	1	1	–	24
Manufacturing		23	7	3	27	10	2	72
Mining		–	–	2	–	–	–	2
	Total	34	31	36	57	161	50	369

simplify their work, Brazilian geographers have introduced the notion of *zonas fisiograficas*" (physiographic zones) which define the situation of various municipios.

The present study, which encompasses type of economy, degree of urbanization, population density, and growth in the years 1950-60, was carried out at the level of the municipios. To obtain comparable data, the administrative division of 1950 was adopted and statistical data for 1960 were calculated to correspond to the 1950 divisions The typology of the agricultural economy was conducted on the basis of value of output. If, for instance, a particular crop prevailed in terms of value (more than 50 per cent of the total output), the economy of the municipio was classified as monocultural. If two crops ranked almost equally, the economy was classified as mixed, e.g. coffee-cotton, with the first-mentioned crop taking the lead. The same system was adopted for industrial production.

The average output of the years 1954, 1955, and 1956 was used for classification purposes, and on the basis of the criteria mentioned above, six demographic-economic regions were singled out, taking into account the existing division of 23 *zonas fisiograficas*.

The economy in all the municipios of each region was classified according to eight major types. Within each municipio the leading crop, as well as the predominant mixture of two crops, was determined. The classification of municipios shown below is based on the 1950 census (5) and statistics for the state (17).

The table above takes into account types with outstanding predominance of a single crop (more than 50 per cent of output value) and mixed types in which the predominating crop accounts for 40 to 50 per cent of the total output value.

The rate of population increase has been highest in the industrial municipios, where densities are more than 50/km² and the percentage of city dwellers is often more than 60 per cent. In the more urbanized municipios, an effective upper limit of density of population cannot be specified. Coffee municipios come next with densities of 25 to 50/km² but rather low percentages of city dwellers (10 to 30 per cent). The rate of population growth is very low, and in many

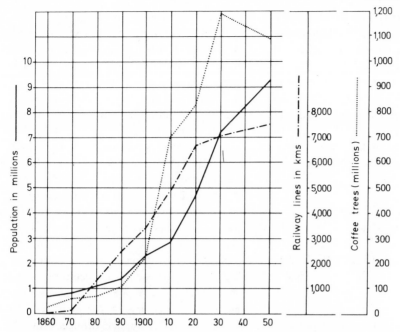

Fig. 32-5. SAO PAULO: POPULATION GROWTH, RAILWAY EXTENSION, AND COFFEE EXPANSION AND DECLINE

instances the population has dropped either in absolute or relative figures. In the cotton municipios, densities are still lower, ranging from 10 to 25/km². Although population growth is somewhat higher, there is frequently a relative drop in population.

The smaller administrative units, whose economy is based on the production of sugar cane, fruit, and vegetables, have a population density from 25 to 50/km², and a relatively low rate of population growth. Densities are lowest in municipios engaged specifically in the cultivation of food crops and stock-breeding.

THE FIRST DEMOGRAPHIC-ECONOMIC REGION
The First Region encompasses the coastal part of the state belonging to the zone of São Paulo (Industrial) and Litoral de Santos. It is a densely populated area with a high percentage of city dwellers, a predominance of industry, and a rapid over-all population growth. The most important mu-

nicipio in this region is the capital, São Paulo. In absolute figures, population growth in this single municipio is unprecendented, and its rate continues to increase. At the same time the percentage of the state's population living here has also increased, as shown below:

Year	Population	Per cent of the State Population
1872	31,000	3.75
1890	65,000	4.69
1900	240,000	10.51
1920	579,000	12.61
1940	1,326,000	18.47
1950	2,198,000	24.06
1960	3,825,000	29.48
1965	4,981,000	32.50
1970	6,498,000	42.40

The rapid growth of population in the nineteenth century was due to the industrialization of the city and its hinterland. This was made possible by the accumulation of capital from the sale of coffee and the inflow of foreign capital. These factors resulted in large-scale migrations to the city and its suburban zone, so that by 1966, the municipio had 5,116,000 inhabitants, and was the largest population unit in Brazil. An analysis of the origins of the city's population made by B. Hutchinson in 1959-60 produced the following results:

Place of Birth	Males	Females
São Paulo	27.1%	29.3%
Other major cities	14.7	16.2
Small towns	32.3	33.1
Countryside	3.9	6.6
Foreign countries	21.2	14.3
No data	0.9	0.6
	100.0%	100.0%

It is an interesting fact that 77.3 per cent of the male migrants and 34.8 per cent of the females arriving in São Paulo were actively searching for employment. The remaining migrants were attracted by the life of the big city.

Difficult living conditions in the Brazilian countryside encourage migration, at first to small towns, then to larger cities. Yet only a small percentage of the immigrants find jobs to suit them. The majority find only seasonal occupation and swell the ranks of the unemployed. Building cannot keep pace with growing needs, and whole districts of the poverty-stricken are appearing in the peripheral zones of the city where about 20 per cent of the population now live. The continuing drift toward the cities causes many difficulties, among them a drop in agricultural production because of the shortage of manpower and almost complete lack of mechanization in field work. Yet the income of farm laborers does not increase. Less agricultural produce means a rise in prices, which in turn makes an increase in wages in the cities inevitable. This process, which is particularly acute in Brazil, is the source of the spiral leading to the devaluation of money and inflation, and may be almost wholly attributed to the fact that urban population growth precedes industrialization.

In São Paulo, new enterprises are highly mechanized and employ relatively small numbers of workers. Thus, population pressure in the city rises and living standards decline. In economic terms, São Paulo is an "enclave of highly developed industry"—a separate region, alienated from the surrounding area of agricultural monoculture. In the years 1950-60, the population of the municipio increased by 74 per cent and the percentage of city dwellers dropped from 96 in 1950 to 87 in 1960. This resulted on the one hand from the tendency, particularly among the wealthy classes, to settle outside the city center. On the other hand, workers, unable to find jobs in industry, began to leave the city, attracted by a growth of employment in agriculture.

Population growth is greatest in the industrial municipios bordering São Paulo, above all in southeastern São Bernardo do Campo, where the density is 212.4/km²; its population increased 228 per cent—from 29,400 in 1950 to 94,700 in 1960. Santo Andre has a density of 732/km²; the number of its inhabitants increased 130 per cent, from 128,100 to 276,000. Growth was no less significant in the most densely populated municipio of São Caetano do Sul (4767.5/km²); its population increased from 60,200 to 114,400. In the municipio of Santo, the second largest city of the region, population increased from 206,900 to 265,000 (29 per cent), which is a little above the average rate of natural increase. The density is lower there, amounting to 366.0/km². The third largest municipio of the region is Campinas: its population increased 60 per cent, from 155,400 to 248,000, and its urban population increased considerably, from 65 to 81 per cent. Even a superficial analysis shows that in the industrial municipios there is no population optimum; on the contrary, in the most densely populated areas, the population increases at relatively quicker ates.

In the agricultural municipios, those specializing in fruit cultivation and sugar cane are the most numerous. Densities vary from 13 to 40/km²; and are greater in the more populated administrative units. This may indicate a concentration of agricultural production and that more profitable farms are developing at the expense of the weaker ones.

In the 37 municipios within the boundaries of the region, there was not one in which the population dropped, and only in five—municipios specializing in fruit, coffee, sugar cane, and commercial food crops— was there a relative drop. This resulted from the adverse balance of migrations (absolute growth of the population was lower than that resulting from natural increase). The specific feature of the First Region is the absence of a monocultural economy: the agricultural municipios cultivated several crops, with no single one predominating.

The First Region is the most dynamic in population growth, both in absolute and relative figures and is economically the most advanced, with great possibilities for development. Population pressure in the sense of exceeding the upper limit of density is non-existent. The largest industrial investments of Brazil are situated in this zone, a factor that certainly will bring further immigration and continuing rapid rises in population.

THE SECOND REGION

The Second Region encompasses the eastern part of São Paulo, namely, the zone of Mantiqueira, Alto Paraíba, and Medio Paraiba. Stock-breeding and industry predominate there; the density of population is high but the rate of growth very low; and there are many instances of absolute decline. This retrogressive tendency is clearly shown in the following statistics:

Year	Per cent of total state population	Per cent of coffee produced in state
1836	46	86
1854	38	77
1886	33	20
1920	13	3
1935	10	2
1950	6	0.5

Population pressure in this area, the oldest coffee plantation zone in the state, is acute. Decreasing yields resulting from badly exhausted soils and the relatively short (25 years) fruit-bearing stage of the coffee tree have led to a change in the economy: many former plantations have been turned into stock-breeding farms. Thus, because opportunities and natural resources are scanty, there has been an outflow of population to the First Region or new coffee plantation areas.

The municipios having a stock-breeding economy accompanied by crops are the most numerous; their population density ranges from 12 to 19/km². The percentage of city dwellers in these units is very low, and in most of them there is either a stagnation or decline of urban population. In the municipio of Lavrinhas, the population dropped from 3996 to 3248 (19 per cent) from 1950 to 1960; the density was 19.1/km² in 1960. In São José do Barreiro (10.2/km²) there was a 13 per cent drop—from 6606 to 5753 respectively. It is characteristic that the most rapid increase took place in the most densely populated municipios with the highest percentage of city dwellers outside the stock-breeding areas. For example, in Guarantingueta (67.3/km²), the population increased from 37,400 in 1950 to 52,600 in 1960—a 45 per cent growth. At the same time, urban population increased from 57 to 72 per cent.

The population of all industrial municipios increased; the rate of growth being the lowest (3 per cent) in the least densely populated Santa Branca (23.3/km²). In the more densely populated municipios with a higher percentage of city dwellers, growth ranged from 40 to 60 per cent. But in the few municipios specializing in coffee and sugar cane there was an absolute drop. Jambeiro showed the largest decrease—4100 to 3200 (22 per cent); Silveiras was next with a drop of 15 per cent—from 6000 to 5100. In both municipios, coffee is the dominating crop and the density of population is particularly low—15 and 12/km², respectively. The fruit-producing municipios are the most dynamic in the agricultural group: Pindamonhangaba and Campos do Jordão have densities of 55.1 and 61.9/km², and growth rates amounting to 38 and 31 per cent. This is an indication of the attractiveness of cultivating fruit and vegetables in the vicinity of the big industrial centers between Rio de Janeiro and São Paulo. All in all, of the thirty-one municipios in the Second Region, there was an absolute drop of population in eleven and a relative drop in ten of them.

THE THIRD REGION

Portions of the southeastern part of the state comprise the Third Region: Litoral de São Sebastião, Baixada do Ribeira, Alto Ribeira, Paranapiacaba, Campos Gerais, and Itaporanga. Vegetable and fruit cultivation and stock breeding predominate; there is a relatively low population density, a high rate of growth, and a low percentage of city dwellers. This area, which plays an important role in supplying vegetables and fruit to the First Region, is one of the least densely populated parts of São Paulo. The maximum density—39.2/km²—and highest percentage of city dwellers—64 per cent—are found in the municipio of Tatui.

Municipios producing fruits and vegetables prevail in this region, and population densities vary from 7 to 34/km². Two out of twelve units showed an absolute population drop during the 1950's, in one the figure remained stable. Characteristically these are situated in the southern coastal region of São Paulo. Population growth was the highest in Caraguatatuba (25.3/km²) increasing from 5500 to 9800. Tourism and banana plantations were the main sources of growth. Another dynamically developing municipio is Juquia (11.9/km²), where the population increased from 6600 to 9600.

Another group in this region is made up of municipios producing food crops and specializing in stock-breeding. Densities range from 6 to 31/km², and of fifteen units, there was a decrease of population in only three, all of them sparsely populated. An example is the maize-producing area of Ribeira (6.9/km²), where the decrease from 6900 to 5800 represented a drop of 18 per cent.

It is interesting to note that another municipio with identical economic structure, Taquarituba (29.5/km²), showed the remarkable growth rate of 71 per cent—from 7500 to 12,000. This was largely due to its location in one of the most dynamic regions of pioneer colonization connected with coffee plantations. Two other nearby coffee-producing municipios, Fartura and Itai, with densities of 31.1 and 10.6/km², also showed a remarkable population growth—46 and 33 per cent respectively. This was due above all to good yields in the area, where coffee plantations were begun as late as the 1940's. On the other hand, administrative units where coffee and stock-breeding are the predominant lines of economy are marked by a much lower growth or even stagnation.

The few industrial and mining municipios in this region are not so densely populated as similar units in other regions. Their rate of growth is much lower; and the percentage of city dwellers is insignificant. Ilhabela, with a population of 5100 and a density of 15.4/km², showed no increase in the decade 1950-60—the result of the dominance of small food-processing enterprises which do not generate significant profit.

Population pressure in the Third Region is not so acute as in the Second Region. The industrial region of São Paulo and more profitable plantations in northern Paraná have attracted considerable numbers. Movement to these areas is facilitated by a good transport system. Nevertheless, because of low population density and lack of typical monocultures it may be expected that the population could increase considerably without exceeding the upper limit of density typical for vegetable and fruit and stock-breeding areas.

THE FOURTH REGION

The Fourth Region comprises zones of the north-central part of the state: Piracicaba, Rio Claro, Bragança Piraçununga, and Araraquara. Here there are great differences in population densities, rate of growth, and urbanization. The economy is based mostly on industrial production and coffee, cotton and sugar plantations. The region borders on that of São Paulo and shares many characteristic features. Industrial municipios are most numerous, totaling twenty-seven, and population densities range from 20 to 231/km². The municipio of Americana is the most densely populated (231.7/km²), and experienced the most rapid rate of growth in the period 1950-60, increasing from 21,800

to 43,600. This growth was due to the rapid expansion of the textile industry, which is supplied with raw material from local cotton plantations. In 1950, 69 per cent of the population of the municipio lived in the town of Americana, where as many as 5700 workers were employed in the factories. Serra Negra (64.2/km²), was the only industrial unit to show a decline in population, from 13,300 to 11,900 (11 per cent), while the percentage of city dwellers rose from 35 to 44. The loss resulted from lower profits in the food industry, mostly the processing of sugar cane. In seven other municipios there was a relative drop, caused by migration.

It must be stated that industrial municipios, although they have the highest density of population, generally are the most dynamic in population growth.

Municipios where coffee, coffee with industry, or coffee with another crop (especially cotton and sugar cane) constitute the second group in this region. Of the twenty-one units within the group, seven were marked by an absolute decline in population and eleven by a relative drop, largely caused by deteriorating conditions on coffee plantations that were initiated in the late nineteenth century.

For example, in Anhembi (4.4/km²) the population dropped from 5200 to 3100 (40 per cent); in Joanópolis (25.8/km²) there was a 10 per cent drop—from 9800 to 8800. It may be concluded that exhaustion of the soil resulted in the deterioration of this type of economy and consequent pressure of population in the area. Nine municipios produce sugar cane, fruit, cotton, and livestock. Densities in this group vary from 20 to 45/km², and there are great differences in growth rates. Out of nine municipios, an absolute loss was recorded in four. In Capivari (34.1/km²), where the economy is based on sugar cane and cane processing, the population dropped from 23,000 to 19,700. At the same time in Cosmopolis (43.8/km²), which has an identical economic structure, there was an increase of 28 per cent—from 6800 to 8800. This was the result of geographical location: Cosmopolis borders on the dynamically developing Americana, where it finds a good market for agricultural products; Capivari, on the other hand, is not only situated near another area producing sugar cane, but is also close to the industrial centers of Piracicaba and Santa Barbara d'Oeste, which continually attract workers from surrounding areas.

THE FIFTH REGION

The Fifth Region covers the northern and central part of the state: São José do Rio Pardo, Riberão Prêto, Franca, Barretos, Catanduva, São Carlos e Jau, Piraju, Botucatu, Marilia, and Rio Prêto. The density of population is moderate and the rate of growth rather slow. It is a region of extensive monoculture with coffee plantations predominating. Stock-breeding, the production of cotton and sugar, and industry contribute to the area, but all are secondary to coffee.

Coffee and coffee-industrial municipios are most numerous; 130 units out of a total of 158 have been classified in this group. The general density is 25 to 50/km², but the actual range is from 9 to 109/km². The specific feature of the region is that in 54 of the coffee municipios, population dropped during the period under survey, and in 52 of them growth was below the natural increase. The percentage of city dwellers is low everywhere—from 20 to 40 per cent. Coffee has been grown there since 1920, a period long enough to induce soil exhaustion, lower yields, and migration. Only in more densely populated municipios with a higher percentage of city dwellers, such as São José do Pardo (91/km²) does the population show vigorous growth. This municipio recorded a growth of 40 per cent—from

32,000 to 43,000—and an increase of urban population from 61 to 74 per cent in the period 1950-60. Those units situated farther westward, where coffee was a monoculture only in the 1930's, show higher increases. For example, Osvaldo Cruz, a little town founded in 1941 amidst coffee plantations, had 6600 inhabitants in 1950, 16,000 in 1960, and the population of its municipio increased by 47 per cent—from 27,200 to 40,700.

Another group includes twelve cotton and cotton-industrial municipios. The population has decreased in one of them, and there has been a relative drop in five more. Densities differ greatly, but the modal value is 20/km². The population has increased considerably in several municipios. In Paulo do Faria (13.4/km²) the number of inhabitants rose from 12,400 to 21,600. Here we find features common to the coffee municipios: population increases wherever new plantations are established and after some 15 or more years, when the soil is exhausted and the yields are poor, population pressure is evident.

In each of the five municipios producing sugar cane, the population has increased and growth rates have considerably exceeded crop production. In addition, densities are greater than in the cotton and cotton-industrial municipios: from 30 to 60/km². The municipio of Serrana provides a good example: Its population density is 57.9/km², and its population increased from 5500 to 7400, or 40 per cent. These municipios are especially attractive because plantations were founded only recently, and facilities for processing sugar are internally located.

The last group is composed of ten industrial municipios. Population increased in all of them, irrespective of density, although in five the balance of migration was adverse. Marilia (65.8/km²) is typical of this group, with an 11 per cent increase (87,800 to 97,900). Forty-six per cent of the population in 1960 was urban. The town of Marilia, founded in 1925, already had 20,000 inhabitants by 1933. In 1940 there were 24,000, in 1950 there were 36,000, and in 1960, there were 51,800. The characteristic feature of towns in this region is that their population increases rapidly in the initial stages of colonization, as in Marilia, but in later years the rate of growth lessens as a result of lower yields or a slower growth of industrial production.

THE SIXTH REGION

The Sixth Region of São Paulo encompasses a zone in the western part of the state: Pereira Barreto, Araçatuba, Andradina, Presidente Venceslau, Presidente Prudente, and Assis. Population in this region is rather sparse, the rate of growth differentiated, the percentage of city dwellers low. Coffee and cotton are most important to the economy; industry plays an insignificant role.

One-half or fifteen of the municipios in the region have been classified as cotton and cotton-industrial. In eight of these, there was an absolute decline in population and a relative drop occurred in seven others. In Martinopolis ($24.2/km^2$), a good example of a deteriorating municipio, the population decreased 37,300 to 26,000 (31 per cent), with a simultaneous growth of urban dwellers from 15 to 27 per cent. Growth was particularly impressive in Jales ($55.4/km^2$) a zone colonized in the 1940's, where the population increased from 32,300 to 123,500. The percentage of urban population was particularly low, despite an increase from 12 to 23 per cent. This growth was due—apart from cotton—to the development of rice cultivation and of the food industry.

Coffee and coffee-industrial municipios form another group with a rather higher density of population, ranging mostly from 20 to $30/km^2$. The rate of increase is decidedly lower: out of twenty-five municipios

a decline was recorded in nine and a relative drop in seven others. Yet in five of the units the population increased several times; among them are three coffee-cotton municipios where industry is well developed. The largest growth was recorded in Pauliceia ($17.2/km^2$)—its population increased by 354 per cent—from 3500 to 15,900. It is situated in a zone colonized in the 1940's. On the other hand, Lavinia, where coffee monoculture prevails, offers an example of a deteriorating area: the density there is $24.2/km^2$ and its population dropped from 16,600 to 13,700 (17 per cent).

Two municipios were classified as industrial. In both of them population increased, and the more densely populated one, Ourinhos ($122.9/km^2$), shows a higher growth. Its population rose 62 per cent in 1950 from 21,500 to 34,400 in 1960. At the same time, the percentage of urban dwellers increased from 64 to 75.

Conclusions

Population pressure most strongly affects those areas with a monocultural economy, especially coffee and cotton plantations that have existed for a dozen years or more. On the other hand, each monoculture brings rapid population growth during its first years, as exemplified in the western part of São Paulo during the 1940's and in northern Paraná during the 1950's.

In the first period of monoculture, yields are usually high and the population density is low. With the passage of time, the procedure reverses itself, living standards are lowered and migration begins. When the soil has been completely exhausted, the plantations cease to exist. The introduction of a new type of economy to replace monoculture does not reactivate the area; population growth remains insignificant and people usually continue to migrate, despite relatively low densities. Within the next few years it may be expected that the economic structure of São Paulo will change. Coffee and cotton monocultures in northern and western areas will give way to stock-breeding and the cultivation of food crops. This will result from a continuous drop in yields from old plantations, which in many areas has already reached a critical stage. On the other hand, the rapid development of the industrial metropolis of São Paulo will call for an increased output of foodstuffs. Most probably, extensive migration will be experienced in large areas of the state, caused not so much by the high population densities as by the attraction of industry in the São Paulo region. New industrial investments in this region indicate continuing development.

The exodus of the population from villages and small towns will continue because of the great difference between the living standards of the peasants and manual workers—even seasonal workers. The liquidation of the feudal practices still existing on many farms may bring in its wake the economic growth of agricultural areas. Proper utilization of land is made more difficult by the ladder of feudal allegiances. The owner leases land to tenants who in turn lease it to subtenants, and the latter employ peasants who are often paid in goods. In the case of monocultures, major landowners often sell the harvest directly abroad. There is rational tillage of land and effective use of fertilizers only in an insignificant percentage of farms, because once the soil has been exhausted, there is always the possibility of laying out new plantations in virgin areas. The un-healthy socio-economic situation is occasionally aggravated by natural disasters, such as floods, droughts, and ground frosts, which often cause great losses and subsequent migration.

The rapid population increases makes economic progress more difficult and is one of the obstacles to rational development. The overcoming of this obstacle and the "deglomeration" of the economic potential of the city of São Paulo may bring about the activation of other regions of Brazil and a more even distribution of population. On the other hand, more rational farming and colonization of new areas if accompanied by land reform, may improve the economic situation. Measures such as these could liquidate population pressure in the state of São Paulo and throughout Brazil as well, which has major potential for increasing its population. The growth of the Brazilian population, even at the present level, should not bring a worsening of the material situation, for the country has immense natural resources. The interior has barely been explored or utilized; almost every year brings discoveries of new minerals. Implementation of the plans for irrigating the fertile northeastern part of the country may greatly increase the output of food, on the condition that the new areas are properly utilized. The last problem is convincing the people that in a developing country, a large population is an adverse phenomenon if the possibility of increasing the economic potential is limited. Overcoming backwardness will only be possible when institutional barriers and population pressures hampering economic growth are eliminated.

REFERENCES

(1) Aziz Nacib Ab'Saber: A Terra Paulista, *Boletim Paulista de Geografia,* Vol. 23, 1956, pp. 5-38.

(2) Associação dos Geografos Brasileiros: A Cidade de São Paulo (São Paulo, 1954).

(3) Waldemiro Bazanella: Industrialização e Urbanização no Brasil, *America Latina,* Nos. I-II, 1963, pp. 3-27.

(4) Brazil: Anuario Estatistico do Brasil, 1952, 1956, 1958, 1961, 1962, 1966 (Rio de Janeiro, 1953, 1957, 1959, 1962, 1963, 1967).

(5) Brazil: VI Recenseamento Geral do Brasil 1950—Censo Agricola, Industrial, Comercio e Serviços—São Paulo (Rio de Janeiro, 1956).

(6) Brazil, Ministerio da Agricultura: Produção Agricola do Brasil 1946/1950 (Rio de Janeiro, 1951).

(7) José Francisco de Camargo: Crescimiento do População no Estado de São Paulo e Seus Aspectos Economicos (São Paulo, 1952).

(8) J. P. Cole: Latin America, an Economic and Social Geography (London, 1965).

(9) Diccionario Historico, Geografico e Etnographico do Brasil, Vol. II (Rio de Janeiro, 1922).

(10) Enciclopedia dos Municipios Brasileiros, 3 vols. (São Paulo, 1958).

(11) J. R. Aranjo Filho: A Cafe Riqueza Paulista, *Boletim Paulista de Geografia,* Vol. 23, 1956, pp. 75-135.

(12) Celso Furtado: Formação Economica do Brasil (Rio de Janeiro, 1963).

(13) Sergio Haselman: Algunos Aspectos do Censo Brasileiro de 1960, *America Latina,* No. II, 1963.

(14) Odilon Nogueiro de Matos: O Desenvolvimiento de Rede Ferroviario e a Expansão da Cultura Cafe en São Paulo, *Boletim Geographico,* Vol. 119, 1953, pp. 371-81.

(15) P. Monbeig: As Estructuras Agrarios de Faixa Pioneira Paulista, *Boletim Geografico,* Vol. 116, 1953, pp. 455-65.

(16) P. Monbeig: Aspectos Geograficos do Crescimiento de São Paulo, *Boletim Geografico,* Vol. 119, 1954, pp. 139-53.

(17) Municipios Paulistas 1954 (São Paulo, 1956).

(18) Pasquale Petrone: As Industrias Paulista ao Factores de Sua Expansão, *Boletim Paulista de Geografia,* Vol. 14, 1953, pp. 26-37.

(19) Pasquale Petrone: O Homem Paulista, *Boletim Paulista de Geografia,* Vol. 23, 1956, pp. 39-77.

(20) T. Lynn Smith and Alexander Merchant: Brazil; Portrait of Half a Continent (New York, 1951).

(21) United Nations: Boletim Economico de America Latina, Vols. V & VI (Santiago de Chile, 1962, 1963).

(22) United Nations: Demographic Yearbook 1965 (New York, 1966).

(23) World Population Conference, Rome 1954: Proceedings, 6 vols. (New York, 1955).

PART THREE

CONCLUSIONS

33. REFLECTIONS ON THE SYMPOSIUM: GEOGRAPHY AND POPULATION GROWTH

Pierre George

It has become commonplace to accuse population pressure of being responsible for underdevelopment and to focus the debate on the question of whether it is possible or permissible to limit voluntarily the number of births. The contributions of the participants in the Symposium held at The Pennsylvania State University have shown that although population pressure is not a false problem, it does present itself in different ways depending on the country. They have also shown that the differences are not solely, or even essentially, quantitative, that they defy the application of "plans" and "models." These differences in fact are geographic; they stem from a whole combination of factors that give dissimilar relative values to demographic forces and dynamics.

The relations between economy and demographic pressures are quite variable. Underpopulation is perhaps the only factor which has disastrous consequences everywhere, for, paradoxically, it accelerates the destruction of nature's patrimony, that is to say, the production potential. Knowledge of agricultural systems shows, in fact, that any use of the raw or semi-raw resources by a temporary (itinerant) agriculture is devoid of the essential conservation measures that allow the production potential to be maintained. Many authors who discussed the tropical countries at the beginning of the century affirmed the fact that, conversely, any agricultural overpopulation likewise led to squandering of soil reserves and production capacity. Overpopulation in this case would be defined as exceeding a population rate that is in harmony with a cultivation system involving more or less prolonged fallow periods, one that assures regeneration of production capacity after a moderate period, and avoids regressive modifications in the physical-chemical structure of the soils, thus appearing in the form of an economic equilibrium. This equilibrium, in the examples studied, corresponds to very low densities, below 10 or $20/km^2$ of uncultivated land, in the savanna and tropical forest zones. It became apparent that exceeding these densities meant a shortening of the fallow period, and accelerated clearing along the margins of cultivatable lands, which consequently activated the processes of ravine formation and lateritization. Objectively, these observations were accurate, but they corresponded to the application of certain systems of cultivation, cultivating habits, and, rather frequently, to the extension of speculative cultivation, occasionally in the form of one-crop farming (e.g. the peanut zone in Senegal). A better knowledge of the variety of societies and agricultural economies in Africa, thanks to geographers who have worked assiduously in various regions, with the Sereres and the Diolas of Senegal (Pelissier), with the Agni of Cameroon (Rougerie), with the Bacongo (Sautter), with the Kirdis and the Kabres (Lasserre, Dresch), shows that population pressure caused the appearance, among denser populations, of techniques which are both intensive and conservation-minded, based on a differential use of the lands (in the European sense of the word, that is to say, of homogeneous masses of soils and climate), above all among the Kirdis and the Kabres of North Togo, who are the most numerous per unit area. One is thus led to consider different, and at the same time essential, thresholds of significance:

(i) The lower threshold below which an insufficient population endangers the productive stability of the environment by primitive modes of exploitation (the *Raubwirtschaft* of the German geographers and ethnologists of the early twentieth century), and below which phenomena of demographic isolation may also bring about the degeneration and the more or less long-term destruction of the group;

(ii) The median threshold above which one goes from extensive exploitation, which only partially occupies the available soils, and this at intervals between long fallow periods—thus preserving a low production potential—to an intensive exploitation that very prudently conserves by correlating the instinct of preservation of the species with that of the preservation of the soil;

(iii) The upper threshold, above which the land, even when expertly worked (within the framework of the traditional techniques of the group) is no longer sufficient to feed the population, which produces corresponding crises, especially in years of small harvest, and population migrations.

The distance between these thresholds may be considerable. In the West African forest zone with two rainy seasons, or in the zone of extensive equatorial forests, they lie at less than 5/km², at 40 to 60, and at more than 100.

The necessity of living on limited territory in large and, what is more, growing numbers, has often generated the most ingenious production systems. This is the example supplied by all regions that have served as refuges for populations put into a blockaded situation due to the hostility of surrounding populations. When these refugee populations appeared particularly miserable, it was be-

cause the upper threshold was being approached or had been exceeded. Then, but only then, did the situation become critical.

It is therefore appropriate to distinguish the three thresholds in every country; and it is possible to define an optimum period (not to be confused with a population optimum above the median threshold in which all the techniques that the group could assimilate are being put to use by means of an intensive economy) at which the population has not yet reached a magnitude such that the entire production capacity may be absorbed. One may then have the impression of prosperity for one or two generations.

In the industrial countries, demographic pressure is exerted on the employment market. It is essentially urban, calling for the creation of industrial and service jobs. But since it corresponds to a higher level of existence than that which even an improved agriculture can assure, it has resulted not only in the desertion of the countryside, but also the abandonment of agriculture. The majority of the industrial countries underexploit their agricultural potential, while they are at the same time capable of obtaining the highest surface yields, the greatest productivities from livestock, the highest productivities from investments and labor. Special cases, such as those of Denmark and the Low Countries and certain portions of Italy, are exceptions. On the whole, those industrial countries which have the better lands, probably because they have been treated with care and intelligence for a long time, are those which draw the least revenue in proportion to the potential, for their production rate is determined by the needs of their internal market, which is relatively low overall.

In contrast, the greatest population agglomerations, the rural masses of Asia, have relatively little rich land at their disposal, considering the ways in which they know how to work them. At the brink of famine, they are obliged to undertake their agricultural revolution, that is to say, learn how to make productive hitherto neglected areas, particularly through a grazing or pastoral economy. This is especially the problem of India, traditionally oriented toward cereal and vegetable production.

The problem, excellently stated by René Dumont, is that of knowing whether the agricultural revolution and the mobilization of supplementary foods can be conducted at a rate comparable with that of natural population growth. It is surely a geographic problem in the sense that certain countries seem capable of taking on the challenge; others, however, are outdistanced by the rate of population growth. For the latter, the obvious solution is population reduction. Actually, this hypothesis shifts the terms of the problem without solving it. In the majority of cases, the process of demographic growth has already been set in motion by the revolution in sanitation during the last few decades. A lowering of the birth rate has a relatively remote effect. It does not eliminate the need for immediate palliatives for underproduction (relative to needs) in order to avoid famine. Additional employment, rather than regular contributions of food products (which are an unproductive´ expenditure) can help in bridging this difficult stage, while awaiting the effects of a reduction in the natural growth.

In the industrial economies, population growth also presents sensitive problems. Faced with continuous technical progress, which is translated into a constant increase in the productivity of the work force, an imbalance in the employment market is threatened. This can be stabilized only by a corresponding increase in consumption. At this point in the evolution of the economy, an increase in the number of consumers, following the growth in population, is a stimulant which rekindles the production processes. Experience shows that it is not sufficient to wipe out unemployment. Though the growth in number is reflected—admittedly rather weakly—in the demand for agricultural products, the multiplication of demands for consumption and services on the other hand essentially involves the "secondary" and "tertiary" sectors. Per capita consumption can increase only through an increase in individual purchasing power. Population pressure therefore has a contradictory effect: it disturbs the employment market; constrained by productivity, it offers an opportunity to stimulate production by a cumulative increase in the demand (number of additional inhabitants multiplied by an individual consumption increase coefficient); but it creates difficulties in the distribution of the resultant revenues.

Demographic pressure, when it reaches the critical threshold, leads to the eradication of all the brakes and obstacles to higher production and induces more equitable distribution of wealth, and productive investment of revenues and savings. It is a revolutionary factor if the necessary reforms and sacrifices of privilege have not been made in time. Under these conditions, it is normal for the "forces of order" or the "forces of social conservation" to fear demographic pressure and to pursue the preventative politics of birth control in the manner of the countries where contradictions between the pressure of needs and the persistence of blockages (the *latifundia* structures with low yield and with vast unexploited reserves of Latin America, for example) threaten to upset social and political equilibria and to create crises whose contagious effects are unpredictable. But in this connection, returning to the strictly scientific terms of the study (terms of the geographer), one cannot sufficiently stress the relative character of overpopulation, which is defined relative to a technical level and to economic and financial structures (if the peasants of Southern Asia could purchase fertilizer, they would produce three or four times more rice per hectare than at present, as proved by the Japanese example) as well as to social and political structures. The global nature of geography cannot be better demonstrated. It should not be surprising any longer that geography is considered by some to be a dangerous discipline.

EPILOGUE

The reader who has persevered this far will readily agree that this collection of essays defies neat summation as a coherent aggregation of ideas. The organizers of the Symposium followed the basic strategy of converging upon central issues from multiple directions, and in retrospect find no reason to regret this approach. Thus we have thrust together the thoughts of a highly diverse group of scholars—disparate in age, nationality, philosophy, disciplinary background, and field experience. Indeed, had it been possible, we would have added also the services of students from other fields, notably political science, psychology, anthropology, and biology. It is no great surprise, then, to find at least partial disagreement on almost every vital point concerning that socially and intellectually transcendent group of problems we have labeled as "Population Pressure upon Resources." Given the present state of knowledge, we find such discord healthy, stimulating, and helpful in focusing more sharply on a set of central, as yet unanswered questions. Each of the participants has proved to be highly articulate in his contributions, whether written or oral, and there is no need for any final paraphrase here. What is proposed instead for this Epilogue are the results of reading between the lines, the detection of certain commonalities of axiom, curiosity, and attitude not openly expressed elsewhere, and whatever mutual enlightenment can be espied.

The most difficult part of any research effort is deciding exactly which questions to ask. At the outset of this project, it was rather naïvely assumed, given the interaction of a set of lively minds, it would be feasible to arrive at precise, rigorous definitions of terms, to ask the proper questions, and to begin finding viable answers. All this was hoped for in addition to the parallel objective of mobilizing a latent curiosity among many geographers about issues of population pressure. Now we know better. We may have succeeded in catalyzing a new sector of geographic inquiry—this we will know in a few years—but the other items proved to be much more intractable. No valid answers to major questions were forthcoming. In fact, no full consensus was attained concerning the proper questions to be asked; and the seemingly elementary task of saying exactly what is meant by PPR was never completed.

The old analogy of the blind men and the elephant is still serviceable here. The beast we call PPR is too large, ambiguous, and ambulatory to be simply catalogued. It is bigger than we suspected previously; it has too many appendages, angles, and wrinkles for comfort, and it may travel in herds. We have succeeded only in demonstrating that it is truly multidimensional, that it involves relationships among many different sets of variables—ecological, social, technological, psychological, and historical. It is impossible to produce a simple, universal definition that subsumes all the many kinds of pressure situations observed at different places and in different periods. But we are all uneasily aware that it exists. It is quite possible that the interdisciplinary perplexity concerning the essential nature of PPR reflects a profound truth, that we are in the presence of a highly relativistic concept that must be defined afresh in every new context. The only common thread running through the discussion is a feeling that PPR is a serious set of stresses caused by an imbalance between perceived human needs and the capacity to satisfy those needs, which is intrinsically related to the size and/or rate of increase of a population. However inconclusive the immediate results, we think that the exposure of the dilemma of definition was a useful, chastening exercise. The question of "Precisely what is it we are trying to look at?" was only the first of a series of questions many of us were forced to confront squarely.

Much less attention was accorded another basic issue, one that bedevils many investigations in the social sciences—a profound ignorance of the operating details of the relationships and processes that constitute PPR. The most explicit approach to this matter is Porter's account of the difficulty of assessing environment potential in Tropical Africa. It shows clearly how much more needs to be known of the basic facts of climate, soil, human attitudes, organization, and capabilities, not to mention the complexities of their co-variance, before we can cope with the measurement, let alone the alleviation, of PPR in the region. Similar "ignorance problems" are, however, implicit in nearly all the other essays. For example, we are only just beginning to understand the motivations and actions of migrant cultivators (as noted by Simkins), or of cityward migrants whom we presume to be impelled by PPR (including those described by Brush and C. Clarke). Our discussions are sorely hampered by lack of much genuine knowledge about what really is happening under conditions of population-resource stress; and we often have been obliged to express ourselves in terms of gross aggregate data or the fuzziest of generalities. On an even more elementary level, it is obvious that we still lack even usable first approximations of the surface facts, of gross numbers, densities, and dynamics, for all too many portions of the world. Such initial surveys are among the objectives of several papers included herein, notably those by John Clarke on Cameroon, Kay on Zambia, Rościszewski on Egypt, and Zelinsky on Middle America.

A recurrent question throughout this volume, at least implicitly, is that of scale, not only territorial but temporal and observational scale as well. Again and again, it has been driven home that it matters quite fundamentally whether one is scrutinizing a few hectares, a province, a nation, or the world, a single household, a village, a tribe, or a group of millions, and whether the study period is a year, a generation, or several centuries, or whether a single set or n sets of phenomena are under observation. Questions and answers that may be valid at one point on a scale may be totally unworkable at others; and the serious investigator must learn to reckon with and work with the scalar attributes of his material as productively as possible. Geographers have something of a head start here, since, possibly more than any other group of scholars, they are instinctively sensitive to this issue, but much more needs to be done in the way of conscious, deliberate control of scale problems by geographers and others.

Closely associated with dimensions of space and time is the question of how wide an observational net is being cast: what limits are to be set upon the kinds of phenomena or study techniques to be considered? It is abundantly clear in this Symposium that any thoughtful treatment of PPR will break the bounds of conventional demography and economics. It is not enough to look at vital indices, density figures, or inventories of agricultural and industrial production. History, ethnology, politics, sociology, and many other facets of human experience are constantly obtruding the studies reported here. The rapport established among individuals of different academic disciplines and sub-disciplines helped shed a brighter light on a critical point of which many of us were only dimly aware before the Symposium. The population-resource crisis of the developing countries is only a part of a long evolutionary process, of the transition from an old traditional existence toward one which we cannot yet predict and realistically describe. The large, diverse range of problems considered by the Symposium is actually only a sub-set of a much vaster set of experiences that can probably best be termed the Modernization Process. It has become obvious that studies of PPR cannot be carried on in isolation from the larger enveloping issues of modernization. Possibly because members of the Symposium have perceived this major truth (though usually subliminally) the outlook for a distressed group of countries was rather less gloomy than the immediate facts might seem to warrant. A sense of evolutionary thrust, of future prospects in spite of present problems, often came close to the surface of the discussion.

Another variant of the scale problem, and one that eternally haunts geographers, is the sorting out of the unique case from the general. Symposium participants were often confronted with both old and new forms of this problem. Obviously, at the level of ultimate specificity, every item becomes unique, while with vigorous scaling down and generalization, all observations ultimately become members of a single class. The difficult operational decision, of course, is to choose the appropriate level of generalization, in terms of one or more dimensions, including those of space and time. Among the specific cases considered, some of the more obvious were Brush's treatment of the rather anomalous recent dynamics of Indian city size, Pirie's puzzlement over how to deal with the unprecedented case of American Samoa, or Sandner's presentation of several forms of rural migration and man-land relationships within the relatively constricted confines of Central America. Can one draw valid generalizations from the conflicting testimony of Central America? Is the apparent recent deceleration of metropolitan growth within India simply the beginning of a more widespread occurrence in other developing lands, or is it truly unique? Does contemporary American Samoa form a class of one, or is it the earliest member of a class that will expand in the near future? No ready answers are forthcoming.

An unusual and singularly important version of the "uniqueness" problem presents itself in any attempt to characterize present demographic history or the historical geography of world population. Are we watching a gradual, orderly intensification of past trends and conditions, or a quantum leap into radically different modes of demographic behavior? Take the familiar controversy over the relevance for the Underdeveloped World of the Demographic Transition model as it has been worked out from observing the history of the currently advanced countries. Even though it will be some time before enough conclusive evidence can be gathered, it is already plain that, if the developing countries are passing through stages of the familiar Transition, they are doing so at an accelerated pace and with growth rates far beyond those recorded in the past. It would seem imprudent to bank on a completion of the cycle, with an approaching phase of rapidly declining fertility and near-stability of population numbers. Is the older model totally inapplicable to present and prospective conditions, or can it be overhauled and refined to the point where it becomes useful in understanding and predicting the future course of demographic events in the developing countries? This question was brought before the Symposium repeatedly, but without any clear resolution.

Directly parallel to the question of the viability of the Demographic Transition model is the less explicit question of the relevance of historical models derived from the advanced countries in understanding current metropolitan structure and growth in the underdeveloped lands. Although never fully codified, a certain common set of ideas about the historical development of cities in the currently advanced countries and their internal spatial and functional structure have been evolved by urban geographers—an outstanding achievement in modern geography. Do these notions apply to Brazil, the Congo, the Philippines, or similar countries? The evidence is still obscure; but it is apparent in the essays by Beaujeu-Garnier, Brush, and Colin Clarke among others, that there is some difficulty in fitting their observations into the Western urban mold. Once again, partial replication of past example may be taking place, or, just possibly, a distinctly new set of processes may be emerging.

The stubborn question of whether the present is the more or less simple extension of the past recurs in the frequent consideration given to the "Boserup Model" in this volume, not only in Mrs. Boserup's paper, but directly or by implication in the contributions of Gosal, Kay, Mabogunje, Porter, Robinson, Rościszewski, and Webb. The suggestion that a gradual building up of rural population densities may be the independent variable generating a series of ever more labor-intensive forms of land use and, ultimately, major transformations of the economy is one that intrigued the participants. On the other hand, while the model may be valid for past periods with modest rates of population increment, it is debatable how useful it will prove in an epoch of extremely rapid growth of rural populations. In any case, the evidence presented by Gosal for the Punjab, Pirie for Western Samoa, Robinson for East Pakistan, and by Bonasewicz, Planhol, and Webb seems to point to a simpler intensification, or involution, of land use without any fundamental reordering of crop or labor systems. However, contrary evidence can be selected from the material offered by Brookfield and Mortimore among others. The question of how far and how fast a community forces the limits of traditional practice before something gives way definitely remains an open one.

Comparisons of past with present also inevitably arose every time the issue of an equilibrium—presumably dynamic—between man and resources or between man and habitat was presented to the Symposium. If it can be hypothesized that such a balance was attained by numerous communities at various times in the past, is it possible, or desirable, to achieve equilibrium again under modern conditions? The polarities represented by Vogt and McLoughlin, the viewpoints of the ecologist and the operational economist, are quite familiar to students of the recent literature; and the present volume adds little that is new to these differences. If the notion that a condition of tensions is not only unavoidable but is to be actively developed is authenticated by future experience, it will indeed amount to a bold departure from past doctrine. Or perhaps it will represent a vigorous overhauling of the Boserup Model to meet modern conditions. It should be added, however, that evidence concerning the deterioration of the habitat, either in biotic or agronomic terms, is not reassuring. Destructive tendencies may have been worrisome in the past, but recently they have been greatly magnified with no compensating spurt of human creativity, according to the data furnished by Bonasewicz for São Paulo, Sandner and Vogt for Middle America, Webb for Northeast Brazil, and Tricart for the Third World in general.

As was to be hoped and expected, the theme of territorial mobility was definitely to the fore throughout much of the Symposium. Section 3 of this volume gives special emphasis to this with movements extending toward agricultural frontiers and urban centers as the dominating consideration. But it might be well to note that, in addition to an accelerating freedom of physical movement (at least within national boundaries), which is amply documented not only here but in a great many other recent publications, there has also been a remarkable extension of the mobility of human minds, in both quantitative and qualitative ways. People in the developing as well as the advanced countries are seeing themselves and their immediate surroundings in distinctly different ways than they did in the past (these psychological dimensions are explored to some extent by Mabogunje and Porter); and there is also extension of awareness—to other places, other times, and other levels of human existence. These revolutionary changes in human perception, quite apart from the now familiar shaking loose of human beings from traditional territorial roots, mean new dimensions in future population-resource equations. A consciousness of these new departures appears sporadically in this volume. Specifically, there would appear to be solid consensus on the great significance of the aspirations and expectations of the peoples of the developing lands, and the necessity to deal with this question in analyses of population pressure.

A conclusion to be drawn from the preceding paragraphs is that we are not ready to affirm categorically that PPR—assuming, of course, that we can meaningfully define and measure it—has induced fundamental reordering of geographic structures and processes, either at the macro- or the microscopic level. Still enough evidence has accumulated to suggest that the question ought to be examined; and we are entitled to wonder, and perhaps stimulated to investigate, whether we may be getting modes and rates of environmental deterioration hitherto unobserved, novel patterns and dynamics in urban agglomerations, unexpected shifts in land-use practice, new spatial-temporal patterns in vital events, the emergence of original forms of geographic perception, and other less obvious phenomena. This was certainly one of our basic concerns in organizing the Symposium; and if we have not disposed of the question of the meaning and nature of PPR, at least these papers represent a sharper underscoring of the problem.

Remedial programs to alleviate PPR form one major topic which the organizers had initially intended to evade in the hope of keeping the discourse as dispassionate and analytical as possible. The fact that the issue erupts in several essays would seem to indicate that students of PPR find it extremely difficult to think of diagnosis without worrying simultaneously about therapy. There may be some profound but not clearly definable lesson in this observation. At any rate, if there was lively interest in correcting a troublesome condition, there was an utter lack of unanimity as to how to proceed. Only mild interest was shown in the possibilities of a quick deflation of growth rates of population through any sort of crash program in family limitation. Attention centered rather upon the developmental solution, i.e. the accelerated advancement of socioeconomic levels; but no single specific strategy for the nature and allocation of investments went unchallenged. Should the urban-industrial sector be favored over the rural? Or if agriculture is to be the main sector of growth, should one maximize total product per operator, with a consequent depletion of rural numbers, or else increase the population-absorptive capacity of the countryside through labor-intensive devices? Is a heavy commitment to educational progress the quick and sure way to a balanced demographic regime and prosperity? Will tourism turn the trick? How does one generate entrepeneurial drive? All of these are intriguing questions, but there are no clear answers. Furthermore, beyond the prox-imate question of tactics, there lurks a problem on which consensus among scholars would be hopeless: What ultimate goals should and can be considered for the developing countries? That, of course, is simply another way of phrasing the unanswerable question: What is the best possible sort of society?

Despite an obvious lack of agreement on remedial strategies, a pre-vious comment concerning the basic mood of the Symposium must be repeated and underscored. In large part—and in addition to strong, genuine scientific curiosity—the project was generated by a deep anxiety over the immediate and long-range welfare of countries seemingly destined for an extraordinary series of crises. Much of the literature on the general topic of population pressures in the Underdeveloped World tends to be depress-ing in tone, to put the matter mildly; and several of the essays in this volume, notably those by Colin Clarke, Gosal, Rosciszewski, and Vogt seem to exclude all possibilities of noncatastrophic solutions for the areas they discuss. Yet there was amazingly little outright pessimism in the discussions. (Note the emphasis on "break-up" rather than "breakdown," for example.) If pressed, almost any of the participants would admit to the distinct likelihood of large-scale famine and other varieties of un-pleasantness in several countries during the 1970's and 1980's; but there was almost no gnashing of teeth and crying of havoc for the world in general. The explanation may lie in a guarded confidence in the larger forces of history—an attitude most vigorously expressed by Pokshishev-skii. Or it may simply be a healthy skepticism as to whether we know enough about the workings of the systems that produce, and perhaps circumvent, PPR to indulge in funereal predictions.

Finally, a word on future directions and the role of the geographer. That geographers have a major part to enact in the study and treatment of PPR seems self-evident, but the nature of that role is by no means clearly spelled out. The one safe assertion would seem to be that here, as elsewhere, geographers do not command jurisdiction over any special body of phenomena, nor even private title to specific tools and techniques. Rather it is a peculiar frame of reference, or an angle of vision, which distinguishes them from their brethren: seeing the world and its parts through spatial spectacles, as a set of very complex places, each one somehow unique, yet also somehow like all the others, and each one susceptible to some degree of ordering. Furthermore, there is license to seek out critical intersections among the multitudinous processes and structures that conjoin to create and give character to the various seg-ments of the terrestrial time-space continuum. In the context of PPR, this means three particularly valuable attributes: (i) The geographer is congenitally sensitive to the critical importance of areal and temporal scale in his observations; he is attentive not only to the national unit but to various levels of smaller territory and to a great variety of transnational areal categories as well. Such flexible optics seem mandatory in getting demographic questions into perspective. (ii) He also bears the charge, along with the ecologist, of viewing a phenomenon such as PPR as a many-dimensioned entity, one that is touched by and acts upon many other aspects of human and nonhuman life. This is an extraordinarily difficult responsibility; but however imperfectly it is discharged, the competent geographer knows that population pressure is not simply a defective economic machine, or a malfunctioning set of social institutions, or a group of farmers who abuse fields and pastures. Armed with this knowledge and a willingness to search out the interrelatedness of things, he is a useful addition in any team of scholars attacking such questions. (iii) The patterns of demographic change, development, stress, and resolution can be quite productively viewed as a series of innovations propagated outward over land and time—as processes of spatial diffusion. Too little has been accomplished along this line by geographers working on population topics to date; but the skills developed in other diffusional analyses would seem highly relevant here.

Aside from a reinforced feeling that much more study is feasible and necessary, the Symposium concluded with no detailed program for this. But interest was shown in one scheme that could eventually yield a rich harvest by attacking many urgent questions that have resisted, and will continue to resist, investigation by the single isolated scholar. Furthermore, it is virtually impossible to contrast or compare one area with another in rigorous fashion. There is every good reason to consider planning a simultaneous series of carefully controlled investigations on precisely stated, significant problems in a selected group of places in the developing lands. The value of such studies would be much enhanced if they could either be continued over a fairly long span of years or repeated at appropriate intervals. They would provide the material for the controlled quantitative comparisons that would make it possible to relate experience of PPR in one area with that in others. No comparative studies of this nature now exist. There are many obvious problems in charting so ambitious, complex, and costly an international venture, even apart from matters of money and personnel; but the practical and intellectual rewards could be well forth the heavy investment that would be required.

GLOSSARY OF SPECIAL TERMS

Agreste (Portuguese)—The portion of Northeast Brazil that is transitional between the warm, humid *Zona da Mata* and the dry *Sertão* of the interior.

aiga (Samoan)—Extended family in Samoa.

alpages (French)—High summer pastures.

baitka—A local community association in Mauritius, based upon a particular ethnic group.

barriada (Spanish)—Shanty-town, the term used throughout Latin America.

bidonville (French)—Shanty-town; the term used especially in former French African colonies.

boma (Kiswahili)—Seat of the local administration in the former British colonial territories of South-Central Africa; literally, a stockade.

caatinga (Portuguese)—Desert tropical thorn scrub forest of Northeast Brazil.

campo cerrado (Portuguese)—Brazilian term for savanna, i.e. grassland with scattered trees and shrubs.

cho (Hindi)—Seasonal stream originating in the Siwalik Hills of North India.

citemene or chitemene (Bemba)—(Literally, "a cut place") A system of agriculture practised in parts of Zambia, involving the clearing of an area of woodland several times larger than that to be cultivated. The branches, etc. are stacked in the area to be cultivated and then burned, thus concentrating the ash and nutrients.

conuco (Spanish)—One of several synonyms for the system of forest fallow practised in the Tropics, in this instance in Venezuela. Under this system, land is cleared for a few years of cultivation after an extended period of natural regeneration, then abandoned once again.

cotching—The term used in Kingston, Jamaica, to describe the methods whereby the poorest inhabitants, who have no settled accommodation, put up for the night as best they can.

couloir (French)—A section of forest cleared in the controlled *paysannat* agricultural system introduced by Belgians in the Congo.

creole (French)—The *lingua franca* in Mauritius, based on French, almost unwritten and of low status.

Creoles (French)—Persons of mixed blood in Mauritius.

daimyō (Japanese)—The largest of the landholding magnates in Japan from approximately the tenth century onwards. During the sixteenth century, the term became limited to those with lands assessed at 10,000 koku (1 koku = 180.4 liter) or more of annual grain production. The system and position of *daimyō* underwent many changes and was finally abolished in 1868-1871.

589

dungle—The city's garbage dump in Kingston, Jamaica.

fale (Samoan)—An indigenous Samoan house, consisting of an arched sugar-cane thatched roof supported by wooden pillars, on a raised stone foundation. There are no walls as such, but coconut blinds can be let down to protect the interior from strong winds and rain.

favella (Portuguese)—Shanty-town; the term used especially in Brazil.

feddan (Egyptian)—Areal unit in Egypt, approximately 0.4 hectare or 1 acre.

finca (Spanish)—A rural property in Spanish America, generally a small farm or ranch.

fokon'olona—the local community (village group) among the Mérina in central Madagascar, in the tenth to eighteenth centuries.

gens-de-couleur (French)—Persons of light skin color, the product of racial intermixture in Mauritius.

governorates—administrative units of the first order in Egypt.

gun (Japanese)—A subdivision of a prefecture; no longer politically functional. All land outside the *shi* (q. v.) (incorporated city) is included in the *gun;* the *gun,* in turn, consists of *machi* (*q. v.*) and *mura* (*q. v.*)

jagirdari (Hindi)—Feudal system of land tenure prevalent in the Deccan and northwest India, abolished in the early 1950's.

latifundio (Spanish)—A great landed estate in Italy, Spain, and Spanish America, typically held by absentee owner and employing servile or semi-servile laborers, using crude technology.

mabiki (Japanese)—Literally, the thinning of plants; figuratively infanticide.

machi (Japanese)—An administrative unit with fewer powers and a less complex organization than a *shi,* (*q. v.*) but more powers and a more complex organization than a *mura* (*q. v.*).The *machi* includes both the central settlement and the surrounding agricultural areas; it is usually larger and more urban in character than the *mura.*

mata seca (Portuguese)—Dry forest formation in Northeast Brazil.

mau (Samoan word for "opinion" or "feeling")—A movement among major Samoan leaders and some European commercial interests against some far-reaching changes initiated by the New Zealand administration in Samoa between 1921 and 1926. It was based mainly on civil disobedience, but there were also outbreaks of violence. A new government mended the affair in 1936.

migration de soudure (French—Migration occurring in the hunger period, i.e., the interval between the exhaustion of one season's food supply and the availability of food during the next season.

minifundio (Spanish)—Miniature landholding in Latin America, so small that it yields marginal subsistence or income for the occupant (*minifundista*). Usually the result of the fragmentation of larger units, it is intensively exploited.

miombo (Kiswahili)—Dry savanna woodland in East and South-Central Africa, with *Brachystegia-Julbernardia* species dominant.

municipio (Spanish or Portuguese)—A minor civil division in Latin America, roughly equivalent to the county in the United States. Generally basically rural, but contains a single agglomerated settlement serving as a political and social center.

mura (Japanese)—The most agricultural and rural of the administrative units into which Japan is divided. It often includes several *buraku* or villages.

nago (Japanese)—Feudalistic social relations between landowners and agricultural workers existing until the end of World War II.

panchayati raj (in Hindi, "rural administration by elders")—Popularly elected representative institutions of rural people in India. They are established at different levels: village, the community development block (an administrative unit consisting of about 100 villages), and district, and are responsible for agricultural and rural development.

parasito (Spanish)—Illegal agricultural occupant, or squatter, within privately owned land in Costa Rica.

parcelario (Spanish)—Settler who has been allocated parcel of land within an agricultural colony developed by Guatemalan government.

paysannat (French)—A system of agriculture involving resettlement of population introduced into the Congo by the Belgian colonial administration, with a considerable element of compulsion governing the methods used, crops grown etc.

peon, pl. peones (Spanish)—Landless peasant or farmhand in Latin America.

PPR—Abbreviation for "population pressure upon resources" adopted for use in this Symposium.

precarista (Spanish)—Unauthorized occupant of state-owned land reserves in Costa Rica who acquires certain property rights if he lives upon and uses his land for more than a year.

Ras Tafari movement—A "Back to Africa" movement which gathered momentum very rapidly in Kingston, Jamaica during the late 1950's, promulgating a revolutionary social and racial philosophy. Since independence in 1961, this movement has declined somewhat in importance.

roulement (French)—A system of related indebtedness, ramifying the various economic strata of society in Mauritius.

samurai (Japanese)—A member of the military class in the service of the daimyō (*q. v.*).

scuffling—The term used in Kingston, Jamaica for nonrespectable or illegal occupations, such as pimping and prostitution, begging, stealing, and selling scrap salvaged from the city's dump or "dungle." (q. v.)

Sertão (Portuguese)—Dry zone of interior of Northeast Brazil, the sparsely populated backlands.

shi (Japanese)—an incorporated city.

sirdar (in Hindi, "leader" or "foreman")—A job-contractor, organizing the supply of labor to estates in Mauritius.

tabuleiro (Portuguese)—Low, flat, sedimentary interfluve in Northeast Brazil, where sandy soils usually support savanna formation.

tahsil (Hindi)—Minor civil division in India, roughly equivalent to U.S. county or township.

yayla (Turkish)—High alpine pasture lying above the tree line and grazed only during the summer season (French *alpage*).

zamindari (Hindi)—Feudal system of land tenure in India prevalent in the eastern part of the country, abolished in the early 1950's.

Zona da Mata (Portuguese)—Humid forest zone along or near the littoral of Northeast Brazil.

INDEX